Volume 1
TELECOMMUNICATIONS AND THE LAW
An Anthology

ADVANCES IN TELECOMMUNICATION NETWORKS SERIES
ISSN 0888-2223

Series Editor: Wushow Chou, *North Carolina State University*

BOOKS IN THE TELECOMMUNICATION NETWORKS SERIES

1. **Raymond Pickholtz, Editor**
   *Local Area and Multiple Access Networks**
2. **Walter Sapronov, Editor**
   Telecommunications and the Law: An Anthology, Volume I

OTHER BOOKS OF INTEREST

Fred J. Ricci and Daniel Schutzer
U.S. Military Communications: A C³I Force Multiplier

Marvin K. Simon, Jim K. Omura, Robert A. Scholtz, and Barry K. Levitt
Spread Spectrum Communications, Volumes I, II, III

William W Wu
Elements of Digital Satellite Communication, Volumes I and II

*These previously-published books are not numbered within the volume itself.

Volume 1
TELECOMMUNICATIONS AND THE LAW
An Anthology

□ □

Editor: WALTER SAPRONOV, ESQ.
Hurt, Richardson, Garner, Todd & Cadenhead

COMPUTER SCIENCE PRESS

Computer Science Press
1803 Research Boulevard
Rockville, Maryland 20850

1 2 3 4 5 6   Printing   Year   93 92 91 90 89 88

Library of Congress Cataloging-in-Publication Data

Telecommunications and the law : an anthology / Walter Sapronov, editor.

    p. cm. — (Advances in telecommunication networks series,
ISSN 0888-2223)
Bibliography: p.
Includes index.
ISBN 7 167-8 155-7
1. Telecommunication—Law and legislation—United States.
I. Sapronov, Walter.   II. Series.
KF2765.T45 1988
343.73′0994—dc19
[347.303994]   87-38185
                                                  CIP

CONTENTS

INTRODUCTION TO TELECOMMUNICATIONS AND THE LAW

The works contained in this anthology address legal and regulatory issues associated with the telecommunications industry. During the last decade, this industry has undergone rapid growth and today represents a convergence of the computer and communications technologies. Numerous examples of the convergence are found in new services and products, such as voice-data private branch exchanges, value-added networks, electronic mail, video text, very small aperture satellite terminals, and perhaps one day, integrated services digital networks (ISDN). Throughout this anthology, the term "telecommunications" is used in a broad sense, encompassing communications and computer processing services, equipment and facilities provided by common carriers, independent service providers, computer and communications equipment manufacturers, resellers, third party distributors, and myriad others.

With the advent of an interrelated computer and communications marketplace, the associated legal and regulatory issues become interrelated as well. Resolution of these issues is determined by various bodies of law, including federal and state regulatory laws, administrative laws, antitrust law, contract law, and the emerging law (known as "computer law") which applies to transactions between computer buyers and sellers. To some extent, these issues are complicated by the U. S. regulatory structure, which often resembles a patchwork of dissonant rules and policies, issued by separate and conflicting federal, state, and judicial authorities.

Thus, it is with a view to the profound impact of these legal and regulatory issues on the "high-tech" community that this anthology is published. The purpose is two-fold. First, this anthology provides a collection of some of the finer essays on this theme, published by many of the industry's leading attorneys and decision makers. Second, it attempts to reduce some of the manifold complexities of telecommunications law and regulation to an orderly discussion, combining various perspectives and treatments of the many intertwined issues. To the extent this anthology achieves its purpose, it does so largely because many of the contributing authors are themselves leading figures in this area and have personally affected many of the developments discussed herein.

Following this introduction, the anthology begins with a primer on telecommunications law and regulation as a background review for the essays that follow.

The primer and following essays are organized as follows:

II. TELECOMMUNICATIONS REGULATION (GENERALLY)

This section begins with "The Regulation of Interstate Phone Rates" by Carl Wheat, which first appeared in the *Harvard Law Review* in 1938. Published shortly after the enactment of the Communications Act of 1934, this work sets the stage for subsequent discussions. The author provides prescient insight into the issues associated with telephone industry regulation, then and now. These include, among others, federal and state jurisdictional conflicts, rate determinations, carrier revenue requirements, rate of return calculations, depreciation, regulatory classifications, and judicial separations. This essay was cited by the U.S. Supreme Court in its recent landmark decision, *Louisiana Public Service Commissioners v. FCC* (*"Louisiana* decision"). (See *Primer on Telecommunications Law and Regulation,* p. 6.)

The following two essays, by Herbert E. Marks, represent a classical statement of the issues associated with telecommunications regulation and case law. The two essays "Two Decades of Telecommunications Regulation: An Historical Perspective" and "Regulation and Deregulation in the United States and Other Countries" collectively span the issues from the *Carterfone* era through the Federal Communications Commission's (FCC's) Second Computer Inquiry. Some of the many cases discussed include the early *Carterfone* and *Hush-a-phone* decisions, the Special Common Carrier Cases, the Competitive Carrier Rulemaking, the AT&T Trial & Consent Decree (MFJ), Computer Inquiry II, as well as a discussion of international regulatory policies. Mr. Marks, a partner in the Washington, D.C. law firm of Squire, Sanders and Dempsey, personally argued many of the cases discussed.

The fourth essay in this section is "The End of Monopoly" by Richard E. Wiley. As former Chairman of the FCC, Mr. Wiley is uniquely qualified to trace the gradual transformation of the U. S. telecommunications industry from a once-regulated monopoly to a competitive environment. Mr. Wiley describes the FCC's instrumental role in this restructuring and argues that the resulting environment has yielded immeasurable public benefit. The essay concludes with a discussion of today's most recent developments, including recent congressional legislation and the outlook for future deregulation. Mr. Wiley is a senior partner in the Washington, D.C. law firm of Wiley, Rein and Fielding.

The section's final essay, "Preemption under the Communications Act" is authored by Richard McKenna, general attorney for GTE Service Corporation, and has been updated since its original publication. It addresses the complex area of federal and state jurisdictional conflicts and overlap. The issue of federal preemption of state regulatory authorities is pivotal in determining who will ultimately dictate this country's telecommunications policies—the states or the FCC. In the wake of the *Louisiana* decision, this issue has become largely unsettled and future jurisdictional disputes are almost certain to follow. Mr. McKenna's now famous essay was cited in the Supreme Court's opinion and is a comprehensive treatment of this extremely complex and controversial subject.

III. BREAK-UP OF THE BELL SYSTEM

Section III focuses on the single most dramatic event in telecommunications history: the AT&T divestiture. The divestiture of the Bell Operating Companies (BOCs) from AT&T was a culmination of the Justice Department's seven-year antitrust suit against AT&T. The action was concluded by a consent decree between the parties which was subsequently approved by the District Court for the District of Columbia and styled as a modification to a prior, 1956 Consent Decree (a "modification to final judgment" or "MFJ").

The section begins with excerpts from the proceedings held pursuant to the Tunney Act before District Court Judge Harold Greene in order to determine whether the proposed consent decree was in the public interest. The essays which follow analyze the economic goals of divestiture and critique the results, including the perspective of AT&T's foremost competitor and that of an advocate of the independent communications equipment industry.

The excerpts contain some of the arguments of Herbert E. Marks, attorney of record for the Independent Data Communications Manufacturers Association (IDCMA), heard before Judge Harold Greene on June 30, 1982. The exchange between Mr. Marks and the court sheds light on the crucial issue of AT&T's residual monopoly power following divestiture. Mr. Marks' arguments focus on the lingering anti-competitive potential of the postdivestiture AT&T in areas of setting network standards, customer premises equipment (CPE) distribution, and ownership of the Bell System patent portfolio. The remedies proposed to the court suggested additional modifications to the consent decree whereby AT&T would be subject to compulsory, nondiscriminatory patent licensing obligations to third parties (which the court eventually adopted) and separate subsidiary requirements for AT&T's CPE sales activities (which the court subsequently rejected).

The excerpts are followed by "Economic Goals and Remedies of the AT&T Final Judgment" by Warren G. Lavey, former legal assistant to the Chief, FCC Common Carrier Bureau,[1] and Professor Dennis Carlton of the University of

---

[1] Mr. Lavey co-authored this article while serving as a lawyer/economist at Lexicon, Inc. The views of the authors do not necessarily represent those of the FCC.

Chicago. The authors clarify the sometimes confusing role of the MFJ vis a vis other regulatory constraints imposed upon AT&T and the BOCs by federal and state regulators. As the authors point out, the AT&T divestiture and related determinations of the MFJ are an antitrust remedy and not a regulatory device. In their essay, Messrs. Lavey and Carlton first analyze the antitrust principles and underlying economic theory upon which the MFJ is based. Second, they critique the application of antitrust principles to the prevention of monopoly abuses by common carriers. Looking to the social and economic goals upon which the MFJ is based, the authors further analyze the problem of cross-subsidization between regulated and unregulated carrier subsidiaries and suggest an appropriate approach to raising carrier revenues in the postdivestiture era.

Pursuant to the MFJ, the divested BOCs remained in possession of the local exchange monopolies. However, as a measure of preventing anticompetitive abuses, the MFJ subjected the BOCs to ongoing restrictions and obligations. One of the most important and far reaching of these obligations was that of "equal access:" the requirement that BOCs upgrade their network switches to provide access equal in quality and price to all inter-exchange carriers (e.g., AT&T, MCI) and information service providers (e.g., GTE/Telenet, Tymnet) upon bona fide requests. A further consequence of "equal access" was that the American public now had to select long-distance carriers on an individual subscriber basis. The MFJ deadline for equal access implementation was September of 1986 but delays and disputes have continued well beyond that date.

In his essay, "Equal Access: the View of a Competitive Carrier", Kenneth A. Cox, Senior Vice President, Regulatory, of MCI Communications Corporation, presents an inter-exchange carrier's viewpoint on the aftermath of divestiture and the equal access requirement that it spawned. The author treats "equal access," essentially an antitrust remedy, as a promise that is not without problems and that remains to be fulfilled. Mr. Cox' discussion includes an analysis of the regulatory treatment of access charges: the compensation of local exchange carriers for use of their facilities by inter-exchange carriers and others The access charge issue is one of the traditionally vexatious problems facing both state and federal regulators and remains very much alive today.

The following discussion, "Will Divestiture Affect the Structure of CPE Markets" by Albert H. Kramer, general counsel for the North America Telecommunications Association (NATA), casts some lingering doubts on the putative competitive benefits of the AT&T divestiture. Mr. Kramer takes exception to the treatment of the CPE industry by the combined policies of the MFJ Court and the FCC. The author argues that CPE markets remain generally dominated by AT&T and the BOCs in the post-divestiture environment, but that pre-divestiture regulatory checks, which previously had served to prevent abusive practices by those carriers, have been all but eliminated. Citing the MFJ provision permitting the BOCs to provide but not manufacture CPE, the author contends that the MFJ Court has ignored the interests of the independent CPE sector. Moreover, he alleges that recent FCC policies, which relieve AT&T and the BOCs from separate subsidiary requirements for CPE provision, promote subsidized competition that the independent CPE industry cannot withstand. Thus, he argues that current policies represent the worst of all possible worlds. Mr. Kramer, therefore, challenges the view that post-divestiture regulatory policies facilitate competitive equipment markets and urges that this be addressed by regulators with utmost priority.

In summary, divestiture left the BOCs with control of the local exchange but did little to alleviate disputes over their other activities. And indeed, the local exchange services provided by the BOCs are also not without controversy, as explained by Henry D. Levine, partner in the Washington D.C. office of Morrison & Forester, in the final essay of this section.

In "Defining Local Exchange Service: For Whom May Only Bell Toll," Mr. Levine unravels some of the ambiguities underlying the local exchange service concept, which may be used to connote different types of services and serving areas, depending upon usage. For example, the term "local exchange services" may at times equivocally refer to either "plain old telephone service," voice plus data over private lines, or all electromagnetic transmission of information within an MFJ defined serving area. Mr. Levine perceptively describes how the different definitions of "local exchange" in fact evidence hidden agendas of interested parties, such as BOCs, regulators, and inter-exchange carriers. The essay thus underscores that it is not the semantics of "local exchange services" that is at issue but rather the policy dispute over who and what can serve the public under this talismanic label.

IV. THE FCC'S THIRD COMPUTER INQUIRY

This section covers one of the most widely discussed FCC regulatory proceedings to follow the AT&T divestiture: the Third Computer Inquiry.

For more than a decade, the FCC has attempted to devise a workable framework for regulating the computer and communications industries. The general purpose of such regulation was to set policies for the participation of regulated common carriers in competitive, unregulated computer and communications equipment markets. The regulatory frameworks proposed in the First and Second Computer Inquiries were based in large measure on regulatory classifications and definitions: namely, communications equipment and service types were deemed to be either regulated or unregulated according to their classification under various FCC-prescribed definitions.

However, the definitions and classifications of the First and Second Computer Inquiries proved unworkable from the outset. The regulatory classifications of Computer Inquiry I, the communications (regulated), data processing (unregulated) and hybrid (unclear) categories, led to controversies over the uncertain treatment of the "hybrid" category. Computer Inquiry II replaced that definitional scheme with a revised classification structure: basic services (regulated), enhanced services (unregulated)—with CPE falling into the unregulated category. Examples of basic services included end-to-end transmission circuits, which are unaltered by computer processing from one end of a subscriber's transmission to the other. Examples of enhanced services, on the other hand, included protocol conversion, database inquiry, and other carrier supplied services that added computer processing functions, interaction or other changes to the subscriber's transmitted information. This approach did not prove any more satisfactory than that of Computer Inquiry I.

Under Computer Inquiry II, controversies inevitably arose about the interpretation of the basic and enhanced services definitions, as well as their application to rapidly changing computer/communications technology and to emerging new services that did not readily lend themselves to either classification. Digital Network Channel Termination Equipment (NCTE), multiplexers, and a variety of packet-switching services (with and without protocol conversion) were some of the technologies subject to regulatory definitional disputes.

Further controversies arose over the conditions under which AT&T and the BOCs (but not other carriers) were permitted to offer CPE and enhanced services. These conditions, so-called "structural separations," had originally required AT&T and the BOCs to offer enhanced services and CPE only through deregulated, separate affiliates. However, structural separations have been vigorously opposed by AT&T and the BOCs since their inception. Through grant of various petitions for waiver of Computer Inquiry II rules, the FCC has to some extent relieved AT&T and the BOCs from structural separations on a case by case basis, albeit not without considerable opposition and lengthy FCC pleading cycles. In effect, the Computer Inquiry II policies have been systematically eroded through these *ad hoc* waiver petitions while the underlying controversies have remained unresolved.

The proposed Computer Inquiry III Rulemaking, as originally envisioned in the Notice of Proposed Rulemaking ("Notice") released August 16, 1985, represents a major revision of these earlier FCC policies. These revisions included the following: first, replacement of structural separations for AT&T and the BOCs with other safeguards (so called "nonstructural safeguards") designed to prevent anticompetitive abuses by those carriers in unregulated markets; second, revision and clarification of the controversial enhanced services definition; third, a revolutionary approach to regulation based on marketplace characteristics rather than regulatory definitions. The FCC Computer Inquiry III Order, released July 16, 1986, addressed only some of these issues, deferring others to collateral proceedings and to a supplemental phase of the preceeding. The essays in Section IV examine the policies and issues of the FCC's new framework as originally proposed in the Notice.

The first essay, "Ending Structural Separations for Telephone Companies" by Warren G. Lavey, former assistant to the Chief of the FCC Common Carrier Bureau and now a partner in the Chicago law firm of Skadden, Arps, Slate, Meagher and Flom, sets forth in detail the arguments against structural separations. Mr. Lavey's discussion provides a cost-benefit analysis of the separate subsidiary requirements for BOCs under Computer Inquiry II, concluding (as did the FCC) that such separations are not in the public interest.

The second essay, "Introduction to the FCC's Third Computer Inquiry" by Messrs. Herbert E. Marks and James L. Casserly (partners in the firm of Squire, Sanders and Dempsey), examines the various proposals set out in the Computer Inquiry III Notice of Proposed Rulemaking. The authors discuss the broader implications of this Rulemaking for computer industry professionals, including manufacturers, service vendors, and users. They question the FCC's premise that efficiencies and economies will necessarily result from the integration of computer intelligence with carrier networks. Furthermore, they emphasize the need for additional analysis by the Commission before embarking on a new regulatory framework based on this assumption. The authors conclude their discussion by urging industry participants to assist the FCC in examining the ramifications of Computer Inquiry III in light of its long-range impact on the future nature, quality, and pricing of communications and data processing.

The third essay, "Understanding the FCC's Third Computer Inquiry" by Messrs. Richard E. Wiley and Howard D. Polsky (both with the firm of Wiley, Rein and Fielding), addresses various jurisdictional problems raised by the FCC's revolutionary approach to regulation based on market analysis. Moreover, this essay underscores a broader issue facing FCC regulators: What are the jurisdictional limits of industry-wide implementation of FCC deregulatory policies? As it turns out, the FCC declined to adopt this proposed approach to regulation. Nonetheless, the problems of jurisdictional limits hover over FCC policy making, especially in the wake of the *Louisiana* decision.[2]

The Computer Inquiry III Rulemaking is far from over. While the Commission's orders have been released, future controversies are virtually certain to follow. The foregoing essays address some of the issues and problems facing the FCC. Other issues, such as the regulatory treatment of protocol conversion, the status of multiplexers and other digital equipment types, and the formulation of nonstructural safeguards such as "comparably efficient interconnection," "open network architecture," and new regulatory accounting standards, promise to be the focus of debate for some time to come. (For a very brief sketch of the entire Computer Inquiry III Rulemaking, see A *Primer on Telecommunications Law and Regulation,* p. 18f.)

V. EMERGING ISSUES IN TELECOMMUNICATIONS LAW

Section V contains a variety of discussions on some new, emerging issues in various relevant bodies of law affecting the telecommunications industry today. User strategies and approaches to the acquisition of telecommunications equipment and services are discussed in the first two essays. A following discussion addresses new issues related to an embryonic industry, shared tenant services

---

[2] For example, the California Public Service Commission, citing the *Louisiana* decision as authority, has petitioned the FCC for reconsideration of the Order on grounds that FCC lacks subject matter jurisdiction to impose Computer Inquiry III classifications on purely intra-state services.

(also called "intelligent buildings") created by the marriage of the telecommunications, and real estate industries. The final discussion focuses on technical and regulatory issues associated with a much-discussed development known as "Integrated Services Digital Networks" (ISDN).

The first essay, "Deregulation and Telecommunications Acquisition," is the editor's brief review of various issues pertaining to the procurement of telecommunications equipment and services under tariffed and nontariffed conditions, respectively. The discussion focuses on opportunities for communications users that arise from the de-tariffing of communications carrier services. Subsequent to the original publication of this essay, the District of Columbia District Court reversed and remanded the FCC's Competitive Carrier Rulemaking, Sixth Report and Order, under which the FCC had mandated the cancellation of nondominant carrier tariffs. This and other adverse appellate rulings have rendered questionable the FCC's authority to de-tariff common carrier services. (See discussion in *Primer on Telecommunications Law and Regulation*, p. 10f.)

The second essay is "Procurement of Customer Premises Equipment: Contracting in a Non-tariffed Environment" by Frederick L. Cooper, III, managing partner of the Computer/Communications Department of the Atlanta law firm of Hurt, Richardson, Garner, Todd & Cadenhead. Mr. Cooper discusses the specifics of contracting for CPE in a competitive, nontariffed environment. As noted earlier, the procurement of CPE under competitive, negotiated terms and conditions was made possible by the FCC's deregulation of that industry in Computer Inquiry II. Based on his experience in "high tech" equipment transactions and drawing on precedents from the related area of computer law, Mr. Cooper's essay provides insight into the various contractual issues and priorities relevant to user procurement strategies.

The following discussion on "Shared Tenant Services" by Henry W. Levine, partner in the Washington, D.C. law firm of Morrison and Foerster, provides a thorough review of the unique legal aspects of shared tenant services from the various perspectives of developers, operators, and tenants. Shared tenant services (sometimes called "intelligent buildings") refers to landlord-supplied telecommunications services to building tenants in conjunction with other utilities. As one of the nation's leading experts on this new industry phenomenon, Mr. Levine's leading edge discussions have been widely published in various industry journals. The issues associated with shared tenant services readily illustrate the new problems and concerns raised by the introduction of new technology (telecommunications) into an established body of law (real estate developer-landlord-tenant relationships).

The final discussion "Technical and Regulatory Issues Affecting ISDN Progress" was originally published by the editor in *Data Communications*. ISDN refers to a new technological development, based on digital telephony, which will eventually integrate voice and nonvoice services in carrier networks and will be accessible to users over newly-defined standard interfaces. The discussion here summarizes the technical aspects of ISDN and briefly raises some of the difficulties of ISDN regulation under FCC and MFJ policies. This essay introduced the concept of "ISDN Islands": the provision of different ISDNs in the U.S. by the various BOCs, separated by technological and legal boundaries.

VI. A VISION OF THE FUTURE

The last section consists of a single, famous essay, based upon FCC Chairman Mark Fowler's "Back to the Future" speech given at the January 1986 Communication Networks (COMNET '86) Conference in Washington, D.C. The essay, "Back to the Future: A Model for Telecommunications," based on that speech, was co-authored by the following gentlemen from the Commission: Chairman Fowler, FCC Chief; Common Carrier Bureau, Albert Halprin; and FCC Special Counsel, Policy and Planning Division, Common Carrier Bureau, James D. Schlichting.

"Back to the Future" is a policy statement. In the transition from regulation to competition, the FCC spokesmen point out that something was lost, namely a genuine debate on the future of telecommunication policy in the United States. Their article seeks to rekindle that debate by isolating issues that could serve as a point of departure. In so doing, the authors first presented an analysis of U.S. policies and social goals to date. Second, they put forth a "modest proposal," intended to spark ongoing and meaningful discourse on these issues by interested and affected parties.[3]

This controversial and somewhat radical proposal consists of a three-year deregulatory trial period under which the states would totally suspend telecommunications regulation within their respective jurisdictions. The authors predict that a competitive industry would result, thriving for the first time in a laissez-faire environment, unencumbered by the burdens of governmental authority. This bold experiment would be preconditioned on the development of an Open Network Architecture (ONA), originally discussed in Computer Inquiry III and described by Chairman Fowler as a type of equal access for end users to the local central office.

Furthermore, the trial would require that ONA be implemented for *all* telecommunications services: inter-exchange, local exchange, and enhanced. In order to preserve the socially necessary commitment to universal services, the proposal suggests funding such services through tax revenue subsidies. The proposal does not purport to superimpose FCC policies onto state regulatory regimes. Rather, the trial would be borne only by those states willing to participate in this experiment; therefore, it presumably would not run afoul of the jurisdictional preemption obstacles of the Supreme Court's *Louisiana* decision.

Finally, the proposal is neither detailed nor conclusive in its plan for the transition from regulated monopoly to competitive telecommunications industry.

---

[3] On a somewhat lighter, irreverent note, the proposal of "Back to the Future" reminds one of how the 18th century English author Jonathan Swift similarly stimulated a dialogue among his countrymen by publishing *A Modest Proposal for Preventing the Children of Poor People in Ireland from Being a Burden to their Parents or Country; and for Making them Beneficial to the Public* (1729).

Rather, it is an invitation to dialogue by the very participants whose ideas and debates will serve to fashion tomorrow's policies. Thus, it represents a fitting and salutary conclusion to the theme of this anthology.

*   *   *   *   *

Sic transit gloria mundei. All too often, the finer writings of men of letters are entrusted to the caretaking of philologists, lying unread for years in dusty archives. Consequently, the rich contributions of yesterday's teachers must often be recreated anew by tomorrow's students. So it is likely to happen with essays on a subject as multi-faceted, arcane and esoteric as telecommunications law.

Hence the purpose of this work: to capture in a unified volume—if only for a moment—the finer writings of today's pioneers in this field of study and thus preserve their efforts for tomorrow's practitioners. My own contributions modestly excepted, this anthology represents an attempt to collect the best essays in this all important area of law, graciously provided by those who are its leaders today.

Acknowledgments

As editor, I gratefully acknowledge the invaluable assistance of numerous individuals without whose help this work would not have been possible. Among many others, these include the following: the contributing authors themselves; the Atlanta law firm of Hurt, Richardson, Garner, Todd & Cadenhead (with special thanks to Frederick L. Cooper, III, Esq., J. Reid Hunter, Esq., Pat Smith Wilson, René Ogilvie, and Roberta Tepper-Guerin and her library staff); Dr. Wushow Chou and the editorial staff of Computer Science Press; Danny Adams, Esq., partner in the Washington, D.C. law firm of Wiley, Rein & Fielding; Jeffrey Blumenfeld, Esq., partner in the Washington, D.C. law firm of Blumenfeld & Cohen; Cynthia B. Somervill, Esq., Counsel for Gerber, Alley Associates, Inc., Atlanta, Georgia.

A very special note of thanks goes to Herbert E. Marks, Esq., partner in the Washington, D.C. office of Squire, Sanders and Dempsey, whose sage counsel inspired my efforts in this field of study.

Finally, I wish to thank various members of my family for their support on this effort, especially my mother, Ludmila Turro, my brother, John Turro, and my wife, Susan.

Walter Sapronov, Editor

About the Editor

Walter Sapronov is an attorney and telecommunications consultant, of Counsel to the Atlanta law firm of Hurt, Richardson, Garner, Todd & Cadenhead, with more than thirteen years in the computer and telecommunications industries. He has held senior consulting positions with NCR/Comten, Wang Laboratories, and General Electric Information Services Company. He has also held part-time teaching positions in computer science departments of the Georgia State University system. He has published and lectured extensively on law and technology. His clients include manufacturers, carriers, service providers, and users.

About the Contributing Authors

Dennis W. Carlton is a professor of Business Economics at the Graduate School of Business at the University of Chicago. He is also co-editor of the *Journal of Law and Economics* and a member of the Law and Economics Program at the University of Chicago Law School. His research and teaching interests include industrial organization, anti-trust, corporate finance, and econometrics. He has published numerous articles in journals and books on a variety of topics such as airline mergers, insider trading, futures markets, and pricing behavior. He is currently completing work on a textbook (with J. Perloff) on industrial organization.

Prior to joining the Business School, Professor Carlton was a member of the Law School and the Economics Department at the University of Chicago and the Economics Department at MIT. Mr. Carlton received his Ph.D. in Economics in 1976, his MS degree in Operations Research in 1975, both from MIT, and his B.A. degree (summa cum laude) in Applied Mathematics from Harvard College in 1972. He is a member of Phi Beta Kappa.

Mr. Carlton has served as an economic consultant on numerous occasions and has presented expert testimony before Congress, the Interstate Commerce Commission, the Federal Trade Commission, the Drug Enforcement Agency, and the Department of Transportation. Mr. Carlton is married and has three children.

James L. Casserly is a partner in the Washington, D.C. office of Squire, Sanders & Dempsey. He obtained his B.A. degree from Tufts University in 1973 and his J.D. from Columbia University School of Law in 1976. He then served as a judicial clerk in two courts, which are now known as the United States Claims Court and the United States Court of Appeals for the Federal Circuit. He represented American Indian tribes for several years before becoming involved with telecommunications issues. He currently represents companies and trade associations involved in the computer, communications, and consumer electronics industries before the Federal Communications Commission, the Congress, and the courts. He is active in a number of professional organizations and serves as the Co-Chair of the Committee on Legislation of the Federal Communications Bar Association.

Frederick L. Cooper, III, managing partner, Computer/Communications Department, Hurt, Richardson, Garner, Todd & Cadenhead, Atlanta, Georgia. Responsible for software related practice, specifically, protection of intellectual property rights; contracting for marketing, distribution, and strategic partnering; regulatory and strategic planning. Past Co-chairman of the Computer Law Section of the State Bar of Georgia. Board of Directors, Advanced Technology Development Institute, Atlanta, Georgia. Adjunct Professor of Computer Law at Wake Forest University School of Law. General Counsel to, and a member of, the Board of Directors of the National Association of Value Added Resellers (NAVAR). Editor of the bi-monthly newsletter, *Computer/Communications Report.* Bachelor's Degree and Juris Doctor Degree from Wake Forest University and its School of Law.

Kenneth A. Cox, is currently a consultant to MCI Communications Corporation. He received a B.A. from University of Washington in 1938; and LL.B. from University of Washington in 1940; and LL.M., University of Michigan, in 1941. He practiced law in Seattle, Washington from 1948 to 1961, with periodic service as special counsel to the U.S. Senate Commerce Committee, 1956-1960. He was Chief, Broadcast Bureau, FCC, 1963-1970; Senior Vice President, Regulatory; and Director, MCI Communications Corporation, 1970-Spring 1987. Currently, of Counsel, Haley, Bader, and Potts, 1970 to date and chairman, National Advertising Review Board, 1976 to date.

Mark S. Fowler, Former FCC Chairman—Republican. Nominated FCC Chairman by President Reagan; confirmed by the Senate May 14, 1981; sworn in May 18, 1981. Term ended April 17, 1987. Born in Toronto, Ontario, October 6, 1941, but a U.S. citizen from birth. Formerly senior partner in Washington, D.C. communications law firm of Fowler & Meyers. Communications counsel to the Reagan for President Committee in 1975-76, 1979-80. Coordinated 26 transition teams for upcoming President Reagan, including Department of Justice and FCC. Ten years broadcasting experience, including part-time announcing at radio stations during high school; announcer at WDVH (AM), Gainesville, while attending University of Florida. After graduation was full-time announcer, WKEE-AM-FM, Huntington, W. Va. (1963-64); announcer and sales representative, WMEG, now WMEL, Melbourne, Florida (1964-65); announcer, sales representative, program director and production manager at WDVH while attending law school (1965-70). Joined Smith & Pepper, Washington, D.C. communications law firm (1970). University of Florida (1966); University of Florida College of Law (1969). Currently, Mr. Fowler is Senior Communications Counsel for the Washington law firm of Latham & Watkins.

Albert Halprin is Chief, Common Carrier Bureau, Federal Communications Commission. Prior to this appointment, he was President of Albert P. Halprin Associates, Inc. and a partner in Kestenbaum and Halprin. Mr. Halprin also served as the Chief of the Policy and Program Planning Division in the Common Carrier Bureau, Federal Communications Commission. He previously worked for the Civil Aeronautics Board, the Department of Energy in the Office of Special Counsel, and the Commonwealth of Massachusetts. Mr. Halprin graduated from Western Washington State College and Harvard Law School.

Albert Kramer is a partner in the Washington, D.C. law firm of Wood, Lucksinger & Epstein. He is the general counsel to the North American Telecommunications Association, a trade association of independent telecommunications equipment manufacturers.

Warren G. Lavey is a partner in the Chicago office of Skadden, Arps, Slate, Meagher & Flom. He works on federal and state regulatory matters and communications ventures. He received a B.A. (summa cum laude) and an M.S. in applied mathematics, Harvard University; Diploma in Economics (first class honors), Cambridge University; and J.D.

(magna cum laude), Harvard Law School. Lavey served as Special Assistant to the Chief, Common Carrier Bureau, Federal Communications Commission in 1983-84. He has written numerous articles on telecommunications regulation and economics, and antitrust.

Henry D. Levine is a partner in the Washington, D.C. law firm of Morrison & Foerster, where he specializes in telecommunications law. He is the executive editor of *Telematics,* a monthly communications policy journal, and was a member of the National Academy of Sciences Committee on Technology Enhanced Buildings. Over the past four years, he has represented more than 30 building owners and developers in negotiating shared service contracts with providers of communications equipment and services.

Herbert Marks is a partner in the Washington, D.C. law firm of Squire, Sanders & Dempsey. He is a graduate of the University of Michigan and Yale Law School. Since 1970, Mr. Marks has participated in proceedings before the Federal Communications Commission, state regulatory agencies, the courts and the Congress on matters related to telecommunications regulation and industry structure. His work has been on behalf of clients in a variety of sectors, including data communications equipment, remote computer services and computer communications. These proceedings have addressed a wide variety of specific issues, including interconnection standards, pricing of services and products, corporate relationships, information transfer, the Computer Rules, the 1956 AT&T Antitrust Consent Decree, the jurisdiction of the Federal Communications Commission, and other matters.

Richard McKenna is General Attorney of Telephone Operating Group, GTE Service Corporation, and is responsible for legal representation of the GTE telephone companies before the FCC. Mr. McKenna took his bachelor's and law degrees from Fordham University in 1956 and 1960 respectively. His M.B.A. is from Columbia, 1961. He was with the New York law firm of Kirlin, Campbell & Keating 1962-1967, ITT World Communications Inc. 1967-1971, and GTE since 1971. He lives in Stamford, Connecticut with his wife, Lucy, and their four children.

Howard Polsky is a partner in the Washington, D.C. law firm of Wiley, Rein & Fielding. From 1976-1979, he served on the staff of the FCC's Common Carrier Bureau and from there became associated with the law firm of Kirkland & Ellis. As an adjunct professor of law at the Delaware Law School, Mr. Polsky taught telecommunications regulation from 1981-84. Mr. Polsky received a B.A. from Lehigh University in 1973, and was elected to Phi Beta Kappa. He received his law degree from Indiana University in 1976.

James D. Schlichting is Special Counsel for Domestic Policy in the Policy and Program Planning Division of the Common Carrier Bureau, Federal Communications Commission. Before working for the Commission, Mr. Schlichting was an attorney with the law firm of Wilmer, Cutler and Pickering in Washington, D.C., and clerked for Judges Philip W. Tone and Luther M. Swygert on the United States Court of Appeals for the Seventh Circuit in Chicago. Mr. Schlichting graduated from Yale College, *summa cum laude,* and Harvard Law School, *magna cum laude,* and pursued graduate research at Cambridge University.

Richard E. Wiley is a senior partner in the Washington law firm of Wiley, Rein & Fielding. From 1974 to 1977, Mr. Wiley served as Chairman of the Federal Communications Commission. His tenure with the FCC began in 1970 as General Counsel and, in 1972, he was appointed as a Commissioner. During Mr. Wiley's years at the FCC, he was associated with policies favoring the development of increased competition in the telecommunications field. He also was a leading force in the Commission's program to lessen regulation of industries within its jurisdiction. In addition to his FCC service, Mr. Wiley was appointed by both Presidents Nixon and Ford to the Council of the Administrative Conference of the United States. More recently, he served as head of the Reagan Administration's transition team for the Justice Department and as senior advisor in the FCC transition.

This work is dedicated to the memory of Eugene Turro,
Nicholas Ledkowsky, Helen and Vladimir Bastunov.

A PRIMER ON TELECOMMUNICATIONS LAW AND REGULATION

WALTER SAPRONOV, Esq.

TABLE OF CONTENTS

I. INTRODUCTION TO THE TELECOMMUNICATIONS REGULATORY ENVIRONMENT

A. Subject Matter of Telecommunications Regulation*

1. This outline summarizes some of the key elements of U.S. telecommunications regulatory policies as determined by Congress, federal and state regulatory authorities, and the courts.‡

---

*"Regulation" is defined as a "rule or order having force of law issued by executive authority of government." BLACK'S LAW DICTIONARY 1156 (5th ed. 1979).

‡This discussion addresses *selective* topics only and does not purport to be a complete or exhaustive treatment of the subject.

1

2. The subject matter of U.S. telecommunications regulation includes the provision of telecommunications services and equipment.

    a) Examples of telecommunications services include voice and data communications circuits, digital and high-speed services, radio microwave, cellular and mobile radio, packet-switching networks, satellite links, fiber optic links, electronic mail, voice mail, and remote database inquiry services.

    b) Examples of telecommunications equipment include multiplexers, concentrators, channel banks, circuit switches, carrier supplied exchange facilities (*e.g.*, CENTREX), and packet switches; examples of customer premises equipment (CPE) include modems, digital termination devices (data service units, channel service units, other digital network channel termination equipment (NCTE)), private branch exchanges (PBXs), protocol converters, packet assembler disassemblers (PADs), and computers.

    c) Regulatory policies change with the pace of the industry. As telecommunications technology advances, new services and equipment appear on the marketplace. Furthermore, as computers become increasingly linked to telecommunications facilities, and as communication networks become increasingly "intelligent," the line between computer and communications technology becomes blurred. Thus, both new telecommunication services and computers form part of the subject matter of regulation.

B. Telecommunications Regulation—Significance

    1. Regulation—generally

        a) Regulation of telecommunications equipment and services is a function of federal, state, and local laws, rules and policies affecting the provision of such equipment and services by carriers and others. "Deregulation" entails the removal or lessening of such rules and policies.

        b) From a public policy perspective, deregulation of the telecommunications industry has as its goal, the replacement of government regulatory oversight with a free, competitive telecommunications marketplace.[1]

    2. Regulatory policy changes directly affect the following:

        a) The scope of carrier participation in computer and communications markets;

---

[1] *See generally* Marks, *Regulation and Deregulation in the United States and Other Countries*, 25 JURIMETRICS 1 (1984); TELECOMMUNICATIONS IN THE U.S.: TRENDS AND POLICIES, (L. Lewin ed. 1981).

b) The scope of noncarrier (*e.g.*, computer manufacturers) participation in carrier-related markets;

c) The nature of transactions (*e.g.*, regulated, tariffed, contractual) between carriers, customers-subscribers, equipment suppliers, value-added suppliers, and others.

3. Role of counsel

a) Advocate in regulatory pleadings and litigation;

b) Contract negotiator for telecommunications equipment and services transactions; and

c) Counselor on impact of legal and regulatory developments on business planning.

C. Background: U.S. Domestic Regulatory Policies

1. Generally—telecommunications regulation involves the Communications Act of 1934 (as amended),[2] the rules and policies of the Federal Communications Commission (FCC),[3] state regulatory regimes, and the D.C. District Court's Modification of Final Judgment (MFJ)[4] which concluded the U.S. Justice Department's antitrust suit against AT&T by modification of an earlier, 1956 Consent Decree.[5]

2. U.S. Telecommunications Regulatory Authorities

a) *Federal* telecommunications regulation is empowered by the U.S. Constitution (Commerce Clause) and subsequent legislation (the Communications Act of 1934 (as amended)).

(1) Congress created the FCC pursuant to Communications Act "for the purpose of regulating interstate and foreign commerce in communication by wire and radio so as to make available...a rapid, efficient, nationwide, and world-wide wire and radio communication service with adequate facilities at no reasonable charges...."[6]

(2) Federal regulation of interstate communications carriage (*e.g.*, telegraph) falls under broad power of Congress to regulate commerce to the exclusion of conflicting state law.[7]

---

[2]47 U.S.C. §§ 151 (1976).
[3]47 C.F.R. §0.1 (1986).
[4]*United States v. AT&T Co.*, 552 F.Supp. 131 (D.D.C. 1982), ["MFJ"] *aff'd sub nom. Maryland v. United States*, 460 U.S. 1001 (1983).
[5]*United States v. Western Electric Co.*, 1956 Trade Cas. (CCH) ¶68, 246 (D.N.J. 1956).
[6]47 U.S.C. §151 (1976).
[7]*See, e.g., Gardner v. Western Union Tel. Co.*, 231 F. 405 (C.C.A. Okl. 1916), *cert. denied*, 243 U.S. 644. *See also Western Union Tel. Co. v. Spencer Bank*, 53 Okl. 398, 156 P. 1175 (1916); *Western Union Tel. Co. v. Orr*, 60 Okl. 39, 158 P. 1139 (1916).

(3) Such broad exercise of Congressional power over "communications" extends *inter alia* over radio broadcasting[8] and private allocation of the electromagnetic spectrum (*i.e.,* FCC has exclusive jurisdiction over radio transmission under Title III of the Communications Act).[9]

(4) The FCC establishes technical registration requirements for attaching customer premise equipment to the public telephone network, encompassing analog, digital, switched and non-switched devices.[10]

(5) The FCC establishes electromagnetic frequency emission limitations, licensing and labeling requirements for various computing devices (*e.g.,* computers, terminals, and personal computers).[11]

b) *State* telecommunications regulations is limited to purely intrastate communication; powers of state regulatory authorities (*e.g.,* intrastate telephone rate regulation) are authorized by state statutes.[12]

c) *Joint federal and state* regulation is expressly intended by the Communications Act, as amended in 1971, to cover telephone company property used for both interstate and intrastate communications.

(1) The Communications Act authorizes a Joint Board, comprised of three FCC and four state commissioners, having powers and jurisdiction equivalent to that of hearing examiner, to determine "jurisdictional separations" of costs of assets jointly used for interstate and intrastate communications. (47 U.S.C. §410(c)) The "jurisdictional separations" process allocates costs of jointly used assets into their respective interstate and intrastate components for rate making purposes.[13]

3. Federal vs. State Regulatory Policies

The area of federal-state relationships in United States regulatory policies is extremely complex. The following is a very brief sketch only.

---

[8]*See, e.g., Regents of University System of Georgia, et al v. Carroll,* 78 Ga. App. 292, 50 S.E. 2d 808, (1948), *aff'd,* 338 U.S. 586 (1950).

[9]47 U.S.C. § 301 *et seq.* (1976) *See, e.g., Motorola Communications and Electronics, Inc. v. Mississippi Public Service Comm'n,* 515 F.Supp. 793 (S.D. Miss. 1979), *aff'd,* 648 F.2d 1350 (5th Cir. 1981).

[10]47 C.F.R. §68 (1986).

[11]47 C.F.R. §15 (1986); *see generally* FCC Bulletin Office of Science and Technology No. 61, May 1984.

[12]*See, e.g.,* O.C.G.A. §§46-2-20-46-2-32 (1982).

[13]*See, e.g., Amendment of Part 31,* 92 F.C.C. 2d 864 (1983).

a) Generally, disputes concerning carrier provision of *interstate* services are governed solely by federal law; state action is precluded in this area.[14]

b) However, both the FCC and state regulators exercise concurrent jurisdiction over telephone plant which is used jointly for intrastate and interstate service; historically, this has been a source of conflicts.[15]

c) Until recently, federal/state jurisdictional conflicts have often been resolved in favor of federal preemption under various interpretations of federal preemption authority.[16] Some examples are as follows:

(1) States may not assert interconnection requirements over customer equipment which attaches to state telephone facilities. Customer premises equipment used jointly for interstate and intrastate communications has been ruled exclusively subject to FCC regulation.[17]

(2) The FCC has exclusive jurisdiction over radio regulation under Title III of the Communications Act; for example, the Georgia Public Service Commission has jurisdiction to regulate cellular radio telecommunications when provider is telephone utility but not when provider is radio utility.[18]

(3) FCC regulation preempts state and local zoning restrictions on receive-only satellite earth stations where local interests would frustrate federal policies.[19]

(4) The FCC thus far has declined to preempt state regulation of local telephone service resale in shared tenant services

---

[14]*Ivy Broadcasting Co. v. AT&T Co.*, 391 F.2d 486 (2d Cir. 1968).

[15]*See, e.g., Smith v. Illinois Bell Telephone Co.*, 282 U.S. 133 (1930).

[16]Federal preemption power over State law is ultimately based on the Supremacy Clause (Art VI, §2) of the U.S. Constitution. *See, e.g., Jones v. Rath Packing Co.*, 430 U.S. 519, 97 S. Ct. 1305 (1977); *Free v. Bland*, 369 U.S. 663, 82 S. Ct. 1089 (1962); *Florida Lime & Avocado Growers, Inc. et. al. v. Paul*, 373 U.S. 132, 83 S.Ct. 1210 (1963); *Rice v. Santa Fe Elevator Corp.*, 331 U.S. 218, 67 S.Ct. 1146 (1947); *Hines v. Davidowitz*, 312 U.S. 52, 61 S.Ct. 399 (1941); *Fidelity Federal Savings & Loan Assn. v. De La Cuesta*, 458 U.S. 141, 102 S.Ct. 3014 (1982). *See generally* McKenna, *Preemption under the Communication Act*, 37 FEDERAL COMMUNICATIONS LAW JOURNAL 1 (1984).

[17]*See Telerent Leasing Corp.*, 45 F.C.C. 2d 204 (1974), *aff'd, sub nom. North Carolina Utilities Comm'n v. FCC*, 537 F.2d 787 (4th Cir. 1976), ["North Carolina I"] *cert. denied*, 429 U.S. 1027 (1976); *North Carolina Utilities Comm'n v. FCC*, 552 F.2d 1036 (4th Cir. 1977), ["North Carolina II"] *cert. denied*, 434 U.S. 874 (1977); *Communication Services, Inc. v. Murraysville Tel. Co.*, 87 F.C.C. 2d 644 (1981), *aff'd*, 100 F.C.C. 2d 210 (1985) (Memorandum Opinion).

[18]83 Op. Georgia Att'y. Gen. 65 (1983).

[19]*Preemption of Local Zoning Regulations or Receive-Only Satellite Earth Stations*, 50 Fed. Reg. 13986 (April 9, 1985) (CC Docket No. 85-87).

("smart buildings") operations but has initiated an inquiry into that issue.[20]

(5) Under the Pole Attachments Act (47 U.S.C. §224(b)(1)), the FCC may prescribe "just and reasonable" rates for CATV use of utility poles.[21]

d) Communications Act Exception to Federal Preemption

(1) An exception to FCC preemption of state communications regulation is found in 47 U.S.C. §152(b) ("152(b) Exception") which reads in part as follows:

"Nothing in this chapter shall be construed to apply or to give the Commission jurisdiction with respect to...charges classifications, practices, services, facilities or regulation for or in connection with intrastate communications service by wire or radio of any carrier."

(2) Prior to the Supreme Court's decision in *Louisiana Public Service Comm'n v. FCC* ("Louisiana Decision"),[22] the old rule of law adopted by the courts in applying the 152(b) Exception to federal preemption limited its application to local services, facilities and disputes that are "separable from and do not substantially affect the conduct or development of interstate communications."[23]

e) The "Louisiana Decision"

(1) The Louisiana Decision reversed lower court cases which had reaffirmed FCC preemption of state regulation of depreciation rates for telephone company property.

(a) Holding: The Louisiana Decision held that the Communications Act (specifically, §152(b)) bars federal preemption of state regulation over depreciation of telephone property falling under joint federal and state jurisdictions for intrastate rate making purposes.[24]

(b) The Supreme Court's Discussion

[20]*In re Policies Governing Provision of Shared Telecommunications Services*, (CC Docket No. 86-9) (Released January 27, 1986).

[21]*Florida Power Corp. v. FCC*, 772 F.2d 1537 (11th Cir. 1985) rev'd 107 S.Ct. 1107 (1987). *See generally* Lipman and Knoble. *Pole Attachment Decision Threatens to Detach Telcom Regulatory Framework*, 3 TELEMATICS 5 (1986).

[22]*Virginia State Corporation Comm'n v. FCC*, 737 F.2d 388 (4th Cir. 1984) *rev'd and remanded sub. nom. Louisiana Public Services Comm'n v. FCC*, 106 S.Ct. 1890 (1986).

[23]*North Carolina I* at 792. *See* discussion in McKenna *supra* Note 16 at 33 *et seq.*

[24]106 S.Ct. at 1898-1904.

      (i) The Commuications Act is properly interpreted as enacting a *"dual* regulatory system" (emphasis in the original)—both federal and state.[25]

      (ii) The FCC may not take preemptive action over state law merely to effect its policy; The FCC is an agency that has no power to "act, let alone preempt the validly enacted legislation of a sovereign state" unless authorized by Congress. Thus, the FCC may not limit the application of the 152(b) exception without express statutory authority.[26]

      (iii) Legislative intent for dual regulatory system evidenced by "jurisdictional separations" process for allocating portions of joint assets to federal and state jurisdictions.[27]

      (iv) However, the Supreme Court distinguished earlier court cases which had affirmed FCC preemption of CPE attachment regulation on the basis that FCC may preempt state regulation where it is not possible to separate the interstate and intrastate components.[28]

(c) Implications: the Louisiana Decision may render area of federal/state policy conflicts unsettled; decision may hold authority for state assertion of exclusive jurisdiction over other areas of intrastate communication, thereby conceivably frustrating FCC policy objectives.[29]

II. FCC REGULATIONS AND POLICIES

A. FCC —Jurisdiction

1. FCC is an administrative agency, created by Communications Act of 1934—assumed powers formerly held by Interstate Commerce Commission; commissioners are appointed by the Executive Branch, responsible to Congress. (47 U.S.C. §151)

---

[25]*Id.* at 1899.
[26]*Id.* at 1901.
[27]*Id.* at 1902; *See* 47 U.S.C. §410(c) (1976).
[28]*Id.* at 1902 n. 4 (distinguishing *North Carolina I,* 537 F.2d 787 and *North Carolina II,* 522 F.2d 1036).
[29]*See generally* Levine.*Louisiana PSC v. FCC: What will the Gorilla Eat?,* 3 Telematics 9 (1986).

2. Common Carrier Regulation

a) *Common Carrier:* defined as "any person engaged as common carrier for hire, in interstate or foreign communications by wire or radio or in interstate or foreign radio transmission of energy" (excluding radio broadcasting). (47 U.S.C. §153(h)(13))

b) A common carrier "undertakes to carry for all people indifferently."[30]

c) Common carrier regulation attaches to resale carriers[31] but not to so called "private carriers."[32]

3. Statutory Basis for Exercise

a) Administrative provisions of Communications Act,[33]

b) Code of Federal Regulations,[34]

c) Administrative Procedures Act,[35]

d) Enforcement provisions of Communications Act authorizing enforcement of FCC decisions through courts of competent jurisdiction.[36]

4. Judicial Limitations on FCC Decisions

a) FCC rulemaking subject to appellate review; courts can reverse FCC rulemaking when its actions exceed scope of authority granted under Communications Act.[37]

b) Carrier compliance with FCC decisions does not confer antitrust immunity.[38]

c) Doctrine of "Primary Jurisdiction."

(1) Under this doctrine, courts of general jurisdiction may refuse to hear complaints against carrier and defer such actions to regulatory agency."[39]

---

[30]*Naruc v. FCC*, 525 F.2d 630, 641 (D.C. Cir. 1976).

[31]*See American Tel. & Tel. Co. v. F.C.C.*, 572 F.2d 17 (2nd Cir. 1978) *cert. denied*, 439 U.S. 875 (1978). *See generally* 46 ALR Fed. 626.

[32]*See In re Norlight, Declaratory Ruling* (File No. PRB-LMMD 86-07) (Released Jan. 13, 1987)

[33]47 U.S.C. §§402-409 (1976).

[34]47 C.F.R. §1 (1986).

[35]*See* 5 U.S.C. §§551, 701 (1976).

[36]47 U.S.C. §401 (1976).

[37]*See, e.g., Louisiana Decision*, 106 S.Ct. 1890; *MCI Telecommunications Corp. v. FCC*, 765 F.2d 1186 (D.C. Cir. 1985).

[38]*See, e.g., Southern Pacific Communications v. AT&T Co.*, 740 F.2d 980, 999 (D.C. Cir., 1984) (citing *Otter Tail Power Co. v. United States*, 410 U.S. 366, 372 (1973)). *Compare Phonetele, Inc. v. AT&T Co.*, 664 F.2d 716 (9th Cir. 1981) (Regulatory compliance relevant as a defense to antitrust action but does not confer immunity).

[39]*See In re Long Distance Telecommunication Litigation*, 612 F.Supp. 892, 895-899 (E.D. Mich. 1986), (citing *United States v. Western Pacific RR Co.*, 352 U.S. 59, 77 S.Ct. 161 (1956)); *Oasis Petroleum Corp. v. U.S. Dept. of Energy*, 718 F.2d 1558, 1564 (Temp. Emer. Ct. App. 1983). *See generally* 67 A.L.R. 3d 84, 89.

(2) Criteria for referring actions to regulatory agency includes factors such as judiciary experience in technical questions and dangers of inconsistent rulings.[40]

(3) Referral to regulatory agency under this doctrine does not deprive antitrust court of authority to decide ultimate issues.[41]

(4) State regulatory statutes are unenforceable to the extent they prevent compliance with antitrust decree.[42]

5. Areas of FCC Jurisdiction

  a) *Interstate* Communications Regulation

    (1) Interstate common carriage is regulated by the FCC under Title II of Communications Act. Regulatory mechanisms include:

      (a) Entry and exit authority ("Section 214" Authority);[43]

      (b) Tariff filing and reasonable rate requirements;[44]

      (c) Nondiscrimination in providing service and interconnection to other carriers upon reasonable request;[45]

      (d) Financial reporting, record keeping, and regulatory accounting requirements;[46]

      (e) Complaint procedures.[47]

    (2) Jurisdictionally Intrastate Communications

      (a) FCC jurisdiction does *not* reach communication between points within the same state-regulated jurisdiction, even if through a point outside that jurisdiction (*i.e., FCC does not exercise authority over jurisdictionally intrastate communications even if they cross state boundaries).*[48]

---

[40] *See RCA Global Communications, Inc. v. Western Union ,Telegraph Co.*, 521 F.Supp. 998, 1006 (S.D.N.Y. 1981) (citing *Orange & Rockland Utilities, Inc. v. Howard Oil Co.*, 416 F.Supp. 460, 466 (S.D.N.Y. 1976)).

[41] *United States v. AT&T Co.*, 461 F.Supp. 1314, 1329 (D.D.C. 1978). *Compare United States v. AT&T Co.*, 427 F.Supp. 57, (D.C. C. 1976), *cert. denied*, 429 U.S. 1071 (1977) (Antitrust court may consider deferring issues to FCC under primary jurisdiction doctrine at an appropriate stage of proceedings).

[42] *MFJ*, 552 F.Supp. at 155.

[43] 47 U.S.C. §214 (1976).

[44] 47 U.S.C. §§203, 201(b) (1976).

[45] 47 U.S.C. §§201(a), 202 (1976).

[46] 47 U.S.C. §§219, 220 (1976).

[47] 47 U.S.C. §§207, 208 (1976).

[48] 47 U.S.C. §153(e) (1976). *Compare Diamond International Corp. v. FCC*, 627 F.2d 489, (D.C. Cir. 1980) (where FCC determined that state rather than interstate tariffs applied to PBX access to interstate facilities). *But cf. Komatz Const., Inc. v. Western Union Telegraph Co.*, 290 Minn. 129, 186 N.W. 2d 691 (1971), *cert. denied*, 404 U.S. 856 (1971) (where telegraph message transmitted from one point within state to another *via* interstate route was determined to be "interstate communications").

b) Other Areas of FCC Regulation

(1) Radio licensing and allocation of radio spectrum for private microwave, direct broadcast satellite, mobile radio (under Title III of Communications Act);[49]

(2) Carrier provision of communications equipment and services other than common carriage. (*e.g.*, CPE, enhanced services); these are not regulated under Title II but are subject to so-called FCC "ancillary jurisdiction."[50] (See discussion in *Computer Inquiry II infra*).

B. FCC Regulatory Policies: A Pattern of Deregulation

1. FCC Forbearance Policies

a) Under the *Competitive Carrier Rulemaking*, the FCC has attempted to exercise varying degrees of regulation over common carriers according to their marketplace "dominance":[51]

(1) The term "dominant carrier" is used by the FCC to designate common carriers having "substantial opportunity and incentive to subsidize the rates for (their) more competitive services with revenues derived from (their) monopoly or near monopoly-services";

(2) "Dominant" common carriers are treated with full Title II regulation; examples of dominant carriers include AT&T Co. and the Bell Operating Companies ("BOCs");

(3) "Non-dominant" common carriers are treated with reduced or eliminated tariff filing requirements, presumption of tariff lawfulness, reduced reporting and Section 214 requirements; examples of non-dominant carriers include resale carriers, domestic satellite companies, specialized common carriers, and international record carriers;

(4) Title II complaint procedures, reasonable rate and non-discrimination requirements remain operative for all (dominant and non-dominant) carriers.[52]

b) The FCC's forbearance policy under the *Competitive Common Carrier* Rulemaking was adopted in stages.

---

[49]47 U.S.C. §301 *et seq.* (1976); 47 C.F.R. §§73, 90, 94, 100. *See Allocation of Frequencies Above 890*, Report and Order, 27 F.C.C. 359 (1959).

[50]47 U.S.C. §152, 153 (1976); *see Final Decision In re: Amendment of Section 64.702 of the Commission's Rules and Regulations*, ["Computer Inquiry II"] 77 F.C.C. 2d 384, 431-35, 450-52 (1980).

[51]*In re Policy and Rules Concerning Rates for Competitive Common Carrier Services and Facilities Authorizations Therefor*, ["Competitive Common Carrier"] First Report and Order, 85 F.C.C. 2d 1 (1980).

[52]*Id.* at 6.

(1) *Permissive Forbearance:* Under the *Competitive Common Carrier* Second Report and Order, the FCC *permitted* non-dominant common carriers to cancel existing tariffs on file.[53]

   (a) The permissive forbearance policy was challenged by MCI Communications Corporation on appeal of the FCC's *AT&T Resale Order* (under which the FCC had permitted AT&T's deregulated subsidiary to resell AT&T basic service without tariff); the appellate court dismissed the appeal as moot when AT&T withdrew the service and did not reach the issue as to whether the FCC has authority to *permit* carriers to offer services without tariffs.[54]

(2) *Mandatory Forbearance:* Under the *Competitive Common Carrier* Sixth Report and Order, the FCC *required* non-dominant common carriers to cancel their existing tariffs.

   (a) The *Sixth Report and Order* was reversed on appeal; the mandatory forbearance policy was held to be unlawful in that the FCC had exceeded the scope of its statutory authority by requiring carriers to cancel tariffs.[55]

c) *Streamlined Basic Services:* The FCC has proposed to "streamline" regulation of certain classes of dominant carriers' services, including packet switching services and services provided under competitive procurement.[56]

2. Computer Inquiry I[57]

   a) In *Computer Inquiry I,* the FCC attempted to distinguish between regulated and unregulated services according to the following definitional distinctions:

   (1) Communications—regulated,

   (2) Data Processing—unregulated,

   (3) Hybrid (mixed communications and data processing)—regulatory status unclear.

---

[53]*Competitive Common Carrier,* Second Report and Order, 91 F.C.C. 2d 59 (1982), *reconsideration denied* 93 F.C.C. 2d 54 (1983).

[54]*In re AT&T: Provision of Basic Service Via resale Separate Subsidiary,* Report and Order, 98 F.C.C. 2d 478 (1984), *vacated and remanded sub nom. MCI Telecommunications Corp. v. FCC,* No. 84-1402 (D.C. Cir. decided Sept. 5, 1986).

[55]*Competitive Common Carrier,* Sixth Report and Order, 99 F.C.C. 2d 1020 (1985) *vacated and remanded sub. nom. MCI Telecommunications Corp. v. FCC,* 765 F.2d 1186 (D.C. Cir. 1985).

[56]*In Re Decreased Regulation of Certain Basic Telecommunications Services,* Notice of Proposed Rulemaking, (CC Docket No. 86-421) (Released Jan. 9, 1987).

[57]*First Computer Inquiry,* 28 F.C.C. 2d 291 (1970), 28 F.C.C. 2d 267 (1971), *aff'd,* in part *sub nom. GTE Service Corp. v. FCC,* 474 F.2d 724 (2d Cir. 1973), *on remand,* 40 F.C.C. 2d 293 (1973).

(a) The Hybrid category created uncertainty over the regulatory status of certain equipment (*e.g.*, the Dataspeed 40 terminal).[58]

b) Eventually, *Computer Inquiry II* was initiated to clear up *Computer Inquiry I* uncertainty by establishing new regulatory definitions.

3. Computer Inquiry II[59]

a) In *Computer Inquiry II*, the FCC again attempted to draw a definitional distinction between regulated and unregulated services as follows:

(1) Basic Services—regulated,

(2) Enhanced services—unregulated,

(3) Customer Premises Equipment—unregulated.

b) Definitions:

(1) *Basic* Services: "a pure transmission capability over a communications path that is virtually transparent in terms of its interaction with customer supplied information."[60]

(2) Enhanced Services: "combines basic service with computer processing applications that act on the format, content, code, protocol or similar aspects of the subscriber's transmitted information, or provide the subscriber additional, different, or restructured information, or involve subscriber interaction with stored information."[61]

c) Examples:

(1) Basic Services—Long-distance voice, leased lines.

(2) Enhanced Services—database inquiry services; electronic mail; packet switching with protocol conversion.

d) Regulatory Distinctions

(1) The FCC distinguished *basic* services as regulated under (Communications Act) Title II from *enhanced* services and *customer premises equipment* (CPE) which are *not* regulated

---

[58]*See In re AT&T Co.*, 62 F.C.C. 2d 21 (1977), *aff'd sub nom. International Business Machines Corp. v. FCC*, 570 F.2d 451 (2d Cir. 1978).

[59]*Computer Inquiry II*, 77 F.C.C. 2d 384, *on reconsideration*, 84 F.C.C. 2d 50 (1980), *on further reconsideration*, 88 F.C.C. 2d 512 (1981), *aff'd sub nom. Computer and Communications Industry Association v. FCC*, 693 F.2d 198 (D.C. Cir. 1982), *cert. denied*, 461 U.S. 938 (1983).

[60]77 F.C.C. 2d at 419-20.

[61]*Id.* at 387.

under Title II but which are only subject to FCC's ancillary jurisdiction under Title I.[62]

    (a) Common carriers required to provide basic service only under tariff and on equal basis to all subscribers.

    (b) Enhanced services and CPE may *not* be provided under tariff or "bundled" with other regulated services.

c) Structural Separations

    (1) "Structural separations" is a requirement that regulated carrier can provide enhanced services or CPE *only* through a separate, deregulated affiliate (*e.g.*, separate subsidiary); example—AT&T and AT&T Information Systems.

    (2) The FCC imposed structural separations, first, on AT&T and subsequently, on the BOCs.[63]

        (a) The rationale for a structural separations is prevention of cross subsidy between regulated and unregulated services by dominant carriers.

        (b) The requirement entails separation of corporate structure, personnel, marketing, sales, accounting, customer records, and physical facilities.

6) Computer Inquiry II—Areas of Dispute

    (1) The "enhanced services" definition has required ongoing interpretation.

        (a) Some controversial examples of basic services include speed calling, call set-up and cessation, call progress signalling, packetized data transmission, inter-networking; these were eventually permitted to be provided as a part of "basic" services.[65]

---

[62]*Id*. at 431-35.

[63]47 C.F.R. §64.702 (1986). Structural separations were subsequently imposed upon the BOCs following the AT&T Divestiture, *see Policy and Rules Concerning the Furnishing of Customer Premises Equipment, Enhanced Services and Cellular Communications Services by the Bell Operating Companies*, 95 F.C.C. 2d 1117 (1983) ["BOC Separation Order"], *aff'd sub nom. Illinois Bell Tel. Co. v. FCC*, 740 F.2d 465 (7th Cir. 1984), *on reconsideration*, 49 Fed. Reg. 26,056 (June 26, 1984), *aff'd sub nom. North American Telecommunications Assn. v. FCC*, No. 84-2216 (7th Cir. August 27, 1984). For arguments for and against structural separations, see ENDING SEPARATE SUBSIDIARIES FOR TELEPHONE COMPANIES? NEW BUSINESS OPPORTUNITIES IN THE COMMUNICATIONS MARKETPLACE, Law and Business, Inc./Harcourt Brace Jovanovich, Publishers (1985).

[64]*Computer Inquiry II*, 77 F.C.C. 2d at 475.

[65]*Communications Protocols under Section 64.702 of the Comm'n Rules and Regulations*, 95 F.C.C. 2d 584 (1983); *Petitions for Waiver (X.25/X.75)*, Memorandum Opinion and Order, (F.C.C. No. 84-561) (released Nov. 28, 1984).

(b) "Net protocol conversion" (*e.g.*, asynchronous-to-X.25), permitting dissimilar computers to intercommunicate, is classified as an *enhanced* service; protocol conversion services therefore could only be provided under structural separations (via *separate* facilities and corporate organization) if offered by AT&T or BOCs. However, packetized transmission *without* net protocol conversion could be provided as part of regulated, *unseparated* telephone network.[66] [See Appendix "A" for illustration of structural separations as applied to packet switching facilties.]

(2) FCC Waiver of Structural Separations for BOC Packet Networks

(a) Waiver relief from structural separation requirements has been granted to some BOCs for provision of certain types of protocol conversion (asynchronous-to-X.25), thereby allowing use of central office switching equipment for *both* basic and enhanced services and further allowing joint marketing of combined packet switched and protocol conversion services by a single sales force.[67]

(b) The FCC's *Asynchronous/X.25 Waiver Order* allows BOCs to offer limited asynchronous protocol conversion as part of their regulated X.25 packet switched networks; however the *Asynchronous/X.25 Waiver Order* also imposes strict conditions on BOCs to show compliance with FCC rules concerning accounting separations, tariffed surcharges, and nondiscrimination vis-a-vis other enhanced service providers; to date, grant of such waivers has been subject to considerable opposition.[68]

(3) CPE Controversies

(a) The CPE classification encompasses terminals, modems, input/output devices, PBXs and, on the Justice Department interpretation, computers.[69]

---

[66]*In re AT&T, Bell Packet Switching Services (BPSS)*, 91 F.C.C. 2d 1 (1982); *BPSS*, 94 F.C.C. 2d 48 (1983); *IBM Petition for Declaratory Ruling re Southern Bell Telephone & Telegraph Company LADT Service*, Memorandum Opinion, (ENF File No. 83-84) (June 11, 1985) ["IBM Petition"].

[67]*In re Petitions for Waiver under Section 64.702 of the Commission's Rules*, 100 F.C.C. 2d 1057 (1985) ["Asynchronous/X.25 Waiver Order"].

[68]*See, e.g., In re New Jersey Bell Telephone Co., Petition for Waiver*, Memorandum Opinion and Order, (ENF File No. 84-22) (Released October 24, 1985).

[69]The MFJ defines "CPE" as "equipment employed on the premises of a person (other than a carrier) to originate, route, or terminate telecommunications, but does not include equipment used to

    (i) Disputes arise over what types of equipment qualify as CPE (*e.g.*, multiplexers, digital services equipment).[70]

    (ii) "Demarcation point" issue: what equipment can be provided by regulated carriers as part of network versus what equipment can be provided by unregulated customers/suppliers? (*i.e.*, where does regulated network end and unregulated customer premises begin?)[71]

(b) Other CPE-related issues

    (i) What are carrier disclosure obligations regarding network specifications necessary for independent manufacturers to attach their devices to the carrier network?[72]

    (ii) Under what conditions can CPE be provided by regulated carriers?

(c) Background of CPE disputes

    (i) The right of customer to attach its own CPE was established in *Carterfone*.[74]

    (ii) The rule of law is that attachment of non-telephone company devices is permissible if it is privately beneficial without being publicly harmful; furthermore, the carrier is under a heavy burden to show public (*i.e.*, network) harm.[75]

    (iii) The FCC enacted an equipment registration program in 1976, permitting direct customer attachment of non-carrier-supplied CPE to telephone net-

---

multiplex, maintain or terminate access lines." 552 F.Supp. at 228. For Justice Department's view that computers "interconnectible to telecommunications facilities" are CPE, *see United States v. Western Electric Co.*, 604 F.Supp. 256, 265 n.40 (D.D.C. 1984) (Memorandum Opinion).

[70]*See Petitions Seeking Amendment of Part 68*, 94 F.C.C. 2d 5 (1983), *reconsideration denied*, 97 F.C.C. 2d 527 (1984) ["NCTE Decision"].

[71]*See, e.g., ISDN*, First Report, 98 F.C.C. 2d 249 (1984).

[72]*See, e.g.*, 47 C.F.R. §64.702(d)(2)(1983) ("disclosure rule"); MFJ, 552 F.Supp. at 227; *Computer and Business Equipment Manufacturers Assn.*, 93 F.C.C. 2d 1226 (1983).

[73]*See Furnishing of Customer Premises Equipment and Enhanced Services bY AT&T Co.*, 102 F.C.C. 2d 655 (1985) ["AT&T CPE Relief Order"], *modified on reconsideration*, FCC No. 86-341 (released Aug. 7, 1986); *Provision of Customer Premises Equipment by the Bell Operating Companies and the Independent Telephone Companies*, 2 F.C.C. Rcd 143 (1987) ["BOC CPE Relief Order"].

[74]*Carterfone*, 13 F.C.C. 2d 420, *reconsideration denied*, 14 F.C.C. 2d 571 (1968).

[75]*Id.* at 424. *See Hush-A-Phone Corp. v. United States*, 238 F.2d 266 (D.C. Cir. 1956).

work equipment upon showing compliance with minimal technical specifications.[76]

(iv) The requirements for attachment (CFR Part 68) change as new CPE technology introduces technical changes.[77]

(d) *NCTE Decision*

(i) The deregulated CPE classification was extended to digital termination devices generally known as digital network channel termination equipment (NCTE).[78]

(ii) The deregulated digital NCTE classification includes Integrated Services Digital Network (ISDN) termination devices (known as "NT-1" in ISDN parlance.)[79]

(iii) Implication of the *NCTE Decision:* digital termination devices are to be provided by customers and suppliers on deregulated, non-tariffed basis and may *not* be provided by carriers as part of the regulated network.

(e) Carrier Provision of CPE

(i) Although digital NCTE was deregulated, the issue of provision of digital NCTE by carriers was reopened in Computer Inquiry III.[80] [See discussion *infra*]

(ii) *Centrex* service, although functionally similar to PBX equipment, was determined to be part of the regulated network—not CPE.[81]

---

[76]47 C.F.R. Part 68; *Docket No. 19528,* First Report and Order, 56 F.C.C. 2d 593 (1975); *on reconsideration,* 57 F.C.C. 2d 1216, 58 F.C.C. 2d 716, and 59 F.C.C. 2d 83 (1976); Second Report and Order, 58 F.C.C. 2d 736 (1976); *on reconsideration,* 61 F.C.C. 2d 396 (1976), *aff'd sub nom. North Carolina Utilities Comm'n v. FCC,* 552 F. 2d 1036 (4th Cir. 1977), *cert. denied,* 434 U.S. 874 (1977).

[77]*See, e.g., Petitions Seeking Amendment of Part 68 of the Commission Rules,* Third Report and Order (CC No. 81-216) (Released Nov. 4, 1985).

[78]*NCTE Decision,* 94 F.C.C. 2d at 22.

[79]ISDN is characterized as the provision of integrated services, both voice and non-voice, using digital transmission facilities over a limited set of subscriber interfaces. *See Integrated Service Digital Networks (ISDN),* Notice of Inquiry, 94 F.C.C. 2d 1289 (1983); *ISDN,* First Report, 98 F.C.C. 2d at 259.

[80]*Amendment of Section 64.702 of the Commission's Rules and Regulations, Third Computer Inquiry* (CC No. 85-229), Notice of Proposed Rulemaking, 50 Fed. Reg. 33581, at ¶141 (August 20, 1985), ["Notice"] Report and Order, 104 F.C.C. 2d 958, 1114-1123 (1986), ["Report and Order"] Supplemental Notice of Proposed Rulemaking, at ¶69 (Released June 16, 1986).

[81]NATA Petition for Declaratory Ruling Under Section 64.702 of the Commission's Rules Regarding the Integration of Centrex, Enhanced Services and Customer Premises Equipment, (FCC 85-248) (May 29, 1985).

(iii) The status of multiplexors, (i.e. as regulated network equipment or as deregulated CPE) remains ambiguous.[82]

(iv) Both AT&T[83] and the BOCs[84] have been granted relief from structural separations for purposes of providing regulated carrier services and deregulated CPE on a sole-source basis.

(v) Removal of separate subsidiary requirements for CPE provision by regulated carriers entail concerns over discrimination by regulated carriers against independent suppliers and dangers of cross-subsidy of unregulated CPE operations by carriers' regulated operations.[85]

(vi) In order to prevent carrier discrimination and cross-subsidy, the FCC's removal of structural separations for BOC provision of CPE is conditioned upon their compliance with various, so-called "non-structural" safeguards: disclosure of technical network information, nondiscriminatory treatment of customer proprietary information, availability of installation and maintenance to third party suppliers, and mandatory joint marketing opportunities for independent vendors to market their CPE with BOC regulated network services.[86]

(vii) Full removal of structural separations from BOCs' CPE operations further requires compliance with new regulatory accounting requirements designed to prevent cross-subsidy.[87]

(viii) Carrier interconnection barriers to customer-supplied CPE have historically held anticompetitive significance for antitrust proceedings.[88]

---

[82] See In re U.S. Transmission Systems, Inc., Petition for Declaratory Ruling to Remove Uncertainty Concerning the Status of Central Office Channel Termination Equipment, 100 F.C.C. 2d 517 (1985); IBM Petition at ¶11.

[83] See AT&T CPE Relief Order, 100 F.C.C. 2d at 655.

[84] See BOC CPE Relief Order at 2 F.C.C. Rcd at 143.

[85] Id. at ¶¶17-30; See also In re American Information Technologies Corp., et. al. 98 F.C.C. 2d 943 (1984).

[86] BOC CPE Relief Order at ¶¶34-94.

[87] Id. at ¶140. See Separation of Costs of Regulated Telephone Service from Costs of Nonregulated Activities, Report and Order, 2 F.C.C. Rcd 1298 (1987) ["Joint Cost Order"].

[88] See, e.g., U.S. v. AT&T Co., 524 F.Supp. 1336, 1349 (D.D.C. 1981); Jack Faucett Associates v. AT&T Co., 744 F.2d 118 (D.C. Cir. 1984), cert. denied, 105 S.Ct. 980 (1985).

4). Computer Inquiry III

   a) Generally speaking, the *Computer Inquiry III* proceeding represents a thorough revision of FCC policies regarding the provision of enhanced services and CPE by regulated common carriers. The proceeding developed in multiple phases as summarized below.[89]

   b) Issues Raised in the *Notice*:[90]

     (1) Whether and how the enhanced services "definition" should be revised in order to permit certain protocol functions to be provided by regulated carriers as part of the regulated network?

     (2) Should the regulatory treatment of digital NCTE be changed to allow regulated carriers to provide NCTE as part of the network?

     (3) What nonstructural safeguards should replace structural separations?

     (4) Should the enhanced/basic service definitional scheme of *Computer Inquiry II* be replaced with a new approach based on carrier market analysis?

   c) Synopsis of the *Order*

     (1) Structural separations' requirements for provision of enhanced services by AT&T and the BOCs will be removed subject to their showing compliance with "nonstructural safeguards."

     (2) Nonstructural Safeguards

       (a) Comparably efficient interconnection ("CEI"): CEI refers to technical parameters and pricing conditions which the BOCs and AT&T must implement in their networks to provide competitors with "equal access" to BOCs and AT&T network facilities whenever those carriers wish to provide enhanced services.[91] (See Appendix "B" for details on CEI).

       (b) Open network architecture ("ONA"): ONA is a logical extension of CEI; it represents an "unbundling" of the BOCs and AT&T basic networks into tariffed, "basic

---

[89]*See Report and Order supra* note 80, *on reconsideration,* Memorandum Opinion and Order, (Relesed May 22, 1987) (CC Docket No. 85-229) ["Reconsideration Order"]; *Amendment of Section 64.702 of the Commission's Rules and Regulations (Third Computer Inquiry) Phase II,* Report and Order, 52 Fed. Reg. 20714 (June 3, 1987) (CC Docket No. 85-229) ["Phase II"].

[90]*See Notice supra* note 80.

[91]*Id.* at ¶¶115-129; *Report and Order supra* note 80 at 1021-1059. *See generally* Marks, "Comparably Efficient Interconnection: Equal Access is Better," proceedings of EIA Conference on COMPARABLY EFFICIENT INTERCONNECTION, Washington, D.C., February 7, 1986.

service elements" ("BSEs") available on equal conditions to the carriers themselves and to others (*i.e.,* users and enhanced service providers). Theoretically, such "unbundling" or "opening" of the carrier networks will make carrier discrimination technically difficult or impossible and thereby will reduce the need for regulation. (Carriers must file ONA plans, including an initial BSE list, with the FCC by February 1988.)[92] (See Appendix "B" for an example of one BOC's approach to the ONA unbundling process).

(c) Other Nonstructural Safeguards

    (i) Prior to the removal of structural separations, carriers must adopt new regulatory accounting procedures for separating costs of regulated from costs of unregulated operations.[93]

    (ii) Additional requirements will be imposed on AT&T and the BOCs to assure adequacy of network information disclosure to competitors and nondiscriminatory treatment of customer proprietary network information.[94]

d) Synopsis of the *Phase II* Order

    (1) The FCC decided not to replace the "basic/enhanced" service definitions and ruled on the following issues regarding enhanced services:

        (a) Protocol processing (*e.g.,* asynchronous-to-X.25 protocol conversion) will continue to be classified as an enhanced service; CEI requirements for BOC provision of protocol conversion will be based on the *Asynchronous/ X.25 Waiver Order.*[95]

        (b) Relief from structural separations for BOC provision of enhanced services is conditioned on implementation of CEI/ONA and other non-structural safeguards including nondiscriminatory use of support personnel, network disclosure obligations, and nondiscriminatory use of customers' proprietary information.[96]

---

[92]*Report and Order supra* note 80 at 1059-1068.
[93]*Id.* at 1068-1077; *Joint Cost Order supra* note 87 at 1298.
[94]*Report and Order supra* note 80 at 1077-1092.
[95]*Phase II supra* note 89 at ¶¶43-71; *see Asynchronous/X.25 Waiver Order,* 100 F.C.C. 2d at 1057.
[96]*Phase II supra* note 89 at ¶77-186.

(2) Digital NCTE will remain classified as unregulated CPE.

  (a) However, carriers may provide NCTE loopback testing as part of the regulated network.[97]

  (b) The regulatory treatment of multiplexers remains unchanged; multiplexers may be provided as either deregulated CPE (by independent vendors) or as part of the regulated network by carriers in order to provide i) two or more channels to a single customer or ii) individual channels to two or more customers (the so-called "multiplexer exception").[98]

e) Synopsis of the *Reconsideration Order*

  (1) Upon review of various petitions for reconsideration of its decision, the FCC concluded that it would not change its decision to relieve AT&T and the BOCs from structural separations. Various clarifications of its decisions are as follows.

  (a) CEI requirements are optional and service-specific; ONA requirements, however, are mandatory.[99]

  (b) While full technical equality of access to carrier networks is the goal of CEI and ONA, equal access as perceived by the end user is a key factor in determining whether that standard has been met; ONA does not demand "impossible or grossly-inefficient over-engineering."[100]

  (c) Design of BSEs must address only the needs of enhanced service providers; however, BSEs must be available to any customer for any use when offered under federal tariffs; furthermore, states may impose additional customer or use restrictions for BSEs offered under state tariffs so long as they do not limit the availability of BSEs to enhanced service providers.[101]

f) State Opposition to *Computer Inquiry III*

  (1) The California Public Service Commission has appealed the Computer Inquiry III rulemaking on the issue of federal preemption, arguing that the FCC's preemption of state regulation of intrastate services is unlawful.[102]

---

[97]*Id.* at ¶¶213-227, 231-234.
[98]*Id.* at ¶¶228-230, 235-237.
[99]*Reconsideration Order supra* note 89 at ¶156.
[100]*Id.* at ¶92.
[101]*Id.* at ¶106.
[102]*People of the State of California and the Public Utilities Comm'n of the State of California v. FCC*, No. 87-7233 (9th Cir. filled June 4, 1987).

III. STATE TELECOMMUNICATIONS REGULATION

A. State Telecommunications Regulations—Generally

1. Regulatory regimes of state public service commissions ("PSCs") typically resemble federal regulations (*e.g.,* tariffs, entry and exit authority, complaint procedures).[103] Regulatory policies regulating local exchange competition, resale, and "private tariff" arrangements, however, vary from state to state.[104]

2. State and municipalities exercise regulation over *private* telecommunications facilities and construction (*e.g.,* local area networks) through right-of-way regulation, building and fire codes, electrical contractor requirements.[105]

B. Georgia Public Service Commission—An Example of State Regulation*

1. The Georgia Public Service Commission ("GPSC") is empowered by state legislation, consisting of five elected officials serving six-year terms.

2. GPSC Jurisdiction

   a) "Except as otherwise provided by law, the commission shall have the general supervision of...telephone and telegraph companies...within this state."[106]

   b) GPSC has exclusive ratemaking authority to determine "just and reasonable rates and charges."[107]

3. GPSC Regulatory Procedures

   a) Ratemaking procedures are subject to GPSC notice, hearing and review.[108]

   b) Administrative procedures are generally subject to Georgia Administrative Procedure Act.[109]

   c) The GPSC conducts hearings according to wide discretion.[110]

---

[103] *See, e.g.,* O.C.G.A. §46-2-20 *et seq. See generally* McCarren and Dworkin, "State Regulations and State Competitors" in proceedings of PLI Conference on THE NEW TELECOMMUNICATIONS ERA AFTER THE AT&T DIVESTITURE, Washington, D.C., Dec. 12, 1985.

[104] *See, e.g.,* Southern Bell Telephone and Telegraph Company Georgia General Subscriber Service Tariff: Sharing and Resale of Exchange Service (Issued April 16, 1984). *See generally* Levine and Kiser, *Customized Tariffs: The Dawn of a New Era,* 3 TELEMATICS 3 (1986).

[105] *See generally* Sapronov, "Networking: the Legal Links," *Data Communications Magazine,* January, 1985.

[106] O.C.G.A. §46-2-20(a) (1985).

[107] O.C.G.A. §46-2-23 (1985).

[108] O.C.G.A. §46-2-25 (1985).

[109] *See* O.C.G.A. §50-13-1 (1985).

[110] O.C.G.A. §§46-2-50, 51 (1985).

(1) Hearings are conducted when deemed to best serve public interest;

(2) Hearings are not bound by strict rules of pleading or evidence;

(3) The grant of application for certificate of convenience is matter of GPSC discretion, not a matter of right.[111]

d) Judicial Review

(1) Administrative remedies (i.e. GPSC hearings) must be exhausted before courts may exercise jurisdiction over reasonableness of rates.[112]

(2) Appeal procedures from GPSC decisions (*e.g.*, telephone company rate cases) as set forth in Georgia Administrative Procedures Act provide exhaustive remedy—injunctive relief from GPSC decisions is not available.[113]

4. Telephone Company Liability

a) Companies under jurisdiction of GPSC which unlawfully injure a person are liable for damages. Action may be brought in any court of competent jurisdiction. (Court may hear issues of damages only—not rates.)[114]

IV. AT&T DIVESTITURE AND THE MFJ

A. Historical Background

1) 1956 Western Electric Consent Decree was entered into by U.S. and AT&T to settle U.S. antitrust action filed vs. AT&T in 1949 for alleged anticompetitive practices.[115] Under that decree

a) The Bell System AT&T Long Lines, Western Electric, Operating Companies) remained intact;

b) AT&T was prohibited from entering business other than common carrier communications (*e.g.*, computers);

c) Bell Laboratories was precluded from manufacturing equipment other than for the Bell System and was required to make patent licenses available upon request.

---

[111]*Tamiami Trail Tours, Inc. v. Georgia Public Service Comm'n*, 213 Ga. 418, 99 S.E.2d 225 (1957); *RTC Transp., Inc. v. Georgia Public Service Comm'n*, 165 Ga. App. 539, 301 S.E. 2d 896 (1983).

[112]*Norman v. United Cities Gas Co.*, 231 Ga. 788, 204 S.E.2d 127 (1974).

[113] *Georgia Public Service Comm'n v. Southern Bell Telephone and Telegraph Co.*, 254 Ga. 244, 327 S.E. 2d 726 (Ga. 1985).

[114]*See Columbia Baking Co. v. Atlanta Gas Light Co.*, 78 Ga. App. 24, 50 S.E. 2d 382 (1948).

[115]*See United States v. Western Electric Co.*, 1956 Trade Cas. (CCH) ¶68,246 (D.N.J. 1956), 1956 Trade Cas. (CCH) ¶71,134 (D.N.J. 1956).

2) Entry of the MFJ

a) Antitrust action vs. AT&T, *et al.* was filed by U.S. Department of Justice ("DOJ") in 1974 for violation of Section 2 of Sherman Act.[116]

  (1) Trial began on January 15, 1981.

  (2) Proposed settlement between the parties presented to D.C. District Court ("Consent Decree Court") Judge Harold Greene on January 8, 1982.

b) New Consent Decree was styled as a "Modification of the (1956) Final Judgment" or "MFJ."

c) Following Tunney Act proceedings, including Competitive Impact Statement submitted by DOJ, Consent Decree Court accepted the settlement with modifications August 24, 1982, thereby vacating the 1956 Consent Decree and replacing it with the MFJ.[117]

d) Consent Decree Court retained jurisdiction and visitorial rights to ensure compliance with MFJ provisions, thereby assuming a regulatory-like role over BOC activities.[118]

e) The AT&T Plan of Reorganization (divestiture) was submitted to Consent Decree Court as a condition of acceptance of the antitrust settlement.[119]

  (1) Divestiture of the BOCs was effected by the transfer of AT&T stock ownership of the operating companies to seven regional holding companies (RHCs);

  (2) The RHCs serve a logistical purposes only and are bound by all provisions of MFJ.[120]

B. MFJ Restrictions on BOC Activities

1) The MFJ restricts the BOCs to role of local exchange carriers and expressly prohibits them from the following:

a) Providing interexchange services;

b) Providing information services;

c) Manufacturing CPE or telecommunications equipment.

---

[116]For opinions of the court on earlier phases of this case, *see United States v. AT&T Co.,* 461 F.Supp. 1314 (D.D.C. 1978); *United States v. AT&T Co.,* 524 F.Supp. 1336 (D.D.C. 1981).

[117]*MFJ,* 552 F.Supp. at 131.

[118]*Id.* at 230-231.

[119]*United States States v. Western Electric Co.,* 569 F.Supp. 1057 (D.D.C. 1983) *aff'd,* California v. United States, 464 U.S. 1013 (1983).

[120]*United States v. AT&T Co.,* No. 82-0192 slip op. at 2 n.2 (D.D.C. January 13, 1985), ["January Opinion"] *rev'd in part on other grounds sub nom. United States v. Western Electric Co.,* Nos. 86-5118, 86-5163, 86-6164 (D.C. Cir. Aug. 15, 1986).

      d) Providing any product or service except exchange telecommunications service and access that is not a tariffed monopoly.[121]

  2) BOC local exchange activities are circumscribed by local access transport areas ("LATAs"). [See illustration of LATAs in Appendix "C"]

  3) Comparison of MFJ and FCC Restrictions on BOC Activities

      a) Provision of CPE:

          (1) Under the MFJ, BOCs are unconditionally permitted to provide (but not manufacture) CPE;[122]

          (2) Under FCC restrictions, BOCs may provide CPE only through structural separations or by compliance with the FCC's *BOC CPE Relief Order.*[123]

      b) Provision of Information Services:

)(1) "Information Services," the MFJ equivalent of "enhanced services" under *Computer Inquiry II,* is defined as follows:

             (a) The offering of a capability for generating, acquiring, storing, transforming, processing, retrieving, utilizing, or making available information which may be conveyed via telecommunications, except that such services does not include any use of any such capability for the management of a telecommunications service.[124];

          (2) The extent to which BOCs may offer enhanced services, even under compliance with FCC policies, is unclear in light of the MFJ's information services prohibition and is subject to varying opinions by the FCC, the DOJ, and the Consent Decree Court.[123]

  4) BOC Obligations regarding Equal Access

      a) The BOCs are required to provide equal access to their exchange facilities to interexchange carriers and information service providers upon "bona fide" request.[126]

  5) BOC Entry into Other Markets

      a) BOC activities other than local exchange access and local ex-

---

[121]*MFJ,* 552 F.Supp. at 227-228
[122]*Id.* at 192-193.
[123]*See BOC CPE Relief Order supra* note 73 at 143.
[124]*MFJ,* 552 Fed. Supp. at 229.
[125]*See, e.g., Report and Order,* 104 F.C.C. at 976-977
[126]*MFJ,* 552 Fed. Supp. at 233.

change service requires DOJ recommendation and "line of business restriction" waiver from the Consent Decree Court.[127]

b) The controlling antitrust standard for granting line-of-business waiver requests to BOCs is that the waived activity will not create substantial possibility of anticompetitive conduct.[128]

c) Conditions for Consent Decree Court approval of line-of-business waivers are summarized as follows:

  (1) The line-of-business must be conducted through a separate subsidiary;

  (2) The subsidiary must obtain its own debt financing without creditor recourse to ratepayer assets;

  (3) The total revenues generated by a BOC under line-of-business waivers must not exceed ten (10%) per cent of its gross revenues;

  (4) The line-of-business is subject to DOJ monitoring and visitorial provisions of the MFJ.[129]

d) BOC waiver requests submitted to the DOJ are subject to comments by opposing parties. [See Appendix "C" for List of BOC Waiver Requests Submitted to the Justice Department]

6) Some Subsequent Interpretations of the MFJ

a) The Consent Decree Court has ruled that the interexchange services prohibition of the MFJ prohibits the BOCs from providing shared tenant services.[130]

b) Appellate Review of BOC Restrictions

  (1) The D.C. Circuit Court reversed and vacated the Consent Decree Court's Opinion and Order which had directed BOCs to cease operating outside their regions, ruling that the MFJ did not impose territorial restrictions on permissible BOC activities (e.g., two-way radio, paging.)[131]

c) The Consent Decree Court has ruled that absent a waiver, the BOCs may not market CPE to interexchange carriers for interexchange use (i.e., central office switching).[132]

---

[127]*United States v. Western Electric Co.*, 592 F.Supp. 846 (D.D.C. 1984) (Opinion).

[128]*Id.* at 869; MFJ, 552 F.Supp. at 231.

[129]*United States v. Western Electric Co.*, 592 F.Supp. at 870-872.

[130]*January Opinion, supra* note 120 at 20-33.

[131]*See United States v. Western Electric Co.*, Nos. 86-5118, 86-5163, 86-6164 (D.C. Cir. Aug. 15, 1986).

[132]*See United States v. AT&T Co.*, No. 82-0192 (D.D.C. filed April 11, 1985). [Memorandum Order granting Department of Justice motion to compel Bell Operating Company to cease providing telecommunications equipment].

C. Triennial Review of the MFJ Restrictions

1) Restrictions on BOC activities are currently under review by the Consent Decree Court.[133]

    a) Based on an independent consulting study (the "Huber Report"), the DOJ has recommended that the Consent Decree Court remove the manufacturing, information services and non-local exchange provisions of the MFJ (other than interexchange service which the DOJ recommends be permitted to BOCs under waiver.)[134]

    b) A decision as to the removal or modifications of MFJ restrictions is expected in the fall of 1987.

---

[133]*See* Report and Recommendations of the United States Concerning the Line of Business Restrictions Imposed on the Bell Operating Companies by the Modification of Final Judgment, *United States v. Western Electric Co.*, No. 82-0192 (D.D.C. filed Feb. 2, 1987).

[134]*See* Response of the United States to Comments on its Report and Recommendations Concerning the Line-of-Business Restrictions Imposed on the Bell Operating Companies by the Modification of Final Judgment, *United States v. Western Electric Co.*, No. 82-0192 (D.D.C. filed April 27, 1987) (relying on P. Huber, *THE GEODESIC NETWORK: REPORT ON COMPETITION IN THE TELEPHONE INDUSTRY,* (1987)).

APPENDIX A

Computer Inquiry II: Illustration of "Structural Separations" Applied to Carrier Facilities for Provision of Enhanced (Packet-switched) Services

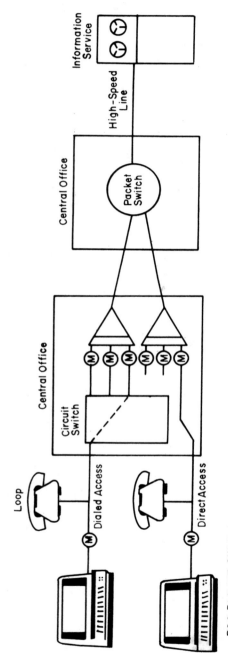

BOC PACKET SWITCHED SERVICES OFFERED WITHOUT STRUCTURAL SEPARATIONS

SOURCE: BELL ATLANTIC

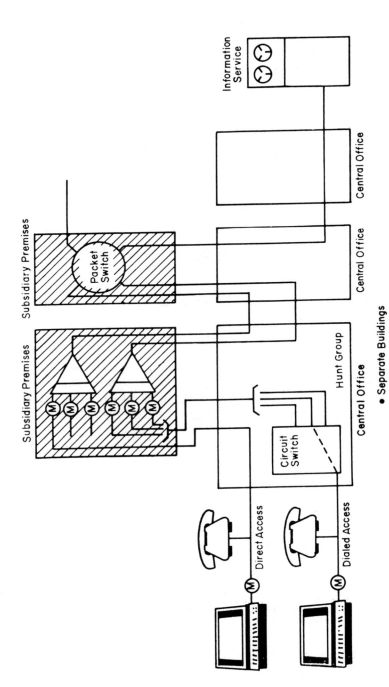

BOC PACKET SWITCHED SERVICES OFFERED UNDER STRUCTURAL SEPARATIONS

SOURCE: BELL ATLANTIC

APPENDIX B

Computer Inquiry III: Supplementary Materials on "Comparably Efficient Interconnection" (CEI) and "Open Network Architecture" (ONA)

I. SUMMARY OF "CEI" PARAMETERS AND PRICING

(FCC Computer Inquiry III Report and Order—CC 85-229)
Released June 16, 1986

Required Parameters for CEI Filings

1) Interface Functionality:

   Carriers are required to disclose standardized hardware/software switching and signalling specifications.

2) Basic Services Unbundling:

   Carriers' enhanced service offerings must include specific rate elements for basic service functions—for example, supervisory signalling, calling number identification; a network utilization rate element (NURE) is required where applicable—for example, in asynch-X.25 protocol conversion.

3) Resale:

   Carriers' enhanced service operations must take basic service at unbundled, tariffed rates.

4) Technical Characteristics:

   Equality of technical characteristics is required for basic services provision to both carriers and enhanced service competitors, including such elements as bandwidth, bit error rate, and mean time between failure.

5) Installation, Maintenance, and Repair:

   Identical time periods are required for servicing carriers and enhanced service competitors.

6) End-User Access:

   Equality of signalling capability is required for user access to carriers' and enhanced service competitors—for example, Data-Over-Voice, abbreviated dialing.

7) CEI Availability:

Carriers' CEI offerings must be available on same date that carrier offers its (unseparated) enhanced services. A reasonable CEI testing period must precede this date.

8) Minimized (Competitors') Transport Costs:

Where carriers do not elect co-location, they must provide minimized transport costs for competitors' access to their facilities through use of techniques such as trunk or loop multiplexing.

9) Recipients of CEI:

CEI must be generally available and not restricted to a particular class of subscribers or enhanced service providers.

Summary of CEI Pricing Principles

1) Transmission Rates:

Competitors' "distance sensitive" transmission rates will be cost based according to an unbundled, tariffed rate element.

2) Interconnection Charges:

Carriers' and competitors' interconnect charges must be equal; where interconnection interfaces for carriers and competitors are not identical (i.e. not co-located), such interconnection charges will be averaged over carrier and competitor interconnection facilities.

3) Concentration Equipment:

Concentration equipment located at carriers' central offices will be price averaged. Concentration equipment located at the competitor's premises will be cost-based; competitors have an option to acquire such equipment in unregulated customer premise equipment (CPE) markets.

4) Pre-Existing Services:

Pre-existing basic network services will be charged to both carriers and competitors at standard, tariffed rates.

II. STATEMENT OF "CEI" PRINCIPLES, PUBLISHED BY
CEI TASK FORCE (IBM, PACIFIC TELESIS, TYMNET)

RECOMMENDATIONS OF THE TASK FORCE
ON COMPARABLY EFFICIENT INTERCONNECTION (CEI)

<u>Task Force Members</u>

International Business Machines Corporation

Mr. E. Clark Grimes,
IBM Director of Telecommunications Practices
Mr. Dennis W. O'Shea,
Telecommunications Consultant

Pacific Bell

Mr. L. G. Camp,
Vice President, Marketing
Mr. T. C. Edrington IV,
Executive Director-Technology Assessment and Planning
Mr. Gary W. McBee,
Vice President, Washington Operations

Tymnet, Inc.

Mr. John J. Hainaut,
Directory, Technology Planning
Mr. Warren F. Prince, Task Force Chairman
President

March 25, 1986

COMPARABLY EFFICIENT INTERCONNECTION (CEI) PRINCIPLES

Opening Statement

CEI applies to enhanced services as defined by CI-II and is intended to enable users to access a range of enhanced service providers and to allow enhanced service providers to compete in the provision of such services. Enhanced services may be offered by a range of providers, including dominant carriers and/or their affiliates. CEI is composed of two major components: interface and connection.

"Interface" details the exact specification required to connect between the dominant carrier and the Enhanced Service Provider (ESP) without regard to whether the connection to the interface is colocated with the dominant carrier's central office or located off-site. The interface should be well defined, provide to

ESPs the same electrically transparent signal and complete functional equivalence, and generally be at a common point.

"Connection" refers to the means by which the interface is delivered to the ESPs, either to a colocated ES capability, such as when offered by a dominant carrier, or to the noncolocated facilities of an ESP. It includes transmission devices and associated media.

The appropriate benchmark for determining whether or not a particular interconnection proposal is comparably efficient is embodied in the attributes of colocation (e.g., transparency, functionality, quality, and cost).

Different classes of Enhanced Services (e.g., voice mail, protocol conversions) may require different types of loop technology (e.g., data-over voice, spread spectrum, time division multiplexing, copper wire) may require different types of interfaces and connections. The detailed issues relating to CEI will need to be resolved with respect to individual enhanced services. However, the Task Force participants endorse the following principles as appropriate to transform CEI from a concept to a useful set of regulatory principles. Each of the following principles presumes the implementation of all the other principles.

These proposals with respect to CEI are not intended to address all of the related but separate regulatory issues. A complete resolution will require agreement on or confirmation of other safeguards, such as the development of adequate cost accounting techniques, network interface disclosure requirements, the treatment of proprietary information, provision of underlying transmission at tariff rates, and other issues directly incorporated in the Third Computer Inquiry Notice of Proposed Rule Making.

CEI PRINCIPLES

A. Transparency to User

Dominant carriers will offer a transparent transport option to all service providers. A transparent offering is one in which there is no change in signal from the user to the service provider, including independence of bit sequence and of protocol. The interface should be well defined, provide to ESPs the same electrically transparent signal and complete functional equivalence, and generally be at a common point. Quality of service parameters attributable to CEI, such as bit error rate, transmission losses, and noise must be perceived as equal among all providers by the end user customers.

B. Choice to User

Users have a need to access a range of services and of ESPs and to support a variety of terminal protocols. The dominant carrier will offer efficient transparent option(s) for all enhanced services. In addition, the dominant carrier may offer other interconnection arrangements to ESPs with differing capabilities for satisfying user needs.

C. CEI Offerings Are Only Required When the Dominant Carrier Offers Enhanced Services

CEI is based on the principle that dominant carriers will offer access to others, comparable to access the carrier offers to itself, for enhanced services.

D. Cost/Pricing

CEI will be offered as a tariffed service, under the appropriate regulatory jurisdiction.

All parties agree that pricing equality at the point of interface is achievable. What has not yet been achieved is a means for accomplishing comparability in connection costs. Until further technical developments reduce costs, prices between the interface and the ESP will require deviation from cost based pricing (for some time) to achieve acceptable comparability by minimizing differences.

Dominant carriers will work with service providers to find mutually acceptable, comparable, cost efficient solutions to interconnection requests. Costing and pricing methodologies for connection should be consistent among dominant carriers.

E. Unbundling

Dominant carriers will unbundle any network building blocks necessary to provide CEI access to enhanced services.

F. Availability of Information

Information that the dominant carrier provides itself from the interface, to provide the enhanced service, (e.g., calling party identification, routing treatment such as satellite transmission utilized) and that is not proprietary to its relationship with its customer, will be provided to all ESPs as an element of CEI.

G. ISDN

CEI to subscriber information on the D channel can be achieved for enhanced services by routing Data Packets to the provider chosen by the subscriber. This can be accomplished through use of a Level 2 packet routing function based on the address in the D channel Link Access Procedure (LAP-D). This approach will also permit transparency above Level 2 and enable support of both X.25 and non-X.25 packet networks and terminals.

Without the above, the proposed CCITT ISDN implementation of packet switched information over the signalling ("D") channel does not permit CEI for enhanced service providers. Some additional technical definition is required. Provisions are needed for the link management, operations, and usage recording functions, etc. between the exchange and the service provider (these would otherwise be provided above Level 2). Figure B.1 illustrates this principle.

H. CEI Included In New Service Designs

The choice to end users of various ESPs should be assured through simple, easy to use ESP selection. Whenever a dominant carrier offers an enhanced service, it is incumbent upon them to include a CEI arrangement in the service design which adheres to these principles. CEI will be made available in the same exchanges to all interested ESPs simultaneously with competing dominant carriers' offerings. The current network interface disclosure safeguard can provide the means to initiate a dialogue between a dominant

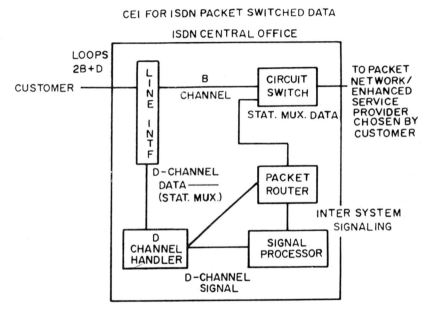

CEI FOR ISDN PACKET SWITCHED DATA

ISDN CENTRAL OFFICE

- APPROACH:
  (1) SEPARATE PACKETS USING D CHANNEL HANDLER
  (2) ROUTE DATA PACKETS TO ENHANCED SERVICE PROVIDER
      CHOSE BY CUSTOMERS
    - PACKET ROUTER
- PROVIDE ROUTING FUNCTION BASED ON LAP-D (LEVEL 2) ADDRESS
    - COMPETIVE ACCESS TO DATA PACKETS
    - EFFICIENT ROUTING
    - FACILITATES SUPPORT OF X.25 & NON-X.25 PACKET NETWORKS
      AND TERMINALS
      - TRANSPARENT L3 & ABOVE

Figure B.1

carrier and interested ESPs in order to expedite determination of acceptable CEI solutions.

III. "OPEN NETWORK ARCHITECTURE" (ONA) EXAMPLE: ONE BOC'S APPROACH TO ONA UNBUNDLING PROCESS

PACIFIC⊠BELL℠

A Pacific Telesis Company

OPEN NETWORK ARCHITECTURE

LOS ANGELES, CALIFORNIA

March 31–April 2, 1987

PACIFIC BELL PRESENTATION OVERVIEW

- Goals of ONA
- Network Capability Summary
- BSE Analysis Process
- Examples of Current and Future Network Capabilities
- Opportunity and Challenge
- The Future

PACIFIC BELL ONA GOALS

- Expanded Information Industry
- Equal Access to the Network and Underlying Capabilities
- Menu of Cost Effective Equal Access Interfaces
- End User Equal Access to ESPs
- Continued Commitment to Universal Service

"EQUAL ACCESS" HAS THREE COMPONENTS

- Functionality
- Cost
- Provisioning/Maintenance

OPEN NETWORK ARCHITECTURE

"(W)e require each carrier... to develop an initial set of key basic service elements that can be used in a wide variety of enhanced services . . . We would expect such a set to contain unbundled basic service functions that could be commonly used in the provision of enhanced services to the extent technologically feasible."
(*Computer Inquiry III*, Report and Order, Paragraph 216)

COMPLEXITY OF PACIFIC BELL'S NETWORK

- 12 Million Access Lines
- 500 Wire Centers
- 700 Switching Systems
- Over 11,000 Interoffice Carrier Routes
- $21 Billion Embedded Investment

DIVERSITY TO THE MARKETPLACE

- Voice and Data
- Numbers of Providers
- Evolving Standards
- Evolving Networks
- Dynamic Markets

NETWORK CAPABILITY MATRIX
List of Items Derived from ONAF1 Breakout Sessions

SUBJECT	TECH. AVAILABLE	TECHNICALLY INTEGRATED	TARIFFED AS NEEDED	TARIFFED BUNDLED	INVENTION REQUIRED
TRANSPORT/ CONCENTRATION					
Cost Effective Transmission	Yes				YES
Access to Clear Channel Transmission					Yes
Access to Derived Channels	Yes				
Access to ISDN "D" Channel Data Packet		Yes			Yes
Trunkside Access to Switch (EO)					Yes
Performance Parameters					Yes
3-6 db Loss Correction	Yes			Yes	Yes
Rework Feature Groups	Yes			Yes	
FG-D (W/O NTS)	Yes			Yes	
SIGNALING					
Direct ISDN "D" Channel Access		Yes			Yes
End User/Network Signaling		Yes			Yes
Faster Signaling/SS7		Yes			Yes
Supervision (Answer, Hang-Up, Disconnect, Seizure)	Yes	Yes			Yes
Line Status—Busy, Idle		Yes			Yes
Suppressed/Distinctive Ring				Yes	Yes
Screening (Class Type Service)					
Message Waiting	Yes	Yes		Yes	Yes
Inband Signaling on Analog Channels	Yes	Yes			Yes

SUBJECT	TECH. AVAILABLE	TECHNICALLY INTEGRATED	TARIFFED AS NEEDED	TARIFFED BUNDLED	INVENTION REQUIRED
ROUTING					
Call Forwarding: Enhanced Busy/Don't					Yes
SWITCHING					
Switching	Yes	Yes		Yes	Yes
4-Wire Interconnection	Yes		Yes		
Class Features (Ubiquitous Class)					Yes
Called Party Identification	Limited	Yes		Yes	
Calling Party Identification	Limited	Yes		Yes	Yes
Billing Number	Limited	Yes		Yes	Yes
NETWORK MANAGEMENT					
Access to 4kb Data Channel	Yes	Yes		Yes	Yes
User-Initiated Diagnostics	Yes				Yes
Management Functions/ Control	Yes	Yes			Yes
LOOP					
Presubscription to Local Loop		Yes		Yes	Yes
DIALING					
Abbreviated Dialing	Limited				Yes
BILLING					
Open Billing	Yes				Yes
SYNCHRONIZATION					
Internetwork Synchronization	Yes	Yes			Yes

PACIFIC BELL'S POSITION IS NOT NECESSARILY REFLECTED IN THE ABOVE LIST

APPROACH TO DEFINING BSEs

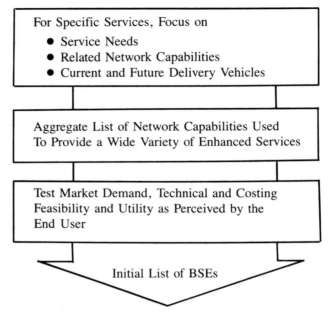

For Specific Services, Focus on
- Service Needs
- Related Network Capabilities
- Current and Future Delivery Vehicles

Aggregate List of Network Capabilities Used To Provide a Wide Variety of Enhanced Services

Test Market Demand, Technical and Costing Feasibility and Utility as Perceived by the End User

Initial List of BSEs

MECHANISM FOR INPUT INTO BSE DEVELOPMENT

- Forums
- Individual ESP Contacts
- Telecommunications Policy Symposium
- Consultant Conducted Interviews
- Ongoing Dialogue

REQUESTS FOR NETWORK FUNCTIONALITY

- Transparent Access to Core Network
  Switching
  Transport
- Equal Access Costs
- Access to End User/Network Signaling
- Maintenance and Diagnostic Information
- Less Functionality—Lower Price
- Other

NETWORK CAPABILITIES

- Available Today
- Available in the Future

NETWORK CAPABILITIES AVAILABLE TODAY:
VOICE MAIL/TELEPHONE ANSWERING SERVICE

BOC CENTRAL OFFICE

SERVICE NEEDS

Access to the End User

Called Party ID for Personal Service

Calling Number ID for Billing Information Plus ESP Access Security

Notify Customer of Message Waiting

Calling Party's Type of Forwarding for Personalized Service

Spread Call Demand Over Attendant Positions for Efficiency

ESP Transfer of Calls to Another Location for Personalized Service

End User Ability to Forward Calls to be Answered by the ESP

Cost Effective Transport

Information for Billing

-
-
-

NETWORK CAPABILITIES
Switched Access to Network

Called Number

Calling Number

Message Waiting

Type of Forwarding

Hunting

3-Way Call Transfer

Call Forwarding

Billing Number

Distinctive Ringing

AMA Information on Forwarded Calls

Multiplexing Options for Long Loops

Disconnect Supervision

Selections/Dialing Plan

-
-
-

VEHICLES TODAY

DID
SMDI*

PLANNED NETWORK ENHANCEMENTS

SS7

SMDI DN
DMS-100/5ESS

*SMDI is tariffed in California as "Forwarded Call Information"

ISDN "D" CHANNEL DATA ACCESS

ISDN Plan

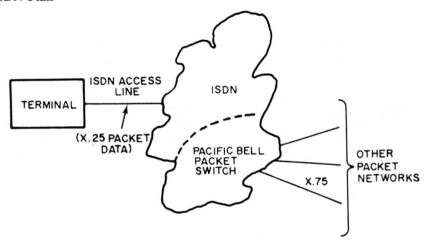

Future ONA Concept

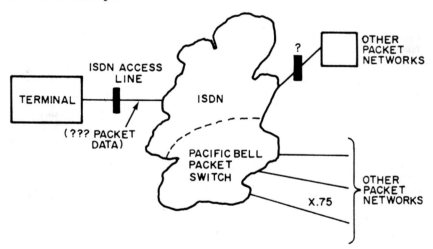

ONA WILL SUPPORT NEW OPPORTUNITIES: THE CHALLENGE

- Economic Evolution of the Network for ESPs and End Users
- Maintain Efficiencies While Providing a More Flexible Network
- Meet Reasonable Needs of ESPs Without Adversely Affecting the Broad Base of Existing Customers

CONTINUING PACIFIC BELL ACTIVITIES

- Continuing Dialogue
  Industry
  Regulatory Bodies
- Discuss Initial Set of Draft BSEs with Industry Participants and Regulatory Bodies
- Develop Ongoing BSE Definition Process for Evolution Beyond 2/1/88

PACIFIC BELL'S ONA PLAN

- Initial Set of BSEs
- Ongoing BSE Definition Process
- Future Network Capabilities
- Other Considerations

APPENDIX C

The AT&T Consent Decree ("MJF"): Supplementary Materials on Bell Operating Company Antitrust Restrictions and Line of Business Waiver Requests.

DEPARTMENT OF JUSTICE

ADVANCE FOR RELEASE AT 12 NOON E.S.T.   AT
TODAY, MONDAY, FEBRUARY 2, 1987   202-633-2016

The following statement was issued today by Charles F. Rule, Acting Assistant Attorney General in charge of the Antitrust Division:

Introduction
Today the government is filing with the court—U.S. District Judge Harold Greene in the District of Columbia—recommendations that the seven regional Bell Operating Companies created by the breakup of the American Telephone and Telegraph Company three years ago be allowed to enter a variety of new businesses from which they are now barred.

The Bell companies are barred from entering such businesses by temporary restrictions imposed by the 1982 consent decree which ended the antitrust suit brought by the Justice Department against AT&T in 1974.

When the decree was approved by the court in 1982, the court asked for, and the Department committed itself to provide, the report being filed today.

The government is also filing with the court a factual study of competition in the telecommunications industry made by Peter Huber, a lawyer and former engineering professor at the Massachusetts Institute of Technology.

He made the study while serving as a consultant to the Antitrust Division. Independenly of the Department, Huber studied the industry for almost a year, soliciting the views of telecommunications companies, consumer groups, and regulators. While the report does not make recommendations to the court, it provides a significant part of the basis for our recommendations.

LONG-DISTANCE RECOMMENDATIONS

We recommend that the restrictions on the Bell companies be removed in order to allow them to enter most types of businesses, but we recommend that certain restrictions be retained to limit their activity in the long-distance or interexchange area—carrying messages from one local exchange to another. The decree barred them entirely from such business, which is now carried on by AT&T and its competitors.

The government recommends that the decree continue to bar each of the seven Bell companies from providing long distance service to, from, or within areas in which that Bell company is the local telephone company. For example, Nynex, the Bell company that provides local telephone service in New York and New England, could not provide long distance service between New York City and Boston.

We recommend that in the future the prohibition on such "in region" service be lifted only in those areas where the states remove the regulatory protection that guarantees the local Bell company a monopoly franchise for local telephone service.

Until that time, the prohibition is needed to prevent the likelihood that a Bell company could exploit the local monopoly it enjoys under state regulation by discriminating against potential long-distance competitors that must hook up to its local exchange.

Our recommendations, however, would allow the Bell companies to provide long-distance service outside their own areas. There the Bell companies do not control the local exchange monopoly and cannot unfairly disadvantage long-distance rivals.

Our recommendations, for example, would allow Nynex to provide long-distance service between Los Angeles and Atlanta because such service would neither originate nor terminate in any exchange where Nynex controlled the local exchange facilities.

BACKGROUND

In the 1982 consent decree, which was agreed to by the government and AT&T and approved by the court, there were provisions to separate AT&T from its monopolies on local telephone service by creating the seven Bell companies to handle local service in the seven regions across the country.

The divestiture of the local companies from AT&T was carried out on January 1, 1984. At the time the decree was approved by the court, it was also agreed that the government would report to the court every three years therafter on how the restrictions on the Bell companies were working and to recommend any appropriate changes.

Since the only authority the government has in this matter derives from the antitrust laws, the standard that is incorporated in the decree and that we must apply is whether the restrictions are still required to prevent anticompetitive behavior by the Bell companies in the new markets that they seek to enter. Unless we find such a likelihood, we are compelled to recommend removal of the restrictions.

Apart from the restrictions on long-distance services by the Bell companies, the decree imposed three additional sets of restrictions, which we believe should be removed because they serve no purpose in protecting competition.

Those restrictions involve the provision of information services, the manufacture of telephone equipment and the entry into any non-telecommunications business without special permission from the court. I'll discuss them one at a time.

INFORMATION SERVICES RECOMMENDATIONS

The government recommends removal of the decree prohibition on the Bell companies' provision of information services because that prohibition is not necessary to protect competition and may be depriving large parts of our society of the benefits of the information age.

Information services include, for example, services that allow computers to communicate with each other; message services that do not require a customer to buy a separate answering machine; automated listings, accessible by telephone, that provide an alternative to newspaper classified advertising or allow customers to obtain information about such things as airline schedules; and meter reading or alarm monitoring from a central location that may reduce utilities' costs and rates.

Many information services are closely related to local telephone service and can at times be provided most efficiently by local telephone companies. Such services often depend on new technology that was not available anywhere at the time the decree was entered.

Information services that the Bell companies are prohibited from providing under the current decree restrictions already are available in local telephone systems in Western Europe and Japan, and we believe it is important that similar benefits be made available to American consumers.

Removal of the decree prohibition on Bell company provision of information services will not leave the Bell companies free to unfairly disadvantage rival information service providers.

Some rivals will not need access to the local exchange. Those that do will be ensured equality of access by the Federal Communications Comission's new Computer III rules, which have been specifically devised to advance the decree's goal of promoting competition. Computer III, as many of you know, is the FCC's rulemaking proceeding that set out the rules under which telephone companies would be allowed to provide so-called enhanced services—basically information services.

Continued duplication of FCC regulation in the information services area by the court and the Department, neither of which have the FCC's specialized expertise, is both unnecessary to protect competition and wasteful.

MANUFACTURING RECOMMENDATIONS

The government also recommends removal of the decree restrictions on Bell companies manufacturing and marketing equipment for themselves and other telephone companies and manufacturing telephone equipment for consumers, which they already are permitted to market.

Since divestiture, the equipment markets have become increasingly competitive, with foreign companies making significant inroads. While AT&T remains a leading firm, other industrial giants such as IBM and foreign telephone firms such as Siemens (West Germany), NEC (Japan), and Northern Telecom (Canada) have increased their share of the U.S. market. Lifting the decree's equipment restrictions will allow seven of this country's biggest telecommunications companies to enter these important and valuable high-tech markets.

In addition, any Bell company equipment business would be subject to several FCC rules designed to preserve equality between the Bell companies and other providers of equipment, as well as new FCC rules designed to restrict a carrier's ability to engage in anticompetitive cross-subsidization—using funds generated by inflated telephone rates to support the competitive equipment enterprise.

As a result of the divestiture and subsequent changes in competitive conditions, we have concluded that Bell company entry into the manufacture and marketing of telecommunications equipment does not raise sufficient antitrust dangers to warrant a judicial prohibition in addition to the existing FCC rules that are designed to protect and promote competition.

NONTELECOMMUNICATIONS BUSINESS RECOMMENDATIONS

Finally, the government recommends removal of the decree's restrictions that prohibit the Bell companies from entering any nontelecommunications businesses without the need to obtain special permission from the court.

The current waiver process, which requires individual application to the court in each case, already has allowed the Bell companies to enter businesses such as real estate, insurance, financial services, and a variety of foreign businesses.

Removal of the decree restriction would eliminate the burdensome waiver process and allow Bell companies to enter new businesses more easily as the FCC and state regulators consider appropriate.

THE FUTURE

The recommendations made by the government today will not take effect until they are approved by the court. The Department of Justice has asked the court to provide an opportunity for public comment and briefing on the proposed changes in the decree.

After considering the views of interested persons, the government will respond to the comments and modify its recommendations, if appropriate. The court may also decide to hold a hearing before reaching its decision on the recommendations.

I think it is important to note that the introduction of competition has been a major factor in decreasing prices in long distance service and in expanding the variety of telephone equipment available to consumers. We expect similar benefits from competition in many aspects of local telephone service.

Furthermore, all users of telephone service are likely to benefit from the increased efficiencies that would result from removal of the decree restrictions.

The government's recommendations will not have an adverse effect on either local or long-distance telephone rates. Nor do they call for any sudden changes that might be disruptive to consumers.

Rather, they provide for gradual growth and development, subject to regulatory controls where Congress, the FCC or state regulators consider such controls necessary to protect the public interest.

Competition is always unsettling and a bit chaotic, especially when technology is changing as fast as it is in the telephone business.

But competition is also the American way. In the end, competition is what works best for consumers.

Other countries—Japan and Britain, for example—are moving toward a competitive telephone industry too.

In many areas we are ahead of them, and it is important to maintain that advantage. We have much more competition in our long-distance business, for example. American consumers are already the winners.

In other areas we are falling behind. Foreign telephone companies—especially in France, Japan, and Britain—are already offering a host of 21st century electronic information services that are not yet offered here. The reason is that they permit their phone companies to compete in these markets, and we don't.

It's time for us to move prudently toward competition.

That means looking at what the Bell companies have to offer competitively in these new markets, many of which are critical to the future of the American economy.

BENEFITS TO CONSUMERS

The technology already exists to offer many new telephone services. For example, videotext and audiotext—which let computers talk to people—can provide directory information, yellow pages, classified ads, stock quotes, and so on. Protocol services can let computers talk to other computers. Alarm monitoring services can let sensors in the home talk to hospitals, security services, and so on, to alert them about home emergencies.

More competition will not be bad for American consumers. We are not proposing any change in local services or local rates. We are proposing to open the door to more competition in certain other markets.

Competition from the Bell companies could bring the consumer cheaper classified ads, faster and more efficient alarm services, perhaps even lower electric bills once we get to electronic meter reading and load-management services.

More competition in the equipment businesses may yield better telephones, more sophisticated business equipment or cheaper telephone cable.

If state regulators permit competition to come to the local exchange, we expect overall benefits to consumers here too. And at that point, though not before, we

ILLUSTRATION OF "LATAs"

● PRE-DIVESTITURE TOPOLOGY

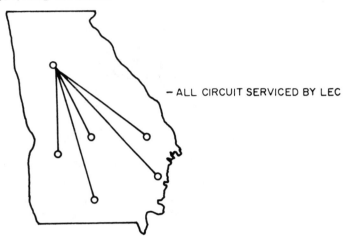

— ALL CIRCUIT SERVICED BY LEC

● POST-DIVESTITURE TOPOLOGY

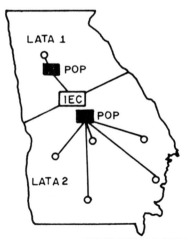

LATA 1

POP

IEC

POP

LATA 2

— ONLY INTRA LATA CIRCUITS SERVICED BY LEC
— POP = CARRIER POINT OF PRESENCE
— LEC = LOCAL EXCHANGE
— IEC = INTER EXCHANGE CARRIER

will also be able to let the Bell companies get into the long distance business to compete against AT&T, IBM/MCI, GTE/US Sprint, and the other giants already established in that industry.

CONCLUSION

The 1984 decree had the healthy effect of creating a business climate in which competition and the technological genius of the United States could flourish.

The changes that divestiture brought about caused some short-term discomfort, but the United States is today in a much better position to meet the telecommunications challenges of the 21st century.

While it would have been more comfortable, in the short run, to retain the old ways, the tough international competition we face today in many areas has taught us that competition and innovation are vital if we are to be able to meet foreign competition head on.

Nobody knows what all of the possibilities are that these recommendations suggest for telephone companies both now and in the future. Nor will it necessarily make sense for local phone companies to offer all of the services that are possible. But we have to prepare to move forward, and welcome more competition.

Most markets in the telephone industry no longer represent antitrust problems. They represent exciting new competitive opportunities—for American business and the American consumer.

LINE OF BUSINESS WAIVER REQUESTS
SUBMITTED TO THE DEPARTMENT OF JUSTICE
PURSUANT TO SECTION VIII(C)

Section I: Line of Business Waivers Submitted to (and Pending
                     Before) the Department of Justice

Section II: Line of Business Filings Pending Before the Court

Section III: Line of Business Waivers Approved by the Court

Section IV: Commentors

Section V: Regional Holding Companies

SECTION I

LINE OF BUSINESS WAIVERS SUBMITTED TO
(AND PENDING BEFORE) THE DEPARTMENT OF JUSTICE*

Date Submitted   Company

July 13, 1985   AMERITECH

Request for Waiver to Permit Ameritech to Provide Financial Services and to
Engage in Financing Transactions.

Comments Received: August 21, 1985:   Independent Data
                                        Communications Manufacturers
                                        Association, Inc.

                   August 21, 1985:   American Telephone and
                                        Telegraph Company

                   September 20, 1985: Ameritech Response

                   September 30, 1986: Ameritech

<u>Date Submitted</u>	<u>Company</u>
July 31, 1985	AMERITECH

Request to Construct InterLATA Transmission Facilities.

Comments Received:	August 21, 1985:	American Telephone and Telegraph Company
	September 16, 1985:	Midwestern Relay Company
	Sept. 20, 1985:	Ameritech Response
	October 11, 1985:	American Telephone and Telegraph Co.
	November 6, 1985:	Indiana Switch, Inc.
	November 12, 1985:	National Telecommunications Network
	Dec. 11, 1985:	MCI Communications Corporation
	Dec. 12, 1985:	Ameritech Reply
	Dec. 20, 1985:	Ameritech Response to MCI Comments

September 16, 1985	BELL ATLANTIC

Request to Permit it to Provide Direct Marketing Services.

Comments Received:	October 7, 1985:	American Newspaper Publishers Association
	October 7, 1985:	National Data Corporation
	October 8, 1985:	Lee Enterprises, Incorporated
	October 16, 1985:	Howard Publications, Inc.
	October 16, 1985:	Direct Marketing Association (as amended 10/21/85)
	October 16, 1985:	The Baltimore Sun
	November 12, 1985:	Bell Atlantic Reply
	December 18, 1985:	Direct Marketing Association, Inc.
	February 10, 1986:	Mega-Dial Comm. Inc.

Date Submitted   Company

November 21, 1985   U S West

Request by Pacific Northwest Bell Telephone Company for Authorization to Enter the Utility and Communication Facilities Construction Business.

Comments Received: December 11, 1985: American Telephone and
                                                     Telegraph Company

                                  December 13, 1985: United States
                                                     Telecommunications Suppliers
                                                     Association

                                  March 21, 1986: U S West Response

December 2, 1985   BELL ATLANTIC

Request to Continue to Provide Time and Weather Information as a Public Service.

Comments Received: December 20, 1985: Communications Ventures, Inc.

                                  December 20, 1985: D.C. Public Service
                                                     Commission

                                  February 13, 1986: Communications Ventures, Inc.

                                  February 14, 1986: Capital Weather Line

                                     March 7, 1986: Bell Atlantic Response to
                                                     Capital Weather Line
                                                     Comments

                                    March 18, 1986: Capital Weather Line
                                                     Opposition to Bell Atlantic
                                                     Response

                                      May 19, 1986: Telephone Time Temperature
                                                     Service

                                       June 5, 1986: D.C. Public Service Comm.

                                     June 20, 1986: Colorado Carphone

Date Submitted   Company

December 13, 1985   BELL ATLANTIC

Request of Bell Atlatnic Mobile Systems to Provide Cellular Service in Northeastern Maryland Through its Philadelphia/Wilmington System.

Comments Received: January 15, 1986: Washington/Baltimore Cellular Telephone Company

February 10, 1986: Washington/Baltimore Cellular Telehone Company Supplemental Comments

August 19, 1986: MCI

Sept. 25, 1986: Bell Atlantic Response

July 8, 1987: Bell Atlantic

July 20, 1987: Amtrak

January 29, 1986   AMERITECH

Request to Provide Voice Storage and Retrieval Services to Cellular Customers. (revised 2/4/86)

Comments Received: February 19, 1986: Detroit Cellular Telephone Company

February 19, 1986: The Cellular Telecommunications Division of Telocator Network of America

February 27, 1986: Associated Telephone Answering Exchanges, Inc.

March 14, 1986: MCI Communications Corporation

March 26, 1986: Ameritech Reply

April 10, 1986: The Cellular Telecommunications Division of Telocator Network of America Response

Date Submitted   Company

March 18, 1986   SOUTHWESTERN BELL

Request to Enter the Marketing Support Services Business.

Comments Received: April 11, 1986: National Data Corp.

                            April 29, 1986: Direct Marketing Association

                            May 6, 1986: American Newspaper
                                    Publishers Association

June 25, 1986   AMERITECH

Request to Provide Non-Telephone Directory Service.

Comments Received: July 15, 1986: Infotext International, inc.

                            July 16, 1986: American Newspaper
                                    Publishers Association
                                    ("ANPA")

June 26, 1986   US West

Request to Enter the Consumer Electronics Line of Business.

Comments Received: July 21, 1986: Tandy Corporation.

June 26, 1986   US West

Request to Enter the Market Research and Business Consulting Line of
Business.

Comments Received: Sept. 5, 1986: American Newspaper
                                    Publisher's Association
                                    ("ANPA")

June 27, 1986   AMERITECH

Request to Permit Its Software Affiliate, Applied Data Research, Inc., to Offer
Updates of Its Software Using Ordinary Telephone Facilities.

Comments Received: July 18, 1986: American Newspaper
                                    Publishers Association

                            August 1, 1986: Ameritech's Reply

<u>Date Submitted</u>   <u>Company</u>

June 27, 1986   US West

New Vector Motion to Amend Order of the Court Respecting Waiver of Section II(D) of the Modification of Final Judgment Regarding the Provision of Cellular Service in the Gulf of Mexico.

Comments Received: July 10, 1986: MCI Communications
                                         Corporation

                                 July 15, 1986: Petroleum Communications
                                         Incorporated

July 3, 1986   AMERITECH

Request to Permit its Operating Companies to Provide Customer-Name-Address Service.

Comments Received: July 18, 1986: American Newspaper Publishers Association ("ANPA")

                                 August 5, 1986: Response of Ameritech to ANPA.

                                 Sept. 30, 1986: MCI Communications, Inc.

                                 Oct. 17, 1986: Ameritech Operating Companies

July 15, 1986   US West

Request to Enter the Securities Line of Business.

Comments Received: Jan. 29, 1987: American Newspaper Publishers Association

July 22, 1986   BELL ATLANTIC

Request to Permit It to Offer Exchange Access Services on an Untariffed Basis.

Comments Received: Aug. 13, 1986: AT&T

                                 Aug. 27, 1986: MCI Communications
                                       Corporation

                                 Sept. 29, 1986: Bell Atlantic Request to Defer Justice Action

Date Submitted   Company

Aug. 28, 1986   SOUTHWESTERN BELL

Request to Provide Cellular Equal Access Services on an Untariffed Basis.
Comments Received: None to date.

Sept. 15, 1986   NYNEX

Request to Provide Office Equipment and Related Services Through Retail Store Outlets.

Comments Received: Oct. 1, 1986: Inacomp Computer Centers

                          Oct. 6, 1986: IDCMA

                          Oct. 6, 1986: MicroAge Computer Stores

                          Oct. 7, 1986: New York Department of
                                        Public Service

                          Nov. 12, 1986: North American
                                         Telecommunications
                                         Association ("NATA")

                          Dec. 4, 1986: NYNEX

Sept. 30, 1986   AMERITECH

Request to Permit Licensing to Third Parties Technology Developed or Acquired by Ameritech Non-Operating Companies for Use in Decree-authorized Lines of Business.

Comments Received: Oct. 20, 1986: USTSA

                          Oct. 21, 1986: IDCMA

                          Oct. 30, 1986: AT&T

                          Oct. 31, 1986: Pacific Telesis Group

                          Nov. 4, 1986: MCI

                          Dec. 11, 1986: Bell Atlantic

Date Submitted   Company

Oct. 20, 1986   SOUTHWESTERN BELL

Request to Provide Certain Billing and Collection Services on an Untariffed Basis.

Comments Received: Oct. 23, 1986: Southwestern Bell agreement to bifurcate request

Oct. 23, 1986   NYNEX

Request to Engage in Market Research and Business Consulting.

Comments Received: Jan. 29, 1987: American Newspaper Publishers Association

                                  Feb. 11, 1987: NYNEX's Response to ANPA

Oct. 24, 1986   BELL ATLANTIC

Request of Bell Atlantic Mobile Systems, Inc. to Provide Cellular Service in Five New Jersey Counties through Its Philadelphia and Atlantic Coastal Cellular Switches.

Comments Received: Nov. 14, 1986: American Cellular Network Corp. ("AMCELL")

                                  Nov. 14, 1986: Telocator Network of America

                                  Nov. 24, 1986: AWACS, Inc. (d/b/a Metrophone)

                                  Dec. 17, 1986: Cellular Telephone Company

                                  Feb. 13, 1987: Bell Atlantic Mobile Systems

                                  June 17, 1987: Bell Atlantic

                                  July 8, 1987: Bell Atlantic

Nov. 12, 1986   AMERITECH

Request to Expand Wisconsin Cellular Service Area.

Comments Received: Dec. 8, 1986: Ameritech

                                  Dec. 31, 1986: Milwaukee Telephone Co.

                                  Feb. 13, 1987: Ameritech

Date Submitted   Company

Nov. 20, 1986   BELL ATLANTIC

Request of Bell Telephone of Pennsylvania to Continue to Provide Time and
Weather Information as a Public Service.

Comments Received: Dec. 11, 1986: Com/unique, Inc.

                              Jan. 12, 1987: Bell Atlantic

                              Jan. 26, 1987: Com/unique, Inc.

Nov. 25, 1986   NYNEX

Request to Permit it to Enter [the Springwich] Partnership Which Would
Provide Cellular Service Beyond LATA Boundaries.

Comments Received: Metro Mobile CTS of Fairfield County
                              Jan. 29, 1987: NYNEX

Dec. 12, 1986   SOUTHWESTERN BELL

Request to Provide Paging Services on a Nationwide and International Basis.

Comments Received: Jan. 30, 1987: Cybertel Corporation

                              Feb. 20, 1987: Southwestern Bell

                              Mar. 6, 1987: Cybertel Corporation

                              Mar. 10, 1987: Southwestern Bell

                              Mar. 25, 1987: Telefind, Inc.

                              May 8, 1987: Southwestern Bell

                              May 19, 1987: Telefind, Inc.

*Dec. 19, 1986   BELL ATLANTIC

Request to Enter Certain Segments of the Electronics Business.

Comments Received: Being held in abeyance at Bell Atlantic's request.

---

*The Department of Justice requests that comments relating to these waivers be made within
twenty-one days.

Date Submitted   Company

Dec. 23, 1986   U S West

Request to Permit its Operating Companies to Provide Non-Tariffed Access Services.

Comments Received: Jan. 13, 1986: AT&T

                          Jan. 21, 1987: Ameritech Network, Inc.

                          Feb. 13, 1987: MCI Communications
                                         Corporation

Jan. 28, 1987   BELLSOUTH

Request to Permit its Acquisition of a Limited Interest in Mobile Communications Corporation of America.

Comments Received: Feb. 2, 1987: BellSouth Corporation

Feb. 11, 1987   PACIFIC TELESIS

Request to Provide Cellular Service in Detroit and Surrounding Areas.

Comments Received: Mar. 4, 1987: Non-Wireline Cellular
                                        Telephone Companies in
                                        Detroit Region

                          Apr. 10, 1987: Pacific Telesis Group

                          June 4, 1987: TRAC Communications, Inc.

Feb. 19, 1987   BELL ATLANTIC

Request to Continue to Coordinate Chespeake & Potomac and Diamond State Telephone Companies' One-Call Notification Services for Utilities.

Comments Received: Mar. 11, 1987: One Call Concepts

                          Mar. 27, 1987: Bell Atlantic

Date Submitted   Company

Mar. 10, 1987   AMERITECH

Request for Clarification or Waiver to Permit its Operating Companies to Continue their Existing Participation in One-Call Notice Systems.

Comments Received: Mar. 30, 1987: One Call Concepts

Mar. 30, 1987: Ohio Public Utilities
                        Commission

Mar. 31, 1987: Illinois Commerce Commission

Apr. 6, 1987: One Call Concepts

Apr. 10, 1987: Diggers Hotline

May 21, 1987: Detroit Edison

June 26, 1987: State of Michigan and the
                        Michigan Public Service
                        Commission

Mar. 13, 1987   U S West

Request to Provide Inter-LATA Paging Services in Connection with its Planned Acquisition of Contact Communications.

Comments Received: None to date.

Mar. 13, 1987   U S West

Request to Own and Operate Voice Storage and Retrieval Services Within Region in Connection with its Planned Acquisition of Contact Communications.

Comments Received: None to date.

Mar. 13, 1987   US West

Request to Own and Operate One Inter-LATA Microwave Link in Connection with its Planned Acquisition of Contact Communications.

Comments Received: None to date

<u>Date Submitted</u>   <u>Company</u>

Apr. 7, 1987   BELL ATLANTIC

Request to Amend and Clarify Bell Atlantic's Line of Business Authority.

Comments Received: Apr. 28, 1987: IDCMA

                            May 22, 1987: Bell Atlantic

Apr. 10, 1987   BELLSOUTH

Request for waiver to allow BellSouth Mobility Inc. to Provide Cellular Mobile Telephone Service Across LATA Boundaries within the Lexington, Kentucky Metropolitan Statistical Area.

Comments Received: None to date.

May 1, 1987   NYNEX

Request to Provide International Telecommunications To and From the United States.

Comments Received: May 22, 1987: ITT World Communications,
                                           Inc.

                            June 9, 1987: AT&T

                            June 16, 1987: STC plc

                            June 19, 1987: MCI Communications Corp.

                            June 19, 1987: U.S. Sprint

                            June 24, 1987: Teleport Communications

May 4, 1987   NYNEX

Request to Permit NYNEX Mobile Communications Company to Provide Cellular Service in the Nashua/Manchester, NH New England County Metropolitan Area (NECMA) and the Rockingham County, NH Portion of the Boston NECMA through its Eastern Massachusetts LATA Cellular switch.

Comments Received: May 25, 1987 New Hampshire Public Utilities
                                        Commission

Date Submitted   Company

May 29, 1987   NYNEX

Request to Permit Uninterrupted Service between the New York and Connecticut Cellular Systems.

Comments Received: July 10, 1987: AMCELL

                          July 10, 1987: Cellular Telephone Company

                          July 22, 1987: NYNEX Response to ANCELL

                          July 23, 1987: NYNEX Response to Cellular
                                         Telephone Company

June 4, 1987   NYNEX

Request to Permit Cellular Service Beyond LATA Boundaries between a NYNEX LATA and an area of the State of New York which is not served by NYNEX and for which no LATA has been established.

Comments Received: July 10, 1987: Syracuse Telephone Company

                          July 17, 1987: Syracuse Telephone Company

                          July 17, 1987: Buffalo Telephone Company

                          July 29, 1987: NYNEX Reply

*June 15, 1987   PACIFIC TELESIS

Request to Enter the Advertising Business.

Comments Received: None to date.

June 30, 1987   BELL ATLANTIC

Request to Provide Cellular Service to Three New Jersey Counties through Cellular Switches in Philadelphia and Atlantic City.

Comments Received: July 20, 1987: Amtrak

                          July 21, 1987: Canaan Industries, Inc.

                          Aug. 4, 1987: AMCELL

                          Aug. 4, 1987: AWACS, Inc.

---

*Submitted Pursuant to the Court's March 13, 1986 *Memorandum Order* establishing expedited procedures for identical waiver requests.

Date Submitted   Company

July 21, 1987   BELLSOUTH

Request to Allow Houston Cellular Telephone Company to Provide Cellular Mobile Service Across LATA Boundaries in the Houston and Beaumont, TX LATAs.

Comments Received: None to date.

August 7, 1987   SOUTHWESTERN BELL

Request to provide Cellular Service between San Antonio and Austin, Texas.

Comments Received: None to date.

SECTION II

LINE OF BUSINESS FILINGS PENDING BEFORE THE COURT*

Nov. 17, 1986   Motion and Proposed Order for a Waiver of the
Modification of Final Judgment to Permit NYNEX
Corporation to Provide Procurement and Support Services
Outside of the NYNEX Family of Companies.

Nov. 26, 1986   Motion and Proposed Order for a Waiver of the
Modification of Final Judgment to Permit Southwestern
Bell Corporation to Provide Extraterritorial Intraexchange
Specialized Telecommunications Services and MultiLATA
Paging and Mobile Radio Services.

Dec. 3, 1986   Motion and Proposed Order for a Waiver of the
Modification of Final Judgment to Permit Southwestern
Bell to Enter Certain Segments of the Electronics Business
(Southwestern Bell filed Motion for Reconsideration on
Jan. 13, 1987)

Jan. 9, 1987   Motion and Proposed Order for a Waiver of the
Modification of Final Judgment to Permit Ameritech
Mobile to Expand its Michigan Cellular Service Area
(beyond LATA boundaries).

Jan. 15, 1987   Motion and Proposed Order for a Waiver of Section II(D)
of the Modification of Final Judgment to Permit Bell
Atlantic to Provide Procurement and Support Services.

Feb. 12, 1987   Motion and Proposed Order for a Waiver of Section II(D)
of the Modification of Final Judgment to Permit Pacific
Telesis to Provide Voice Storage and Retrieval Services in
Connection with its Extraregional Cellular Business.

---

*Responses due 14 days after DOJ filing. *See* September 14, 1984 and March 13, 1986
Memorandum Orders.

SECTION III

Line of Business Waivers Approved by the Court

Waiver Issue	Regional Holding Company	Date Court Approved
Advertising	Bell Atlantic	4/13/87
	NYNEX	4/13/87
	Southwestern Bell	4/13/87
	U S West	6/18/87
	BellSouth	6/18/87
Cellular Monitoring & Consulting Services	Ameritech	8/16/85
	BellSouth	8/16/85
	NYNEX	8/16/85
	Southwestern Bell	8/16/85
	U S West/New Vector	8/16/85
	Pacific Telesis	11/06/85
	Bell Atlantic	4/08/86
Computer Sales, Service, & Maintenance	Bell Atlantic	12/14/84
Financial Services	Bell Atlantic (lease financing)	12/14/84
	Southwestern Bell (lease financing)	3/01/85
	US West/US West Financial Services, Inc.	8/22/85
	Ameritech	3/13/86
	Bell Atlantic (additional services)	3/13/85
	Pacific Telesis	5/22/86*
	NYNEX	11/14/86
	BellSouth	1/21/87*
Fleet Services	US West	2/28/86
	Bell Atlantic	9/26/86*
	Pacific Telesis	11/14/86

---

*Deemed approved pursuant to March 13, 1986 *Memorandum Order.*

Foreign Business Ventures	Ameritech (cellular)	12/14/84
	Ameritech (cnsulting)	12/14/84
	NYNEX	12/14/84
	Pacific Telesis	12/14/84
	US West	12/14/84
	BellSouth	3/01/85
	Southwestern Bell	3/01/85
	Ameritech (additional services)	5/01/85
	Bell Atlantic	8/13/85
	BellSouth (cellular)	9/10/85
	Southwestern Bell (cellular)	9/10/85
	Pacific Telesis (cellular)	9/10/85
	Ameritech	6/26/86
	BellSouth	8/20/86*
	US West	8/21/86*
	Southwestern Bell	9/08/86*
	Bell Atlantic	9/26/86*
	Pacific Telesis	11/14/86
	NYNEX	12/9/86*
Insurance	Ameritech (self-insurance)	10/14/86
	Bell Atlantic (separate sub.)	10/23/86
	NYNEX (self-insurance)	11/14/86
	Southwestern Bell (self-ins.)	11/14/86
	Pacific Telesis (self-ins.)	11/14/86
	US West (self-insurance)	12/11/86*
	US West (separate sub.)	12/11/86*
	Bell Atlantic (self-insurance)	1/21/87*
	US West	2/26/87
	US West (meet own needs)	2/26/87
Multi-LATA Paging	Ameritech	6/20/86
	Bell Atlantic	6/20/86
Nontariffed Billing Services	Ameritech (separate sub.)	5/24/85
	US West (separate sub.)	9/24/85
	Bell Atlantic (separate sub.)	9/24/85
	Southwestern Bell (sep. sub.)	1/27/86
	NYNEX (separate sub.)	10/8/86*
	BellSouth (operating cos.)	11/14/86
	BellSouth	
	Ameritech (operating cos.)	12/23/86
	Bell Atlantic (operating cos.)	12/23/86
	Bell South (operating cos.)	12/23/86

	NYNEX (operating cos.)	12/23/86
	Pacific Telesis (op. cos.)	12/23/86
	Southwestern Bell (op. cos.)	12/23/86
	US West (operating cos.)	12/23/86
Office Equip.	BellSouth	12/14/84
	NYNEX	12/14/84
	Pacific Telesis	12/14/84
	Southwestern Bell	3/01/85
	US West	8/21/86*
Out of Region	US West/NewVector (Gulf)	12/14/84
Cellular and	Pacific Telesis	2/26/86
Paging	NYNEX (Connecticut)	3/13/86
	US West/NewVector (San Diego)	4/11/86
	NYNEX (paging)	8/08/86
	BellSouth	10/31/86
	NYNEX	1/28/87
	Pacific Telesis	2/24/87
Print Media	Pacific Telesis	3/01/85
	Southwestern Bell	9/20/85
	NYNEX	10/28/85
	Ameritech	10/28/85
	BellSouth	10/28/85
	Bell Atlantic	1/27/86
	US West	3/12/86
Real Estate	Pacific Telesis	12/14/84
	US West	12/14/84
	BellSouth	3/01/85
	NYNEX	3/01/85
	Southwestern Bell	3/01/85
	Bell Atlantic	3/01/85
Software	Ameritech (separate subsidiary)	5/24/85
	BellSouth (separate subsidiary)	5/24/85
	BellSouth (operating companies)	5/24/85
	Bell Atlantic (separate sub.)	8/14/85
	Southwestern Bell (separate sub.)	8/14/85

	NYNEX (separate subsidiary)	8/14/85
	Bell Atlantic (operating co.)	8/16/85
	NYNEX (operating companies)	8/16/85
	Pacific Telesis (separate sub.)	1/27/86
	Pacific Telesis (operating co.)	4/11/86
	Ameritech (operating companies)	4/11/86*
	Southwestern Bell (operating co.)	4/11/86*
	US West (separate subsidiary)	5/13/86*
	US West (operating company)	5/13/86*
Telephone Answering Services and VSR	US West (NewVector—interim basis)	3/3/87
Training and Education	NYNEX	1/14/87
	Ameritech (operating companies)	2/24/87
	Bell Atlantic (op. companies)	2/24/87
	Pacific Telesis (op. companies)	2/24/87
	Bell Atlantic (sep. subsid.)	2/24/87
	Pacific Telesis (sep. subsid.)	2/24/87
	NYNEX (sep. subsidiary)	2/24/87
	US West	6/18/87
	US West (operating companies)	6/18/87

SECTION IV

Commentors

Organization	Address
American Bankers Association	William J. Bosies, Jr. Federal Administrative Counsel Federal Agency Relations American Bankers Association 1120 Connecticut Ave., N.W. Washington, DC 20036 (202) 467-4200
American Cellular Network Corp.	Kenneth E. Hardman Fortas and Hardman 1200 Twenty-Ninth Street, N.W. Washington, D.C. 20007
American Newspaper Publishers Association	Michael Yourshaw Wiley & Rein 1776 K Street, N.W. Washington, DC 20006 (202) 429-7028
AT&T Communications	Francine J. Berry Assistant General Counsel AT&T Communications Room 17-3244J1 295 North Maple Avenue Basking Ridge, NJ 07920 (202) 221-3327
American Network, Inc.	Michael L. Glaser Gardner, Carton & Douglas 1875 Eye Street, N.W. Suite 1050 Washington, D.C. 20006 (202) 872-0200
American Telephone and Telegraph Company	Jim G. Kilpatric Corporate Vice President-law 1120 20th Street, NW Suite 520 South Washington, D.C. 20036 (202) 457-7491

Organization	Address
Amtrak	Elyse G. Wander National Railroad Passenger Corporation 400 N. Capitol St., NW Washington, D.C. 20001
Associated Telephone Answering Exchanges, Inc.	David L. Hill Audrey P. Rasmussen Shack, Buenzle & Hill 1140 Connecticut Avenue, N.W. Suite 1005 Washington, DC 20036 (202) 293-5900
AWACS (d/b/a Metrophone)	Steven C. Schaffer Schwartz, Woods & Miller Suite 206, The Palladium 1325 18th Street, N.W. Washington, D.C. 20036
The Baltimore Sun	Reg Murphy President and Publisher The Baltimore Sun 501 North Calvert Street P.O. Box 1377 Baltimore, Maryland 21278 (301) 322-6000
Capital Weather Line	Gilbert B. Lessenco Wilner & Scheiner Suite 300 The Thurman Arnold Building 1200 New Hampshire Ave., N.W. Washington, DC 20036 (202) 861-7800
Canaan Industries, Inc.	Larry A. Blosser Fisher, Wayland, Cooper and Leader 1255 Twenty-third Street, N.W. Suite 800 Washington, DC 20037 (202) 659-3494

Organization   Address

Cellular Telephone Company   John Q. Hearne
                                      Fisher, Wayland, Cooper and Leader
                                      1255 Twenty-third Street, N.W.
                                      Suite 800
                                      Washington, DC 20037
                                      (202) 659-3494

Colorado Carphone   Larry J. Whitaker
                                      Colorado Carphone
                                      100 West Eleventh Ave.
                                      Denver, Colorado 80204
                                      (303) 893-8999

Communications Ventures, Inc.   Michael D. Ridberg
                                      Bergson, Borkland, Margolis and Adler
                                      11 Dupont Circle
                                      Washington, DC 20036
                                      (202) 462-5930

Com/unique, Inc.   Daniel Van Horn
                                      Arent, Fox, Lintner, Plotkin &
                                          Kahn
                                      Washington Square
                                      1050 Connecticut Avenue, N.W.
                                      Washington, D.C. 20036

CyberTel Corporation   Raymond G. Bender, Jr.
                                      Dow, Lohnes & Albertson
                                      1255 23rd Street, N.W.
                                      Suite 500
                                      Washington, DC 20037
                                      (202) 857-2500

Detroit Edison   Burkhard H. Schneider
                                      2000 Second Avenue
                                      Detroit, MI 48226

Diggers Hotline   Donald H. Gordon
                                      President
                                      2040 W. Wisconsin Ave., Suite 10
                                      Milwaukee, WI 53233
                                      (414) 344-7398

Organization	Address
Direct Marketing Association	Ian D. Volner N. Frank Wiggins Cohn and Marks 1333 New Hampshire Ave., N.W. Suite 600 Washington, DC 20036 (202) 293-3860
D.C. Public Service Commission	Howard C. Davenport General Counsel 451 Indiana Aenue,N.W. Washington, DC 20001 (202) 727-3050
Detroit Regional Cellular Telephone Companies	Patrick J. Whittle Heron, Burchette, Ruckert & Rothwell 1025 Thomas Jefferson St., N.W. Suite 700 Washington, D.C. 20007
Howard Publications, Inc.	Alfred C. Cordon Cordon and Kelly 1920 N Street, N.W. Second Floor Washington, DC 20036 (202) 293-2300
Inacomp Computer Centers	David L. Steinberg, Esq. 1800 West Maple Road Troy, Michigan 48084-0309 (303) 649-5580
Independent Data Communications Manufacturers Association, Inc.	Herbert Marks James L. Casserly Squire, Sanders & Dempsey 1201 Pennsylvania Avenue, N.W. Washington, DC 20004 (202) 626-6624 (202) 626-6717

Organization   Address

Indiana Switch, Inc.   Gerald White
                                      President
                                      P.O. Box 1785
                                      Indianapolis, IN 46206

Infotext International   Fritz Golman
                                      President
                                      875 North Michigan Avenue
                                      94th Floor
                                      John Hancock Center
                                      Chicago, IL 60611-1755
                                      (312) 670-4300

ITT World Communications, Inc.   John A. Ligon
                                      100 Plaza Drive
                                      Secaucus, NJ 07096
                                      (201) 330-5000

Lee Enterprises, Incorporated   W. Theodore Pierson, Jr.
                                      Richard M. Singer
                                      Pierson, Ball & Dowd
                                      1200 18th Street, N.W.
                                      Washington, DC 20036
                                      (201) 331-8566

MCI Communications Corporation   Michael H. Salisbury
                                      Jenner & Block
                                      21 Dupont Circle, N.W.
                                      Washington, DC 20036
                                      (202) 223-4400

Mega-Dial Communications, Inc.   Katherine M. Holden
                                      Wiley & Rein
                                      1776 K Street, N.W.
                                      Washington, DC 20006
                                      (202) 429-7245

Metro Mobile CTS of   Robert Kellor
Fairfield County   Fleischman & Walsh
                                      1725 N St. N.W.
                                      Washington, D.C. 20036
                                      (202) 828-7800

Organization

Address

Michigan Public
Service Commission

James G. Berry
Assistant Attorney General
1000 Long Boulevard
Suite 11
Lansing, MI 48911

MicroAge Computer Stores

Ross W. Blair, Esq.
Rudnick and Wolfe
30 North LaSalle Street
Chicago, Illinois 60602
(312) 368-8923

Midwestern Relay Company

William S. Reyner, Jr.
Robert M. Frieden
Hogan & Hartson
815 Connecticut Avenue, N.W.
Washington, DC 20006
(202) 331-4510
(202) 331-2624

Milwaukee Telephone Company

Douglas B. McFadden
McFadden, Evans & Sill
2000 M Street, NW
Washington, D.C. 20036

National Data Corporation

Joseph P. Markoski
Squire, Sanders & Dempsey
1201 Pennsylvania Ave., N.W.
P.O. Box 407
Washington, DC 20044
(202) 626-6634

National Telecommunications
Network

Martin F. McDermott, III
Vice President and General
    Manager
1350 Piccard Drive
Suite 400
Rockville, MD 20850
(301) 258-9717

Organization   Address

New Hampshire Public   Mary C. Hain, Esq.
Utilities Commission   Utility Analyst
                                      8 Old Suncock Road
                                      Concord, NH 03301-5185
                                      (603) 271-2431

North American Telecommnica-   Albert H. Kramer
    tions Association ("NATA")   Wood, Lucksinger & Epstein
                                      2000 M St., N.W.
                                      Suite 500
                                      Washington, DC 20036
                                      (202) 223-6611

Ohio Public Utilities   Ann E. Henkener
Commission   Asst. Attorney General
                                      Public Utilities Section
                                      180 East Broad Street
                                      Columbus, OH 43266-0573

One Call Concepts, Inc.   Lawrence L. Bell
                                      1011 Chevy Chase Lake Building
                                      8401 Connecticut Avenue
                                      Chevy Chase, MD 20815

Petroleum Communications Inc.   Dennis C. Brown
                                      Brown and Schwaninger
                                      1919 Pennsylvania Avenue, N.W.
                                      Suite 504
                                      Washington, D.C. 20006
                                      (202) 223-8837

STC plc   Andrew D. Lipman
                                      Pepper, Hamilton & Scheetz
                                      1777 F Street, N.W.
                                      Washington, D.C. 20006
                                      (202) 842-8100

Syracuse Telephone Company   Eliot J. Greenwald
                                      Fisher, Wayland, Cooper & Leader
                                      1255 23rd Street
                                      Suite 800
                                      Washington, D.C. 20037
                                      (202) 659-3494

Organization	Address
The Radio Common Carrier Division of Telocator	R. Michael Senkowski Katherine M. Holden Wiley & Rein 1776 K Street, N.W. Washington, D.C. 2006 (202) 429-7000
Tandy Corporation	John W. Pettit Hamel & Park 888 Sixteenth Street, NW Washington, DC 20006 (202) 835-8062
Telefind, Ltd.	David J. Kaufman Brown & Finne Suite 510 1920 N Street, N.W. Washington, D.C. 20036 (202) 887-0600
Telephone Time Temperature Service	Dudley S. Powell, Jr. 110 Winston Street Huntsville, Alabama 35801 (205) 539-5620
Teleport Communications	Michael Yourshaw Wiley, Rein & Fielding 1776 K Street, N.W. Washington, D.C. 20006 (202) 429-7028
TRAC Communications, Inc.	Donald E. Ward Ward & Mendelsohn, P.C. 1100 17th St., N.W. Washington, D.C. 20036 (202) 785-0200
US Sprint	Leon M. Kestenbaum 1850 M Street, N.W. 11th Floor Washington, D.C. 20036 (202) 857-1030

Organization	Address
Washington/Baltimore Cellular Telephone Company	Jonathan D. Blake Covington & Burling 1201 Pennsylvania Avenue, N.W. P.O. Box 7566 Washington, DC 20044 (20) 662-5264

SECTION V

REGIONAL HOLDING COMPANIES

AMERITECH

Thomas P. Hester
Senior Vice President
—General Counsel
Ameritech Corporation
30 South Wacker Drive
Chicago, Illinois 60606
(312) 750-5200

Jeffrey J. Kennedy
Kirkland & Ellis
200 East Randolph Drive
Chicago, Illinois 60601
(312) 861-2000

BELL ATLANTIC

John M. Goodman
General Attorney
Bell Atlantic, Inc.
1710 H Street, N.W.
8th Floor
Washington, D.C. 20006
(202) 392-1497

BELLSOUTH

Mark Hallenbeck
General Attorney
BellSouth Corporation
4300 Southern Bell Center
675 West Peachtree Street, N.E.
Atlanta, Georgia 30375
(404) 529-5555

Abbott Lipsky
King & Spalding
1730 Pennsylvania Ave., N.W.
Washington, D.C. 20006-4706
(202) 737-0500

NYNEX

Raymond F. Burke
Vice President and
   General Counsel
1113 Westchester Avenue
White Plains, NY 10604
(914) 683-2263

Martin Silverman
Washington Counsel
NYNEX Corporation
1828 L Street, N.W.
Washington, DC 20036
(202) 955-1170

PACIFIC TELESIS

Robert V. Dalenberg
Executive Vice President,
  General Counsel and
  Secretary
Pacific Telesis Group
140 New Montgomery Street
(415) 546-5700

Stanley J. Moore
Washington Counsel
Pacific Telesis Group
444 N. Capitol St., N.W.
Suite 718
Washington, DC 20001

SOUTHWESTERN BELL

Liam S. Coonan
Vice President, General
  Attorney—Washington
Southwestern Bell Telephone
1667 K St., N.W.
Suite 1000
Washington, D.C. 20006
(202) 283-8563

US WEST

C. Scott McClellan
Associate General Counsel
US West, Inc.
7800 East Orchard Road
Englewood, CO 80111
(303) 793-6339

David Sather
Washington Counsel
US West, Inc.
1020 19 St., N.W.
Suite 700
Washington, D.C. 20036
(202) 429-0303

Chapter 1

The Regulation of Interstate Telephone Rates*

CARL I. WHEAT

Charges for the interstate transmission of telephone messages were first subjected to federal administrative regulation by the Mann-Elkins Act of 1910,[1] which required such charges to be "just and reasonable,"[2] and indicated an apparent intent on the part of Congress to "occupy the field."[3]

That the concrete results of this legislation were relatively limited, both in nature and extent, may doubtless be attributed largely to the lack of adequate congressional appropriations, over the years,[4] and apparently in part to the more

---

*Reprinted with permission from 51 *Harvard Law Review 846*. Copyright 1938, Harvard Law Review Association. All rights reserved.

†The writer desires to acknowledge the assistance and counsel rendered in connection with the preparation of this article by his associates, Harold J. Cohen, of the Illinois Bar; Robert E. May, of the District of Columbia Bar; and Milford Springer, of the California Bar.

[1]Act of June 18, 1910, §7, 36 STAT. 544.

[2]Since the requirements of §6 of the Interstate Commerce Act in respect to the filing of tariffs seemed applicable only to transportation carriers, the Commission deemed itself without authority to require such filing. Unrepeated Message Case, 44 I.C.C. 670 (1917).

[3]Of this Act, the Interstate Commerce Commission, in one of the few formal telephone matters which arose before it, stated: "By the amendatory act of June 18, 1910, telephone and telegraph companies were declared to be common carriers and we were given jurisdiction and control over their interstate rates and practices, as well as the rules, regulations, conditions, and restrictions affecting their interstate rates." Huntington Engineering Co. v. Chesapeake & P. Tel. Co., 112 I.C.C. 377, 379 (1926).

[4]The Preliminary Report on Communication Companies [H.R. REP. No. 1273, 73d Cong., 2d Sess. (1934)], submitted on April 18, 1934, pursuant to H. R. RES. 59, 72d Cong., 1st Sess. (1932), and H. J. RES. 572, 72d Cong., 2d Sess. (1933) (the so-called "Splawn Report"), declared that: "At the present time there is little, if any, Federal regulation of the rates, practices, and charges of the several branches of the communication industry. This is, however, not due to any lack of interest or sense of responsibility by the Interstate Commerce Commission; rather it has been due to the absence of an effective mandate from the Congress. Congress has not had enough interest in, or information about, the communication companies to respond in a mandate to make inquiries coupled with appropriations sufficient to carry on an investigation." (p. xvi.)

or less "judicial" attitude adopted by the Interstate Commerce Commission in respect to telephone rate problems. In the field of railroad rate making the practice of that body had long been to rely upon shippers to draw to its attention, usually through formal complaint, any inequalities or improprieties in the charges made by common carriers subject to its authority. No exception was made when jurisdiction over interstate telephone charges was acquired. The relatively large sums ordinarily involved in railroad rate controversies, and the resultant monetary incentives to positive shipper action, had apparently rendered the Commission's traditional practice feasible in that field. But reliance upon "complaints" as the moving force in the regulatory process was obviously unsuited to effective telephone rate regulation. Individual monetary incentive was so largely absent in that field that no individual user of the service could fairly have been expected to bear the large costs necessarily incident to the prosecution of a telephone rate case.[5]

Meanwhile the states went forward with their individual exploration of the intricate and at times vexing regulatory problems posed by the telephone industry. Indeed, prior to 1930 all but three states (Delaware, Texas, and Iowa) provided themselves with regulatory commissions, clothed with comprehensive intrastate telephone rate jurisdiction. The complex nature of the telephone business, however, and in particular the organization and methods of control over local operating companies adopted by the American Telephone and Telegraph Company, has frequently rendered state regulatory efforts ineffective, and in certain respects wholly nugatory. Problems arising out of the relations between local operating companies and their parent corporation, as well as problems relating to equipment manufacturing costs and prices, to depreciation practices, and to many other phases of broad operating and regulatory policies, have constantly arisen to plague the state commissions, faced as they are with limited geographical jurisdiction and with lack of authority over units of the system other than the individual operating company serving their own state. In many respects their hands have been tied.[6]

---

[5]Practically the only concrete result of the Mann-Elkins Act, insofar as it applied to interstate telephone practices, related not to rates but to accounting. In 1913, the Interstate Commerce Commission adopted its Uniform Classification of Accounts for Telephone Companies, a system which has largely been followed by the State Commissions; which was broadly revised in 1933, and which has now been superseded by the Uniform System of Accounts for Telephone Companies adopted in 1935 by the Federal Communications Commission. See American Tel. & Tel. Co. v. United States, 299 U.S. 232 (1936).

Certain activity in respect to the depreciation accounting practices of telephone companies followed the enactment of the Transportation Act, 1920 (41 STAT. 456, §20(5)). See Depreciation Charges of Telephone Cos., 118 I.C.C. 295 (1926), and 177 I.C.C. 351 (1931).

[6]Due to the fact that the American Telephone and Telegraph Company was incorporated under the laws of the State of New York, the commission of that state, in a state-wide rate case, was able to require, by subpoena, the production of certain information bearing upon the intercorporate relationships between the parent company and the local company. Re New York Tel. Co., P. U. R. 1923B, 545, 575. Other state commissions have not been so fortunately situated. For example, the Maryland Commission in sseeming exasperation, commented upon its inability to secure information as follows: "No information bearing on this matter [intercorporate relationship] that the company or companies could prevent this Commission from obtaining was secured. The Commission was met

1.1 THE COMMUNICATIONS ACT OF 1934

By the early nineteen-thirties, therefore, a movement had developed looking toward more positive federal occupation of this field. There followed an extensive congressional investigation of the entire group of communications industries, and in a voluminous report, dated April 18, 1934, the enactment of a comprehensive regulatory statute was recommended. Provision of adequate funds was declared essential, and a full investigation of the telephone problem was suggested, since:

> The American people are entitled to know if they are being overcharged for this service [*i.e.*, telephone service] though they may be satisfied with the quality of the service. . . . The importance of the industry, and the magnitude of its operations call for *actual and not nominal regulation*. Telephone business is a monopoly—it is supposed to be regulated. Thus far regulation, particularly by the Federal Government, has been nominal largely because Congress has not made appropriations sufficient to enable the Interstate Commerce Commission to give effect to existing statutes.[7]

Even before the publication of this Report, the President (on February 26, 1934) had recommended the subjection of all phases of communication service, by wire or wireless, to the authority of a single regulatory body, and Congress responded by including in the Communications Act of 1934[8] comprehensive provisions for the regulation of interstate telephone and telegraph rates and practices, as well as for the regulation of "all the channels of interstate and foreign radio transmission."

Since little data on interstate telephone operations was readily available in published form to the newly-established Commission, one of its first steps was to conduct a thorough investigation of the telephone situation, under a further mandate of Congress.[9] The final report of this investigation will doubtless bring together for the first time a mass of factual material, covering the entire field of telephone operations in this country, particularly with respect to the American Telephone and Telegraph Company and its associated and subsidiary corporations, which together constitute the so-called "Bell Telephone System."

1.2 THE BELL TELEPHONE SYSTEM

Starting in 1878 as an outgrowth of Alexander Graham Bell's invention of "the speaking telephone," that system now embraces a closely integrated group of

---

with a positive refusal of any information relating to the American Telephone & Telegraph Company affairs that was not a matter of public record, or which could not be found in the records of the Chesapeake & Potomac Telephone Company of Baltimore City. The fact that most of the important books and records of the local company are kept outside the state made the securing of information more difficult than it otherwise would have been. Nevertheless much information, vital in character, concerning the relationship between the parent company and its subsidiaries was secured and put into the record." Public Serv. Comm. v. Chesapeake and P. Tel. Co., P.U.R. 1925B, 545, 566 (1924).

[7]"Splawn Report," *supra* note 4, p. xxxi (italics supplied).

[8]Act of June 19, 1934, c. 652; 48 STAT. 1064.

[9]Act of March 15, 1935, 49 STAT. 43.

more than two hundred corporations, with total book assets well in excess of five billion dollars,[10] constituting the largest single aggregation of wealth ever concentrated in private hands. Although there are more than six thousand so-called "independent telephone companies," operating today in the United States, their individual insignificance, as compared with the "Bell System," becomes apparent when it is noted that the latter owns or controls some ninety percent of the total book value of telephone plant and equipment used for the rendition of telephone service in this country; that its wires constitute ninety-five percent of the nation's total telephone wire mileage; that it operates all but two percent of telephone toll line mileage; and that its earnings constitute approximately ninety percent of total gross telephone reveues in the United States, while its operating plant serves as the medium for more than eighty million separate telephone conversations *per day,* or some twenty-four billion such messages each year.[11] Obviously, public interest demands that the regulation of telephone operations in this country concern itself largely with this powerful and dominating group of operating companies.

Because of the very concentration of interstate telephone business in the Bell System, the opportunity for effective federal regulation seems greatly simplified, and the integration of this business may be contrasted with the lack of integration in the railroad, gas, electric power, maritime, and automotive fields of federal regulatory effort. But this unified operating organism, possessed of unequalled corporate resources and a highly-developed personnel may well offer a formidable obstacle to successful regulation, unless the efforts of the public authorities can be directed along positive and constructive lines. The importance of developing efficient machinery for the continuous scrutiny of interstate telephone operations is apparent.

Although the nation over intrastate and interstate telephone operations, respectively, must at all times be kept in view, the field is so extensive and the problems

---

[10]The corporate pyramid topped by the American Telephone and Telegraph Company includes twenty-one so-called "Associated Companies," which handle most of the actual operations in their several areas. Eighty-five controlled connecting companies also perform actual telephone operating, as do forty-four "Bell Interest Companies" in which the Associated Companies hold slightly less than a majority of outstanding capital stock. There are four affiliated companies which engage in international and foreign service, and, finally, there are certain research, manufacturing, and marketing subsidiaries engaged in both telephonic and nontelephonic activities, and certain corporations formed because of state law statutes and other similar technical reasons.

The American Telephone and Telegraph Company, itself, is primarily a holding corporation, but it also renders certain advisory and technical services to the operating companies, and handles in large part the financing of those companies. These functions are performed through what is known as its "General Department," while it directly operates, through its "Long Lines Department," some seventy-five percent of the interstate telephone toll busines of the country. Six of the Associated Companies are if a multi-state character, and handle all or a large part of the interstate business within their respective areas. "Independent Telephone Companies" account for only a negligible proportion of interstate operations.

[11]As of December 31, 1937, the Bell System had book assets of $5,057,800,000 with $1,198,500,000 of depreciation and amortization reserves; it served some 15,332,000 separate telephones with over eighty million miles of wire, and its gross telephone operating revenue during the year 1937 amounted to no less than a billion dollars.

so compelling that it is not believed that serious jurisdictional conflict or "jealousy" should arise. The Federal Communications Commission has expressed its desire to be of service to the state bodies, and to offer them its full cooperation in their efforts to solve these difficult and vexing questions. Since, on certain of such questions, only the federal body is in a position to develop the basic facts, frank and continuous cooperation in connection with these joint problems can hardly fail to produce results of permanent social significance.[12]

1.3 TELEPHONE RATE "CLASSIFICATION"

Public utility rate regulation is, of course, twofold in character. Fundamentally, the economic function of the rates as a whole is to bring in revenues sufficient to cover reasonable operating expenses, including taxes and proper depreciation accruals, and also to provide a "return" which will enable the operating utility to develop and maintain such a "credit position" as will make possible the obtaining of required additional capital at the lowest reasonable "cost of money." Subject to this fundamental overall earning requirement, the individual rates for the several classes of service rendered by the company must be "spread" among the several classes of consumers in such manner as to preclude undue or unreasonable discrimination or preference in respect to any consumer or group of consumers, and also in such manner as to develop the maximum economic usage of the plant consistent with such nondiscriminatory rate classification. The investigation of any public utility's rate structure must take into consideration both of these factors, in order to inform the regulatory body of (1) over-all corporate revenue requirements, and (2) the reasonableness of the "spread of rates" within the general structure. A properly developed rate structure should afford the needed total revenue and should be so constructed as to make for constant expansion of service and an ever-increasing and more efficient use of the plant devoted to that service. This is as true in the telephone field as it is in any other sphere of utility regulation.

Telephone rates are therefore primarily classified between "exchange" and "toll" services; charges for the former are frequently developed on the "flat

---

[12]Under §410(a) of the Communications Act of 1934, the Federal Communications Commission may refer any matter arising out of the administration of the Act to a joint board of representatives selected by state regulatory commissions, or by state governors where no such agencies exist. Joint hearings with state commissions are also authorized, and co-operation with state commissions is specifically mentioned. (§410(b).) Machinery somewhat similar to that for many years in use in Interstate Commerce Commission co-operative proceedings is apparently in the process of development, a committee of state commissioners having been appointed to co-operate in connection with the pending "fifteen per cent" telegraph rate increase cases.

Under existing statutes, the regulation of local, or "exchange," telephone rates falls exclusively within the authority of state agencies. These agencies also possess exclusive jurisdiction over toll, or "inter-exchange," operations of an intrastate character. The federal authorities, on the other hand, are given exclusive control over interstate toll rates and services. The only exception to exclusive federal jurisdiction over interstate telephone operations is in the case of exchange service which may in part overlap a state boundary, where such service is "subject to regulation by a state commission or by local governmental authority." Communications Act of 1934, §221(b), 48 STAT. 1080.

rate," or fixed monthly payment basis, and charges for the latter are almost exclusively constructed on the unit rate basis, the individual message being the usually adopted unit. Telephone "exchange" rates are further classified between business and residential usage, each main use group being subdivided to reflect the type and extent of service required by various major groups of subscribers. Telephone toll rates also cover several types of service and usage, the most important being "message toll service," which involves the commonly-termed "long distance" or "interexchange" telephone call. Other services falling within the general group of toll rates include private line service (usually consisting of a leased wire, used by the customer either for telephone conversations or for transmitting "Morse Code" telegraph signals or teletypewriter exchange service (offering rapid connection) between any two subscribers to such service, wherever located); program transmission service (used largely in connection with chain radio broadcasting); telephoto service; conference service (offering the connection of three or more telephones for general conference purposes); ship-to-shore and coastal harbor service (partly by radio telephony); international service (through point-to-point radio connections with foreign countries, in conjunction with the domestic telephone toll network), and certain miscellaneous services. Of these numerous toll services, the telephone message toll business accounts for approximately eighty-seven percent over the entire Bell System (both interstate and intrastate), and for some seventy-five percent of the "Long Lines" business of the American Telephone and Telegraph Company (which is wholly interstate). Special attention must obviously be given by the federal regulatory body to this major class of service and to the rates which apply to it.

In like manner to the exchange services, telephone message toll service is further classified according to usage requirements, as by (1) length of conversation, (2) distance covered, (3) whether a particular person or merely a given telephone station is called, and (4) the time of day when the call is made, this process of toll service classification resolving itself into a complex process of averaging, based on each fundamental use requirement.[13] Day-by-day examination of these "spread of rate" problems must go hand in hand with the overall study of general rate levels if the regulation of telephone toll rates is to be rendered effective, in the public interest.[14]

---

[13] An extensive report on the existing toll rates of the Bell System was published on May 1, 1937, by the Federal Communications Commission (Telephone Rate and Research Department) under the title, "Message Toll Telephone Rates of Long Lines Department and Associated Companies of American Telephone and Telegraph Company at January 15, 1937." This report covered all toll schedules, both interstate and intrastate, of the system, and offered a means for ready and accurate comparison between all such schedules. In general, it was found that the Long Lines Department rates were the lowest in the system; that the interstate rates of the multi-state Associated Companies were somewhat higher, and that the intrastate toll rates were still higher. A total of eighteen basic schedules was found to exist over the system as a whole.

[14] As of January 15, 1938, the Federal Communications Commission (Telephone Rate and Research Department) published a report entitled "The Classified Toll rate Structure and Basic Rate Practices for Message Toll Telephone Service (as developed by the American Telephone and Telegraph Company and 'The Associated Bell Companies' in the United States)." This report constituted an

1.4 ORGANIZATION OF POSITIVE FEDERAL REGULATORY MACHINERY

During the first three years of its existence, little positive telephone rate regulatory effort was undertaken by the Federal Communications Commission, save as particular elements of the rate problem were considered and their implications developed in connection with the Special Telephone Investigation.[15] Late in 1936, however, informal negotiations looking directly toward rate adjustments were commenced by representatives of the Commission and of the American Telephone and Telegraph Company, based largely upon studies by members of the Special Investigation staff in respect to the Long Lines Department's operations. The result of these negotiations was an agreement (announced on December 2, 1936) that Long Lines rates would be reduced by an amount totaling $12,000,000, on an annual basis, and that this large reduction would be applied to the company's rates for message toll telephone service, with special attention to messages over distances of less than 234 miles, as to which the most recent rate reductions on this system had not generally been made applicable. In its announcement of this successful rate negotiation, the Commission declared:

> It is the Commission's view that in acceding informally to its request for an immediate and material rate reduction, without the necessity of long-drawn-out formal rate proceedings, this company is pursuing a forward-looking policy. And the Commission further believes that the many advantages to the public which will flow from this immediate rate reduction, thus informally obtained, greatly outweigh any possible advantage of somewhat greater future reductions that might result from lengthy formal proceedings at this time, especially since under the law rate orders of regulatory commissions cannot be given retroactive force. Under the informal methods which have been adopted the expected large savings to the public will become available at once, rather than being delayed by hearings, arguments and possible litigation, as has been the situation in many rate proceedings in the past.

---

attempt to fill, in at least a preliminary fashion, an apparent hiatus in regulatory "literature," and represented an effort to outline the "principles" which have apparently actuated the Bell System in developing its existing toll rate schedules, and to pose certain queries in respect to the application of these apparent principles. It was pointed out that positive and detailed regulation of toll rates (even intrastate) is as yet in its infancy, and that the development of "a much larger backlog of factual data than is now available" will be required before a final critique of the toll rate problem, from the public point of view, may be achieved.

[15]Among such items may be mentioned the question of special charges for use of the handset or "French type" combination receiver and transmitter, and the question of night and Sunday reduced rate periods. On January 15, 1936, the American Telephone and Telegraph Company altered and unified its evening reduced rate periods, eliminating the midnight to 4:30 A.M. reduction period, and lengthening the night discount period to 7:00 P.M. to 4:30 A.M. Similar discounts were also made available all day on Sunday. The extra handset charge, which was criticized in certain Special Investigation reports, has now (March 1, 1938) either been greatly reduced or entirely eliminated in most states.

The new rates will be given a reasonable test, thus permitting time for intensive study of the effect on revenues and expenses of the changes now being made. In this connection, it is the purpose of the Commission to set up as soon as possible a specialized, expert rate and research staff which will be made responsible for the continuous examination of the company's operations under the new rates. This staff will thus be in a position to recommend to the Commission from time to time such further and additional rate adjustments as the financial results of the company's operations may justify. It is recognized by the Commission that its jurisdiction over interstate telephone rates is one of its most important responsibilities under the Communications Act, and through the creation of this highly specialized staff department it is expected that a nucleus of experts familiar with all phases of such interstate telephone services may be developed.

Early in 1937, the Telephone Rate and Research staff, thus formally announced, was set up, as a mechanism for developing methods of active, continuous, and positive interstate telephone rate regulation. A comprehensive program for such regulation was at once prepared, but since the financing of the group had been accomplished through the final appropriation for the Special Telephone Investigation (under which funds for this work were to be available only to July 1, 1938) particular accent was placed upon the more immediate problems, as to which the accumulation of data seemed most essential.[16]

1.5 GENERAL PROBLEMS OF INTERSTATE TELEPHONE RATE REGULATION

Certain problems of interstate telephone rate regulation are common to all public utility rate control, others are special to the telephone industry, while still others stem from the specific organization and operating practices of the Bell Telephone System. The problems common to all utility regulation will in general require no more than mention here. Among them are the question of rate base (whether it is to be "fair value," "reproduction cost," "prudent investment," or some other figure);[17] the propriety of using price and cost "indices" (and their specific

---

[16]No sums have been included in the Commission's July 1, 1938–June 30, 1939, budget, either to cover additional personnel for this effort in the regular staff departments, or to provide for the carrying forward of this work through the existing Telephone Rate and Research group. Nor has provision for such additional funds been made in the current "deficiency" appropriation bill.

[17]No attempt has as yet been made by the Federal Communications Commission to "value" interstate telephone plant, either for rate-base purposes, or otherwise. At the same time it should be pointed out that the Commission has not officially expressed any opinion or attitude respecting the "fair value" rule of rate making. The vagaries of the usual "valuation" process seem to the writer peculiarly inconsistent with either sound or businesslike methods of regulating public utility rates, both from the point of view of the consuming public and from that of the public utilities whose required earnings are under consideration. See Wheat, *The Structure and Regulation of Interstate Telephone Rates* (1937) 20 P. U. Fort. No. 9, 583.

significance in telephone toll rate making),[18] and the vexing but strangely neglected question of the "rate of return."[19] These problems, though still productive of much acrimonious debate, apply generally to the entire field of public utility regulation, and, with the exception of the "rate of return," have so frequently been discussed that repetition of time-worn argumentation respecting them would hardly further an understandin of the specialized problems of interstate telephone rate control. They will not be considered further here.

1.5.1 Operating Expenses

Among the problems common to all utility regulation, however, that of operating expenses apparently deserves a word, if only because it has so often been passed over lightly by the regulatory agencies.[20] The complexity of telephone operations has rendered this especially the case in the telephone field.

---

[18]If variations between the original cost of utility property (*i.e.,* an amount approximating so-called "prudent investment") and "the present cost of construction" [mentioned in Smyth v. Ames, 169 U.S. 466 (1898)] are to be considered in rate base development, the sensible use of pertinent price and cost indices and trends seems indicated. Such action is believed wholly consistent with the remarks of the United States Supreme Court in West v. Chesapeake and P. Tel. Co., 295 U.S. 662 (1935), if the trends utilized are carefully selected and bear directly upon the specific types of property under consideration. *Cf.* McCart v. Indianapolis Water Co., 58 Sup. Ct. 324 (1938). For a discussion of this problem, see Wheat, *The Present as Compared with Original Cost of Construction* (1937) 20 P.U. FORT No. 3, 131. A detailed study of price and cost trends in the telephone field is now well under way by members of the special Telephone Rate and Research Department staff.

[19]Solution of the problem of "return" (usually considered as the product of "rate base" times a selected "rate of return") appears at this time to offer a fertile field for regulatory thought and action. Even minor variations in a selected "rate of return" are equivalent to large variations in the rate base, and the strategic import of this factor in rate making is rapidly becoming recognized. Much discussion of apparent factors to be considered in arriving at a proper "rate of return" is to be found in the decisions of courts and commissions, but the factual backlog of corporate financial data on which to apply these theoretical factors is still lacking. The prime economic function of "return"is, of course, to provide sufficient revenue to enable the corporation to maintain a healthy "credit position," in order to obtain required new capital at the lowest reasonable "cost of money." Possibly the most succinct statement of the problem was that contained in a *New York Times* editorial, published on November 3, 1937, and reading, in part, as follow:

" . . . What we need are rates just high enough to insure that the public is continuously furnished with the utility services it needs at the minimum cost to itself. The 'prudent investment' theory, or the 'cost of reproduction' theory, or a rate-making theory that ignored valuation altogether, must be judged not by its moral grandeur, nor by the elegance of its legal logic, but by the degree to which it promises to accomplish that end.

"The 'fairness' of utility rates depends entirely upon how they function. And from a functional viewpoint, what is needed are rates that will yield a return just sufficient to keep attracting the necessary new capital into utilities, but no higher."

See Bluefield Water Works & Imp. Co. v. Public Serv. Comm., 262 U.S. 679 (1923); United Rys. & Elec. Co. v. West, 280 U.S. 234 (1930); Smith v. Illinois Bell Tel. Co., 282 U.S. 133 (1930); Wabash Valley Elec. Co. v. Young, 287 U.S. 488 (1933); Los Angeles G. & E. Corp. v. Railroad Comm., 289 U.S. 287 (1933).

[20]The jurisdiction of regulatory authorities over the question of reasonableness of public utility operating expenses has so long been recognized that it seems almost axiomatic. The import of this factor was early accented by the Supreme Court when, in Chicago and Grand Trunk Ry. v. Wellman, 143 U.S. 339 (1892), it declared: "While the protection of vested rights of property is a supreme duty

Roughly eighty cents out of every dollar paid by consumers for telephone service goes to pay operating expenses. Taxes at the present time consume approximately fifteen percent of this expense total; depreciation accruals account for a further twenty to twenty-five percent; current maintenance takes about twenty-five percent; current maintenance takes about twenty-five percent; "commercial" expenses total some ten percent; "traffic" expenses amount to approximately eighteen percent, and the remainder is consumed by general administrative salaries and expenses, and by certain miscellaneous items.

Excluding taxes and depreciation, much of the expense in question is represented by wages and salaries, and the general efficiency of the management of any public utility may doubtless be tested by the general levels of such residuary expenses. Whether one man or ten shall be employed to perform a given task, whether maintenance routines shall be accomplished once a month or once a week, whether a certain grade of service shall be rendered at all times and at all points served—these, and many similar factors of a managerial nature, delimit in the usual case the levels of operating expense.

The difficulty of analyzing the propriety of such practices and their resultant expenses is obvious. But mere complexity can hardly form a valid excuse for failure to recognize and examine this, or any other, regulatory problem. Much of the time and energy hitherto wasted on the vagaries of so-called "valuation" might apparently have been better devoted to this potentially much more fertile field.[21]

Past regulatory methods have often placed a distinct penalty on "littleness," since the errors of both omission and commission by a small utility are ordinarily much more readily discernible than are those of statewide or nationwide operators. The fundamental functions of management should not be unreasonably invaded, but the dangers inherent in too great freedom of managerial control in the operating expense field should be recognized, and machinery should be developed to protect consumers against wasteful methods.[22]

---

of the courts, it has not come to this, that the legislative power rests subservient to the discretion of any railroad corporation which may, by exorbitant and unreasonable salaries, or in some other improper way, transfer its earnings into what it is pleased to call 'operating expenses'." (p. 346.)

[21] Professor C. O. Ruggles, of the Graduate School of Business Administration of Harvard University has recently termed the examination of managerial efficiency in public utility rate making "a field that is ripe for the harvest," remarking that: "In spending so much time nad money on long drawn out and, in some instances, almost useless valuations, we have overlooked the highly important problems of trying to work out fair and reasonable operating cost standards or yardsticks. . . . Focusing the spotlight on operating costs will have a wholesome effect upon privately owned and operated utilities." *Some Aspects of Public Utility Management and Regulation in* ANNUAL REPORT OF THE CONNECTICUT SOCIETY OF CIVIL ENGINEERS (New Haven, 1937) 98–112. See also Ruggles, *The Public's Interest in Public Utility Management* in (Dec. 1937) PROC. THIRTY-FIRST ANNUAL CONVENTION OF ASSOC. OF LIFE INS. PRESIDENTS 108–19.

[22] Charges to operating expenses may be as important as valuations of property. Thus, excessive charges of $1,500,000 to operating expenses would be the equivalent of 6 percent on $25,000,000 in a rate base." Lindheimer v. Illinois Bell Tel. Co., 292 U.S. 151, 164 (1934).

1.6 BASIC RATE PROBLEMS OF SPECIAL IMPORT IN TELEPHONE RATE REGULATION

1.6.1 Depreciation

The problem of developing a constructive and consistent treatment of depreciation, from both the annual expense and the accrued loss in plant service value viewpoints, has proved peculiarly difficult in the telephone field, largely because of certain attitudes adopted by the Bell System companies.[23]

The fact that property devoted to public utility service is used up or exhausted in that service must, of course, be considered in counting the cost of operations, and it is essential to make provision to take care of this cost in fixing the rates to be charged against the consumers.[24] Obviously, all potential causes of the ultimate retirement of operating property should be taken into consideration, whether their nature by physical (as decay, deterioration, or ordinary wear and tear) or functional (as obsolescence, inadequacy, or public requirements).

Several methods of accounting for depreciation accruals have been developed. Under both the "straight line" and "sinking fund" methods, equal annual charges are made to operating expenses over the estimated lives of property units, but the "sinking fund" method requires smaller annual accruals because of interest credits to the accumulated "reserve." Both methods result in the accumulation of such balances, or "reserves," from which requirements are taken care of, as and when necessary. It has repeatedly been pointed out that, whereas "sinking fund" accruals are consistent with use of an undepreciated rate base, the "straight line" method of handling accruing depreciation requires the adoption of a depreciated base.[25] Since the "straight line" method has been adopted for telephone accounting purposes by the federal regulatory body, the problem is to select the fairest and most reasonable measure of such depreciation deduction from the rate base, consistent with the charges made for annual accruals.

---

[23]For the purpose of simplifying the consideration of a necessarily complex subject, numerous subfactors, such as salvage, cost of removal, and the like are not here discussed. Nor has mentioned been made of the many problems incident to the development of estimated "lives" of various classes of property for the purpose of fixing annual depreciation accruals. On the general subject of depreciation, see: Perry Mason, *Princples of Public Utility Depreciation,* AMERICAN ACCOUNTING ASSOC. MONOGRAPH No. 1 (Chicago, 1937); *Depreciation,* PUBLIC SERVICE COMM. OF WISCONSIN (1933).

[24]See Knoxville v. Knoxville Water Co., 212 U.S. 1, 13 (1909).

[25]In its brief before the Interstate Commerce Commission in respect to depreciation accounting for telephone companies, the Public Service Commission of Oregon stated this proposition concisely, as follows:

"Manifestly, the straight-line method of calculating depreciation cannot properly be used in conjunction with an undepreciated rate base, nor should the sinking-fund principle be followed where a depreciated rate base is considered. In other words, the public cannot equitably be required to pay for capital as it is consumed, *i.e.,* on the straight-line basis, and at the same time be required to pay a return upon such consumed capital, *i.e.,* on an undepreciated rate base. Nor should a utility company be asked or required to forego its legitimate return upon the full undepreciated value of its property unless its capital is fully repaid as rapidly as it is consumed." 118 I.C.C. 295, 355 (1926).

It has been the practice of the Bell System companies to charge regularly to operating expenses sufficient sums on the "straight line" basis to take care of all potential causes of telephone plant retirement, both physical and functional. These accruing depreciation charges commonly amount to from twenty to twenty-five percent of total operating expenses, and over the years "depreciation reserves" in large amounts have been accumulated.[26] These reserves have generally been reinvested in operating telephone plant, which thus consists in part of property provided by the company's consumers[27], through charges made to cover the progressive loss in service value suffered over the years by the original property.

Since the "straight line" method of distributing annual depreciation charges equally over the life of the property results in the accumulation of the accruals in the "depreciation reserve," and since the reserve has been developed for no other purpose than to provide against the loss in service value of the plant units, it becomes, from the accounting viewpoint, the equivalent of such loss. This is not to say that any purely mathematical machinery for spreading the accruing loss of service value over the useful life of plant units could be so devised as necessarily to produce a reserve in fact equal *at any given moment* to the theoretical total loss in service value then existing in the plant. The "straight line" method of depreciation accounting is no exception to this rule. By its very definition, it spreads in equal annual installments a loss which may in fact be proceeding along a very different curve. There will therefore be times in the life of any plant unit when the sum of the annual depreciation accruals made in respect to it will exceed, and other times that sum will be less than, the loss measured along that other curve. But this variation is of no moment. The important fact is that the rate payers have contributed certain sums by way of operating expenses for the sole purpose of taking care of the progressive loss in service value, and that these sums have been accumulated over the years in the "depreciation reserve," which thus represents the accumulated provision to date for this purpose. It therefore seems both logical and fair to use this reserve as the most available and most equitable measure of the rate base deduction to be made on account of the progressively accumulating "accrued depreciation," or loss in service value, in the property.[28] If this deduction is not made, the ratepayers will obviously be

---

[26]Prior to the close of 1936, the Bell Telephone System had accumulated on its books an aggregate of "reserves for depreciation" totalling $1,145,000,000. This prodigious sum equalled 28 percent of the System's book investment of over four billion dollars, and the annual depreciation charges from which such reserves have been accumulated, and which continue to increase their total, loom large in operating expenses. On the Long Lines System alone, such annual depreciation charges amount to some seventeen million dollars per year, or almost a million and a half dollars *each month*. An error equivalent to but one month's such charges would obviously be equivalent to a variation in "return," at 6 percent, on twenty-five million dollars in the rate base.

[27]In addition to capital supplied directly by investors, certain elements are, of course, derived through investment of pension "reserves" and accrued corporate surplus, the total capital thus provided being here contrasted with the operating capital secured through investment of the depreciation reserve.

[28]In instances where sufficient operating expense, or annual accrual, charges have not been made to take care of the depreciation which is going on in the property, reserves equivalent to the accrued depreciation will not accumulate. It has been suggested that, in such cases, an estimate should be

forced to pay a return on the company's full original investment, part of which
has been amortized and returned to the investors through the subscribers' own
contributions by way of "straight line" accruing depreciation charges. Doubtless
this was what the Interstate Commerce Commission had in contemplation when it
declared that:

> It is essential to bear in mind, however, that there is an inseparable connection
> between the straight line method and the principle that accrued depreciation repre-
> sented by the depreciation reserve must be deducted in ascertaining the rate-base
> value.[29]

The Bell Telephone companies have agreed that *some* deduction should be
made in arriving at the base rate to cover what they term "existing depreciation."
But they have taken issue with the use of the depreciation reserve as a measure of
that deduction, even in connection with "straight line" annual accruals. "Existing depreciation," say they, is a fact wholly distinct and apart from the accumulation of annual depreciation charges in the depreciation reserve. They express a
willingness to deduct accrued and visible physical depreciation in calculating the
rate base, but they in effect deny that functional causes result in "actual" or
"existing" depreciation until retirement for such causes actually becomes necessary.[30] Though they have collected large sums by way of annual depreciation
accruals to provide for such functional losses, on the apparent theory that they do
in fact exist throughout the life of the property as potential causes of retirement,
they nevertheless urge that such losses have not yet actually come to pass for rate
base purposes, but are merely clouds hovering about some future, but as yet
indeterminable sunset.

Under the "straight line" method of annual depreciation accruals, however, the
proper and equitable rule seems clear,[31] and in its telephone accounting case the
Interstate Commerce Commission declared that if any other principle than the

---

made of the "reserve requirement," based on currently used depreciation accrual studies, and that this
"requirement," rather than the actual reserve, be deducted for rate-base purposes. In this connection,
it is essential to consider the financial history of the company in question. Inadequate reserves
combined with a history of excessive dividends are to be contrasted with excessive reserves accumulated at the expense of the stockholders or subscribers. The Bell Companies have, without apparent
exception, followed a conservative policy in respect to annual depreciation accruals; have accumulated depreciation reserves largely equivalent to their present "reserve requirements," and have
enjoyed generally excellent dividend records.

[29]Depreciation of Telephone Companies, 118 I.C.C. 295, 356 (1926).

[30]In this connection, the Bell Companies attempt to distinguish between the obsolescence and
inadequacy which has "actually occurred" and that which is merely "potential." The latter they
reject as a deduction in arriving at the rate base, regardless of the collections already made from the
ratepayers to take care of it.

[31]In New York Tel. Co. v. Prendergast, 36 F.(2d) 54, 66 (S.D.N.Y. 1929), the court, speaking of the
company's position in respect to the deduction of "observed depreciation" only, in developing the
rate base, remarked: " . . . When it built up its reserve, it claimed the reserve as its actual
depreciation. It cannot now take an inconsistent position about depreciation, without fully establishing it, and it has weakened its proof of present value accordingly. The plaintiff was right about
depreciation when it created its reserve, and it is wrong, in its position now, in its claim for a lesser
sum as actual depreciation in this effort to establish fair value."

deduction of accrued depreciation "represented by the depreciation reserve" in ascertaining the rate base were to be adopted by the courts, "a reconsideration of the entire question of depreciation accounting would at once become necessary."[32] There seems to be no logical escape from this conclusion. In its second decision in the same matter, the Interstate Commerce Commission pointed out the "absurd incongruities" which must flow from the consideration of all causes of retirement in measuring "accruing depreciation" charges, and the elimination of all save purely physical causes in measuring "accruing depreciation" charges, and the elimination of all save purely physical causes in measuring "accrued depreciation" for rate base purposes.[33] In a recent local telephone rate case, the California Railroad Commission remarked upon "the extreme and inequitable results" indicated by the company's arguments in this connection, and declared that these results "negative the soundness of the company's position in respect to depreciation."[34] The California Commission's depreciation engineer went so far as to assert from the witness stand that the propositions advanced by the company in that case seemed to him "so at variance with reason and facts as to cause the collapse of the method by its own inconsistencies."[35]

Authority for the deduction of "observed depreciation" only, without consideration of annual depreciation accruals, or of their purpose under "straight line" accounting methods, or of the reserves accumulated for the sole purpose of taking care of "accrued depreciation," has been sought by the Bell companies in the opinions of the United States Supreme Court in *Pacific Gas and Elec. Co. v. San Francisco*[36] and *McCardle v. Indianapolis Water Co.*[37] Extended and careful examination of these decisions by the Interstate Commerce Commission[38] led that body to conclude that no such proposition was intended by the Supreme Court,

---

[32] 118 I.C.C. 295, 356 (1926).

[33] Depreciation Charges of Telephone Cos., 177 I.C.C. 351, 401 (1931).

[34] Los Angeles v. Southern Calif. Tel. Co., 14 P.U.R. (N.S.) 252, 271 (1936).

[35] Under the theory thus criticized the deduction for accrued depreciation in the rate base is measured not by the collections for accruing depreciation which have been included in subscribers' rates over the years, but by a judgment approximation of the "existing depreciation" which can be seen with the eye upon examination of the property. This judgment approximation is derived by application of the so-called "condition percent" theory. This theory assumes the possibility of deriving mathematical "percent" figures from which to calculate accrued physical depreciation. Observation is made of units of property, and the observers set down their "judgment" of the percent relation of such property in its present "condition" to like items of property "similarly placed but new." The difference between thbe percentages thus obtained and 100% is labeled "existing depreciation." This has ordinarily amounted to some 5% to 10%, and such percentages have been applied to book alues of property in arriving at the rate-base deductions for accrued depreciation admitted as proper by the Bell System Companies. These percentages are to be contrasted with depreciation reserves of from 20 to 30 percent of property cost. In the Wisconsin Telephone Company case [13 P.U.R. (N.S.) 244 (1936)], the admitted accrued depreciation under the "condition percent: theory was 7.3%, while the depreciation reserve aggregated 30.1% of total book cost. In the Illinois Bell Telephone Company Chicago Exchange case [Lindheimer v. Illinois Bell Tel. Co., 292 U.S. 151 (1934)], these figures were 8% and 28.1%, respectively.

[36] 265 U.S. 403 (1924).

[37] 272 U.S. 400 (1926).

[38] 177 I.C.C. 351, 405–08 (1931).

and that the issue here under discussion was not, in fact, directly raised in those cases. It declared that adequate presentation of the facts relative to "the infirmities of ocular evidence" and of the necessity for also analyzing past experience and applying "informed judgment as to future trends" seemed to be the sole requisite to obtaining judicial recognition of the Commission's conclusion that "the principles are identical which govern the estimating of loss in service capacity for both accounting and valuation purposes."[39]

In order that some reasonable harmony may be reached in the treatment of these two important aspects of the depreciation problem, it has recently been seriously urged that allowed annual depreciation charges to operating expenses be reduced to a sum sufficient to take care of physical deterioration alone. In the light of the necessity for proper accounting recognition of functional causes of property retirement, this suggestion seems unsound, since many important and indubitable causes of losses in plant service value which must be faced by operating public utilities would thus be removed from the protection of depreciation accounting. Alternative suggestions have been to place the accounting for depreciation on the "retirement" basis, thus eliminating the large reserves which result from the "straight line" method. This suggestion would apparently be more practicable in almost any other field of public utility service that in that of telephone operations, as to which the functional causes of property retirement

---

[39]No final determination on this important regulatory problem has yet been rendered by the Supreme Court, its remarks in West v. Chesapeake & P. Tel. Co., 295 U.S. 662, 678–80 (1935), being inconclusive on the point. The decisions of the lower federal courts are in conflict, though it is doubtful whether the question has as yet been presented to any court in the manner suggested by the Interstate Commerce Commission. See New York Tel. Co. v. Prendergast, 36 F.(2d) 54, 66 (S.D.N.Y. 1929); Chesapeake & P. Tel. Co. v. Whitman, 3 F.(2d) 938, 951 (D. Md. 1925); Chesapeake & P. Tel. Co. v. West, 7 F. Supp. 214, 226–28 (D. Md. 1934), aff'd, 295 U.S. 662 (1935); Michigan Bell Tel. Co. v. Odell, 45 F.(2d) 180 (E.D. Mich. 1930); Pacific Tel. & Tel. Co. v. Whitcomb, 12 F.(2d) 279, 283–84 (W.D. Wash. 1926), the issue not arising on appeal [Denney V. Pacific Tel. & Tel. Co., 276 U.S. 97 (1928)]; and Southern Bell Tel. & Tel. Co. v. Railroad Comm., 5 F.(2d) 77, 96 (E.D.S.C. 1925).

Recent decisions rendered by state commissions indicate a determination not to accept the contention of Bell Telephone Companies that "observed" depreciation should be the sole criterion in determining accrued depreciation; and some commissions have used the amount in the depreciation reserve as the basis for determining the deduction to be made for accrued depreciation. For recent decisions of state commissions discussing this subject, see Los Angeles v. Southern Calif. Tel. Co., 14 P.U.R. (N.S.) 252, 270–76 (Cal. 1936); Lousiana Pub. Serv. Comm. v. Southern Bell Tel. & Tel. Co., 8 P.U.R. (N.S.) 1, 8–17 (La. 1935); Re Chespeake & P. Tel. Co., 1 P.U.R.(scn.s.) 346, 371–85 (Md. 1933); Re New York Tel. Co., P.U.R. 1930B, 439, 446–49, P.U.R. 1930C, 325, 337–52, 14 P.U.R. (N.S.) 443, 448 (N.Y. 1936); Re Southern Bell Tel. & Tel. Co., 7 P.U.R. (N.S.) 21, 25–26 (N.C. 1934); Re Ohio Bell Tel. Co., 2 P.U.R. (N.S.) 113, 125–30 (Okla. 1935); Re Southern Bell Tel. & Tel. Co., P.U.R. 1933B, 181 (S.C. 1933); Memphis v. Southern Bell Tel. & Tel. Co., 6 P.U.R. (N.S.) 464 (Tenn. 1934); Re Wisconsin Tel. Co., 13 P.U.R. (N.S.) 224, 298–305 (Wis. 1936). See also re Northwestern Bell Tel. Co., 11 P.U.R. (N.S.) 337 (Neb. 1935), in connection with the necessary relationship between accrued depreciation and the balance in the depreciation reserve. In a later decision [Re Northwestern Bell Tel. Co., 17 P.U.R. (N.S.) 458, 469 (Neb. 1937)], the Nebraska State Railway Commission specifically found that an excess in depreciation reserve over the accrued depreciation must be considered in fixing future annual depreciation "rates." The right of the states to prescribe such annual depreciation "rates," in the absence of federal action in this regard, was discussed and sustained in Northwestern Bell Tel. Co. v. Railway Comm., 297 U.S. 471, 479 (1936), aff'g Northwestern Bell Tel. Co. v. Nebraska State Ry. Comm., 128 Neb. 447, 259 N.W. 362, 8 P.U.R. (N.S.) 46 (1935), aff'g Re Northwestern Bell Tel. Co., 5 P.U.R. (N.S.) 20 (Neb. 1934).

loom so large and might at times prove overwhelming in the absence of proper reserve provision.

A suggestion of much greater equity would seem to be to place telephone depreciation accounting on the "sinking fund" basis, or possibly to leave the accounting for purely physical deterioration on the "straight line" basis, but to adopt the "sinking fund" method for functional retirement causes. Since the "sinking fund" method is consistent with an undepreciated rate base, this division of depreciation accounting would do complete equity to the Bell companies. In any event, a consistent and harmonious treatment of depreciation in all its aspects is imperative, and if "straight line" accruals are to continue the "reserve" balance apparently represents the minimum necessary rate base deduction.

Finally, the essential interdependence of the concepts of functional depreciation and of business risk must be recognized. A corporation whose plant may be expected to become obsolete in ten years is doubtless a greater investor risk than one with longer potential functional serviceability. Other things (as competition, market for services, managerial efficiency, and the like) being equal, comparability of business risk seems largely dependent on the weighing of these relative expectancies of property retirements due to such non-physical causes. And if, as the courts have suggested, risk constitutes one of the primary functions of "return," duplication of allowance for this factor would seem to flow from a practice which authorizes recovery of its cost both in depreciation charges to operating expense and in the adopted "rate of return." The limitation of depreciation accounting to physical causes of property retirement, and the consideration of functional causes in the allowance for "risk of the business," as part of the "fair return" allowance, may therefore constitute the ultimate solution of this curious and vexing problem.

1.6.2 The "Separation of Property, Revenues, and Expenses

The modern telephone plant consists of a highly complicated aggregation of wire, cables, pole lines, land, rights-of-way, buildings, central office equipment, and station apparatus, much of it jointly used. Obviously, if each general class of consumer is to bear its fair proportion of over-all operating costs, the exchange properties, revenues and expenses must be allocated or "separated" from those involving toll service, and because of the separation of basic jurisdiction between the states and the nation, adequate and accurate allocations of operative property, revenues and expenses between intrastate and interstate uses are essential to the successful regulation of interstate questions.[40] Concretely, the problem is to

---

[40] Although intrastate exchange-toll separation had previously been considered and attempted in numerous instances, it was not until the Supreme Court's decision in the Chicago telephone rate case that the necessity for a detailed separation between interstate and intrastate toll operations became acute. In that case the Court remarked: "The separation of the intrastate and interstate property, revenues and expenses of the company is important not simply as a theoretical allocation to two branches of the business. It is essential to the appropriate recognition of the competent governmental authority in each field of regulation." Smith v. Illinois Bell Tel. Co., 282 U.S. 133, 148 (1930).

develop adequate data from which may be determined, with reasonable accuracy, the respective exchange, intrastate toll, and interstate toll uses to which the joint plant is being put. Present accounting methods do not afford such information,[41] and in practice the "proportionate use" separation studies now in vogue have been expensive, complicated, and time-consuming.

The reasonableness of the over-all "return" of Long Lines may be determined without separation studies, since it offers no intrastate services, but allocations will eventually be essential in connection with the several major types of service which this organization renders,[42] and will also become necessary in the evaluation of Long Line rate "divisions." Moreover, with respect to those Associated Bell companies which offer interstate, as well as exchange and intrastate toll services, interstate rate regulation will obviously be impracticable in the absence of basic separation data derived from complete and detailed separation studies. The development of cheaper and more expeditious methods of arriving at satisfactory separations in respect to all phases of telephone operations is therefore a matter of major importance to the future of effective interstate telephone rate regulation. Comparatively inexpensive additions to existing engineering and accounting records would apparently afford the necessary data, though much additional effort will be required before the problem can be fully solved.

The basis upon which separation is to be developed remains to be determined. With few exceptions, the Bell companies have maintained that their toll rates are established upon the so-called "board-to-board" basis, under which the toll charge is intended to cover the costs from the toll sides of the exchange switchboards at the originating and terminating ends. The cost of completing toll connections between the toll boards and the subscribers' telephones is, under this theory, included in rates paid by the subscriber for exchange service. Numerous state regulatory agencies and public representatives have taken this position, however, that the toll charge should cover all costs involved in transmitting toll messages between subscribers' telephones. This is known as the "station-to-station" method of toll rate making, and since the decision in the Chicago rate

---

[41]Plant accounting by telephone companies in respect to pole lines, cables, wire circuits and other "outside plant" is commonly developed on the so-called "major use" basis, which some have interpreted as "predominant use," others as a reflection of originally planned use, and still others as allowing a classification to toll of all structures carrying toll circuits, regardless of the proportion of exchange circuits. Central office equipment, land and buildings are not ordinarily divided on the books between exchange and toll usage. It therefore becomes necessary to provide machinery for the division of recorded investments between exchange and toll in accord with actual use, and further to subdivide the toll factor between intrastate and interstate use, on some more accurate basis than is afforded by presently accepted accounting methods.

For example, if a pole supports both exchange and toll circuits, the investment which it represents must be separated between exchange and toll, and further between intrastate and interstate toll, regardless of the particular account in which it is carried on the company's books according to its "major use". The complexity of such a process over the intricate and highly specialized aggregate of telephone operating properties is obvious. And the separation of expenses is equally difficult, though revenue segregations do not offer quite as complex a problem.

[42]See p. 852, *supra*.

case[43] the telephone companies have apparently considered it necessary to make "station-to-station" separation studies.

However, on the theory, above mentioned, that exchange rates have been established in such manner as to include subscriber access to the toll board, the companies have allocated a portion of exchange service revenues to intrastate and interstate toll. Many of the state commissions apparently do not agree with this final revenue separation, maintaining that exchange rates do not include these particular toll costs. Doubtless some understanding in respect to this problem satisfactory to both state and federal regulatory agencies must shortly be reached.[44]

---

[43]Smith v. Illinois Bell Tel. Co., 282 U.S. 133 (1930).

[44]Prior to the Supreme Court's remarks respecting separation in the Chicago rate case most Bell System companies followed the strict board-to-board theory, and presented testimony on that basis before state commissions. Apparently the only important exception was the New York Telephone Company. See Re New York Tel. Co., P.U.R. 1926E, 1 (N.Y.); New York Tel. Co. v. Prendergast, 36 F.(2d) 54 (S.D.N.Y. 1929). Certain of the state commissions had sanctioned board-to-board separations. See Re Indiana Bell Tel. Co., P.U.R. 1922C, 348 (Ind.); Re Michigan State Tel. Co., P.U.R. 1923A, 30 (Mich.); Re Northwestern Bell Tel. Co., P.U.R. 1922C, 762 (Minn.); Re Northwestern Bell Tel. Co., P.U.R. 1923B, 112 (Neb.); Buck v. New York Tel. Co., P.U.R. 1921E, 798 (N.Y.); Public Utilities Comm. v. New England Tel. & Tel. Co., P.U.R. 1926C, 207 (R.I.); Re Rock Hill Tel. Co., P.U.R. 1928E, 221 (S.C.); Re Wisconsin Tel. Co., P.U.R. 1925D, 661 (Wis.). Others had already favored the station-to-station theory of separation. See Re Southern Calif. Tel. Co., P.U.R. 1925C, 627 (Cal.); Re Missouri & Kansas Tel. Co., P.U.R. 1918C, 55 (Kan.); City of Kansas v. Kansas City Tel. Co., P.U.R. 1922A, 466 (Mo.); Re Pacific Tel. & Tel. Co., P.U.R. 1924D, 39 (Ore.); Re Chesapeake & P. Tel. Co., P.U.R. 1926E, 481 (Va.), sustained in Chesapeake & P. Tel. Co., v. Virginia, 147 Va. 43, 136 S.E. 575, P.U.R. 1927B, 484 (1927).

In the Chicago case, the United States district court at first approved the company's board-to-board theory of rate making. Illinois Bell Tel. Co. v. Moynihan, 38 F.(2d) 77 (N.D. Ill. 1930). But the Supreme Court, in remanding the case for further findings, referred to the fact that the company, in its computations submitted to the lower court, had attributed entirely to the intrastate service "what it called exchange property, that is, the property used at the subscriber's station and from that station to the toll switchboard, or to the toll trunk lines," and held that "unless an apportionment is made, the intrastate service to which the exchange property is allocated will bear an undue burden—to what extent is a matter of controversy," and that the subject should be given further consideration "to the end that by some practical method the different uses of the property may be recognized and the return property attributable to the intrastate service may be ascertained accordingly." Smith v. Illinois Bell Tel. Co., 282 U.S. 133 (1930).

The district court's later findings with respect to separation of property and expenses [3 F. Supp. 595 (N.D. Ill. 1933)] were not contested when the case again reached the Supreme Court [Lindheimer v. Illinois Bell Tel. Co., 292 U.S. 151 (1934)]. While the city and the commission objected to the lower court's apportionment of exchange revenues to toll, the Supreme Court did not pass upon this issue.

Decisions rendered since the Supreme Court's opinion in the Smith case indicate a definite preference for the station-to-station theory, and, in the application of that theory, rejection of any apportionment of exchange revenues to toll. See Los Angeles v. Southern Calif. Tel. Co., 14 P.U.R. (N.S.) 252 (Cal. 1936); Louisiana Pub. Serv. Comm. v. Southern Bell Tel. & Tel. Co., 8 P.U.R. (N.S.) 1 (1935), sustained in 187 La. 137, 174 So. 180, 18 P.U.R. (N.S.) 1 (1937); Re Pacific Tel. & Tel. Co., 8 P.U.R. (N.S.) 111 (Ore. 1935) (order enjoined by Oregon Circuit Court in Pacific Tel. & Tel. Co. v. Thomas, 13 P.U.R. (N.S.) 337 (Ore. 1936), aff'd, Pacific Tel. & Tel. Co. v. Wallace, 26 Ore. Advance Sheets 187 (1938); Re Michigan Bell Tel. Co., 10 P.U.R. (N.S.) 149 (Mich. 1935); Southwestern Bell Tel. Co. v. San Antonio, 2 F. Supp. 611, P.U.R. 1933D, 405 (W.D. Tex. 1933), rev'd, 76 F.(2d) 880 (C.C.A. 5th, 1935), cert. denied, 295 U.S. 754 (1934).

1.6.3 The Division of Toll Revenues

The problem of "division of rates" between two or more rail carriers has long received the attention of the Interstate Commerce Commission, as well as of numerous state regulatory agencies.[45] This question is also of importance in the telephone field, since Long Line messages, though transmitted wholly or in part over Long Lines toll circuits, are originated and terminated by use of Associated or connecting operating company facilities. It has been the practice of the American Telephone and Telegraph Company to compensate the Associated companies for their terminal services by means of a uniform "originating commission," assertedly based on average costs over the entire system, and the revenue remaining after deduction of these originating commissions is "prorated" between the involved companies in approximate proportion to the toll circuit mileage provided by each company.

Since the originating commissions are uniform over the system, and are based upon average terminal costs, they necessarily exceed the actual costs of certain of the Associated companies, and are less than those costs in other instances.[46] Studies of the overall adequacy of such payments have been made from time to time by the American Telephone and Telegraph Company, but no such study is apparently of sufficiently recent date to form a basis for a current critique of originating commission adequacy.

A much more detailed examination of this important problem will be required before alterations in either the method or in the amounts of such payments should be recommended.[47]

1.6.4 Toll Rates as Specialized Problems

Studies of existing Bell System toll rate schedules[48] and of the apparent "philosophy" underlying such toll rates[49] have already been published. Numerous other specialized rate problems remain for further examination. For example, tele-

---

[45] See Sharfman, The Interstate Commerce Commission (4 vols. 1931–37); United States v. Abilene & S. Ry., 265 U.S. 274 (1924); Morgantown & Kingwood Divisions, 40 I.C.C. 509 (1916); Denver & S.L.R.R. v. Chicago, B. & Q.R.R., P.U.R. 1916E, 403 (Colo.); Marion & E.R.R. v. Chicago & E.I.R.R., 5 Ill. C.C. 424 (1926).

[46] They have been increased in recent years, purportedly from a desire to prevent decreases in revenue to the Associated Companies resulting from rate reductions on the Long Lines system. Originating commissions totalled $165,170,000 between 1913 and 1936, inclusive, and equalled 38.16% of Long Lines net revenues during that period. The prorate payments equalled 36.58% of such net revenues during the same span of years, and amounted to $158,337,000.

[47] Commissions paid to "independent" connecting companies frequently vary from those paid to Bell Associated companies, and also vary considerably among themselves. Many "independents" assert that commissions received by them are materially insufficient to cover their necessary operating costs, and that connection with Bell System lines is afforded them only on allegedly "arbitrary" basis, without regard to such individual costs.

[48] See note 13, *supra.*

[49] See note 14, *supra.*

phone toll rate reductions apparently exert a considerable stimulating effect upon the volume of business to be expected. The repricing of the existing message business under a proposed new schedule will, of course, disclose the extent of the potential reduction "to the public" on the basis of the number of messages of various classes experienced under existing rates. However, net losses in revenue to the telephone companies in connection with such reductions are ordinarily less than this "repricing effect" upon the public, because of the natural stimulation of business resulting from the reduced rates.[50] Existing company studies seem inconclusive as to the exact nature or extent of this stimulating effect, but na examination of recent interstate rate reductions discloses increases in business volume, apparently flowing directly from the reductions, and varying in magnitude from 20 to 40 per cent of the repricing measure.[51]

The problem of properly evaluating this "stimulation" factor is highly complicated, because of the many variations in demand occasioned by other causes, particularly in connection with changes in general business levels. The question is one of concrete moment, however, since as close an approximation as possible of the relation between the net effect of potential rate changes on the business and the gross effect of such changes on the patrons must be developed in connection with any proposed rate adjustment.[52] Experience indicates that telephone toll business, and in particular the interstate toll business, has in no sense "struck its level." Indeed, the ultimate potentialities of long distance telephone service in this country seem hardly to have been touched. And wherever possible such stimulating effects should be fostered in the interest of the telephone-using public.[53]

Estimates of the monetary effect upon the public and upon the company of various types of potential rate adjustments, and the careful evaluation of such potentialities on the basis of comparative public interest, seem essential to any positive and active regulation of the telephone industry. Such studies should enable the regulatory bodies to discuss intelligently and to rule advisedly upon the details of proposed rate adjustments of any given magnitude, as and when such adjustments may come before them for consideration.

---

[50]See Louisiana Pub. Serv. Comm. v. Southern Bell Tel. Co., 8 P.U.R. (N.S.) 1, 25 (1935).

[51]Estimates by Long Lines officials made at the time of the $12,000,000 reduction of January 15, 1937, indicated that the net loss in revenues to the company would be about $8,000,000 or $9,000,000, rather than the full $12,000,000. Actual operations under the new rates for a full year indicate that these estimates were remarkably accurate.

[52]For example, if Long Lines revenues were at any time found to be in excess of a reasonable return by $5,000,000, a repricing reduction "to the public" aggregating almost $7,000,000 would appear to be indicated on the basis of the company's past experience.

[53]Calculations of rate change effects include certain other factors, in addition ot that of "stimulation." Thus, it was recently remarked: "Because of the incidence of taxes and certain operating charges which are proportioned to gross and net revenue, a reduction in gross revenue affects net revenue to a lesser degree." Los Angeles v. Southern Calif. Tel. Co., 14 P.U.R. (N.S.) 252 (Cal. 1936).

The "short-haul" interstate toll problem is also of importance,[54] particularly in relation to service between heavily populated areas which adjoin one another on either side of a state line, such as between New York City and adjacent populous New Jersey communities; between Philadelphia, Pennsylvania, and Camden, New Jersey; between Chicago, Illinois, and Gary, Indiana; and between St.Louis, Missouri, and East St. Louis, Illinois. Of these situations, the most noteworthy is that between New York City and the neighboring New Jersey communities, not only because of the magnitude of the business involved, but also because the rates in effect for such service are on a higher level than are those for seemingly comparable services. With this exception, the rates generally applicable to short-haul interstate toll business compare favorably with the intrastate rates of the associated companies which render the service. These short-haul problems apparently differ in nature from the long-haul interstate telephone rate problems, and they also seem to differ in kind among themselves. The eventual determination of short-haul propriety must therefore depend largely upon local operating conditions, costs, and results.

1.7 REGULATORY PROBLEMS RESULTANT FROM BELL SYSTEM ORGANIZATION AND PRACTICES

1.7.1 The "License Contract"

Much controversy has arisen in Bell Telephone rate cases with respect to the so-called "license contract fee" charged by the American Telephone and Telegraph Company to its Associated operating companies for services allegedly rendered and work allegedly performed under the "license contract" in effect with those companies.[55] Such service fees are not uncommon in connection with corporate holding and operating systems,[56] but the Bell System's license contract fees have raised numerous distinctive issues and have, therefore, been given particular

---

[54]Practically all interstate toll business for distances under forty miles is accomplished through the facilities of the Associated Bell companies. The Long Lines operates an exclusively interstate message toll business, and while its tariffs include charges for service from zero mileage upward, its actual service over distances of less than forty miles is negligible. The problem of short-haul interstate telephone rates is therefore almost exclusively an Associated company problem.

[55]The "license contract" was originally an agreement between the Bell parent organization and its licensees which provided for the leasing of the telephone instruments and the licensing of their use. Hence its name. For many years prior to 1926, the license contract fee amounted to 4½% of the licensee's gross operating revenues, but covered the rental of telephone instruments, in addition to recompense for asserted services. In 1926 the fee was reduced to 4%, and in the following year the instruments were sold to the licensees, and the fee was cut to 2%. A subsequent reduction resulted in the fee of 1½% of gross revenues, the current charge.

The somewhat haphazard character of this method of determining the amount of the licensee's payment should be noted. It bears no exact relation to the alleged license contract services, and gross operating revenues might be affected by any number of factors extraneous to the license contract relations. See HERRING AND GROSS, TELECOMMUNICATIONS (1936) 339–40.

[56]SEE NOTE (1936) 49 HARV. L. REV. 957. There is some discussion of the Bell System license contrat in this Note at 982–85.

attention by regulatory bodies. From the monetary standpoint, these payments do not loom large in the determination of individual subscriber rates,[57] but they have provoked much criticism from state commissions, largely because the Bell System's corporate organization has at all times made it impossible for the local regulatory authorities to examine and properly to rule upon the ultimate facts, as a result of their inability to reach the parent company and its operations by direct process.

Prior to the Supreme Court's decision in the Chicago rate case, it was the position of the American Telephone and Telegraph Company that the costs incurred by it in rendering the alleged license contract services were immaterial to the validity of the contract fee as an operating expense. The company contended that, in the absence of showing of bad faith or an abuse of discretion by the directors of the licensee company, it was sufficient to prove that the value to the lilcensees of the instruments and services furnished was greater than the amount of the fee paid, and that the charge was less than would have been the cost of obtaining those instruments and services elsewhere. For many years, the courts appeared to sympathize with that position,[58] but, in the Chicago rate case, it was held that

> . . . there should be specific findings by the statutory court with regard to the cost of these services to the American Company and the reasonable amount which should be allocated in this respect to the operating expenses of the intrastate business of the Illinois Company in the years covered by the decree.[59]

Although that decision has been of assistance to regulatory bodies, it by no means solved the problem of the propriety of the license contract payment, for the books of the American Company's "General Department" are not kept in such fashion as to record separately and currently the several costs attributable to the license contract. The determination of license contract costs, as distinct from the nonlicense contract costs of the General Department, must therefore depend upon "judgment allocations" made by various officials and employees of the American Company. Since the Chicago rate case it has been the American Company's practice to offer, in rate cases of its licensees, usually through representatives of its Comptroller's Department, testimony respecting costs allegedly incurred by it and which it asserts properly apply to the rendition of the alleged license contract services, as developed by these "judgment allocations." Included in such asserted costs are expenses incident to the carrying forward of fundamental research projects; to "holding money available" for Associated

---

[57]Over the System as a whole, however, the fees collected totalled over fifteen millions of dollars in 1936.

[58]See Houston v. Southwestern Bell Tel. Co., 259 U.S. 318, 323 (1922); Southwestern Bell Tel. Co. v. Public Serv. Comm., 262 U.S. 276, 288–89 (1923).

[59]282 U.S. 133, 157 (1930). See Note (1936) 49 Harv L. Rev. 957, 982–89. It is the clear implication of this decision that the burden of proof as to showing the cost of these services is upon the company seeking to sustain the license contract payment.

company financing; to practically all of the work of its operation and engineering, legal, accounting, advertising, and personnel departments, and to most of its remaining general functions. When totalled, these claimed costs have managed, since 1928, to amount each year to a sum greater than the total payments actually received from the operating companies.

If the contentions of company witnesses are to be accepted, the American Telephone and Telegraph Company, despite its holdings of more than two billion dollars of stock in Bell System companies and its large advances to those companies, exists for virtually no other purpose than the rendering of these license contract services, since, except for the operation of its Long Lines Department, practically all its costs have been allocated to these services. This is not to say that many of the services in question lack value. The primary question, however, is the propriety of the costs so allocated, and thus claimed to be rightfully recoverable from the telephone ratepayers.[60]

There appears to be no good reason why the long-continued controversy over these license contract payments and costs may not be brought to an end, through some reasonable application of accounting methods in respect to the costs of rendering such services as are of actual value to the Associated companies and are required for their efficient operation. Unless or until some such reasonable machinery be adopted, the controversy over these fees will doubtless continue to rage. It would be interesting to be able to contrast the American Company's asserted license contract service costs with teh costs (by way of salary and expenses to witnesses, attorneys' fees, transcripts of testimony, and the like) which that company and its Associated companies have incurred over the years in the attempt to defend these license contract fees, as well as with the far greater but more intangible costs resultant from the long-continued impairment of Bell

---

[60]There has been as yet no Supreme Court pronouncement on the validity of the American Company's claimed costs of rendering the alleged license contract services. Since the decision in the Smith case, the showings of the American Company have been held deficient, in whole or in part, in the following cases: Southern Bell Tel. & Tel. Co. v. Georgia Pub. Serv. Comm., 2 P.U.R. (N.S.) 234, 237–39, 240 (N.D. Ga. 1933); Illinois Bell Tel. Co. v. Gilbert, 3 F. Supp. 595 (N. D. Ill. 1933), *rev'd on other grounds,* Lindheimer v. Illinois Bell Tel. Co., 292 U.S. 151 (1934); Ohio Bell Tel. Co. v. Public Utilities Comm., 131 Ohio St. 539, 3 N.E.(2d) 475 (1936), *rev'd on other grounds,* Ohio Bell Tel. Co. v. Public Utilities Comm., 3 or U.S. 292 (1937); *Re* Pacific Tel. & Tel. Co., 13 P.U.R. (N.S.) 337, 386–89 (Ore. C.C. 1936), *aff'd,* Pacific Tel. & Tel. Co. v. Wallace, 26 Ore. Advance Sheets 187, 244–46 (1938); *Re* Wisconsin Tel. Co., 13 P.U.R. (N.S.) 224, 259–68 (Wis. 1936); *cf. Re* Michigan Bell Tel. Co., 10 P.U.R. (N.S.) 149, 199, 212–16 (Mich. 1935); *Re* Northwestern Bell Tel. Co., 19 P.U.R. (N.S.) 455, 458–59 (Minn. 1937); *Re* New York Tel. Co., 19 P.U.R. (N.S.) 443, 452 (N.Y. 1936). The license contract payment was allowed as an operating expense in the following cases: Chesapeake & P. Tel. Co. v. Public Utilities Comm., 62 Wash. L. Rep. 486, 490 (D. C. Sup. Ct. 1934), overruling *Re* Chesapeake & P. Tel. Co., 4 P.U.R. (N.S.) 346, 353–55 (1934); Los Angeles v. Southern Calif. Tel. Co., 14 P.U.R. (N.S.) 252, 269, n. 18 (Cal. 1936); *Re* Customers of New England Tel. & Tel. Co., 5 P.U.R. (N.S.) 333, 337–38 (Mass. 1934); Chesapeake & P. Tel. Co. v. West, 7 F. Supp. 214, 231, 3 P.U.R. (N.S.) 241, 267 (D. Md. 1934), *aff'd* (without mention of license contract), 295 U.S. 662 (1935); *Re* Southwestern Bell Tel. Co., 9 P.U.R. (N.S.) 113, 122, 142 (Okla. 1935), *aff'd* (without mention of license contract), 71 P. (2d) 747 (Okla. 1937), *appeal dismissed,* U.S. Sup. Ct., Feb. 28, 1938; *Re* Southwestern Bell Tel. Co., 16 P.U.R. (N.S.) 1, 7 (Okla. 1936); Memphis v. Southern Bell Tel. & Tel. Co., 6 P.U.R. (N.S.) 464, 475–76 (Tenn. 1934).

System public relations which may be traced directly to the American Company's insistence that virtually all costs incurred by it in its operations are applicable to these license contract fees.[61]

1.7.2 The Western Electric Company

Prices paid for apparatus, equipment, and materials used in public utility operations enter directly into the rate base, and to a degree into operating expense, and are therefore pertinent subjects of inquiry in rate investigations. Were the telephone instruments used by the Bell System companies manufactured directly by them in shops maintained as parts of their own plants, the expenditures incurred in such manufacture would, if "prudent," become proper capital charges. As a matter of fact, the Bell System's manufacturing department is a separate corporation, the Western Electric Company, wholly owned by the American Telephone and Telegraph Company. This corporation has contracted with the Bell System operating companies, including the Long Lines, to furnish them with apparatus and materials. Its prices and its underlying costs are therefore of direct pertinency in any consideration of operating company rate bases. And this is true, whether the inquiry be as to the "reproduction cost" of the company's property, or as to the "prudent investment" represented by it.[62]

This Western Electric price and cost problem is one of the knottiest encountered in the regulation of Bell System rates. No state operations, and even the Federal Communications Commission has found great difficulty in ascertaining that corporation's true manufacturing costs. Apparently its existing accounting system is not so constructed as to present sufficiently accurate data on this subject, with the result that the costs in question cannot even be approximated, in respect to individual items or groups of apparatus, from an examination of the

---

[61]The Long Lines Department, being a department of the American Company, cannot, of course, legally have a contract with that company, but with reference to servicing arrangements with the General Department, it is treated much as one of the Associated companies. The effective license contract percentage charge was formerly made on its books and credited to the General Department, but in 1936 the interdepartmental credits for these purposes were placed on a "cost" basis, the result being to increase the amount of such transfers of funds. The total billing to the Long Lines Department on this basis in 1936 was $1,762,160, as against an estimated total of $1,340,000 on the 1½% basis.

[62]The practical importance of the question becomes apparent when it is realized that from 1925 to 1930 Western Electric sales to the Bell companies averaged over $290,000,000 each year; that from 1926 to 1934 Western made approximately ninety percent of the total sales of telephone apparatus, equipment, and materials enjoyed by the major manufacturers of such products in the United States, and that during the entire period from 1913 to 1931, no less than sixty percent of the gross cost of plant and equipment constructed by the Bell operating comapnies was represented by materials purchased from Western. (The remainder was largely made up of labor, company overheads, freight, and like items.) Inasmuch as this period of nineteen years may be said roughly to constitute a complete life cycle of Bell System Plant, it is apparent that almost two-thirds of the Associated companies' present plant must today be represented by apparatus and materials originally purchased from Western.

company's books. A more satisfactory cost accounting system seems greatly to be desired.

Much of Western's business is of a noncompetitive nature, and the conditions under which it operates are such that its overhead costs loom particularly large. The result has been that during periods when the general prices of manufactured articles have been dropping, because of lack of demand in competitive markets, Western's prices have risen—and vice versa. "Reproduction cost" estimates based upon such curiously inverted price trends demand the most careful attention by the regulatory bodies, and historical or recorded costs of equipment to operating companies likewise reflect this odd manufacturing situation.[63]

If Bell System operating company rate bases have, in fact, been inflated through use of excessive Western Electric prices, this is a matter of wide import to the telephone-using public. Indeed, no future consideration of Bell telephone rates can apparently hope to be complete without careful examination of this problem. Effective exercise of jurisdiction over, and positive scrutiny of, all phases of this manufacturing cost and price question are the prime requisites, and the federal commission can doubtless render invaluable assistance to state regulatory bodies by compiling accurate Western Electric Company cost and price data, and making such data available to the public agencies of the states.

---

[63]The reasonableness of the prices charged the Bell operating companies by Western Electric cane before the Supreme Court in Smith v. Illinois Bell Tel. Co., 282 U.S. 133 (1930) the finding of the lower court, based upon the average profit made by Western Electric, being held insufficient. When the case came before it a second time, the Court rested its decision primarily upon a finding that excessive charges had been made to operating expenses for depreciation, and took the position that it was unnecessary to pass further upon the Western Electric price problem. Lindheimer v. Illinois Bell Tel. Co., 292 U.S. 151 (1934).

Since the Supreme Court's decision in Smith v. Illinois Bell Tel. Co., *supra,* several state commissions and courts have considered the Western Electric Company price problem, the weight of opinion apparently being that "reproduction cost" appraisals based on Western Electric price increases, made during periods when other prices were decreasing, should not be deemed controlling. In this connection, see: Los Angeles v. Southern Calif. Tel. Co., 14 P.U.R. (N.S.) 252, 267–68 (Cal. aff'd, 62 Wash. L. Rep. 486 (D.C. Sup. Ct. 1934); Louisiana Pub. Serv. Comm. v. Southern Bell Tel. & Tel. Co., 8 P.U.R. (N.S.) 1, 7–8 (La. 1935), aff'd, 187 La. 137, 174 So. 180, 188–89 (1937); Re Chesapeake & P. Tel. Co., 1 P.U.R. (N.S.) 346, 369–71 (Md. 1933), enjoined, 7 F. Supp. 214, 231–32 (D. Md. 1934) (although the district court stated that it would, for the purpose of comparison of reproduction cost with book cost, give effect to the Commission's contentions with respect to Western Electric prices), injunction upheld, 295 U.S. 662 (1935) (but the Supreme Court did not discuss the reasonableness of Western Electric prices); Re Customers of New England Tel. & Tel. Co., 5 P.U.R. (N.S.) 333, 338–39 (Mass. 1934); Re Michigan Bell Tel. Co., 10 P.U.R. (N.S.) 149, 209–16 (Mich. 1935); Re New York Tel. Co., 14 P.U.R. (N.S.) 443, 452 (N. Y. 1936); Re Southern Bell Tel. & Tel. Co., 7 P.U.R. (N.S.) 21, 26–27, 32 (N.C. 1934); Re Ohio Bell Tel. Co., 2 P.U.R. (N.S.) 113, 123–26 (Ohio 1934), aff'd, Ohio Bell Tel. Co. v. Public Utilities Comm., 131 Ohio St. 539, 3 N.E.(3d) 475 (1936), rev'd, 301 U.S. 292 (1937) (but neither court discussed the reasonableness of Western Electric prices); Re Southwestern Bell Tel. Co., 9 P.U.R. (N.S.) 113, 121–24 (Okla. 1935), aff'd, 71 P.(2d) 747, 756 (Okla. 1937), appeal dismissed, U.S. Sup. Ct., Feb. 28, 1938; Pacific Tel. and Tel. Co. v. Thomas, 13 P.U.R. (N.S.) 337, 360 (Ore. C.C. 1936), aff'd, Pacific Tel. & Tel. Co. v. Wallace, 26 Ore. Advance Sheets 187, 210–11 (1938); Southwestern Bell Tel. Co. v. San Antonio, 2 F. Supp. 611, 620–21 (W. D. Tex. 1933), remanded for further findings, 75 F.(2d) 880, 883 (C.C.A. 5th, 1935), cert. denied, 295 U.S. 754 (1935), and case settled without further litigation; Re Wisconsin Tel. Co., 13 P.U.R. (N.S.) 224, 275–80 (Wis. 1936), now pending in the state circuit court.

1.7.3 Interstate Toll Rate "Uniformity"

Six of the Bell Associated companies are multi-state in character, rendering at least some interstate toll service within their respective areas,[64] and it has already been pointed out that complete "separations" of the property, expenses, and revenues incident to such interstate business will be necessary before effective regulation of the interstate rates of these companies will become practicable. This would not be the case were all interstate operations in these territories handled by or through Long Lines, since its business is wholly interstate in character and does not require intrastate-interstate separation. Long Lines already handles the major portion of the total interstate telephone business of the country, particularly the "long-haul" interstate business over distances greater than forty miles, and such an extension of its operations would therefore not seem illogical. It would, of course, greatly simplify the problem of interstate telephone rate regulation.

Even more important would be the fact that such unified interstate operation should automatically result in a single, uniform interstate schedule, applicable to practically all interstate toll messages in the entire country over distances beyond the forty-mile Long Lines minimum.[65] The possibility of attaining such nation-wide interstate telephone rate uniformity,[66] and at the same time of eliminating the necessity for the expensive separation studies which must otherwise soon be undertaken, apparently renders the suggestion one of importance. No "monop-oly" problem seems to be here involved, since the Bell System already domi-nates the interstate telephone field, and the transfer of business mentioned would merely represent the turning over by the left hand to the right hand of operations already handled in their entirety by Bell System companies.

---

[64]The Pacific Telephone and Telegraph Company, the Mountain States Telephone and Telegraph Company, and the New England Telephone Company handle all the interstate business in their territories. The Southwestern Bell Telephone Company, the Northwestern Bell Telephone Company and the Southern Bell Telephone Company handle a portion of such intracompany interstate business, the Long Lines supplying the balance.

[65]There have been times during the past two decades when the Associated Company interstate rates have been identical with those of Long Lines. Such was the case just prior to the $12,000,000 Long Lines reduction of January 15, 1937. Since that date, only one of the Associated companies (the Southwestern Bell Telephone Company) has reduced its interstate schedule to the new Long Lines levels. This reduction was voluntarily made by that company, no separation studies having as yet been undertaken. Informal efforts to obtain similar action from other Bell multi-state companies have so far proved ineffective, and mandatory regulation of rates for interstate services now handled by these companies must remain ineffective—in fact, practically impossible—in the absence of complete separation studies, unless their interstate operations were in some manner to be assumed by the Long Lines.

[66]The nationwide interstate telephone rate schedule uniformity here discussed signifies merely the extension into the multi-state Associated company areas of the Long Lines rate schedules, which are already uniformly effective for interstate service throughout most of the more populous sections of the United States (*i.e.*, wherever Long Lines now operates).

1.8 THE RELATION OF TELEPHONE RATES TO THOSE OF OTHER COMMUNICATION FACILITIES

Doubtless there exists a place in the national economy for the type of service offered by the telegraph companies, but few persons would today assert with any degree of confidence that the ultimate nature and extent of that place is as yet clear. It must be at least partially the task of the federal body charged with regulating interstate communications to assist in finding the solution of this problem, as well as of those which arise from many other rapidly developing phases of communications. For example, point-to-point radio telephone and telegraph service must be given due to consideration. Such service is today largely confined to the international communications field. What it may be tomorrow is another question.

The relation between rates for telephone message toll service and those for the transmission of telegrams is obvious. Private line service and teletypewriter service impinge even more directly upon the traditional telegraph field. And the growth of the "teletypewriter exchange" business is a threat to the existing telegraph service that no informed observer of communications trends can over-look. On the other side of the picture, the telegraph companies find themselves confronted with an equally serious threat resultant from the rapid development of the air mail.

Questions arising out of the control and pooling of patents; the necessity of considering, from the economic viewpoint, the vast investments already made in existing plant, both for telephone and telegraph service; the import of recent air mail developments; the effect of technological advances on labor, and of the ascendancy of any one purveyor of communication services upon the men and women who derive their livelihood from rendering those services—these and many other serious social and economic problems beset the investigator in the communications field. The Federal Communications Commission could not, if it would, escape the necessity of straight thinking on these problems, and of leading in the development of national policies in respect to them.

1.9 INFORMAL VERSUS FORMAL METHODS

Many of the problems of interstate telephone rate regulation are continuing in nature, calling at all times for frank, informal discussion between company and commission representatives. The atmosphere of the council table seems or-dinarily much more conducive to the development of positive results in such matters than does the adversary air which tends to surround most formal proceed-ings. The aspect of a game or contest which inevitably envelops the respective advocates (be they lawyers, accountants, engineers, or what not) in formal rate cases makes for bickering and bitterness, as well as for delay and expense.

If the essential factors can be soundly defined and weighted, and if their factual background can be fully and frankly developed the positive and direct methods of informal negotiation should prove effective, and desired ends should be attainable with a minimum expenditure of time, money and effort. Only through some such concept of regulatory functions can an end apparently be brought to the sorry spectacle of "ten year rate cases." *In rate making, time is always of the essence,*[67] and certain of the state commissions are today making notable progress in the development of informal regulatory machinery.

Interstate telephone rates have grown up almost wholly outside the boundaries of regulation, and particularly careful scrutiny of schedules and basic practices is therefore essential, in the public interest. The very absence of a background of federal regulatory experience renders basic factual development especially important. Though informal methods are still on trial, and are to be judged wholly from the standpoint of their practical results, there will always be time for formal proceedings, if and when the more direct and expeditious methods fail.

1.10 CONCLUSION

The concentration of over ninety-five percent of the nation's interstate telephone business in the hands of a single, integrated group of corporations, not only poses a challenge in respect to the development of regulatory machinery of high capacity and efficiency in one of the subtlest and most difficult fields of public regulatory effort, but at the same time presents an unparalleled opportunity for positive and effective action in this direction. Experience in federal regulation of telephone rates leads to the conclusion that a purely "judicial" attitude can hardly be expected to produce desirable results. Furthermore, "continuous scrutiny" must apparently replace the practice of "regulation by explosion" which has so frequently characterized much state regulatory effort. Basic and continuous "research" in connection with interstate telephone rate problems is an imperative and fundamental requirement. The regulatory agency must develop effective machinery which will enable it at all times to keep fully abreast of the factual operating situation.

In this effort, the traditional separations of the regulatory function obviously do not apply. For in this problem considerations ordinarily labeled "legal" blend inextricably with those of "accounting," of "engineering," and even of "public policy." If this complex problem is squarely to be met, the regulatory body must avoid any attempt to fit these individual considerations into the separate pigeonholes of law, or economics, or what-not. The lawyer, the economist, the accountant and the engineer who are to share in this process must possess an awareness of the whole—an awareness and an understanding of factors which cannot be the sole concern of any one such area of effort. The appropriate process

[67]Examples of such lengthy rate hearings are numerous. See *Re* Wisconsin Tel. Co., 13 P.U.R. (N.S.) 224 (Wis. 1936); also the discussion by Mr. Justice Brandeis, concurring, in St. Joseph Stock Yards Co. v. United States, 298 U.S. 38 (1936), and the remarks of Mr. Justice Black, dissenting, in McCart v. Indianapolis Water Co., 58 Sup. Ct. 324 (1938). The staggering cost of such futile methods of public utility rate making must, in the end, be borne by the rate payers.

of experience and of training for those who are to give effectiveness to the scheme of regulation in this field must be such as will develop understanding in spheres which cannot be the individual concern of law schools, or of schools of economics, or of business administration, or of engineering. Here, as in many other fields of the interaction of business and government, there must be developed a special body of public administration, if the regulatory machinery is to be rendered truly effective.

It has been the considered view of the writer that positive and effective interstate telephone rate regulatory processes may successfully be developed only through the establishment, under proper direction, of an integrated and fully coordinated group of people trained and experienced in all the interrelated fields of appropriate inquiry—a group freed from responsibility for the details of routine administration, but charged collectively with full responsibility for the development of all types of basic factual data, for the continuous scrutiny of all phases of this complex problem, and for the fundamental "research" which seems so essential to its solution.[68]

No federal body has ever faced a regulatory opportunity offering greater possibilities for successful effort than does the Federal Communications Commission today. The course which it may adopt in meeting this opportunity, and the concrete methods and program which it may develop in respect to positive interstate telephone rate control will doubtless be followed with close attention by other administrative bodies, and will prove of large moment in the history of American public utility regulation.

---

[68]Professor C. O. Ruggles, in his recent monograph, ASPECTS OF THE ORGANIZATION, FUNCTIONS, AND FINANCING OF STATE PUBLIC UTILITY COMMISSIONS (HARVARD UNIV. BUSINESS RESEARCH STUDIES NO. 18, VOL. XXIV, NO. 2, APRIL 1937), REMARKS UPON THE ERECTION OF SPECIAL "RATE AND RESEARCH" DIVISIONS IN THE STAFFS OF SEVERAL LEADING STATE COMMISSIONS, ADDING, "IN GENERAL, HOWEVER, THE COMMISSIONS HAVE NOT GIVEN THIS MATTER THE ATTENTION TO WHICH IT IS ENTITLED." ID. AT 39.

Chapter 2

Two Decades of Telecommunications Regulation: An Historical Perspective*

HERBERT E. MARKS[†]

ABSTRACT   This article was completed before the announcement, on January 8, 1982, of the proposal to settle the Government's antitrust actions against American Telephone & Telegraph Company (AT&T). This article provides an historic perspective from which to judge this and other recent developments. The development of telecommunications regulation during the past two decades is a uniquely American story of how the nation's policy-making machinery responds to technological innovation and its concomitant industrial proliferation and growth. This review focuses on the significance of these recent developments for the information science professions and their associated industries. The Federal Communications Commission has attempted, in a number of ways, to promote competition in telecommunications. In each case, the dominant telephone carrier—American Telephone and Telegraph Company (AT&T) and its affiliated companies—vigorously resisted, on an element-by-element basis, all such attempts to undermine its monopoly position. In the first section of this article, we shall briefly outline the course of this struggle. As the Commission was moving to increase competition in a number of telecommunications markets, several other factors coalesced to generate an atmosphere conducive to widespread acceptance of competition in the telecommunication industry and to an accelerated pace of change. AT&T itself became increasingly aware of the potential benefits of increased competition. The year 1982 may well be the crucial point in the evolution of telecommunications policy for the next two decades. The resulting laws, regulations, decrees, and decisions will have profound effects on the structure of telecommunications markets and the nation's technology.

---

* Reprinted from *Journal of Telecommunication Networks*, Vol. 1, No. 2. © 1982, Computer Science Press, 1803 Research Blvd., Rockville, MD 20850. All rights reserved.

†Mr. Marks is a partner in the Washington, D.C. law firm of Squire, Sanders & Dempsey. Any views expressed in this article do not necessarily represent the views of any client of the firm.

2.1 INTRODUCTION

The development of telecommunications regulation during the past two decades is a uniquely American story of how the nation's policy-making machinery responds to technological innovation and its concomitant industrial proliferation and growth. This review focuses on the significance of these recent developments for the information science professions and their associated industries. Space limitations do not permit discussion of all the proceedings or even all of the policy areas. Thus, certain proceedings and areas have been selected as illustrative of the process.

The Federal Communications Commission ("Commission") has attempted, in a number of ways, to promote competition in telecommunications. For example, the Commission fostered competition in the terminal equipment market by eliminating telephone company tariff provisions which severely restricted the interconnection of nontelephone company-supplied terminal equipment to telephone company facilities. The Commission promoted competition in transmission services by permitting new entities to provide such service without first showing a specific economic need for their offerings. Finally, the Commission spurred the proliferation of new telecommunications services by invalidating telephone company tariff provisions which restricted the resafe and sharing of telephone company facilities.[1]

In each case, the dominant telephone carrier—American Telephone and Telegraph Company ("AT&T") and its affiliated companies—vigorously resisted, on an element-by-element basis, all such attempts to undermine its monopoly position. In the first section of this article, we shall briefly outline the course of this struggle.

Before this struggle for increased competition in telecommunications was resolved, the trend toward promoting greater competition converged with the movement toward deregulation. The distinction between the two is sometimes lost, but it is important to bear it in mind. In the deregulatory process, a regulatory agency removes itself wholly or partially from the marketplace, primarily in the belief that market forces have developed sufficiently to render government regulation unnecessary and, very likely, burdensome. Effective competition is generally seen as a precondition to deregulation. In the last section of this paper, the process of deregulation in the telecommunications industry will be discussed.

---

[1]Because telecommunications services have become a vital resource for businesses and government, these and other Commission decisions have affected a number of non-telecommunications markets and industries. Thus, the "competitive" issues discussed in this article are of interest beyond the telecommunications context.

2.2 THE INITIAL CHAPTER: COMPETITION EVOLVES

The first portion of our historical analysis focuses on the attempts by firms not affiliated with telecommunications common carriers to obtain and maintain the authority to compete with established common carriers and to utilize carrier-provided transmission facilities to provide a variety of telecommunications services. These attempts were energetically resisted by the existing carriers, particularly AT&T, which did not yet see the advantage of an open competitive environment for the Bell System. As a result, the struggle to win the right to compete was lengthy, as each barrier to competition was contested one at a time.

2.2.1 Competition: Terminal Equipment

The first major impulse toward significant competition in telecommunications probably arose in the terminal equipment market. The history of the struggle to foster competition in this market is interesting because it illustrates both the step-by-step nature of the struggle and the tenacity of those who resisted competitive forces. Competition developed dramatically in this area because the potential variety of such equipment is immense.[2] Competition is of relatively recent vintage, however, because telephone carriers for years barred the interconnection of any noncarrier-supplied equipment to their facilities. Although the *Hush-a-Phone* decisions in 1957 and 1958[3] had established the principle that a customer may attach any equipment to carrier-provided facilities which is privately beneficial without being publicly detrimental, significant interconnection rights were not fully enforced by the Commission until the *Carterfone* decision in 1968.[4]

Nevertheless, while the *Carterfone* decision represented a first step towards broader interconnection rights for the communications user, it did not eradicate the discriminatory restrictions of the past. In 1969, AT&T filed tariffs in response to *Carterfone* which permitted the interconnection of customer-supplied terminal equipment to switched telephone network facilities, but only if the customer also obtained a connecting arrangement from the serving telephone company.[5] No connecting arrangement was needed, however, if the customer obtained his terminal equipment from the telephone company. Thus, a customer was free to supply his own terminal equipment, but only at an added cost and using a different interface to telephone company facilities.

---

[2]Generally speaking, terminal equipment includes all that equipment on the subscriber's premises which is owned or leased by the subscriber and which is attached to the facilities of a communications common carrier.

[3]See *Hush-a-Phone Corp. V. United States*, 238 F.2d 266 (D.C. Cir. 1956); *Hush-a-Phone Corp. v. AT&T*, 22 FCC 112 (1957).

[4]*Carterfone*, 13 FCC 2d 420, *recon. denied*, 14 FCC 2d 571 (1968).

[5]*See AT&T Foreign Attachment Tariff Revisions*, 15 FCC 2d 605 (1968), *recon. denied*, 18 FCC 2d 871 (1969). The Commission allowed these tariff provisions to become effective without investigation.

These restrictive tariff provisions—i.e., the requirement of a different and discriminatory interface and added charges for the interconnection of customer-provided terminal equipment—survived intact until 1975. In that year, the Commission ruled that AT&T's connecting arrangement tariffs were unreasonable, unjust and discriminatory, and adopted a registration program for all terminal equipment.[6] Embodied in Part 68 of the Commission's Rules,[7] the registration program permits the direct interconnection of all terminal equipment, whether provided by the telephone company or by an independent vendor, to the switched telephone network so long as that equipment meets certain technical requirements. Additionally, all such terminal equipment now connects through a standard interface.

These new interconnection privileges were a long time in coming, however, as the telephone companies steadfastly resisted the Commission's registration program. The Commission first instituted its investigation of AT&T's connecting arrangement tariff in 1972. The registration program was adopted in 1975, but, because of delays ordered by the Commission and the courts, the program did not become effective until 1977.[8] Even today, this program still does not apply to all telephone company services.

Before and after adoption of the registration program, telephone company resistance to competition persisted in a number of other forms. There were, for example, legislative proposals that would have reinforced the telephone industry's monopoly in the provision of terminal equipment. Additionally, the Commission was presented with a telephone industry "fall-back" proposal—the Primary Instrument Concept—which would have required every subscriber of single line telephone service to obtain from the supplying telephone company at least one terminal at each location served. This proposal was rejected by the Commission in 1978.[9]

Indeed, those pressing for nondiscriminatory interconnection of customer-provided terminal equipment had to run a veritable gauntlet of similarly restrictive tariff provisions. User and competitor complaints were instrumental in forcing the elimination of restrictive tariff provisions which:

a. classified a wholly intrastate private line circuit connected to an interstate private line circuit through terminal equipment as interstate for tariff purposes

---

[6]*See First Report and Order in Docket 19528*, 56 FCC 2d 593, (1975), *on reconsideration*, 57 FCC 2d 1216, 58 FCC 2d 716, 59 FCC 2d 83 (1976). This registration program became a nationwide standard because the Commission had previously held that its decisions and regulations regarding equipment interconnection preempted conflicting state regulation. *See Telerent Leasing Corp.*, 45 FCC 2d 204 (1974), *aff'd sub nom. North Carolina Utils. Comm'n v. FCC*, 537 F.2d 787 (4th Cir.), *cert. denied*, 429 U.S. 1027 (1976).

[7]*See* 47 C.F.R. Pt. 68 (1980).

[8]The registration program was subsequently expanded to include PBX's, key telephone equipment, and main station telephones, and, as expanded, was affirmed on appeal. *See Second Report and Order in Docket 19528*, 58 FCC 2d 736 (1976), *modified*, 64 FCC 2d 1058, *aff'd sub. nom. North Carolina Utils. Comm'n v. FCC*, 552 F.2d 1036 (4th Cir.), *cert. denied*, 434 U.S. 874 (1977).

[9]*See Primary Instrument Concept*, 68 FCC 2d 1157 (1978).

if the terminal equipment were provided by the telephone company, and as intrastate if the terminal equipment were provided by the customer;[10]

b. required all terminal equipment on a private line circuit to be provided by the telephone company or by the customer ("no mix");[11] and

c. prohibited customers from interpositioning nontelephone company terminal equipment between the telephone carrier's transmission service and carrier-provided terminal equipment ("no piece out").[12]

Moreover, because the Part 68 registration program only applies to the interconnection of terminal equipment to the switched telephone network, the effort to secure direct, nondiscriminatory interconnection continues with respect to other services. It has taken further proceedings, for example, to try to extend the Commission's liberal interconnection policy to other services (for example, Dataphone Digital Service) and to resist the reimposition of discriminatory regulations. These efforts have not all been successful.

Further, although terminal equipment other than the basic telephone has usually been subject to a separate charge,[13] proceedings have been necessary to eliminate those situations where the provision of terminal equipment is "bundled" with the furnishing of transmission facilities.[14] Bundling can occur when some of the costs for separately tariffed telephone company-provided terminal equipment are recovered through the transmission charges which all users pay. When this occurs, the customer who does not utilize telephone company terminal equipment is nonetheless forced to assume some of the costs associated with that equipment, thereby permitting the telephone company to underprice the equipment. The *general* principle in favor of unbundling has been confirmed only as a concomitant to deregulation.[15]

The foregoing discussion mentions only a few of the proceedings that have been necessary to secure the right to interconnect customer-provided terminal equipment to telephone company-provided facilities on reasonable, non-discriminatory terms. Enormous progress has been made by users and competitors in seeking and obtaining decisions from the Commission affirming and

---

[10]*See Application of AT&T's Private Line Service Tariff,* 52 FCC 2d 979 (1975), *investigation terminated,* 58 FCC 2d 1288 (1976).

[11]The "no-mix" rule was eliminated by AT&T in 1977. *See* AT&T Transmittal No. 12600 (filed Jan. 23, 1977).

[12]The "no piece out" provision was eliminated by AT&T in 1978. *See* AT&T Transmittal No. 13123 (filed Dec. 12, 1978).

[13]*See Amendment of Section 64.702 of the Commission's Rules and Regulations (Second Computer Inquiry),* 77 FCC 2d 384, 442, *on reconsideration,* 84 FCC 2d 512 (1981), *appeal docketed sub nom. Computer & Communications Indus. Ass'n, v. FCC,* No. 80-1471 (D.C. Dir., filed May 5, 1980) [hereinafter referred to as *"Final Decision"*].

[14]*See, e.g., AT&T Group/Supergroup Facilities,* 84 FCC 2d 1 (1981).

[15]*See Final Decision,* 77 FCC 2d at 443-43. *See also Interface of the International Telex Service with the Domestic Telex and TWX Service,* 76 FCC 2d 61 (1980), *aff'd sub nom. Western Union Tel. Co. v. FCC,* No. 79-2496 (D.C. Cir., 1981).

facilitating the freedom to interconnect. Nevertheless, the struggle continues to the present day. It is interesting and significant that during the prolonged struggle over interconnection there was little apparent interest in this important issue within the Congress.

2.2.2 Competition: Transmission Services

The Commission's commitment to greater competition in the provision of transmission services dates from the early 1960's, when it approved private microwave systems which could be substituted for telephone company intercity transmission facilities.[16] The dramatic changes in this area, however, began in 1969 when Microwave Communications, Inc. ("MCI") was authorized to construct microwave transmission facilities between Chicago and St. Louis over which to offer common carrier services.[17]

The Commission soon received a flood of applications from other non-telephone company firms proposing to offer telecommunications services over specialized microwave facilities.[18] In 1971, the Commission granted many of these applications and established a policy favoring competitive entry in certain intercity private line service markets.[19] In so doing, the Commission ruled that open entry could benefit the public without impairing the telephone common carriers' ability to provide universal telephone service.[20] The Commission, however, reserved judgment on the wisdom of permitting competitive entry into the Message Telecommunications Service ("MTS") and Wide Area Telecommunications Service ("WATS") markets.

Despite the adoption in principle of a policy favoring competitive entry with respect to certain telecommunications services, the struggle to implement competition in this area proceeded, as was the case with the interconnection of terminal equipment, on a step-by-step basis. After MCI's initial certification as a specialized carrier, for example, AT&T refused to interconnect its local exchange facilities with MCI's intercity microwave facilities, thus preventing MCI from extending its interstate services to local exchange customers. MCI appealed to the Commission, and the latter ordered AT&T to cease and desist from denying reasonable interconnection to MCI and the other SCC's for their authorized private line services.[21]

---

[16]See *Allocation of Frequencies in the Bands Above 890 Mc.*, 27 FCC 359 (1959), *recon. denied*, 29 FCC 825 (1960).

[17]See *Microwave Communications, Inc.*, 18 FCC 2d 953 (1969), *recon. denied*, 21 FCC 2d 190 (1970).

[18]These firms are now often referred to as specialized common carriers ("SCCs").

[19]See *Specialized Common Carrier Services*, 29 FCC 2d 870, *recon. denied*, 31 FCC 2d 1106 (1971), *aff'd sub. nom. Washington Utils. & Transp. Comm'n v. FCC*, 513 F.2d 1142 (9th Cir.), *cert. denied*, 423 U.S. 836 (1975).

[20]See 29 FCC 2d at 920.

[21]See *Bell System Tariff Offerings*, 46 FCC 413, *aff'd sub nom. Bell Telephone Co. of Pa. v. FCC*, 503 F.2d 1250 (3d Cir. 1974), *cert. denied*, 422 U.S. 1026 (1975).

Despite this victory, MCI's difficulties with AT&T continued when MCI began marketing its metered Execunet service in competition with AT&T's switched MTS/WATS services. At AT&T's request, the Commission rejected MCI's Execunet tariff, holding that MCI's initial certification implicitly restricted it to the provision of private line services.[22] The Commission was reluctant to open MTS and WATS services to competition for fear that competitive entry would impair the ability of local telephone companies to provide universal telephone service. On appeal, however, the Court of Appeals nor the District of Columbia Circuit ruled that the Commission could not prohibit MCI from offering Execunet service, since the Commission had not imposed such a restriction on MCI's initial certification.[23] Nonetheless, further litigation was necessary to vindicate MCI's rghts because AT&T, with the Commission's approval, refused to interconnect its local exchange facilities with MCI's Execunet service. The court of appeals again ruled in favor of MCI's favor and, in a sharply worded decision, ordered the Commission to require AT&T to provide the requested interconnection.[24]

Once the SCC's right to reasonable interconnection had been established, the focus of the debate shifted to the terms and conditions pursuant to which that interconnection would take place. Thus, the specialized carriers have filed a series of cases against AT&T claiming that AT&T has not acted in good faith in providing them transmission facilities. In addition, extensive discussions are proceeding between the SCCs and the telephone carriers to establish the charges which the latter can exact for providing the SCCs with access to the telephone companies' local distribution facilities.[25] Finally, the SCCs are involved in proceedings intended to obtain local exchange access on economical and technical terms similar to those provided by the telephone companies, particularly AT&T, to their own intercity services. Thus, critical policy issues in this area are still being resolved.

2.2.3 Competition: Resale and Shared Use

The next great competitive advance was precipitated by the dramatic advances in computer technology since World War II, which have made it possible to improve vastly the quality and capacity of standard transmission facilities. A new computer services industry exploited these transmission improvements and provided a wide variety of innovative communications and data processing services to customers at a profit. The industry's progress was stifled, however, by the fact

---

[22]*See MCI Telecommunications Corp. (Execunet)*, Docket No. 20640, FCC 75-799 (released July 2, 1975), *on reconsideration*, 60 FCC 2d 25 (1976), *rev'd*, 561 F.2d 365 (D.C. Cir. 1977), *cert. denied*, 434 U.S. 1040, *on remand.*, FCC 78-142, *rev'd*, 580 F.2d 590 (D.C. Cir.), *cert. denied*, 439 U.S. 980 (1978).

[23]*See MCI Telecommunications Corp. v. FCC*, 561 F2d 365 (D.C. 1977).

[24]*See MCI Telecommunications Corp.*, 580 F.2d 590 (D.C. Cir. 1978).

[25]*See Exchange Network Facilities (ENFIA)*, 71 FCC 2d 440 (1979). *See also MTS/WATS Market Structure*, 77 FCC 2d 224 (1980).

that telephone company tariffs generally placed sharp restrictions on the resale or the sharing of telephone company transmission services. The telephone carriers viewed their transmission facilities as stand-alone communications networks, whereas the information sciences industry saw those facilities as merely one component of a geographically-extended computer/communications system.[26]

In 1976, the Commission reshaped the regulatory environment by requiring domestic common carriers to permit unlimited resale and sharing of their private line transmission services.[27] The Commission also defined when an unregulated "sharing" arrangement becomes a regulated "resale" activity, thus providing companies some useful guidance on the point at which regulation would attach to their communications offerings. Still, the Commission resisted requests to deregulate all resale carriers.

2.2.4 Competition: Questioning the Legal Monopolies

It is important to remember that the Commission's *Resale and Shared Use* decision applied only to private line services. It was not until 1980, when the deregulatory era was phasing in, that the Commission endorsed unlimited resale and shared use of MTS/WATS-type services.[28] In order to reach that decision, the Commission had to reassess whether the concept of "natural monopoly"—the notion that some communications facilities and services should be provided on a sole source basis—should continue to have a place in the telecommunications realm.

The Commission's commitment to that concept diminished with the proliferation of its pro-competitive telecommunications decisions. Thus, in 1979, the Commission concluded that domestic public message service and telex/TWX markets should be open to competitive entry.[29] In 1980, the Commission categorically ruled that MTS and WATS service should no longer be provided on a sole source basis.[30] These decisions effectively abandoned the notion of natural monopoly and extended the pro-competitive *Specialized Common Carrier* and *Resale* and *Shared Use* decisions to all domestic telecommunications services.

---

[26]Resale and sharing arrangements may be viable simply by passing on savings achieved from buying transmission capacity in bulk. The impetus for growth in this area, however, came from the use of computer technology to improve capacity and quality of services.

[27]*See Resale and Shared Use,* 60 FCC 2d 261, *modified,* 60 FCC 2d 588 (1976), *amended on reconsideration,* 62 FCC 2d 588 (1977), *aff'd sub nom. AT&T v. FCC,* 572 F.2d 17 (2d Cir.), *cert. denied,* 439 U.S. 875 (1978).

[28]*See Resale and Shared Use,* 83 FCC 2d 167 (1980). Although this was a landmark decision, the result was not unexpected in light of the *Execunet* litigation.

[29]*See Domestic Public Message Services,* 71 FCC 2d 471, *modified,* 73 FCC 2d 151 (1979).

[30]*See MTS/WATS Market Structure,* 81 FCC 2d 177 (1980).

2.2.5 Competition: International Services

The Commission has sought to extend its competitive policies into the international telecommunications service arena as well. Regrettably, foreign authorities, which retain the authority to approve services and facilities entering their jurisdictions, have considerably slowed the Commission's initiatives in this area. A current proceeding which would require unlimited resale and shared use of international facilities, for example, is apparently dormant.[31]

Nonetheless, the Commission has acted to increase competition in the international area through alternate means. Historically, domestic carriers were restricted to providing only the domestic segment of international traffic. The overseas segment was provided by one of the international record carriers ("IRCs"). The IRCs in turn were forbidden to provide domestic except to a few gateway cities. The Commission has attempted to increase competition in the international area by breaking down this dichotomy. Thus, in 1980, the Commission permitted the IRCs to provide direct service to a number of new domestic points.[32] It also allowed AT&T to offer switched data services over its international voice facilities on a secondary basis.[33] Additionally, the Commission is reassessing a 1964 policy decision which generally restricts AT&T to the provision of international voice services and the IRCs to the offering of international record services.[34]

Equally important, Congress has moved to reinforce the Commission's efforts to expand competition in the international communications arena. For example, a bill to repeal Section 222 of the Communications Act, which prohibits Western Union from furnishing international services, has recently been enacted into law.[35]

2.3 THE SECOND CHAPTER: DEREGULATION AND ANTITRUST

As the Commission was moving to increase competition in a number of telecommunications markets, several other factors coalesced to generate an atmosphere conducive to widespread acceptance of competition in the telecommunications industry and to an accelerated pace of change. AT&T itself became increasingly aware of the potential benefits of increased competition. Specifically, AT&T recognized that it might gain substantially, if through open competition, AT&T were allowed to enter markets previously denied to it. Further, a restructuring of

---

[31]See *International Telecommunications Competition*, 77 FCC 2d 831 (1980).

[32]See *International Record Carriers Scope of Operations*, 76 FCC 2d 115, *recon. denied*, 80 FCC 2d 303 (1980).

[33]See *AT&T (Dataphone)*, 75 FCC 2d 682 (1980).

[34]See *Overseas Communications Services*, 84 FCC 2d 622 (1980).

[35]See P.L. 97-130, 95 Stat. 1687 (1981). Previously, the Commission had made it clear that it viewed the limitations of Section 222 as obsolete. *See, e.g., Western Union Tel. Co.*, 75 FCC 2d 461, 465-70, 483-502, *vacated sub nom. ITT World Communications Inc. v. FCC*, 635 F.2d 32 (1980).

the regulatory scheme for the telecommunications industry could have an important impact upon the ongoing Justice Department antitrust suit against AT&T.[36] A 1956 antitrust consent decree,[37] however, limited the markets which were open to AT&T. Even allowing for disputes over the scope of that decree, it was clear that the 1956 Consent Decree limited AT&T's participation in the computer services and computer equipment markets. AT&T recognized that the drive for "competitive" principles might help AT&T obtain relief from the strictures of the 1956 Consent Decree. In brief, the Bell System could very well gain much more than it would lose by joining the movement for increased competition.

Second, the 1970s were years in which there was a noticeable decline in confidence in the government's ability to analyze economic problems and develop workable solutions. The period was one of economic stagnation, inflation, an increasingly unfavorable balance of payments, and cartel pricing of foreign oil. Increasingly, goverment regulation of business was subject to criticism. The conviction arose that, assuming sufficient competitive forces, market forces would assure a more efficient allocation of the nation's increasingly scarce resources, without the administrative costs and burdens imposed by administrative regulation. A movement arose, therefore, to reduce, and eventually eliminate, the government's role in telecommunications regulation.

2.3.1 Deregulation: Competitive Common Carriers

This deregulatory mood manifested itself most clearly in late 1979 when the Commission instituted a rulemaking to determine whether the full range of administrative regulation should apply equally to all classes of carriers.[38] In the first phase of this proceeding, the Commission determined that nondominant (competitive) carriers should be relieved from many of the regulatory strictures previously imposed upon them pursuant to the Communications Act.[39] Thus, nondominant carriers were given greater flexibility in instituting or discontinuing service; they were allowed to submit far less economic data in support of their proposed tariffs; and these tariffs were made less susceptible to challenge by other parties.[40] Nondominant carriers were defined as those firms which lack "market power" (defined as a firm's ability to set the prices of its output independently) and, therefore, which have no incentive to price unreasonably or discriminatorily.[41] Initially, all carriers were deemed to be nondominant, except for AT&T and its operating companies, the independent telephone companies,

---

[36]See *United States v. AT&T,* No. 74-1698 (D.D.C., filed Nov. 20, 1974).

[37]See *United States v. Western Electric Co.,* 1956 Trade Cases ¶71,134 (D.N.J. 1956) [hereinafter referred to as "1956 Consent Decree"].

[38]See *Competitive Carrier Rulemaking,* 77 FCC 2d 308 (1979).

[39]See *Competitive Carrier Rulemaking,* 85 FCC 2d 1 (1980).

[40]See *id.* at 6-8.

[41]See *id.* at 20-21.

Western Union, domestic satellite carriers and resellers and a variety of video microwave carriers.[42]

In the second phase of this proceeding,[43] the Commission has proposed even more sweeping changes. Most critically, the Commission now intends to deregulate on a market specific, rather than a firm specific, basis. Thus, the Commission will focus on those services, rather than those firms, which appear to be sufficiently competitive to justify deregulation.[44] At least tentatively, the Commission has determined that all telecommunications services should be substantially free from regulation except

1. MTS/WATS and private line services offered jointly by AT&T and the independent telephone companies and
2. Telex/TWX service provided by Western Union.[45]

In so doing, the Commission suggested two legal bases for its proposal to deregulate all competitive services:

• Firms which provide these services are not "common carriers" and should not be regulated as such.
• Even if these firms are "carriers," the Commission has discretion to forbear from regulating item.

2.3.2 Deregulation: The Second Computer Inquiry

The deregulatory impetus is further illustrated by the Commission's decisions in the *Second Computer Inquiry,*[46] a proceeding prompted by Commission dissatisfaction with the inability of existing rules to keep pace with the ever-changing technology of the telecommunications industry. In the early phases of the *Second Computer Inquiry,* the Commission was intent upon fashioning a regulatory framework which adequately distinguished between communications services, which can be regulated pursuant to Title II of the Communications Act, and data processing services, which cannot be so regulated. As it proceeded, however, the Commission decided that no such definitional scheme could keep abreast of advancing technology. Consequently, it shifted focus and radically altered the way in which the telecommunications industry had traditionally been regulated.

Briefly, the Commission decided to regulate only basic transmission services, broadly defined as transparent pipelines for the delivery of communications.

---

[42]*See id.* at 22-30.

[43]*See Deregulation of Telecommunications Services,* 84 FCC 2d 445 (1981).

[44]*See id.* at 496-500.

[45]*See id.* at 500-15.

[46]*See Amendment of Section 64.702 of the Commission's Rules and Regulations (Second Computer Inquiry),* 77 FCC 2d 384, *on reconsideration,* 84 FCC 2d 50 (1980), *on further reconsideration,* 88 FCC 2d 512 (1981), *appeal docketed sub nom. Computer & Communications Industry Associaton v. FCC,* No. 80-1471 (D.C. Cir., filed May 5, 1980).

Other services, classified as "enhanced" services, are deregulated. Enhanced services include a variety of computer (data processing) services, as well as services—such as transmission services offering protocol and code conversion—which were previously deemed to be "communications." The borderline between the two classes of service remains a topic of dispute.[47] The Commission also deregulated the provision of terminal equipment by common carriers. AT&T may enter these deregulated markets, but only through a "fully" separate subsidiary.[48] Separation, however, is largely limited to sales and marketing activities for terminal equipment and to marketing, operations, and certain software activities for enhanced services. Other facility-owning carriers (so-called "underlying carriers") can offer enhanced services without any corporate separation, but these services must be unbundled from basic services. Finally, the Commission's decision preempts virtually all state regulation of enhanced services and terminal equipment.

The *Second Computer Inquiry* orders are now on appeal.[49] A variety of parties have challenged virtually every aspect of the Commission's decision, including the adequacy of the separation between AT&T's regulated and unregulated activities, the Commission's interpretation of the 1956 Consent Decree, the preemption of conflicting state regulation, and the deregulation of those "enhanced" services which previously were deemed regulated "communications" services. The Department of Justice has challenged the adequacy of the Commission's Rules that prescribe separation.

Although these appeals are pending, the Commission is proceeding to implement certain aspects of its *Second Computer Inquiry* decision. In a recent order,[50] the Commission outlined its implementation scheme as well as the method by which it will effect the structural separation of AT&T. Telephone company terminal equipment which is in service or in inventory on or before January 1, 1983 will continue to be regulated. Equipment acquired by a carrier or manufactured by a carrier affiliate after that date, however, will be deregulated. AT&T must form its separate marketing subsidiary by January 1, 1983, and the capitalization plan for that subsidiary must be submitted at least 180 days before its formation.

---

[47]For example, the Commission is considering whether to permit AT&T to provide some levels of protocol and code conversion as a part of its basic services. *See Digital Communications Protocols*, 83 FCC 2d 318 (1980). Additionally, the Commission has denied AT&T's request for a waiver of the Second Computer Inquiry separation requirements to allow AT&T to offer call answering as part of its basic service. *See AT&T Petition for Waiver of Section 64.702 of the Commission's Rules and Regulations*, 88 FCC 2d 1 (1981).

[48]The Commission construed the 1956 Consent Decree as permitting AT&T to conduct unregulated activities in this manner.

[49]*See Computer & Communications Indus. Ass'n v. FCC*, No. 80-1471 (D.C. Cir., filed May 5, 1980).

[50]*See Amendment of Section 64.702 of the Commission's Rules and Regulations (Second Computer Inquiry)*, 88 FCC 2d 512 (1981).

The order also further clarified the structural separation rules. For example, Western Electric (AT&T's manufacturing affiliate) may sell new equipment to the separate subsidiary or to unaffiliated wholesalers, but it may not sell directly to the end user. AT&T must also submit a plan for implementing a Commission-granted waiver which permits the Bell System Operating Companies (including AT&T Long Lines) to provide installation and maintenance for business terminal equipment for 18 months after January 1, 1983. Finally, the Commission stated that the question whether the research, development, and manufacturing components of AT&T's terminal equipment business should be separated will be considered at a later date.[51]

2.3.3 Deregulation: Antitrust Considerations

The Commission's ability to implement its *Second Computer Inquiry* decision is limited in part by the need to conform the regulatory scheme adopted therein to the antitrust laws. To permit AT&T to provide enhanced services and terminal equipment on an unregulated basis, for example, the Commission had to harmonize its *Second Computer Inquiry* decision with the terms of the 1956 Consent Decree. This Decree specifically limits AT&T to the provision of common carrier communications services, "the charges for which are subject to public regulation."[52] The Commission accomplished this by concluding that "public regulation" does not require tariff regulation.[53] Marketplace forces can be relied upon to regulate AT&T's activities, the Commission ruled, and, so long as the Commission retains discretion to reimpose tariff regulation if the need arises, the requirements of the 1956 Consent Decree are satisfied.[54]

Shortly after the Commission issued its *Second Computer Inquiry* decision. AT&T moved the United States District Court for New Jersey—the court which entered the 1956 Consent Decree—for a construction of the Decree which was consistent with the Commission's interpretation.[55] In September, 1981, the New Jersey court so ruled.[56] This decision was appealed to the United States Court of Appeals for the Third Circuit,[57] and is also in issue in the challenge to the

---

[51] The Commission preferred to complete its investigation into AT&T's License Contract, by which the development and administrative expenses for Bell Labs and the General Departments are funded by a payment from the Bell Operating Companies based on gross receipts from transmission services.

[52] *See* 1956 Consent Decree, Section II(i).

[53] *See Final Decision*, 77 FCC 2d at 494.

[54] *See id*. at 490-95.

[55] *See* Motion for Construction of Final Judgment of January 24, 1956, *United States v. Western Electric Co.*, Civ. Action No. 17-49 (D.N.J., filed Mar. 4, 1981). This step was necessary because only the New Jersey court could issue a binding construction of the 1956 Consent Decree. The Commission's interpretation was therefore merely an advisory opinion.

[56] *See* Opinion, *United States v. Western Electric Co.*, Civ. Action No. 17-49 (D.N.J., filed Sept. 3, 1981).

[57] *See United States v. Western Electric Co.*, No. 81-2837 (3d Cir., filed Oct. 30, 1981). This appeal has been dismissed.

Commission's new Compuer Rules now pending before the Court of Appeals for the District of Columbia Circuit.

The regulatory structure established by the Commission's *Second Computer Inquiry* decision may also be significantly affected by the outcome of a 1974 antitrust suit in which the government is seeking the divestiture from AT&T of the Bell Operating Companies' local exchange operations, Western Electric, and other components of the Bell System. The government has completed its direct case and the presiding judge has ruled, in response to a motion to dismiss from AT&T, that the government's evidence demonstrates that AT&T "has violated the antitrust laws in a number of ways over a lengthy period of time."[58] AT&T is currently presenting its defense and the presiding judge plans to issue a decision in July, 1982.[59] The 1974 case has been linked to pending legislative efforts to rewrite the Communications Act of 1934. The Assistant Attorney General (Antitrust) has represented to the court that the government would consider abandoning the case if the government's goals can be attained through legislation. The matter of a "legislative" solution or settlement of the case continues to be discussed.

2.3.4 Deregulation: Legislative Aspects

In recent years, the Commission's actions have sparked increased congressional interest in telecommunications issues. At first, legislative initiatives focused on rolling back the landmark Commission decisions which increased competition in communications services and equipment markets. In 1976 and again in 1977, the telephone industry secured the introduction of bills entitled the Consumer Communications Reform Act ("CCRA").[60] As introduced, these bills would have overturned many of the Commission's interconnection decisions. These bills were never formally considered by any congressional committees, but they did receive strong sponsorship. Additionally, these bills increased the interest of Congress in common carrier legislation and the relevant regulatory and antitrust issues.

After these first attempts to restrict the Commission's pro-competitive decisions, Congress increasingly turned its attention to telecommunications regulation, deregulation, and the structure of AT&T. In 1981, this trend culminated in Senate passage of the "Telecommunications Competition and Deregulation Act of 1981."[61] The more important aspects of this bill may be summarized as follows:

---

[58]*Opinion* at 73, *United States v. AT&T,* No. 74-1698 (D.D.C., filed Sept. 11, 1981).

[59]The Department of Justice has recently announced that settlement negotiations are under way, although earlier settlement discussions proved unsuccessful. A settlement will be subject to Court review under the Antitrust Procedures and Penalties Act, 15 U.S.C. §16(b)-(h) (1976).

[60]*See, e.g.,* S. 3912, 94th Cong., 2d Sess. (1976); H.R. 12323, 94th Cong., 2d Sess. (1976).

[61]*See* S. 898, 9th Cong., 1st Sess. (1981).

1. Except for MTS, all telecommunications services are deregulated, except those which the Commission determines are not subject to "effective competition." It is not clear which services will fall into this latter category. There is no requirement that unregulated services be provided when reasonable demand exists, that the rates for such services be reasonable, or that interconnection with other services and facilities or terminal equipment be permitted.

2. Information services, resale telecommunications services, and customer-premises equipment provided by common carriers will not be regulated, subject to certain transition provisions.

3. State regulation of customer-premises equipment, information services and federally deregulated telecommunications services is preempted; jurisdiction over intrastate, intercity toll services is transferred to the Commission.

4. AT&T may enter an unregulated market only through a "fully separated affiliate" (FSA), although this affiliate may be wholly-owned and controlled by AT&T. After a transition period, the FSA must have separate facilities and personnel. Unlike the minimal separation requirements prescribed by the *Second Computer Inquiry* decision, the separation between AT&T and the FSA will eventually extend to manufacturing, research and development and software activities. Transactions between the FSA and regulated affiliates must be on a nonpreferential basis. Nevertheless, there is still significant dispute over the adequacy of separation, the procedures for implementing separation, and the mechanisms for its enforcement. Concern has been expressed over such matters as the ability to shift personnel freely between the FSA and AT&T's regulated entities, joint financing, joint institutional advertising, the long transition period, joint use of property, the FSA's ownership of transmission facilities and the like. It is beyond the scope of this article, however, to discuss the many aspects of this crucial subject in depth.

5. The 1956 Consent Decree is modified so as to permit AT&T to undertake unregulated activities through an FSA and the bill has some provisions affecting AT&T's patent obligations under the Decree. AT&T is barred from certain media activities, and its offering of burglar and fire alarm services is also curtailed until competitive telecommunications facilities develop.

6. The bill disclaims any effect on the government's 1974 antitrust case against AT&T. There is concern, however, that a bill restructuring AT&T will have this effect in any event.[62] This concern is increased by the Administration's decision to link the prosecution of the antitrust case with legislation reforming the Communications Act.

7. Although the bill does not purport to affect international telecommunications services, it does have a number of provisions directed toward foreign trade

---

[62]*See* H. Rep. No. 96-1252 (Pt. 2), 96th Cong., 2d Sess. 10-13 (1980).

issues. These include reciprocity provisions which direct the Commission to consider, in passing an applications from foreign entities, whether a foreign applicant's government bars or discriminates against domestic companies with regard to activities similar to those for which Commission authorization is sought. In addition, restrictions on AT&T's FSA are relaxed for its overseas operations.

8. Local exchange service carriers must provide interconnection to all intercity carriers on an equal basis. There is substantial dispute over how "equal" this treatment must be.

9. The present mechanism for allocating joint costs between local and long distance services will be replaced by a cost-based system, but with provisions for some subsidies for local services. The effect of this mechanism on local rates is another hotly contested matter.

10. Except for certain low-density, rural areas, telephone companies are generally barred from providing cable services in their own operating areas, unless they can show that the telephone company-provided cable services will provide significant additional diversity and competition.

The House Subcommittee on Telecommunications, Consumer Protection and Finance has conducted extensive hearings into a broad spectrum of telecommunications issues. Those hearings have resulted in a massive report (released on November 2, 1981) on the status of competition in the telecommunications industry. On December 10, 1981, the Chairman of the House Subcommittee introduced H.R. 5158. Although this bill drastically revises Title II of the Communications Act of 1934 and covers many of the same subjects as S. 898, H.R. 5158 nonetheless differs from S. 898 in many significant ways, including the following:

1. The bill adopts a "user" perspective. Before a service can be deregulated, it must be demonstrated that there are adequate alternatives to such service. Deregulation is also phased in more gradually.

2. The AT&T separate subsidiary for unregulated activities must have outside ownership and outside financing. The subsidiary must either forego owning basic transmission facilities or must acquire such facilities wholly from outside sources. If the separate subsidiary is to offer transmission services, it must accept a larger degree of separation.

3. All carriers and providers of inside wiring are required to provide nondiscriminatory interconnection to customer-provided terminal equipment.

4. All currently installed terminal equipment must continue to be made available under tariff until fully depreciated. If the customer desires to purchase this equipment from the carrier, he can do so at a price set by State regulatory commissions.

5. Inside wiring, at the customer's choice, will remain under tariff or be sold to the customer.

6. The bill more severely limits potential increases in local rates when existing cost allocation schemes are changed.

The House Subcommittee expects to hold hearings on H.R. 5158 in February of 1982, with Subcommittee and Committee consideration scheduled for March and April. It is conceivable that a Senate-House Conference Committee could address the various bills during the summer of 1982.

2.4 CONCLUSION

Competition has now been accepted as a guiding principle for governmental policy decisions affecting telecommunications. Changes in technology, particularly computer technology, have done much to compel its acceptance. Such technology has made it possible to improve telecommunications functions by utilizing equipment and software external to the telephone company-controlled telephone system. Technology has produced and continues to promise new and improved transmission systems, and the Commission is now more inclined to authorize new telecommunications facilities and services.[63] For example, the Commission has recently

1. proposed to increase satellite capacity by reducing orbital spacing;[64]
2. authorized omni-directional microwave Digital Termination Systems to serve as a transmission alternative to local wireline facilities;[65] and
3. allocated spectrum for an advanced cellular mobile radio service.[66]

Deregulation has also gained acceptance as a policy for encouraging the expansion and proliferation of telecommunications facilities and services. Deregulation of telecommunication is also perceived by some as a way to avoid the regulation of data processing services. The exact rules by which deregulation will proceed, however, have not yet been agreed upon.

The antitrust problems of the dominant provider of telecommunications services in the United States, AT&T, have not been resolved. The need to resolve these problems, to establish the framework for deregulation, and to complete the process of injecting more competition into telecommunications and other affected industries *all at one time* creates much of the complexity for decisionmaking in telecommunications policy. For example, deregulation by definition contemplates a relaxation of governmental regulation. Encouraging competition in the

---

[63]This does not mean, of course, that these authorizations occur promptly, or that the Commission's actions do not have controversial aspects.

[64]*See Licensing of Space Stations in the Domestic Fixed-Satellite Service and Related Revisions of Part 25 of the Rules and Regulations,* 88 FCC 2d 318 (1981).

[65]*See Digital Termination Systems,* 86 FCC 2d 360 (1981).

[66]*See Cellular Communications Systems,* 86 FCC 2d 469 (1981).

face of an entrenched government-sanctioned monopoly, however, often requires governmental intervention. Similarly, the restructuring of that monopoly, whether in an antitrust case, legislation, or a Commission proceeding, requires active government involvement. Indeed, to assure that effective competition can evolve, such involvement may have to continue, at least for some transition period. These countervailing pressures require careful consideration.

The year 1982 may well be the crucial point in the evolution of telecommunications policy for the next two decades. It is possible that a new Communications Act will become law, that the government's antitrust case against AT&T will reach judgment or be settled, and that the 1956 Consent Decree will be altered, one way or the other. The Commission and the courts will also render decisions dealing with the Commission's Computer Rules and other pertinent policies. The resulting laws, regulations, decrees, and decisions will have profound effects on the structure of telecommunications markets and the nation's technology. These effects will be felt far beyond the telecommunications, computer services, equipment, and information industries. For the nation's telecommunication system is not only an essential building block for the ever-expanding information industry; it is also a part of the infrastructure for all business and government.

This means that 1982 is the year to become involved in the formulation of national telecommunications policy. Those who have previously been uninvolved should get involved. Those who have previously participated should increase their participation. To adopt a comment by a seer from another discipline, it is fair to state that for telecommunications policy decision-making—"the future is now."

Chapter 3

Regulation and Deregulation in the United States and Other Countries*

HERBERT E. MARKS

INTERNATIONAL TELECOMMUNICATION UNION TELECOM '83
WORLD TELECOMMUNICATIONS FORUM; PART 3
LEGAL ASPECTS OF INTERNATIONAL TELECOMMUNICATIONS

Geneva, Switzerland
October 28–29, 1983

Panel On

THE STRUCTURE OF TELECOMMUNICATION
REGULATION AND MARKETS

Outline of Presentation of:

Herbert E. Marks, Esquire
Squire, Sanders & Dempsey
Washington, D.C.[†]

Regulation and Deregulation
in the United States and
Other Countries

*With contributions by Robert L. Jillson and Guy J. Pevtchin, Squire, Sanders & Dempsey, Brussels, Belgium.

Reprinted with permission from *Jurimetrics Journal,* American Bar Association Section of Science and Technology, Fall 1984, Volume 25, Number 1. Copyright 1984, American Bar Association. All rights reserved.

3.1 REGULATION OF U.S. DOMESTIC TELECOMMUNICATIONS

3.1.3 Traditional Regulatory Pattern

In the United States, public telecommunications services are provided by private companies using privately-owned facilities. These companies are regulated both by state and federal government units, but this discussion focuses on the regulation of interstate common carriage by the Federal Communications Commission ("FCC") primarily[2] pursuant to the Communications Act of 1934, as amended.[3] The FCC does not itself provide telecommunications services or facilities; its role is limited to regulating the nongovernment entities.

Traditionally, the Federal Government has regulated common carriage in the following manner:

1. Common carriers are required to obtain a certificate of public convenience and necessity before constructing, acquiring, or operating lines (facilities) subject to the Federal Government's jurisdiction and before existing services can be discontinued.[4]

2. Common carrier services are offered pursuant to tariffs filed with the FCC before the service is offered.[5]

3. Tariffed rates and conditions for such services must be just and reasonable and not unreasonably discriminatory.[6]

4. Rates are generally based on costs and should be based on the carrier recovering a reasonable rate of return, at least in theory.[7] Such rates must be supported by cost data submitted to the FCC when the tariff is submitted.[8]

---

[1]The material set forth in this outline does not represent the views or position of any client of the author; it is intended to provide background information that can serve as a basis for discussion and study.

[2]The Communications Satellite Act of 1962, as amended, 47 U.S.C. §735 (Supp. 1983), and the U.S. antitrust laws are also relevant. The FCC must take into consideration antitrust factors, and in certain instances make a determination under such laws. *See e.g.*, 47 U.S.C. §222 (1976). Further, FCC action does not generally accord antitrust immunity. Therefore, there may also be an antitrust action available to the Government (usually acting through the Department of Justice) or to a private party.

[3]Intrastate common carriage is generally regulated by state regulatory agencies and the pattern of state statutory provisions historically has been similar to federal patterns. In certain situations state regulation is preempted by federal (FCC) regulation. This has become increasingly so in recent years. The complex issue of the state-federal relationship in the United States is beyond the scope of this presentation, and is currently the subject of court and Congressional proceedings. This presentation will deal with the statutes, regulations, and policies administered by the FCC.

[4]47 U.S.C. §214 (1976).

[5]47 U.S.C. §203 (1976).

[6]47 U.S.C. §201 (1976).

[7]*See, e.g., American Telephone and Telegraph Co. (WATS)*, 59 F.C.C.2d 671, 678 (1976) (Docket No. 19989); *American Telephone and Telegraph Co. (DDS)*, 62 F.C.C.2d 774, 793 (1976) (Docket No. 20288). Historically, there have also been noncost based services sometimes justified on a "value of service" concept. This is most prevalent in dealing with local service residential rates. To be treated properly, an analysis of court theory would require a separate paper.

[8]47 C.F.R. §61.38 (1982).

5. Common carriers are required to provide service and interconnect with other carriers upon reasonable request.[9]

6. Common carriers must maintain certain financial and corporate records and comply with requirements for filing annual and other reports with the FCC.[10]

This process involved the FCC when an interstate carrier was formed, when it constructed lines, when it offered a new service or discontinued an existing service, and when it changed its rates. Historically, when a common carrier offered customer-premises terminal equipment ("CPE"), such activity was also regulated. Over a decade ago, the FCC determined that the end user could provide its own CPE.[11] When CPE was not provided by a common carrier, such activity was unregulated. In 1976, the FCC adopted an equipment registration program, which allows CPE, whether provided by the telephone company or by the end user, to be connected to telephone company facilities if it meets certain technical specifications.[12] CPE provided by the telephone company and CPE provided by the end user connect in the same manner through standard interfaces.

In addition to its power to regulate common carriers as such, the FCC also regulates the allocation of radio spectrum and the licensing of radio facilities, including those of common carriers. The licensing of these facilities must be in the "public interest." And, for example, where a common carrier seeks to construct or operate radio facilities to offer common carrier services, the proposal must pass muster under both Title II and Title III of the Communications Act. *See* 47 U.S.C. §§301 *et seq.* (1976) (Title III).

3.1.2 Recent Pattern of Diminishing the Regulation of U.S. Domestic Services

During the last five years, the United States has proceeded to lessen government controls on a variety of telecommunications services and facilities. This process is usually referred to as "deregulation" or "unregulation." These terms cover a range of actions—some of which have entirely eliminated government controls and some of which merely lessen, or streamline, such controls. In some cases, the government retains standby powers. The issues relating to such domestic deregulation have been debated in all elements of the federal government concerned with telecommunications: Congress, the courts, the Executive Departments, and the administrative agencies; however, most of the deregulatory initiatives have been the work of the FCC. These deregulatory initiatives, companion administrative actions, and the court-approved settlement of the U.S.

---

[9]47 U.S.C. §201(a) (1976).

[10]47 U.S.C. §§219, 220 (1976).

[11]*Carterfone*, 13 F.C.C.2d 420, *reconsideration denied*, 14 F.C.C.2d 571 (1968).

[12]*See* 47 C.F.R. Part 68 (1982). Disputes continue about what is or is not CPE in particular situations, but the policy statement is clear.

Government's antitrust case against American Telephone and Telegraph Company (AT&T) have led to a restructuring of the telecommunications industry in the United States.[13]

The following is a summary of the changes in the federal regulation of telecommunications in the United States today. Since the issues are still being considered in legislative, judicial, and administrative fora, this list should not be considered as either definitive or final. However, we can say that there is presently a clear U.S. national policy of limiting regulation where it is deemed appropriate to do so. There is a clear preference for letting the marketplace control wherever feasible.

The following are the present rules within the United States:

1. The FCC has distinguished between the so-called "dominant" common carriers, which are fully subject to regulation (*see* Part A above), and all other domestic carriers, classified as "nondominant," which are permitted to take advantage of streamlined regulatory requirements.[14] Nondominant common carriers may thus file tariffs on short notice and need not provide detailed economic support for their rates. They are often excused from filing applications for new facilities.

2. The provision of enhanced services by whatever type of carrier is not deemed common carriage and is thus not regulated by the FCC.[15] The interpretation of the term "enhanced services" has been the subject of several FCC proceedings, but, generally speaking, an enhanced service is one in which a computer-processed code or protocol conversion is offered as a service to the end user. The category of enhanced services encompasses a wide range of telecommunications services and computer services using telecommunications as a media of transmission. Many of these have never been deemed "communications." Others have. Thus, "basic services" are regulated and "enhanced services" are unregulated. The FCC has required all carriers to "unbundle" basic offerings from enhanced services and CPE, so that basic and enhanced services are offered separately. AT&T must offer enhanced services and CPE through a separate subsidiary.[16] The FCC has continued to study the definition

---

[13]For an historical perspective of telecommunications regulation during the past two decades, *see* Marks, "Two Decades of Telecommunications Regulation: An Historical Perspective," *Journal of Telecommunications Networks* 127 (Summer 1982).

[14]*Policy and Rules Concerning Rates for Competitive Common Carrier Services and Facilities Authorizations Therefor,* 85 F.C.C.2d 1 (1980) (CC Docket No. 79-252). The FCC has classified the following carriers as dominant: AT&T, Western Union Telegraph Company, all domestic satellite carriers and resellers, independent telephone companies, and Miscellaneous Common Carriers (Microwve Common Carriers).

[15]*Amendment of Section 67.702 of the Commission's Rules and Regulations (Second Computer Inquiry),* 77 F.C.C.2d 384, *on reconsideration,* 84 F.C.C.2d 50 (1980), *on further reconsideration,* 88 F.C.C.2d 512 (1981), *aff'd sub nom. Computer & Communications Industry Association v. FCC,* 693 F.2d 198 (D.C. Cir. 1982), *cert. denied,* _____U.S._____, 103 S. Ct. 2109 (1983); *see* 47 C.F.R. §64.702 (1982).

[16]*Id.*

of basic service,[17] and is considering whether the requirement of a separate subsidiary should apply to the Bell Operating Companies after divestiture.[18]

3. In 1976 the Commission listed the prohibition on the resale and shared use of communications services and determined that resale services could be offered under tariff.[19] On reconsideration, the FCC concluded that its order should apply only to the resale and shared use of communications services within the boundaries of the U.S.; the advisability of permitting resale and shared use internationally would be considered in a separate proceeding. *See* Part II.B.7 below.

4. The resale of telecommunications is still deemed common carriage, but for carriers that do not own underlying facilities, the Commission has abandoned the requirement that such carriers file tariffs or secure authority before operating or discontinuing services.[20] However, these carriers do remain subject to a statutory requirement that they provide service at reasonable rates and on a nondiscriminatory basis. The definition of what is reasonable in this context and what is nondiscriminatory remains to be tested. This policy of relaxed regulation for resellers was subsequently limited to resellers that are not affiliated with dominant carriers. Resale entities of dominant carriers (*e.g.*, telephone companies affiliated with AT&T or other dominant carriers) remain subject to tariff regulation for the time being, although the FCC will soon be reexamining this point. The Commission has indicated, however, that it would look favorably on requests for waivers of the tariff filing and facilities authorization requirements for resale entities affiliated with independent telephone companies, where the resale entities provide most of their service outside of the serving area of their affiliated companies.[21]

5. The provision of CPE, including such things as PBXs, telephone handsets, modems, etc., may not be conducted pursuant to tariff and does not constitute the provision of a regulated common carrier service.[22] AT&T must offer CPE through a separate subsidiary, and the question of whether the Bell Operating Companies will have to do so after divestiture is under study.

---

[17]*See, e.g., Datapoint Corporation Petition for a Declaratory Ruling Regarding the Mechanized Calling Card Service Provided by the American Telephone and Telegraph Company,* File No. ENF-82-2 (released Mar. 10, 1983).

[18]*Policy and Rules Concerning the Furnishing of Customer Premises Equipment, Enhanced Services and Cellular Communications Services by the Bell Operating Companies,* 48 Fed. Reg. 13.056 (1983).

[19]*Regulatory Policies Concerning Resale and Shared Use of Common Carrier Services and Facilities,* 60 F.C.C.2d 261 (1976), *on reconsideration,* 62 F.C.C.2d 588 (1977), *aff'd sub nom. American Telephone Co. v. FCC,* 572 F.2d 17 (2d Cir. 1978).

[20]*Policy and Rules Concerning Rates for Competitive Common Carrier Services and Facilities Authorizations Therefor,* 91 F.C.C.2d 59 (1982), *on reconsideration,* FCC 83-69 (released Mar. 21, 1983) (CC Docket No. 79-252).

[21]*Id.*

[22]There has been continued regulation of so-called "embedded CPE," that is, the CPE that was offered under tariff as of December 31, 1982. There is probably over $15 billion of such equipment. A plan for its deregulation is pending.

6. The FCC has recently concluded that, since there no longer appears to be a shortage of satellite facilities, it would allow several domestic satellite carriers to sell transponder capacity on their satellites instead of continuing to restrict satellite utilization to common carrier services.[23]

7. The FCC is studying a further relaxation of regulation. It is possible that the Commission will extend its theories of regulatory forbearance. The FCC is currently studying whether to extend its policy of forbearing from regulation to all domestic common carriers, other than AT&T, and whether to forbear from regulating or streamline its regulation of certain of AT&T's services.[24]

The resolution of the government's antitrust case against AT&T and court action thereon has had a significant impact on domestic regulation. The Modfication of Final Judgment,[25] entered on August 24, 1982, eliminated the line of business and patent licensing restrictions imposed on AT&T since 1956, allowed it to enter new markets, and required it to divest its 22 wholly-owned Bell Operating Companies. These changes will take effect January 1, 1984.[26]

The United States Congress it not actively considering legislation that deals with the regulation of carriers. There is however, intense legislative activity focusing on the level of charges for domestic local services and matters relating to the organizational structure that the United States should use to formulate and administer its international telecommunications policies.

3.2 U.S. RULINGS AFFECTING INTERNATIONAL TELECOMMUNICATIONS

3.2.1 Traditional Regulatory Pattern

U.S. regulation of international telecommunications must be handled very differently from domestic regulation since international telecommunications lines are only partly subject to the FCC's jurisdiction; the other part is subject to "regulation" by the telecommunications administrations of other governments ("PTTs"). Policies regulating international telecommunications lines must accordingly be agreed upon by all affected countries.

---

[23]*Domestic Fixed Satellite Transponder Sales,* 90 F.C.C.2d 1238 (1982) (CC Docket No. 82-45).

[24]*See supra* note 13. *See also* United States Independent Telephone Association Petition for Further Rulemaking, CC Docket No. 79-252 (filed Apr. 13, 1983); American Telephone and Telegraph Co. Petition for Further Rulemaking, CC Docket No. 79-252 (filed Aug. 11, 1983).

[25]Modification of Final Judgment, *United States v. American Telephone & Telegraph Co.,* 552 F. Supp. 131, 226 (D.D.C. 1982), *aff'd sub nom. Maryland v. United States,* _____U.S._____, 103 S. Ct. 1240 (1983).

[26]Several FCC proceedings have been examining various implementation issues relating to the court-ordered AT&T restructuring. *See, e.g., Policy and Rules Concerning the Furnishing of Customer Premises Equipment, Enhanced Services and Cellular Communications Services by the Bell Operating Cos.,* FCC 83-71 (released Mar. 4, 1983) (CC Docket No. 83-115); *Procedures for Implementing the Detariffing of Customer Premises Equipment and Enhanced Services (Second Computer Inquiry)* 89 F.C.C.2d 694 (CC Docket No. 81-893).

The U.S. structure is unusual in that telecommunications services are provided by private companies rather than by the government as in most other nations. Nevertheless, there has been cooperation, as there must be, between countries with disparate approaches, in order to effect international telecommunications.

Until recently, the U.S. Government's regulation of U.S. companies providing international telecommunications services resulted in a relatively simple structure:

1. The FCC had required a division between domestic and international markets. Accordingly, no domestic carrier except AT&T could offer international service. International record carriers (IRCs) were prohibited from offering domestic record service, whereas the primary domestic record carrier, Western Union, was barred by statute from entering international markets.[27] Where related corporations other than AT&T offered domestic and international services, the two operations were separated.

2. AT&T was restricted to offering voice services only.[28]

3. The IRCs were presumed to be permitted to offer only record and alternate voice-data service; they were thought to be effectively barred from providing major voice service.

4. The IRCs were limited to providing record services only to certain "gateway" U.S. cities; Western Union was authorized to carry this traffic from the gateway cities to other U.S. destinations.

5. All international carriers were subject to the same tariff and reporting requirements that bound dominant domestic carriers. *See* Part I.A above.

6. In order to receive authorization to provide an international service, a carrier had to show that it had an appropriate operating agreement with a foreign PTT.

7. COMSAT was restricted to being a "carrier's carrier": it was only allowed to lease satellite circuits to U.S. carriers who would in turn provide end-to-end service to their customers. There were no other satellite systems available. Other companies could not provide satellite facilities.

The consequence of this regulatory structure was that the PTTs basically dealt only with a limited group of U.S. carriers providing international service— AT&T, the six dominant IRCs, and COMSAT.[29]

---

[27] *See Western Union Telegraph Co.*, 55 F.C.C.2d 668 (1975), *vacated sub nom. Western Union International, Inc. v. FCC* 544 F.2d 87 (2d Cir. 1976), *cert. denied*, 434 U.S. 903 (1977); *International Record Carriers Scope of Operations*, 38 F.C.C.2d 543 (1972).

[28] *American Telephone & Telegraph Co.*, 37 F.C.C. 1151 (1964).

[29] These six IRCs are FTC Communications, Inc.; ITT World Communication Inc.; RCA Global Communications, Inc.; TRT Telecommunications Corp.; Western Union International, Inc.; and United States-Liberia Radio Corp.

3.2.2 Current U.S. Regulation of International Telecommunications Services[30]

Many of the features of traditional U.S. regulation of international telecommunications services have been changed in the last few years. This international process has been more limited than that which has taken place domestically. This is because of the necessary involvement of the PTTs, which have sometimes expressed concern over U.S. deregulatory initiatives. Nevertheless, the following recent actions by the FCC and Congress directly or indirectly affect or potentially affect the structure and regulation of the international telecommunications market:

1. *Elimination of the domestic/international barrier*
   a. The FCC has authorized the IRCs to enter U.S. domestic markets in addition to providing international services, and has permitted them to serve additional U.S. cities.[31]
   b. The Record Carrier Competition Act of 1981[32] allowed Western Union, the dominant domestic record carrier, to provide international record services, and the FCC approved Western Union's application to enter the international market in August, 1982.[33]
2. *Elimination of the voice/record dichotomy.* In December 1982, the FCC reversed the 1964 TAT-4 decision so that AT&T may now provide international record and data services and the IRCs may provide international vocie services.[34]
3. *Lowering of entry barriers.* A March 3, 1983 FCC order required interconnection among record carriers, as called for by the Record Carrier Competition Act of 1981.[35] In order to help new carriers obtain operating agreements with foreign PTTs, the FCC will now grant short-term authorizations to new international carriers even if they have not yet negotiated an operating agreement.
4. *Possibility of streamlined tariff regulation for carriers.* International carriers currently remain subject to the same tariff and reporting requirements applica-

---

[30]This discussion does not address the U.S. rules governing the operation of non-U.S. common carriers within the United States.

[31]*International Record Carriers' Scope of Operations*, 76 F.C.C.2d 115 (1981), *aff'd sub nom. Western Union Telegraph Co. v. FCC*, 665 F.2d 1126 (D.C. Cir. 1981).

[32]Record Carrier Competition Act of 1981, Pub. L. No. 97-130, 95 Stat. 1687.

[33]*Western Union Telegraph Co.*, 91 F.C.C.2d 1051 (1982).

[34]*Overseas Communications Services*, 92 F.C.C.2d 640 (1982), *appeal docketed sub nom. TRT Telecommunications Corp. v. FCC*, No. 83-1247 (D.C. Cir. filed Mar. 8, 1983).

[35]*Interconnection Arrangements Between and Among Domestic and International Record Carriers: Store-and-Forward and TWX/Telex Conversion*, FCC 83-84 (released Mar. 14, 1983) (CC Docket No. 82-122).

ble to dominant domestic carriers, though several carriers have petitioned the FCC for streamlined regulatory treatment.[36]

5. *Reduced Regulation of Satellite Operations*
   a. Lessening Regulation of COMSAT.
      (1) The FCC's *Authorized User* decision:[37]
          (a) Removes the requirement that COMSAT be only a "carrier's carrier," so that COMSAT may now serve noncarrier users directly rather than through the IRCs. Implementation of this part of the FCC's order is currently stayed, pending appeal.
          (b) Removes the mandatory rate compositing requirement whereby international rates were set by averaging satellite and cable costs. Carriers may now choose to continue with composite rates or file separate satellite and cable rates.
          (c) Limits the FCC's role in prescribing circuit loading for cable vs. satellite to encourage intermodal competition.
      (2) The FCC's *COMSAT Structure* decision[38] allows COMSAT, through a separate subsidiary, to provide end-to-end service in competition with the IRCs.
   b. Other Possible Satellite Deregulatory Initiatives. The FCC is considering (1) whether to allow carriers direct access to INTELSAT rather than access only through COMSAT;[39] (2) whether U.S. INTELSAT earth stations should be owned outside of the current Earth Station Ownership Committee[40] and (3) whether to authorize operation of privately owned satellites to compete with INTELSAT.[41]

6. *Deregulation of international enhanced services.* In August 1982, the FCC determined that the distinction which the Second Computer Inquiry had drawn domestically between regulated common carrier "basic" services and unregulated "enhanced" services also applied to international services.[42] This

---

[36]*See, e.g.*, MCI International Inc. Petition for Rulemaking, CC Docket No. 79-252 (filed Apr. 18, 1983).

[37]*Proposed Modifications of the Commission's Authorized User Policy Concerning Access to the International Satellite Services of the Communications Satellite Corp.*, 90 F.C.C.2d 1394 (1982), *appeal docketed sub nom. RCA Global Communications, Inc. v. FCC*, No. 82-1972 (D.C. Cir. filed Aug. 20, 1982).

[38]*Changes in the Corporate Structure and Operations of the Communications Satellite Corp.*, 90 F.C.C.2d 1159 (1982) (CC Docket No. 80-634).

[39]*Regulatory Policies Concerning Direct Access to INTELSAT Space Segment for the U.S. International Service Carriers*, 90 F.C.C.2d 1446 (1982) (CC Docket No. 82-548).

[40]*Modification of Policy on Ownership and Operation of U.S. Earth Stations that Operate with the INTELSAT Global Communications Satellite System*, 90 F.C.C.2d 1458 (1982) (CC Docket No. 82-540).

[41]*See Application of Orion Satellite Corp. to Construct and Operate an International Satellite System Consisting of Two In Orbit Satellites and One Ground Spare*, File No. CSS-83-002-P (filed Mar. 11, 1983).

[42]*See supra* note 15; *GTE Telenet Communications Corporation/Tymnet, Inc.*, 91 F.C.C.2d 232 (1982).

decision is not yet "final" because of subsequent proceedings and appeals. The Commission also currently has under consideration a proposal that would enable an international enhanced service provider, that would be unregulated if the FCC's August, 1982 decision takes effect, to secure accreditation as a Recognized Private Operating Agency.[43]

7. *International Resale and Shared Use Proceeding.* This rulemaking proceeding was instituted in 1980 to examine whether the FCC's decision to permit resale and shared use of domestic services should be extended to U.S. international service providers.[44] This proposal is objectionable to many PTTs, and accordingly numerous U.S. parties have opposed it, concerned that the reactions of the PTTs to a unilateral U.S. move will offset any procompetitive benefits. No decision has been announced in this important proceeding. In the meantime, AT&T has amended its Message Telecommunications Service (MTS) tariff to permit resale[45] and its private line tariff to permit third party use where the customer has an operating agreement with a foreign administration.[46]

These many changes and proposed changes in U.S. regulation of international telecommunications services will result in an international market structure fundamentally different from the familiar pattern, where AT&T provided voice service, the IRCs offered record or data services, and COMSAT was the only satellite carrier. With the elimination of the voice/record and domestic/international dichotomies, any carrier that can obtain an operating agreement with a PTT is allowed to provide either voice or record service between any U.S. and foreign points; thus, there will be more entrants and more services.

Although there have been changes effected by FCC rulings, certain aspects of U.S. regulation of international services are still uncertain because significant FCC proceedings are unresolved, on appeal, or under reconsideration. For example, the important issues of whether international resale and shared use will be allowed, whether COMSAT may lease circuits to noncarriers, and how international enhanced services will be regulated have not yet been finally resolved. Further, the response of the non-U.S. authorities remains a factor.

---

[43] *See Petition for Rulemaking and Request for Stay of Association of Data Processing Service Organizations, inc.,* RM-4435 (filed Mar. 29, 1983).

[44] *Regulatory Policies Concerning Resale and Shared Use of Common Carrier International Communications Service,* 77 F.C.C.2d 831 (1980) (CC Docket No. 80-176).

[45] *See* American Telephone & Telegraph Co. Tariff F.C.C. No. 263, §2.2.1, at 11th Revised Page 12 (effective Aug. 6, 1982).

[46] *See* Letter from W.E. Albert, Administrator Rates and Tariffs of AT&T Long Lines, to Secretary, FCC, Transmittal No. 14350 (Sept. 1, 1983).

3.3 NON-U.S. RULINGS AND POLICIES AFFECTING INTERNATIONAL TELECOMMUNICATIONS

3.3.1 Non-U.S. Regulatory Authorities

In virtually every country apart from the U.S., telecommunications services are provided by the public sector. In most countries the PTT is both the provider and "regulator" of telecommunications services. In a few countries, such services are provided by a public corporation operating under the authority of a government department.[47]

Outside of the U.S., "regulation" of telecommunications often has a procedural and substantive focus that is very different from the U.S. policy that tries, at least in certain situations, to improve public telecommunications service by promoting competition among private companies. The non-U.S. government telecommunications administrations are interested in providing a range of basic communications services to their public, but are clearly less concerned about using competition as a mechanism to attain this goal. Often, PTTs utilize the revenues generated by telecommunications services to subsidize postal services. PTTs may employ a large labor force, and may be associated either directly or indirectly with local industries such as equipment suppliers.[48]

The role of these administrations thus varies significantly from the role of the U.S. regulators overseeing services provided by private companies. Many PTTs accordingly regard the prospect of increased competition among U.S. private telecommunications service providers with a certain degree of skepticism. The concerns that have been expressed include:

1. diversion of revenues away from the PTTs (and associated industries) by providing competing services or new services that cannot be provided by the PTTs;

2. duplication of resources and possibly poorer service to the public; and

3. increases in the PTTs' administrative costs attributable to dealing with multiple carriers.[49]

It is not clear how non-U.S. administrations will react to the new forces in the international telecommunications market structure created by the deregulatory

---

[47]Examples of this structure are British Telecom, Australia's Telecom and the Nippon Telephone and Telegraph ("NTT") in Japan. Japan also allows Kokusai Denshin Denwa, a private corporation controlled by the government, to be its external carrier. *See* Comptroller General, Report to the Subcommittee on Government Information, Justice, And Agriculture, "FCC Needs to Monitor a Changing International Telecommunications Market," U.S. General Accounting Office Report No. RCED-83-92, at 15 (Mar. 14, 1983) [hereinafter cited as "GAO Report"].

[48]GAO Report at 15; Ramsey, "International Opportunities and Problems: International Regulation," published in *Computer Telecommunications: Business Opportunities in the New Regulatory/Legal Environment*, Law & Business, Inc./Harcourt Brace Jovanovich, Publishers (1982); Address by R. Dumey, "Telecommunications and the EEC Competition Rules," Brussels (June 29, 1983) [hereinafter cited as "Dumey Speech"].

[49]*Id.*

initiatives of the FCC. There has certainly been a hesitancy to develop working relationships with carriers other than the familiar IRCs and AT&T, and much will depend on how they and the U.S. Government cooperate to handle the many issues relating to international service that have not yet been finally resolved.

3.3.2 Current Non-U.S. Regulatory Rulings and Policies

The lessening of regulation of U.S. telecommunications companies is related to a factor that may create an even greater challenge for the PTTs: rapid growth and technological development in the telecommunications field. In addition to their traditional concerns of protecting their revenue base, the PTTs are becoming increasingly aware that keeping up with technological advances may require changes. The technological revolution and the increasingly competitive environment in telecommunications services and equipment has had an impact throughout the world and, I submit, has caused many countries to reexamine their regulatory policies.

Their reactions to this challenge have been varied. It is difficult to characterize the responses of PTTs and their governments generally because their reactions are not only dictated by the unique circumstances of each country, but, in many countries, are also in a state of flux. The following paragraphs attempt, nevertheless, to describe a few of the trends in policies. Some of the trends are a matter of "concern" from a United States perspective, and some would be viewed as helpful in developing a freer flow of information among countries.

Many PTTs or other government agencies have been reacting to the changing technological and competitive environment by adopting policies that appear to protect the status quo. These policies take many forms:

1. reluctance to enter into operating agreements with new carriers;[50]
2. local telecommunications regulations that restrict a foreign company's ability to do business in the country. Such regulations have, for example, required foreign firms:

   a. to procure all or most of their equipment from domestic companies;[51]

---

[50]*See* GAO Report; U.S. National Telecommunications and Information Administration (Department of Commerce), "Long-Range Goals in International Telecommunications and Information, An Outline for United States Policy," at 7-9 (Feb. 1983) [hereinafter cited as "NTIA Report"].

[51]*See* Office of the U.S. Trade Representative, "Trade Barriers to Telecommunications, Data and Information Services," V TDR-Transnational Data Report on Information Politics and Regulations 181, 183 (June 1982) [hereinafter cited as "U.S. Trade Representative Report"]; Clark, "PTTs are accused of being unwieldy," *The London Times,* Jan. 14, 1983, at 13 [hereinafter cited "Clark Article"]; S. Beach & H. Marks, "Working Paper on the Legal Problems of Computer Services Industry Networks," prepared for the International Data Networks Project of the American Bar Ass'n Section on Science and Technology, Committee on Communications, Publication anticipated in the winter, 1983–84, at 5-6 [hereinafter cited as "Beach/Marks Paper"]; Markoski, *Telecommunications Regulations as Barriers to the Transborder Flow of Information,* 14 Cornell Int'l L.J. 287 (1981) [hereinafter cited as "Markoski"]; NTIA Report at 174-75.

   b. to use the domestic public data communications network rather than their own leased lines;[52] or

   c. to terminate their lines and/or perform substantial data processing in domestic computers.[53]

3. legal impediments to foreign firms' operations in the PTT's country, such as foreign investment laws or procedural obstacles, *e.g.*, inspection or approval requirements or other preconditions.[54]

4. regional multilateral opposition to competition to national PTTs. For example, the member PTTs of the Conference of European Post and Telecommunications Administrations ("CEPT") presented a unified response to a proposed private communications network that was intended to serve the needs of the world banking community.[55] The PTTs, faced with the possibility of a substantial diversion of revenues from their operations, changed their rate structure so that the proposed network became much less economical.[56]

Another common reaction of governments to technological developments in the storage and transmission of data and the accompanying increase in the flow of data across borders has been the adoption of data protection laws to address privacy concerns. Many countries have passed data protection laws that are intended, *inter alia,* to safeguard the privacy rights of individuals. Many of these laws also cover a great amount of business information, and may portend obstacles to the transborder flow of information services.[57]

In addition to national laws, several multilateral organizations have proposed privacy protection guidelines in an effort to reconcile the diverse regulatory policies of different countries. The Organization for Economic Cooperation and Development (OECD) has developed a set of guidelines[58] for privacy protection that, while not binding on OECD countries, have helped facilitate information flow between countries that voluntarily adhere to the guidelines. The Council of Europe has also proposed a convention that would regulate privacy protection among signatory nations.[59] Some nations have expressed concern about this

---

[52] *See id.*

[53] *See id.*

[54] *See* U.S. Trade Representative Report; Beach/Marks Paper at 4-5.

[55] The network was organized by the Society of Worldwide Interbank Financial Telecommunications ("SWIFT").

[56] *See* Markoski at 298–99.

[57] *See* Beach/Marks Paper at 7; Marks, *A Perspective on Information Policy, Privacy and Transborder Data Flow Restrictions,* Bigelow CLS §7-5, Article 2, at 4 (1979); Allen, Transborder Data Flow Debate: An Overview of the Issues, Nov. 20, 1979, at 10-14.

[58] Organization for Economic Cooperation and Development, *Guidelines on the Protection of Privacy and Transborder Flows of Personal Data* (Paris 1981).

[59] Council of Europe, *Convention for the Protection of Individuals with Regard to Automatic Processing of Personal Data* (Strasbourg 1981).

treaty because it permits contracting parties to restrict data flows to nonsignatory nations that do not have equivalent privacy legislation.[60]

Finally, a small but growing group of nations are reacting to technological advances by allowing, or at least considering, more open competitive access to their telecommunications markets.[61] The U.S. is obviously the prime example of this trend. A few other countries and international organizations have, however, taken steps to reduce the role of the government administration and increase the participation of private competitors in their telecommunications services or are at least reported to be considering such steps:

1. The United Kingdom in 1980–81 split its postal and telecommunications services into two separate entities: the Post Office and British Telecommunications (British Telecom). Telecommunications revenue will thus no longer subsidize postal services. British Telecom is expected to be made into a 51 percent privately-owned company, and will no longer have a total monopoly since a British competitor, Mercury Communications, has already been authorized to compete with British Telecom.[62]

2. Sweden's PTT has taken steps to structurally separate its competitive activities from its monopoly activities and has allowed more competition in equipment markets.[63]

3. Canada is planning a reorganization of the major telephone carrier, Bell Canada, that will remove certain telecommunications activities from government regulation.[64]

4. In several other countries, commissions or study groups have recommended that the control of the PTTs over certain telecommunications functions (*e.g.*, provision of terminal equipment) should be reduced and more competition allowed.[65]

5. Business and consumer user groups in many countries are pushing for increased privatization of networks, equipment supply, etc., because they be-

---

[60] *See* "Pact Would Restrict Data Flow in Europe," Computerworld, Feb. 28, 1983, at 7; "Data Flow: The U.S. Takes on Europe," IV TDR-Transnational Data Report on Information Politics and Regulations 7 (Jul./Aug. 1981).

[61] *See generally* Clark Article.

[62] *See* Address by R.L. Ford, Chief Executive, International Business Services, British Telecommunications International, "The Wind of Change in International Telecommunication—A View from Over the Water," Anaheim, Cal. (June 1, 1983); Dumey Speech; D. Schiller, "Privatization Trends in World Communications," VI Transnational Data Report 105 (1983) [hereinafter cited as "Schiller Article"]; Johnstone, "On the Changes Being Rung in by the Government at British Telecom," *The London Times*, Jan. 14, 1983 at 16.

[63] *See* National Telecommunications and Information Administration Contractor Reports, *Telecommunications Policies in Seventeen Countries: Prospects for Future Competitive Access* 12, 178 (May 1983) [hereinafter cited as "NTIA Contractor Reports"].

[64] *See* Schiller Article at 105; Clark Article.

[65] *See* note 63 *supra;* Dumey Speech at 2.

lieve private enterprises will modernize the systems more efficiently than the PTTs acting alone.[66]

6. On December 10, 1982, the Commission of the European Communities[67] struck down, as inconsistent with the competitive provisions of the Treaty of Rome, restrictions which British Telecom had imposed on domestic private message-forwarding agencies.[68] British Telecom had imposed these restrictions in response to the demands of other PTTs, which alleged that the British message-forwarding agencies were diverting revenues from the PTTs. The Commission's decision concluded that the restrictions in question limited the development of new markets and technologies and had a detrimental effect on users in other countries, and constituted an abuse of British Telecom's dominant market position in violation of the Treaty.

The British Telecom decision was the first decision to apply the competition policy of the European Communities (EC) as embodied in the Treaty of Rome to the telecommunications sector. The competition policy of the European Communities, which is broadly similar to that of the U.S., is a vital part of its economic policy. The EC Commission's role in competition policy is particularly important, for this is one of the few areas where the Commission has real decision-making powers of its own.

The EC's competition rules are embodied in two articles of the Treaty of Rome: Article 85, which prohibits concerted practices that prevent competition between enterprises, and Article 86, which prohibits abuse of a dominant position. Another article of the Treaty of Rome, Article 92, provides that state aids that distort competition are incompatible with the Treaty of Rome, except in certain conditions such as to promote economic development or other social aims.[69] In many cases, the Comission has prohibited the granting of state aids to given industries, but, up to now, no case has involved the telecommunications industry.

The effect of the decision should be to encourage private telecommunications service/equipment providers to compete with the PTTs. The Italian Government, evidently concerned that the decision's rationale might apply to all telecommunications services, has appealed the Commission's decision to the European Court of Justice, which is not expected to decide the case until 1984.

7. The Commission of the European Communities has also reportedly commenced an "ex-officio" inquiry challenging the right of a PTT to expand

---

[66]See Dumey Speech at 2; Schiller Article at 106; "Newsmaker—The head of an International User Group [INTUG] takes on bureaucrats in Europe's PTTs," Data Communications, June 1982, at 73.

[67]See Official Journal of the European Communities No. L 360/36, Dec. 21, 1982, at 36-42.

[68]The EC Treaty provision at issue was Article 86.

[69]For discussion of the applicability of EC competition rules as well as EC Treaty rules generally, see Ramsey, *Europe Responds to the Challenge of the New Information Technologies: A Teleinformatics Strategy for the 1980's,* 14 Cornell Int'l L.J. 237 (1981).

its telecommunications monopoly to include a monopoly over the supply of equipment that had previously been supplied by private companies. The Commission may also be investigating instances where a PTT has used its standards approval authority as a procedural mechanism to delay or prevent the introduction of privately-supplied equipment.[70] Such inquiries are an appropriate and desirable vehicle for the EC to increase its involvement in regulating telecommunications activities that have traditionally been regulated primarily by national authorities.

The attitudes, policies, and reactions of PTTs and their governments to the demands created by technological innovation, increased competition, and user pressure for better service have thus been varied and multifaceted. Some PTTs have maintained restrictive policies to protect their position, while others have been exploring means of lessening their exclusive control without losing their regulatory power. The only thing that can be said for sure is that national telecommunications policies are the subject of considerable debate and discussion in many countries and multinational organizations, and will probably change a great deal in the years to come.

3.4 OBSERVATIONS

The foregoing is a truncated and *simplified* analysis of the status of rulings by the Federal Communications Commission and other U.S. agencies that affect the regulation and structure of domestic U.S. and international telecommunications markets, as well as an equally simplified summary of regulation in other countries.

The United States has been developing its policy of lessening regulation for more than a decade. The level of activity has increased in recent years. Even though there are many rulings on the subject, the effort is not yet complete. Indeed, it may never be complete, as it is necessary to evaluate the current situation against extant policies. Given technological change and the increased demand for electronic information transfer, it will probably be necessary to continue to make adjustments in government policies. There is, however, a clear United States commitment to keep government regulation to the minimum required and to rely on competition to the fullest extent reasonable. Of course, one can debate what is the "required" amount of government involvement and when reliance on competition becomes unreasonable. The bias of U.S. policy is nonetheless clear.

A lot can be said for the bias of U.S. policy, particularly at a time when technological advances affecting telecommunications call for a high degree of innovation, experimentation, and change. The thrust of U.S. policies is likely to

---

[70]*See* Dumey Speech at 13–14.

make the most of this environment. This does not mean that every U.S. decision is necessarily correct. It is not my intention to defend U.S. policy. No such defense is necessary or has been requested. What I can say is that the private sector, with encouragement to experiment, and the ability to fail on the route to development of improved telecommunications, is a particularly attractive approach to a high technology industry.

Our chairman has asked how the U.S. approach, perhaps appropriately labeled "the U.S. experiment," will mesh with the rest of the world. My response to this question is as follows:

1. U.S. regulation of telecommunications has differed in approach from that of its world partners since its accession to the ITU's predecessor, the International Telegraph Union, in 1908; nevertheless, the need for worldwide telecommunications has provided a basis for negotiation and agreement in the past.
2. The increased demand for information transfer and the obvious benefits for all countries in facilitating such transfer make it more likely that now and in the future there will be even greater incentives for international negotiation and agreement.
3. The United States is a very large market for information services; trade is two way, thereby increasing the incentives for eliminating barriers.
4. There have been indications that other nations perceive that there are benefits from having multiple suppliers of telecommunications services. This recognition becomes more crucial as telecommunications technology becomes more dependent on computers, that is, as networks become more "intelligent." And it certainly becomes more crucial as a country perceives that "telecommunications" comprises or integrally relates to the provision of data processing services.
5. There is a basis for accommodating the U.S. approach and other approaches. The worldwide trends toward the introduction of new vendors, or trends against expanding historic monopolies, will make it easier to reach appropriate accommodations. The essence of such accommodations will be the historic basis of successful diplomacy:
   a. Education about the benefits of each approach and the problems of each party;
   b. Patience with each other's point of view; and
   c. A desire to reach an accommodation, based on a need to reach such an accommodation.

The ingredients for reaching meaningful agreements are present.

Chapter 4

THE END OF MONOPOLY:
Regulatory Change and the Promotion of Competition*

RICHARD E. WILEY[1]

4.1 INTRODUCTION

The preservation of competition in our economic system generally is closely associated with enforcement of the antitrust laws. In that regard, the settlement of *United States v. American Telephone and Telegraph Company*, breaking-up AT&T's national monopoly, must be judged a major event. However, during the preceding 15 years, the Federal Communications Commission played a leading role in promoting a competitive telecommunications industry structure. In fact, AT&T's actions in response to the FCC's pro-competitive decisions set the stage, in large part, for the divestiture.

While regulation has been widely criticized in recent times, the FCC's restructuring of the telecommunications industry has benefited the public immeasurably. The unique aspect of the FCC's efforts was that it used regulation, without significant amendment to its legislative mandate, as a tool to accommodate a shift from a monopoly to a competitive industry structure.

During the late 1960s and early 1970s, advancements in technology and consumer demand for new services and products proved to be more than a single company could handle. Accordingly, the FCC adopted policies designed to encourage entry into selected markets without jeopardizing a public telephone system that had become the envy of the world.

---

* This article is an updated version of a work that first appeared as part of a compilation titled "Disconnecting Bell: The Impact of the AT&T Divestiture."

Reprinted with permission from Harry Shooshan, Copyright 1984, Pergamon Press.

[1]Assisting in the preparation of this chapter were Danny E. Adams, Howard D. Polsky, and Jeffrey S. Linder. Messrs. Adams and Polsky were formerly members of the FCC's Common Carrier Bureau staff.

This chapter reviews the ways in which the FCC brought competition to a highly concentrated industry, and how the competitive market structure that resulted is now paving the way for deregulation in many segments of the telecommunications field.

4.2 BACKGROUND: FCC REGULATION PRIOR TO 1968

4.2.1 Regulated Monopoly Era

When the Communications Act of 1934 was written, telephone service was widely viewed as a "natural monopoly." This belief was premised on the technological limitations of telephony at that time. Although numerous telephone and telegraph carriers originally entered the field, duplicative lines, multiple telephones, and competition for rights of way—either between cities or within cities—made monopoly attractive. The early days of multiple telephone companies were referred to as the era of "destructive competition."

A public consensus emerged favoring only one telephone company in a single locale. As a result, AT&T and its Bell System Operating Companies became the sole supplier of local telephone services to over 80 percent of the nation's population. The remainder of the country was served by local monopoly independent companies. These local companies all interconnected with AT&T's intercity network for long-distance service. For similar reasons, Western Union monopolized the telegraph industry, the only other electronic telecommunications service of the era.

Of course, the ability of these monopolistic entities to engage in anticompetitive activities was well understood at the time. For precisely this reason, Congress created the FCC in 1934, and authorized it to regulate the telephone and telegraph industries. Among other things, the Communications Act of 1934 directs the FCC to ensure that communications carriers do not overcharge or discriminate.[2]

In addition, Congress sought to use regulation to achieve specific social goals. The Act encourages the development of universal telephone service and mandates policies to encourage the construction of the most modern, rapid, and efficient telecommunications system possible.[3] These goals were to be pursued, however, in the context of private ownership of telecommunications companies. Congress preferred economic regulation of private business over government ownership and operation of the nation's telecommunications system (the latter course was chosen by nearly every other nation in the world).

Under this scheme, the FCC regulated AT&T and Western Union as essentially private monopolies for the next three decades.[4] The type of regulation during that

---

[2] 47 U.S.C. Sections 201(b), 202(a).

[3] 47 U.S.C. Section 151.

[4] In fact, in 1943, Congress confirmed its earlier policy determination that a regulated monopoly market structure would best service the nation's needs, enacting Section 222 of the Communications Act which gave the FCC the authority to approve the merger of the Postal Telegraph Company into

period, however, was neither formal nor exacting. For the most part, the FCC followed a concept known as "continuing surveillance." If the agency believed AT&T's overall rate of return was too high, for instance, it would simply negotiate a rate reduction with the carrier. The FCC rarely concerned itself with cost-of-service studies or rate structure issues. Similar informal measures would be taken in response to claims of questionable carrier practices.

Technical Developments Underminding the Monopoly Market

Until the mid-1960s, this regulated monopoly market structure worked well. The national policy objectives of affordable, universal telephone service and the construction of the most rapid and efficient system possible were essentially fulfilled.

In the 1950s, however, technological advances began to eliminate many of the "natural monopoly" elements of telecommunications service. Of primary significance was the new microwave technology, which overcame the alleged natural monopoly traits of cable-based intercity telecommunications transmission. Second, with the widespread development and application of computers, user needs for high-speed communications became increasingly important.

4.2.3 Microwave

Prior to World War II, intercity transmission services depended upon cables connecting telephone and telegraph offices. During the war, however, the Army Signal Corps developed a new technique for transmitting voice communications by means of radio waves only a few centimeters long (i.e., microwaves). Construction of a microwave voice communications system was faster, more economical, and easier than laying cables. Microwave antenna towers could be placed as much as 35 miles apart, with no need for acquiring any rights-of-way in between. The subsequent application of this technology to the nation's telephone system was a means of overcoming the natural monopoly characteristics of intercity transmission services.

4.2.4 Computers

The invention of the computer also brought with it a need for new communications services and equipment that had not traditionally been offered by the monopoly telephone and telegraph companies. At first, computers were ex-

---

Western Union (the only two nationwide telegraph carriers) so as to create a legal monopoly, exempt from the antitrust laws, and subject to FCC regulation. *See* Application for Merger of Western Union and Postal Telegraph, Inc., 10 F.C.C. 148 (1943). Thirty-six years later, the Commission found that competition was again feasible in the domestic telegraph market and eliminated Western Union's monopoly status. *See* Graphnet Systems, Inc., 71 F.C.C.2d 471 (1979), *aff'd sub nom.* Western Union Tel. Co. v. FCC, 665 F.2d 1112 (D.C. Cir. 1981). Shortly thereafter, Congress ratified the FCC's new policy and amended Section 222 to promote the development of a fully competitive domestic telegraph industry pursuant to the "Record Carrier Competition Act of 1981," P.L. 97–130, 95 Stat. 1687.

tremely large in size, housed in special facilities often requiring a user's physical presence. Because of the obvious inefficiencies of that arrangement, the ability to access centrally located computers from remote user terminals became critical. Additionally, as more and more computing devices came into use, the need for computers at different geographic locations to "talk" to each other developed. These physical barriers were ultimately overcome by employing telephone lines to link computers and users to one another.

Expanding computer reliance on telephone company lines soon created another problem. The basic telephone network was originally designed and constructed to carry only human voices. To do that, system designers used "analog" transmission techniques. However, to enable users to communicate with a central computer, or for computers to talk with each other, an entirely different transmission mode was necessary. Specifically, computers require transmission lines which can accommodate "digital" information. Thus, terminal devices and a network optimized for human voice communications had serious limitations for computer data transmission—limitations which led to significant economic and technological pressures to develop alternative transmission techniques.

But if the computer revolution created a demand for specialized communications services and equipment, it also produced many of the solutions. By the mid-1960s, computer technology was being applied to improve the basic operations of the telephone system. Computers started to replace the electromechanical hardware used to switch telephone messages. Computers also permitted telephone companies to introduce new communications services, such as remote call forwarding, message storage, speed dialing, and so on.

In the process of developing these telecommunications applications for computers, large numbers of firms outside the traditional telephone and telegraph industry acquired technical expertise that was directly transferable to communications. Telecommunications companies were also developing computer processing expertise.

Furthermore, the marriage of computer and communications technologies effectively destroyed the homogeneity of the terminal market. The simple telephone handset could no longer satisfy all of the demands placed on the public telephone network. As a result, serious questions arose as to whether it was in the public interest to rely on a single terminal equipment supplier or whether reliance on a competitive marketplace might be more appropriate.

The FCC recognized the importance of these issues and, in 1965, instituted a proceeding which is commonly referred to as the *First Computer Inquiry*.[5] Primarily as a result of its findings in the *First Computer Inquiry*,[6] the FCC began reassessing the monopolistic market structure it had helped foster. The radically

---

[5]Notice of Inquiry, *In re* Regulatory and Policy Problems Presented by the Interdependence of Computer and Communication Services and Facilities (Docket No. 16979) 7 F.C.C.2d 11 (1966), *further notice*, 17 F.C.C.2d 587 (1969).

[6]Computer Use of Communications Facilities (Final Decision), 28 F.C.C.2d 267 (1971), *affd in part sub nom.* GTE Service Corp. v. FCC, 474 F.2d 724 (2d Cir. 1973).

new public needs spawned by the development of data communications altered the way in which the objectives set by Congress in 1934 could best be achieved. While dramatic changes were soon to occur in the terminal equipment and transmission fields, the introduction of competition in each developed separately.

4.3 THE EVOLUTION OF CUSTOMER PREMISES EQUIPMENT COMPETITION

4.3.1 Creation of the "Consumers' Right" to Use Their Own Terminals

As communications needs emerged which the Bell System could not met, AT&T nevertheless prohibited its customers from connecting any device to its lines—no matter how innocuous—if it was not furnished by the telephone company. In once instance, AT&T attempted to enforce this restriction against customers who utilized the Hush-A-Phone, a cup-like device which was placed on the telephone handset to funnel the speaker's voice into the telephone instrument. The device was intended to facilitate private telephone conversations in noisy locations.

When the FCC refused to order the Bell System to remove this limitation, Hush-A-Phone asked the United States Court of Appeals to overturn the Commission's ruling. The Court agreed and held that AT&T had acted unlawfully in disallowing the attachment of the Hush-A-Phone.[7]

After the Hush-A-Phone decision, AT&T made some changes in its regulations, but essentially took the position that the Hush-A-Phone ruling was limited to its facts. Thus, the general prohibition against connection of independently manufactured terminal equipment, or "customer premises equipment" (CPE), to telephone company lines persisted.

But along came Thomas Carter, an entrepreneur who began marketing to private individuals a device called the "Carterfone." This device acoustically and inductively interconnected mobile radio systems with the wireline telephone system. When the telephone companies refused to allow the device to be used, Carter asked the FCC for relief. Thus, the issue of terminal equipment interconnection was presented to the FCC concurrently with its *Computer I* inquiry.

In March 1968, the FCC concluded that AT&T's tariff prohibiting use of the Carterfone was unreasonable and unlawful. The *Carterfone* case[8] therefore firmly established the consumer's right to connect noncarrier-provided, technically compatible equipment to the public telephone network.

As part of the *Carterfone* decision, the Commission also ordered the carriers to submit regulations to protect the telephone system against *technically* harmful devices, but to otherwise allow the customer to provide his own terminal equipment.[9] Subsequently, AT&T filed tariffs which generally allowed free acoustic

---

[7]Hush-A-Phone v. United States, 238 F.2d 266 (D.C. Cir. 1956).

[8]Carterfone, 13 F.C.C.2d 420, *recon. denied*, 14 F.C.C.2d 571 (1968).

[9]AT&T (Foreign Attachments), 15 F.C.C.2d 605, *recon. denied*, 18 F.C.C.2d 871 (1969).

and inductive interconnection of CPE and communications systems, but which permitted the direct electrical connection of such equipment only through "protective connecting arrangements" (PCAs). Bell maintained that PCAs were required to guard the network against technical harm.

The PCAs could only be acquired from the telephone company, for an extra monthly charge. Moreover, the tariff requirement that PCAs be used in connection with independently manufactured (nonBell) CPE obviously made such equipment less attractive to users.

In response to claims by independent manufacturers that such devices were therefore anticompetitive, AT&T maintained that they were necessary to preserve the integrity and usefulness of the network. Nevertheless, the FCC initiated informal proceedings to explore the technical feasibility of liberalizing these restrictions.

4.3.2 The FCC Registration Program: Creation of the "Manufacturer's Right" to Access Directly the Telephone Network

The FCC's investigation concluded that uncontrolled interconnection of customer-provided facilities to the nationwide telephone system could harm the network. But, it was technically feasible to ease the interconnection provisions of the tariffs without causing any harm through an FCC-administered program to certify compatibility of independently manufactured equipment with the telephone networks.

As a consequence, in 1975, the Commission found the tariff regulations requiring the use of telephone company-supplied connecting arrangements to be unjust and unreasonable. It adopted instead a program of standards and procedures to govern FCC registration of protective circuitry and customer premises equipment to provide the necessary minimal protection against technical harm to the network.[10]

In just a few short years, this FCC registration program spawned a whole new "interconnect" equipment industry. The industry grew rapidly and is today highly competitive—both with AT&T and among its members. In 1982, interconnect companies produced $1.7 billion in revenues and captured significant shares of various terminal equipment markets. In the PBX market, for example, interconnect companies accounted for 21 percent of the market in 1982. This share increased dramatically, to 55 percent of new PBXs in 1984, but since that time it has decreased as the industry matures. Clearly, then, the FCC's policies have benefited American consumers by permitting the CPE market to evolve naturally into a multiple supplier market where competitors must be efficient and utilize state-of-the-art technology and innovative features in order to succeed.

---

[10]Interstate and Foreign Message Toll Telephone (Docket No. 19528) (First Report and Order), 56 F.C.C.2d 593 (1975), aff'd sub nom. North Carolina Util. Comm'n v. FCC, 537 F.2d 787 (4th Cir.) cert. denied 429 U.S. 1027 (1976); Second Report and Order, 58 F.C.C.2d 739 (1976), aff'd sub nom. North Carolina Util. Comm'n v. FCC, 552 F.2d 1036 (4th Cir.), cert. denied, 434 U.S. 874 (1977).

4.3.3 The FCC's *Computer II* Decision: Deregulation of the Competitive CPE Market

Having opened the CPE market to competition, the next major issue confronting the FCC was to decide whether rate (or "tariff") regulation of common carrier-provided CPE was still necessary. With competition alive and well in the CPE market, many wondered whether there was still a need to continue to regulate rates in this area.

They pointed out that rate regulation of some participants in a single market, and not others, tends to skew the natural operations of the marketplace. Interconnect companies could sell or lease terminal equipment free of regulation, whereas common carriers that offered the same equipment had to file tariffs and obtain regulatory approvals. Further, by "bundling" transmission and terminal equipment charges into a single end-to-end rate for interstate service, the FCC was concerned that common carriers might cross-subsidize their competitive equipment offerings by unfairly shifting costs to their monopoly service ratepayers.

In its *Comptuer II* decision, the Commission addressed these issues, determining that the provision of all customer premises equipment—whether by common carriers or not—should be completely free from regulation.[11] As of January 1, 1983, telephone companies have been prohibited from offering new CPE under tariff, and all existing on-premises CPE is being phased out of the regulatory process. To ensure nationwide uniformity in CPE detariffing, the FCC has also preempted the states' authority to regulate CPE rates.

Finally, so that telephone companies cannot unfairly burden those who buy regulated communications services with costs properly attributable to unregulated equipment offerings, the *Computer II* decision contained accounting and structural separation requirements. All carriers, except AT&T and the BOCs, must segregate their regulated and unregulated activities by maintaining separate books of account which the FCC can audit to determine whether improper cross-subsidization is occurring. AT&T and the BOCs were required to offer unregulated services and equipment through wholly separated corporate subsidiaries that, in general, could deal with regulated affiliates only on an arms-length basis. The FCC imposed these additional requirements because AT&T has a dominant nationwide position in the CPE market and the BOCs control bottleneck local exchange facilities.

While the *Computer II* decision is extremely important for what it did—forcing all common carriers to detariff and deregulate their provision of CPE—the way it reached that result is equally important. Ever since 1934, the Communications Act has been construed as a mandate from Congress to regulate interstate common carrier activities, and not to allow carriers to deal with the public on an unregulated basis. If circumstances changed, it was thought that

---

[11] Second Computer Inquiry, 77 F.C.C.2d 384 (1980), *recon.*, 84 F.C.C.2d 50, *further recon.*, 88 F.C.C.2d 512 (1981), *aff'd sub nom.* Computer and Communications Indust. Ass'n v. FCC, 693 F.2d 198 (D.C. Cir. 1982), *cert. denied*, 461 U.S. 938 (1983).

only Congress, not the FCC, could alter this fundamental national policy. This traditional view was shattered by the *Computer II* decision.

Through a creative interpretation of the Act, which has been sustained by the federal courts, the FCC decided in *Computer II* that it has the discretion to *forbear* from regulating some common carrier activities, and even to affirmatively require deregulation under certain conditions. The Commission first found that nothing in the Communications Act states that common carriers must offer CPE as part of their communications services. The sale of such equipment is completely severable from the offering of communications transmission services. In fact, the FCC observed that the manufacture, distribution, sale, or lease of CPE by noncariers (such as by independent interconnect companies) has never been rate-regulated under the Act.

Second, the agency was quick to point out that, although the provision of CPE in isolation does not constitute a regulated common carrier activity, all CPE is nevertheless within the overall "subject matter" or ancillary jurisdiction of the Commission. The FCC said that CPE falls within the Act's definition of "wire and radio communications" because it is an instrumentality incidental to communications transmission. Accordingly, the Commission asserted its jurisdiction over any kind of terminal equipment connected to a telephone line.

Having established this jurisdictional basis, the FCC then decided to unbundle and detariff common carrier-provided CPE costs from transmission service rates. Observing that the market for CPE had become competitive, the Commission concluded that there was no longer any public interest need to rate regulate common carrier-provided CPE. Market forces would keep CPE prices at reasonable levels.

In addition, by requiring the removal of CPE from transmission charges, the FCC stated that it could better assure cost-based rates for regulated carrier transmission services. Finally, the agency stressed that its accounting and separate subsidiary requirements were simply different means (as opposed to tariffs) for fulfilling its obligation under the Act.

4.3.4 The Removal of Structural Separation: *Success of the FCC's Deregulatory Policies*

By 1985, the FCC's deregulatory initiatives had fostered a CPE marketplace in which over 2000 suppliers sold over $14 billion worth of terminal equipment. As more and more competitors entered the interconnect industry, AT&T's market share of new PBXs declined from 45 percent in 1980 to approximately 20 percent in 1984, and it sold only about one quarter of new key systems in 1984, as compared to almost one-half in 1980.

In light of this vigorous competition and other industry changes, including divestiture of the BCCs, the final detariffing of AT&T's CPE, and progress toward equal access, the Commission decided in 1985 that structural separation of AT&T's CPE operations was no longer necessary to protect competition and ratepayers from potential cross-subsidization and discrimination.[12] In place of separate subsidiary requirements, the agency ordered AT&T to comply with four "nonstructural safeguards."

First, to guard against cross-subsidization, the FCC required AT&T to file an accounting plan designed to separate the costs of its CPE business from its telephone operations. Second, to prevent discriminatory use of customer proprietary information (such as circuit requirements and usage patterns), AT&T must disclose such information to competitors at the customer's request. Third, to ensure that AT&T does not design its network to favor its own CPE, the agency required AT&T to inform the CPE industry of changes in its network. Finally, to preclude discriminatory provision of network service, AT&T must issue reports at regular intervals regarding the timing of installation and maintenance of its regulated services to its own CPE customers and to customers of other vendors. In early 1987, the Commission replaced separate subsidiary requirements for the BOCs' provision of CPE with similar nonstructural safeguards.[13]

Under the FCC's controlled deregulation of CPE, this equipment has become just another consumer product marketed by specialty phone stores, interconnect companies, department stores, mail-order outlets and, of course, telephone companies. a wide variety of styles, quality, and prices is available. Although federal oversight of the CPE marketplace will soon be a memory, it was only through the FCC's active regulatory efforts that these achievements could have occurred when they did.

4.4 THE EVOLUTION OF INTERCITY TRANSMISSION SERVICE COMEPTITION

Benefits similar to those which have come to pass in the CPE field also have come from competition in intercity transmission services. As discussed above, prior to the 1960s transmission services were viewed as natural monopolies. Only AT&T and Western Union publicly offered intercity services, and those services generally were limited to basic voice and record transmission. The emergence and proliferation of computers, however, created a demand for specialized dedicated or "private line" circuits which were not provided by AT&T or Western Union. And, as indicated, microwave radio provided a technological means of overcoming the "natural monopoly" characteristics of intercity private line transmission.

---

[12]Furnishing of Customer Premises Equipment and Enhanced Services by AT&T, 102 F.C.C.2d 655 (1985).

[13]Furnishing of Customer Premises Equipment by the Bell Operating Companies and the Independent Telephone Companies, CC Docket No. 86–79, FCC 86–529 (January 12, 1987).

4.4.1 Above 890: A Crack in the Wall

In the 1950s, when the three newly established American television networks needed to transmit television signals to their affiliated stations across the country, AT&T provided transmission facilities primarily with coaxial cable. But, when the networks began to seriously consider the establishment of their own private microwave network, AT&T switched to microwave for its television signal relay services despite its initial investment in cable. It did so because privately-owned microwave transmission networks proved to be a competitive threat to its leased coaxial cable service.

The option of constructing a private microwave network was created by the FCC in a 1959 order known as the *Above 890* decision.[14] The Commission found in *Above 890* that an adequate number of microwave frequencies were available to fulfill the reasonably foreseeable needs of both common carrier *and* private microwave systems. As a result, AT&T was impelled by comeptition with private microwave networks to hasten its development of microwave technology for its own network.

Not only did the *Above 890* decision cause AT&T to convert to more efficient transmission facilities, but it also brought above *price* competition. Fearing the loss of business that could occur if its largest customers decided to construct their own private communications networks, AT&T filed its first "Telpak" tariff in 1961. Telpak consisted of bulk quantities of private line circuits offered at substantial "volume discounts" from the rates for individual private line circuits.

Questions were immediately raised as to whether Telpak rates were unduly discriminatory or otherwise below cost. After years of hearings, the FCC concluded that some Telpak rates were justified to meet the competitive threat posed by private microwave (i.e., the "competitive necessity" doctrine), but that other Telpak rates had not been shown by AT&T to be fully compensatory.[15] Because the Commission's "continuing surveillance" approach to regulation had never required AT&T to identify the costs associated with each of its individual interstate services, a determination about the overall lawfulness of Telpak was put aside pending the outcome of another Commission proceeding (Docket 18128) to investigate AT&T's cost allocation practices.

4.4.2 Specialized Common Carriers: The True Beginning

Although the *Above 890* decision brought a kind of competition to telecommunications transmission services, only a handful of very large organizations possessed both the need and the financial resources to install a private microwave system. It was only when the FCC authorized the offering of such service for hire that momentum was really given to the move toward competition.

---

[14] Allocation of Frequencies in the Bands Above 890 Mc., 27 F.C.C. 359 (1959), *recon.*, 29 F.C.C. 825 (1960).

[15] *See* American Trucking Ass'n. v. FCC, 377 F.2d 121 (D.C. Cir. 1966), *cert. denied*, 386 U.S. 943 (1967).

In 1969 a new company known as Microwave Communications, Inc. (MCI) filed an application with the FCC for authority to construct a limited common carrier microwave system to provide specialized voice and data services between Chicago and St. Louis. MCI's proposed services were confined to transmissions between MCI's microwave sites, thereby making it necessary for each subscriber to obtain his own communications link (or "local loop") from his premises to MCI's offices. MCI's proposed rates were lower than those offered by AT&T or Western Union for comparable private line services.[16]

AT&T and Western Union strongly opposed MCI's application. Chief among their objections was that MCI planned to "cream skim"—that is, operate only high-density routes where lower fixed costs per channel permit lower rates with higher profits. They argued that this approach was not in the public interest because the established carriers were required by the Commission to serve all geographical areas. Thus, to compete with MCI, the carriers maintained that they would be forced to discontinue the practice of averaging the costs of high and low density routes to arrive at a uniform nationwide average rate structure. Without nationwide averaging, private line rates would increase except between major cities.

By a 4-3 vote, the FCC found that competition in the common carrier field, like that proposed by MCI, was in the public interest and granted its application.[17] The Commission rejected the argument that the new carrier would be cream skimming. It said that MCI proposed to offer "new and different" services not then provided by the established interstate carriers.[18]

Shortly after the MCI decision, the Commission was inundated with hundreds of applications from companies seeking to construct microwave facilities to provide specialized common carrier services in various parts of the country. The applications contained a wide variety of public offerings, including a nationwide switched digital network specifically engineered for computer data transmissions.

Out of concern that the growing demand for data communications would not be met and that other new and innovative services might not develop, the FCC decided that these myriad applications could be more effectively handled through the development of an overall policy, rather than reviewing each application individually. It therefore initiated a rulemaking which culminated in the *Specialized Common Carrier* decision.[19]

---

[16]MCI claimed that it could offer lower rates because its service utilized smaller channels with less capacity, and customers would be sharing these channels. Moreover, unlike AT&T and Western Union, MCI pointed out that it was not offering a "through" or "end-to-end" service, which included the cost of local loops. MCI estimated that its service would attract a maximum of 204 small business subscribers.

[17]Microwave Communications, Inc., 18 F.C.C.2d 953 (1969).

[18]*Ibid.*, 961.

[19]Specialized Common Carrier Services, 29 F.C.C.2d 870 (1971), *aff'd sub nom.* Washington Util. and Transp. Comm'n v. FCC, 513 F.2d 1142 (9th Cir.), *cert. denied*, 423 U.S. 836 (1975).

The *Specialized Common Carrier* decision was significant in that it established a general policy in favor of new entries in the private line and specialized common carrier markets. The Commission noted that these markets, particularly for data communications, were growing rapidly and were expected to continue to expand.

The specialized common carrier applicants, rather than entering a fixed market with established services, were seeking to develop new services and markets. Thus, they could be expected to satisfy demands which were not being met by the existing carriers and to expand the size of the total communications market. Permitting the entry of specialized common carriers would provide data users with the flexibility and wider range of choices they required. Moreover, competition in the private line market was expected to stimulate technical innovation and the provision of those types of communications services which would attract and hold customers. The agency refused to consider claims of harm to public telephone services generally, stating that the new carriers did not propose such services and the issue was thus not pertinent.

The *Specialized Common Carrier* decision also recognized that the new specialized carriers would need to interconnect with local monopoly telephone companies to complete their transmission services. Without guaranteed access to these facilities, the development of full and fair competition in the interstate transmission markets could not occur. Accordingly, the Commission issued a broad directive to telephone companies to make their local facilities available to the new carriers, on a reasonable and nondiscriminatory basis, for the local origination and termination of their intercity traffic.

Although Bell initially provided dedicated local loops to the specialized common carriers, it refused to provide interconnections for certain private line services which originated or terminated over the local public telephone exchange. Bell argued that the *Specialized Common Carrier* decision did not require such interconnections. The FCC disagreed, ordering the Bell System companies to stop denying specialized carriers reasonable interconnection services similar to those provided to AT&T.[20]

Domestic Satellite Services: "Open Skies"

In 1972, one year after the *Specialized Common Carrier* decision, the FCC adopted a similar competitive entry policy toward domestic satellite communications networks.[21] The Commission said that competitive entry would demonstrate the extent to which satellite technology could provide specialized services more economically and efficiently than terrestrial facilities. The FCC felt that com-

---

[20]Bell System Tariff Offerings, 46 F.C.C.2d 413 (1974), *aff'd sub nom.* Bell Tel. Co. of Pennsylvania v. FCC, 503 F.2d 1250 (3d Cir. 1974), *cert. denied*, 422 U.S. 1026 (1975).

[21]Domestic Communications-Satellite Facilities (DOMSAT), First Report and Order, 22 F.C.C.2d 86 (1970); Second Report and Order, 35 F.C.C.2d 844 (19720, *aff'd sub nom.* Network Project v. FCC 511 F.2d 786 (D.C. Cir. 1975).

petitive sources of supply for specialized services, both among satellite licensees and between satellite and terrestrial systems, would encourage services and technical innovation, as well as minimize costs to the public.

The Commission recognized that to create a successful multiple entry policy, the incentive for competitive entry by financially responsible satellite system entrepreneurs must be meaningful, and not merely token. Thus, to ensure that real opportunity for entry would not be frustrated by any particular applicant, the Commission imposed certain conditions on AT&T's entry into the domestic satellite market, prohibiting AT&T from utilizing its satellite facilities for competitive private line services for three years.[22]

With approval of the FCC's "open skies" policy, several carriers established domestic satellite transmission systems. Today, there are 25 domestic satellites in orbit and 26 more authorized.

Also, in 1983, the FCC reduced the spacing between statellites from four degrees to two degrees to permit even greater entry into the satellite transmission services market.[23] In addition, the Commission has authorized the sale of individual satellite transponders on a noncommon carrier basis.[24] Satellite capacity is therefore now available not only from regulated domestic satellite carriers, but from private operators as well. Thus, as a result of active FCC regulation, the domestic satellite market, along with the terminal equipment field, has become one of the most dynamic and competitive industries in American business.

Controversy continues to surround the FCC's attempt to expand this policy to international satellite services. The agency has approved 11 applications to establish trans-Atlantic satellite systems under private ownership. This action is looked upon with disfavor by the International Telecommunications Satellite organization and most European nations. Whether any of these systems is ever successfully deployed will depend upon the resolution of such differences.

4.4.4 "Value-Added" and Resale Carriers

Still another FCC policy of the 1970s—the *Resale and Shared Use* decision—contributed to the development of competition in telecommunications service. "Value-added networks" (VANs) first appeared in 1973 with FCC approval of a packet-switched communications network offered by Packet Communications, Inc.[25] The VANs emerged to serve data communications users requiring different private line services than were available from the existing carrires. VAN carriers simply lease basic private line circuits from other common carriers, attach computers or other devices to those circuits which will perform addtional functions (or "added-value"), and then resell the new service to the public.

---

[22]The moratorium was terminated in 1979. Satellite Private Line Services, 72 F.C.C.2d 895 (1979).

[23]Report and Order (CC Docket No. 81–704), FCC 83–184 (released August 16, 1983).

[24]Domestic Fixed Satellite Transponder Sales, 90 F.C.C.2d 1238 (1982).

[25]Packet Communications, Inc., 43 F.C.C.2d 922 (1973).

In authorizing Packet Communications, Inc., the FCC recognized that the entry of "value-added" carriers into the communications services market would affect the structure of the communications industry. Nevertheless, it said that entry should be permitted because it would introduce new and improved means for meeting consumers' data transmission requirements in a manner not available from any other type of carrier. The Commission pointed to its philosophy in the *Specialized Common Carrier* decision as supportive of a competitive environment for the development and sales of the type of services proposed.

The Authorization of Packet Communications and other VANs was followed in 1976 by a more general FCC policy decision favoring unlimited resale and shared use of private line services and facilities. In its *Resale and Shared Used* decision, the FCC held that any tariffs prohibiting resale and shared use were unjust and unreasonable as a matter of law.[26] However, because resellers (as opposed to sharers) reoffer interstate communications services to the public for hire, the FCC determined that such entities are common carries and, therefore, should be subject to regulation under the Communications Act.

The impact on the private line market of the *Resale and Shared Use* decision was immediate. AT&T, for example, anticipated that the removal of tariff restrictions on the resale of Telpak—its bulk discount private line offering—would cause a substantial loss in company revenues. With resale and sharing, arbitrageurs (both resellers and sharers) could aggregate individual user needs in order to meet the minimum private line circuit subscription requirements necessary to qualify for the lower Telpak rates. Rather than face this possibility, AT&T discontinued its Telpak offering.[27]

The Execunet Cases: The Last Barriers Fall

In July 1977, just one year after the Commission adopted an open entry policy for the resale carrier private line market, the United States Court of Appeals for the District of Columbia Circuit issued its landmark *Execunet* decision.[28] The Court reversed FCC decisions limiting MCI and other specialized carriers to private line services and held that the agency must allow the specialized carriers to offer ordinary long-distance telephone servickes to the public in competition with AT&T—even though the FCC had never intended to permit such competition in any of its prior rulings. The ramifications of the *Execunet* cases have had a profound and lasting effect on the telecommunications industry and the public.

MCI began to offer its Execunet service in October 1974. A few months after the service was initiated, AT&T complained to the FCC that Execunet was

---

[26]Resale and Shared Use, 60 F.C.C.2d 261, *recon.* 62 F.C.C.2d 588 (1977), *aff'd sub nom.* American Tel. and Tel. Co. v. FCC, 572 F.2d 17 (2nd Cir.), *cert. denied*, 439 U.S. 875 (1978).

[27]AT&T Long Lines Dept. 64 F.C.C.2d 959 (1977), *aff'd sub nom.* Aeronautical Radio. Inc. v. FCC, 642 F.2d 1221 (D.C. Cir. 1980), *cert. denied*, 452 U.S. 920 (1981).

[28]MCI Telecommunications Corp. v. FCC (Execunet I), 561 F.2d 365 (D.C. Cir. 1977), *cert. denied*, 434 U.S. 1040 (1978); MCI Telecommunications Corp. v. FCC, (Execunet II), 580 F.2d 590 (D.C. Cir.), *cert. denied*, 439 U.S. 980 (1978).

simply regulat long-distance message telephone service (MTS)—not a specialized common carrier service. AT&T maintained that MCI was therefore in violation of the Specialized Common Carrier decision restricting interstate carrier competition to the dedicated private line and specialized service field. AT&T further alleged that this placed MCI in violation of the service limitiations included in its FCC microwave licenses. The FCC agreed with AT&T's position, stating that the *Specialized Common Carrier* order had expressly rejected concerns about potential impact on the public telephone system because no services were being authorized to compete in that market. The agency ordered MCI to cease and desist from its offering of Execunet.

Judge Skelly Wright reversed the FCC decision, reasoning that the agency had never said that AT&T's monopoly on long-distance telephone service was in the public interest. Without such a finding, the Court ruled that the FCC erred in restricting the type of service that MCI could offer over its previously authorized microwave facilities.

The next *Execunet* controversy occurred shortly after Wright's decision, when MCI attempted to obtain more interconnections to Bell System's local exchange facilities for its Execunet service. In response to an AT&T petition, the FCC held that MCI was not entitled to additional interconnections for Execunet because the Commission had never conducted a hearing requiring AT&T to connect its local facilities for public switched-message services offered by other interstate carriers. The scope of AT&T's interconnection obligations extended only to interstate specialized and private line services, as established by the *Specialized Common Carrier* decision.

Once again, MCI sought judicial intervention and, as before, Judge Wright held in the *Execunet II* decision that the FCC erred. He concluded that, contrary to the Commission's view, the scope of the interconnection obligation established by the Commission in the *Specialized Common Carrier* decision was broad enough to include services like MCI's Execunet. Moreover, in an Execunet III case,[29] Judge Wright extended this interconnection obligation beyond the Bell System Companies to all independent local exchange telephone companies.

After these rulings, the FCC accepted the invitation of the Court in the *Execunet I* case and conducted a hearing into whether competition in the long-distance public telephone market would serve the public interest. In 1980, the Commission formally opened the public-switched telephone service market to competitive entry.[30]

4.4.6 MTS and WATS Resale

By 1980, the FCC had authorized competition in all interstate transmission markets. However, the tariffs of most interstate carrires still contained prohibi-

---

[29]Lincoln Tel. and Tel. Co. v. FCC, 659 F.2d 1092 (D.C. Cir. 1981) (Execunet III).
[30]MTS and WATS Market Structure (CC Docket No. 78–72), 81 F.C.C.2d 177 (1980).

tions which restricted the resale and shared use of public-switched long-distance services, like MTS and WATS, these tariff restrictions had their origins in pre-*Execunet* times and generally were intended to prevent the aggregation of small MTS users into groups that would resell or share AT&T's lower priced WATS services. Migration of MTS users to WATS, AT&T argued, would necessitate increases in long-distance telephone rates for the average consumer.

As with the resale and shared use of private line services, the FCC found these claims to be unfounded. Consequently, in 1980, it ordered the removal of these tariff restrictions.[31] Today, there are over 200 resale carriers offering interstate public-switched message services.

4.4.7 The Competitive Carrier Proceeding

In keeping with its deregulatory trend, the FCC, in its *Competitive Carrier* proceeding, has decided to minimize regulation of carriers that do not possess "market power." Over the course of six separate *Competitive Carrier* decisions, the agency has examined the market structure of different segments of the transmission services industry and chosen to "forbear" from regulating "non-dominant" carriers. Accordinly, alternative long distance service providers such as MCI and US Sprint, carriers that resell basic terrestrial communications services, domestic satellite carriers, and many other entities no longer need to file tariffs with the FCC or obtain facilities certifications.

Indeed, the Commission even attempted to prohibit "forborne" carriers from filing tariffs, and ordered such carriers to cancel tariffs already on file, in order to avoid creating the perception that it had approved these companies' rates. This decision was overturned on appeal, however, as the D.C. Circuit held that the agency lacked jurisdiction to forbid carrires from submitting tariffs that the Communications Act says they "shall" file.[32] (It is not yet clear how the court's decision will affect the remainder of the framework established in *Competitive Carrier*.)

As a result of the FCC's deregulatory policies, AT&T is essentially the only domestic interstate common carrier subject to full FCC regulation, and the agency is currently considering whether AT&T, too, should be deregulated. The BOCs and other local exchange carriers are also considered dominant.

4.5 THE NEED FOR REGULATED COMPETITION: PROBLEMS OF A DOMINANT CARRIER IN COMPETITIVE MARKETS

FCC policy decisions have opened virtually every segment of the telecommunications industry to competitive entry. But changes in policy do not instantly transform an historically monopoly-based industry into a fully competitive one. Even though MCI earned more than $2.5 billion in revenue in 1985, AT&T still

---

[31]Resale and Shared Use, 83 F.C.C.2d 167 (1980).
[32]MCI Telecomm. Corp. v. FCC, 765 F.2d 1186 (D.C. Cir. 1985), *vacating* 99 F.C.C.2d 1020.

controls over 80 percent of the interstate transmission market. Moreover, the BOCs and other local telephone companies still control interstate access to essential exchange facilities and the provision of local telephone service.

Under these circumstances, the FCC has continued to use its regulatory powers to ensure the transition from a monopoly to a fully competitive marketplace. For the most part, regulation is likely to continue in four areas: 1) cost allocation, 2) interconnection of interstate carrires to the local exchange, 3) interconnection of enhanced service providers to the local exchange, and 4) access charges.

4.5.1 Cost Allocation

One of the most vexing problems in establishing competition in telecommunications services is cross-subsidy. The heart of the cross-subsidy issue is the coexistence of carriers' participation in monopoly and competitive markets. For example, the FCC has long struggled to find a way to permit AT&T to offer competitive services but, at the same time, to keep the costs of those operations separated from its regulated monopoly services. The task has not been easy.

Simply put, the FCC's concern has been that if AT&T sets noncompensatory rates for its competitive communications services, the company might subsidize them with revenues collected from monopoly services (residential and commercial long-distance telephone service). Detection and prevention of this kind of harmful cross-subsidy between services is critical to protecting users and to ensuring that AT&T's competitors are not unfairly driven out of the market.

The manner in which communications services should be priced to avoid unlawful cross-subsidies has been the subject of numerous FCC proceedings, most notably Docket 18128. At that time, only the specialized and private line services markets were open to competition. AT&T maintained that its competitive services should be priced to recover their direct costs, and that all of the company's unattributable joint and common costs (such as overhead) should be borne by the basic monopoly services for which the AT&T network was originally constructed. AT&T contended that the long-run incremental costs (LRIC) of providing its competitive private line services would yield fully compensatory rates.

In its Docket 18128 decision, the Commission rejected LRIC in favor of a fully distributed costing (FDC) methodology for allocating joint and common costs.[33] Under FDC, all of AT&T's services are required to bear a proportionate measure of the company's unattributable costs. The Commission found that the FDC methodology was the best way to ensure that the ratepayers of AT&T's monopoly services were not exploited in the name of competition. The Commission found this to be especially true in the case of AT&T's particular LRIC methodology, because AT&T reserved for itself which of its services would be deemed "incremental" for ratemarketing purposes.

---

[33] AT&T (Docket 18128), 61 F.C.C.2d 587 (1976), *recon.* 64 F.C.C.2d 971 (1977), *further recon.*, 67 F.C.C.2d 1441 (1978).

On appeal, the Commission's choice of FDC was upheld by the United States Court of Appeals for the District of Columbia Circuit in *Aeronautical Radio, Inc. v. FCC*.[34] Since then, the FCC has prescribed an interim cost allocation manual for use by AT&T in computing its interstate rates.[35]

These regulatory measures, in conjunction with separate subsidiary requirements, are meant to provide reasonable assurance that the rates for each of AT&T's major service categories are based on cost. However, with the removal of structural separation, the flood of new equipment and service offerings, the BOCs' entry into competitive markets, and changes in its accounting rules, the FCC has recently adopted a detailed set of cost allocation rules to apply to AT&T, the BOCs, and the independent telephone companies.[36] The effective implementation of these rules will be a prerequisite to further progress toward full competition.

4.5.2 Interconnection of Long Distance Carriers to Local Exchange Facilities

Another area that is critical to the development and maintenance of a fully competitive market structure is equal access to local exchange facilities for all interstate carriers. As mentioned above, the FCC imposed an equal access obligation on local exchange carriers in its *Specialized Common Carrier* decision. Later, it launched enforcement proceedings to ensure that these obligations were met. Now, although equal access for interstate carriers is a reality in much of the nation, AT&T still receives superior access in many locations. Moreover, even in equal access areas, technical difficulties are still arising.

Typically, interstate carriers construct or lease their own intercity networks. But, they must generally utilize the exchange facilities of local monopoly telephone companies to reach the homes and offices of their subscribers. From an interstate carrier's perspective, the local exchange represents a "gateway" or "bottleneck" through which its traffic must pass. In the absence of regulation, the entities that monopolize these essential bottleneck facilities could charge a very high toll, discriminating against, or even refusing access to, others. In the telecommunications industry, this situation has created obstacles to the achievement of full and fair competition.

For years, interstate competitors of AT&T—"Other Common Carriers" or "OCCs"—faced substantial difficulties in attempting to interconnect with the AT&T-owned BOCs. AT&T's efforts to impede competition by such means were a primary reason for the prosecution of the antitrust case against AT&T.

---

[34] 642 F.2d 1221 (D.C. Cir. 1980), *cert. denied*, 451 U.S. 910 (1981).

[35] Amer. Tel. & Tel. Co. (CC Docket No. 79–245), 84 F.C.C.2d 384, *recon.*, 86 F.C.C.2d 667 (1981), *aff'd sub nom.* MCI Telecommunications Corp. v. FCC, 675 F.2d 408 (D.C. Cir. 1982).

[36] Separation of Costs of Regulated Telephone Service from Costs of Nonregulated Activities, CC Docket No. 86–111, FCC 86–564 (February 6, 1987).

During this period, the FCC also played an important role in promoting nondiscriminatory interconnection. For example, when Lincoln Telephone and Telegraph Company refused to provide MCI with the interconnections necessary to terminate its Execunet services, the FCC prevented that local telephone company from frustrating the national policy in favor of competition.

While regulation has been used to secure the right to interconnect, it has also been a means to bring about technical changes. For many years, OCCs received interconnection technically inferior to that provided to AT&T. Thus, an OCC's subscribers would typically need a push-button telephone, use access codes for billing purposes, tolerate a lower quality of voice transmission, and push 10 to 11 extra digits to complete a call. This put the OCCs at a significant disadvantage and demonstrated that equal access is essential to a truly competitive marketplace.

Accordingly, the FCC initiated a proceeding designed to achieve technical interconnection parity for all interstate carriers. By the end of 1986, equal access was available in more than two-thirds of the local exchanges. The BOCs must also provide equal access to all interstate carriers under the terms of the MFJ in the AT&T antitrust case.

4.5.3 Interconnection of Enhanced Service Providers to Local Exchange Facilities

Interconnection is also a prime concern for providers of enhanced services (offerings that incorporate some element of computer processing). The quality and cost of interconnection determines the quality and cost of these vendors' services.

As with CPE, the FCC deregulated enhanced services in its *Computer II* decision and permitted AT&T and the BOCs to offer such services only through separate subsidiaries. Now, in light of changes in the telecommunications industry and inefficiencies perceived to have resulted from structural separation, the FCC has decided, in its *Computer III* proceeding, to remove the separate subsidiary requirement for the provision of enhanced services by AT&T and the BOCs.[37] The agency concluded that, to foster the rapid development and timely introduction of new services, it should replace structural regulation with a combination of interconnection requirements and nonstructural safeguards.

Under *Computer III*, AT&T or a BOC may offer any enhanced service on an unseparated basis if it can provide competitors and end users "comparably efficient interconnection" (CEI) to the basic service elements, such as signalling, switching, and billing, that underlie the enhanced service. CEI requires interconnection that is technically and functionally equal to that provided a carrier's own enhanced service operation, given the current state of technology.

---

[37] Amendment of Section 64.702 of the Commission's Rules and Regulations (Third Computer Inquiry), CC Docket No. 85–229, FCC 86–252 (June 16, 1986).

In the long term, the FCC will remove structural separation requirements for all enhanced services once AT&T and the BOCs develop and implement an "Open Network Architecture" (ONA) that enables all users of the basic network, including the carrier's competitive operations, to enjoy identical interconnection. ONA involves the provision of a universally useful set of basic service elements. AT&T and the BOCs must file ONA plans by February 1, 1988. (Under both CEI and ONA, AT&T and the BOCs must comply with nonstructural safeguards similar to those applied to AT&T's provision of CPE on an unseparated basis.)

Although the FCC has taken substantial steps to deregulate the BOCs, it should be noted that the MFJ currently limits the activities in which these carrires may engage. The MFJ Court has just reaffirmed that the BOCs may not provide interexchange services or information services (a term that includes most enhanced services) and may not manufacture telecommunications equipment. However, the Court did allow the BOCs to provide "gateway functions" necessary to establish a transparent "information services infrastructure," and it sought comments on the proper boundaries of these functions.[38] The BOCs are likely to appeal this decision and to seek Congressional relief from the MFJ's restrictions.

4.5.4 Access Charges

Ensuring interconnection rights and equality of access are not the only areas which may require further FCC regulation. The prices which local exchange carriers charge the OCCs for their interconnections have been, and will continue to be, an especially important factor in a fully competitive telecommunications marketplace.

Immediately after the *Execunet* decision, AT&T filed its first so-called "ENFIA" tariff,[39] raising the interconnection charges for MCI's MTS/WATS-equivalent services by nearly 300 percent. MCI argued that, having lost the battle to keep it out of the ordinary long-distance telephone business, AT&T was now trying to make it too expensive for the OCCs to compete.

In response, AT&T contended that because the interconnection charges it paid to local telephone companies for its MTS and WATS services included a subsidy for local service, fairness required that all carriers offering MTS/WATS-type services compensate local exchange carriers on the same basis.

To resolve this major tariff controversy, extensive negotiations between AT&T and the OCC industry were conducted under the aegis of the FCC. Finally, both sides agreed to a "rough justice" ENFIA arrangement.[40] Under the agreement, the OCCs receive a discount from the interconnection charges paid by AT&T.

---

[38]United States v. Western Elec., Co., Civil Action No. 82-0192 (D.D.C. Sept. 10, 1987).

[39]ENFIA stands for "Exchange Network Facilities for Interstate Access."

[40]*See* Exchange Network Facilities, 71 F.C.C.2d 440 (1979); *see also* Exchange Network Facilities For Interstate Access, 90 F.C.C.2d 6 (1982), *aff'd sub nom.* MCI Telecommunicatoins Corp. v. FCC, 712 F.2d 517 (D.C. Cir. 1983).

Because the discount is primarily designed to reflect the OCCs' inferior interconnection arrangements, as equal access becomes available the discount is eliminated.

ENFIA, however, was intended as a temporary expedient to facilitate the competition mandated by the *Execunet* decisions. In its landmark *Access Charge* proceeding (CC Docket No. 78–72), the FCC devised a long-term solution to access charges, calling for a dramatic change in the way the American public pays for long-distance telephone service.[41]

When the FCC's new plan takes full effect, interstate carriers will no longer be solely responsible for covering the cost of the local exchange facilities used to originate and terminate between telephone subscribers and interstate carriers. Telephone subscribers pay for the interstate costs associated with the copper wire which runs from homes and offices, over telephone poles or through underground conduits, to the telephone company central office. Interstate carriers will pay for the lines and switches necessary to connect their interstate networks to the local telephone company.

The access charge scheme involves a flat monthly fee on all subscribers, to be paid whether or not the subscriber makes any long distance calls. As originally proposed, subscribers were to bear full responsibility for the costs associated with local transmission of interstate traffic after a six-year transition period.

However, requiring subscribers to pay a mandatory flat monthly fee for interstate access—even though no interstate calls are made—sparked sharp Congressional criticism and led to the introduction of numerous bills to repeal the *Access Charge* decision. In reaction, the FCC deferred the effective date of the access charge plan and reduced the initial subscriber line charge.

Residential subscribers began paying a one dollar per month charge in June, 1985. This charge was increased to two dollars in June, 1986 and to $2.60 in June, 1987. The Commission has adopted the recommendation of a Federal-State Joint Board that the subscriber line charge increase to $3.50 by April, 1989. In addition, local exchange carriers may file plans to recover subscriber-caused costs outside of the access charge framework.

As a result of the Commission's access charge plan, long distance phone rates have decreased dramatically. For example, in 1986, AT&T filed rate reductions totalling $2 billion to account for costs it no longer had to bear. AT&T's competitors also lowered their rates. In the next several years, if the FCC succeeds in placing additional access costs on subscribers, long distance rates should decrease even further.

---

[41]MTS and WATS Market Structure, CC Docket No. 78–72, Phase I, Third Report and Order, 93 F.C.C.2d 241 (1983) *recon.*, 48 Fed. Reg. 42987 (1983), *aff'd in substantial part sub nom.* National Ass'n of Regulatory Util. Comm'rs v. FCC, 737 F.2d 1095 (D.C. Cir. 1984), *cert. denied*, 105 S.Ct. 1225 (1985).

4.6 THE ROLE OF CONGRESS

In addition to its power to define the FCC's authority, Congress significantly influences telecommunications policy through its oversight authority and through individual members' reactions to agency actions.

For example, in 1976, some 200 members of the House cosponsored the Communications Consumer Reform Act. That bill would have ended nearly all competition in telecommunications services. It almost passed, primarily because of telephone company lobbyists who claimed that the new FCC policies were going to cause technical and economic harm to the nation's telephone system, at the expense of consumers.

While the Communications Consumer Reform Act did not pass, it focused Congressional attention on the changes taking place in the telecommunications industry. Since then, subcommittees have thoroughly investigated the field. Several Communications Act "rewrites" were introduced in both houses of Congress, ironically fostering competition in telecommunications as national policy.

Startled by the near passage of the Communications Consumer Reform Act of 1976, the FCC adopted a methodical and studious approach to the introduction of competition. The Court of Appeals upset that strategy, however, by ruling that the FCC's 1977 *Execunet* decision erred in holding that public long-distance telephone service was closed to entry by would-be competitors.

By 1978, Congressional views had changed drastically. The *Execunet* rulings did not cause a legislative reversal of the preceding years of procompetitive FCC decisions, as some feared might happen. With Congress pressing for full competition in all markets at the earliest possible time, the Commission issued a rapid-fire series of rulings incorporating nearly all the substantive aspects of the Congressionally-drafted "rewrites." Those decisions, in combination with divestiture, accomplished most of the goals sought by the legislative proposals.

In 1983, Congressional interest in telecommunications legislation again rose in the wake of the FCC's *Access Charge* decision. Fearing that the combination of the AT&T divestiture, access charges, the deregulation of terminal equipment, and other FCC actions moving to a cost-based environment could threaten universal telephone service, over 16 bills were introduced proposing different ways to ensure the continued availability of affordable basic telephone service within a competitive industry structure. Although none of these bills was passed, Congress' wariness of end user access charges forced the agency to modify its original plan and proceed much more slowly.

Also in 1983, Congress acted to promote the rapid introduction of new telecommunications technology by adding Section 157 to the Communications Act. This legislation requires the FCC to determine whether any new proposed technology or service is in the public interest within one year of the filing of a petition or application for its approval.

Throughout 1985 and 1986, Congress focused on the MFJ's line-of-business restrictions. Several bills were proposed that would have modified or removed the restrictions, and one bill, introduced by Senator Dole, would have transferred administration of the MFJ from the antitrust court and the Justice Department to the FCC. None of these bills were passed, but Congress is likely to consider future MFJ-related legislation in the future.

4.7 THE FUTURE

Further common carrier deregulation appears to be the logical next step in the evolution of telecommunications policy. Common sense dictates that regulations established to protect the public from the abuses of a monopolist need not be maintained when competition has supplanted monopoly. Thus, as with CPE, enhanced services, and basic transmission services provided by nondominant carriers, the FCC may foresake economic oversight of services that are currently regulated if they become competitive. In that event, the agency would act only when necessary to preserve or promote competition.

Until AT&T has lost its dominant status as a supplier of interstate communications services, it is likely to require continued close Commission oversight. Precisely how much regulation of AT&T is necessary, and what kind, will continue to be the subject of considerable Congressional and FCC debate. Too little regulation could retard the growth of competition, and too much could unfairly hamper AT&T's ability to compete.

The BOCs, similarly to AT&T, retain monopoly control of the local exchange. Yet, these carriers are entering or seeking to enter a broad range of businesses that go beyond supplying local telephone service. As a result, they are replicating the same regulatory difficulties posed by AT&T's provision of both monopoly and competitive services. With AT&T's market power continuing to erode, regulation of the BOCs is emerging as the major issue before Congress and the FCC in the next several years. The agency's assessment of the proper balance between active administrative oversight and passive reliance on the marketplace will have an important bearing in determining whether the progress made over the last 15 years will continue.

Chapter 5

Preemption Under the Communication Act*

RICHARD McKENNA

5.1 INTRODUCTION

This article will focus on the exercise of preemptive power by the Federal Communications Commission (FCC) under its governing statute, the Communications Act of 1934 as amended.[1] Of primary concern will be the FCC's preemptive decisions involving the domestic telephone industry.

Over the last fifteen years, the telephone industry in the United States has been transformed. In terms of industry structure, competition, regulation, legal theory and practice, and impact on the consumer, among other things, there are vast differences between the environment of 1984 and of the 1960s. FCC preemption has been a key factor in bringing about these dramatic changes.

The question of an appropriate division between federal and state regulatory power was a dominating controversy in 1934. The results were the key jurisdictional provisions of the Act addressed in this article. But for roughly three decades after 1934, jurisdictional conflicts between state and federal regulation of communications were few and not of great moment in terms of practical consequences. This period was relatively peaceful because (i) the philosophies of federal and state regulators were generally in harmony; and (ii) the technology of communications, as then applied to the telephone network, tended to reinforce the essentially non-competitive environment prevailing at that time.

*Reprinted with permission from *Federal Communications Law Journal,* Vol. 37, No. 1. Copyright 1985, *Federal Communications Law Journal.* All rights reserved.
This article was quoted and twice cited in Louisiana Public Service Comm'n v. FCC 106 S. Ct. 1890, 1899, 1900 (1986), *reversing and remanding* Virginia State Corporation Comm'n v. FCC, 737 F. 2d 388 (4th Cir. 1984), discussed *infra* at 202 *et seq.*
[1]47 U.S.C. 151 *et seq.,* often referred to herein as "the Communications Act" or "the Act." This article will follow the convention of referring to Sections 151, 152, etc. of Title I as Section 1, Section 2, etc.; Sections 201, 202, etc. of Title II as Section 201, Section 202, etc.

The great FCC preemption cases did not arise until two sets of Commission activities made the scope of FCC jurisdiction an active issue:

First, the FCC decided to impose regulation on cable television, and to preempt certain forms of state regulation of cable television. Initially, this policy was created to protect the public interest in relation to broadcasting, but it was later extended in order to bring cable television service itself in line with statutory objectives.

Second, the FCC, influenced by the dynamics of communications technology, opened the domestic telephone industry to competition and exercised preemptive power to clear away obstacles at the state level.

These two policy directions—the first suppressing competition and the second stimulating competition—served to force a more precise identification of the regulatory borderline between the state and federal domains.

Prior to the FCC's initiatives, two factors combined to create a complex pattern of cross-subsidies designed to keep residential exchange rates low: the political environment of telephone industry regulation at the state level, and industry objectives looking to a broader base of customers. Dramatic developments in technology after the Second World War—including coaxial cable, microwave radio, satellites, and the computer—generated great per-unit savings in long distance communications, but had far less impact on the costs of exchange communications. This meant that there were significant rate disparities between intrastate and interstate tariff offerings; and further, that rate reductions were being considered by the FCC at the same time state commissions were faced with rate increases. The resulting political implications led the FCC and the states jointly, with the acquiescence of Congress, to adopt policies intended to minimize price increases for residential consumers by requiring long distance customers to contribute toward the costs of the local network.[2] The complex system of cross-subsidies, which was anticipated by, and resulted from, these policies,

---

[2]By virtue of changes in "Jurisdictional Separations," a substantial portion of non-traffic sensitive costs of the local network were transferred to the interstate revenue requirement, to be recovered from customers for interstate (or foreign) service. The most recent stage in this process was the FCC's adoption of the "Ozark" plan, 26 F.C.C.2d 247 (1970). Congress' acquiescence in Ozark is reflected in its 1971 modification of Section 410 of the Act, adding Subsection 410(c); *see* 1971 U.S. Code Cong. & Ad. news 1511, 1514. For a brief discussion of some of this history, *see* Washington Utilities and Transp. Comm'n v. FCC, *infra* note 121, 513 F.2d at 1148 n.7; and *infra* note 25. *See also* J. SICHTER, SEPARATIONS PROCEDURES IN THE TELEPHONE INDUSTRY: THE HISTORICAL ORIGINS OF A PUBLIC POLICY (1977) (publication of the Harvard Program on Information Resources Policy); R. GABEL, DEVELOPMENT OF SEPARATIONS PRINCIPLES IN THE TELEPHONE INDUSTRY (1967) (Michigan State University Public Utilities Studies). The FCC has ordered a fundamental change in the way these non-traffic sensitive costs transferred to interstate are to be recovered, *i.e.* through "access charges." *See* MTS and WATS Market Structure, Third Report and Order in CC Docket No. 78-72 (Phase I), 93 F.C.C.2d 241 (1983), *modified,* 54 R.R.2d 615 (1983), *modified,* 94 F.C.C.2d 852 (1983), *modified,* 54 R.R.2d 1119 (1983), 97 F.C.C.2d —, 55 R.R.2d 785 (1984), *modified,* 55 R.R.2d 1089 (1984), *modified,* FCC 84-201 (May 15, 1984), *aff'd in part and remanded in part sub nom.* NARUC v. FCC, 737 F.2d 1095 (D.C. Cir. 1984), *petitions for certiorari pending,* No. 84-95 and No. 84-504, October Term, 1984 *petitions for further reconsideration pending, further appeals pending.*

Meanwhile, the FCC, on the recommendations of a federal/state "Joint Board" convened under Section 410 of the Act, has taken action modifying the Ozark plan. *See* Amendment of Part 67, CC

resided comfortably within the essentially non-competitive environment of the industry.

But as the FCC, supported and prodded by the federal courts, moved toward an opening-up of telecommunications to competitive forces, many state commissions (as well as the telephone industry) resisted the notion of competition. In large part, this resistance was based on recognition that a system of cross-subsidy could not be maintained once the most profitable portions of the network—which contributed the subsidy—were drained of super-profitability by the pressures of competition.

Nonetheless, the transformation of the industry to a competitive environment has been generally accomplished. A indispensable element in attaining this outcome was a body of FCC decisions endorsed by the courts—decisions founded on and extending jurisdictional and preemptive theory developed in early common carrier and cable television cases. In conjunction with complementary actions by the Department of Justice and the federal courts,[3] the FCC, wielding its preemptive power, succeeded in largely reshaping the domestic telephone industry.

New decisions of the FCC, taking into account the new competitive environment and seeking to reform industry structures and reduce regulation, are being made or implemented, and again the FCC's power to preempt is a critical factor. At this writing, a number of FCC decisions involving the interplay of federal and state power are being appealed to the courts by the states and/or the National Association of Regulatory Utility Commissioners ("NARUC").[4]

FCC preemptive action has been upheld by the courts (i) on the basis of powers explicitly granted by the Act, and/or (ii) on the basis of an FCC finding, with adequate record support, that such action is necessary to make effective the intent of Congress as properly interpreted and applied by the FCC. The governing

---

Docket No. 80-286, 89 F.C.C.2d 1 (1982); 90 F.C.C.2d 52 (1982); *recon denied,* 91 F.C.C.2d 558 (1982); *appeals pending sub nom.* MCI Telecommunications Corp. v. FCC (Nos. 82-1237 and 82-1456, D.C. Cir.); and Decision and Order, 96 F.C.C.2d 781, 55 R.R.2d 659 (1984), *petitions for reconsideration pending, further appeals pending.*

[3]Pursuant to the "Modified Final Judgment" in United States v. AT&T, 552 F. Supp. 131 (D.D.C. 1982), *aff'd sub nom.* Maryland v. United States, 103 S. Ct. 1240 (1983), American Telephone and Telegraph Company (AT&T) has divested itself of the "Bell Operating Companies" or "BOCs." This article will employ the terms "Bell System" or "Bell" to refer to AT&T, together with its affiliates, prior to divestiture.

[4]Pending appeals of FCC decisions by NARUC and/or state commissions include: (i) *See supra* note 2. (ii) California v. FCC and NARUC v. FCC (Nos. 83-1791 and 83-1882, D.C. Cir.), *appealing* Interconnection of Private Radio Systems, Docket No. 20846, Second Report and Order, 89 F.C.C.2d 741, 51 R.R.2d 313 (1982), *reconsideration,* 93 F.C.C.2d 1111, 53 R.R.2d 1469 (1983), *further reconsideration,*—F.C.C.2d —,56 R.R.2d 684 (1984) ("The interconnection of private land mobile systems with the public switched telephone network is now recognized as a statutory right to be protected by the federal government and honored by the states." The FCC will "retain jurisdiction, if necessary, to address in the future any exchange tariffs that might unreasonably restrict the right of private radio licencees and users to interconnect as guaranteed in the legislation." 93 F.C.C.2d at 1120, footnote omitted). *See* the 1982 Amendment to the Communications Act, particularly subsections 3(gg) and 331(c)(1), 47 U.S.C. § 332(a)(1) (1982). *See also* Conference Report on 1982 Amendment, Pike and Fischer Radio Regulations, 10,647-49. (iii) *See infra* note 173. (iv) *See infra* note 103, New York State Comm'n on Cable Television v. FCC.

principle adopted by reviewing courts is that the FCC will be deprived of regulatory power—preemptive, if necessary—over local services, facilities and disputes *only* if the nature and effect of such services, facilities and disputes are separable from and do not substantially affect the conduct or development of interstate (or foreign) communications.[5]

The FCC has not attempted to preempt the full range of state regulation. However, given the interrelationship of virtually all matters affecting the furnishing of interstate and intrastate service, the potential scope of FCC preemptive action appears boundless under the standard established by the courts.

The core problem is that interstate and intrastate service are both furnished by a single integrated system at the exchange level; and yet the jurisdictional provisions of the Act involving common carrier services were constructed around the distinction between "interstate" and "intrastate". Confused and confusing expressions of Congressional intent in 1934 were contained in statutory words of strict jurisdictional limitations on the FCC, in a context that largely stripped these limitations of practical effect. The theme of this article is the resulting anomaly and the ways in which the Commission and the courts have grappled with this conundrum in a changing environment.

5.2 GENERAL PRINCIPLES GOVERNING FEDERAL PREEMPTION OF THE STATES

It would be helpful first to set out the governing principles of federal preemption articulated by the courts in recent years.[6]

The preemption doctrine is based on the Supremacy Clause of the United States Constitution.[7] The central question is whether the agency has acted "within the scope of [its] delegated authority." Assuming the agency has so acted, preemption of the states is a matter of Congressional intent, which may be either expressed or implied. Even without explicit preemptive language, Congress' intent to supersede state law altogether may be inferred because the "scheme of federal regulation may be so pervasive as to make reasonable the inference that Congress left no room for the States to supplement it;" or because "the Act of Congress may touch a field in which the federal interest is so dominant that the federal system will be assumed to preclude enforcement of state laws on the same subject;" or because "the object sought to be obtained by federal law and the character of obligations imposed by it may reveal the same purpose."

---

[5]See *infra* notes 108 through 112.

[6]This discussion is generally taken from Justice Blackmun's summary of current preemption doctrine in Fidelity Savings and Loan Ass'n v. de la Cuesta, 458 U.S. 141, 152 (1982).

[7]The Supremacy Clause, U.S. CONST. art. VI, § 2, reads as follows: This Constitution, and the Laws of the United States which shall be made in pursuance thereof; and all Treaties made, or which shall be made, under the Authority of the United States, shall be the supreme Law of the Land; and the Judges in every State shall be bound thereby, any Thing in the Constitution or Laws of any State to the Contrary notwithstanding.

Where Congress has not completely displaced state regulation in a specific area, state law is nonetheless nullified to the extent that it actually conflicts with federal law. Such a conflict arises when compliance with both federal and state regulation is a physical impossibility, or when state law "stands as an obstacle to the accomplishment and execution of the full purposes and objectives of Congress." Federal regulations consistent with Congressional intent have no less preemptive effect than federal statutes. The court's inquiry must consider the relationship between state and federal laws as they are interpreted and applied, not merely as they are written.[8] Federal regulation of a field of commerce should not be deemed preemptive in the absence of "persuasive reasons—either that the nature of the subject matter permits no other conclusion, or that Congress has unmistakably so ordained."[9]

Finally, if an agency merely announces its intent to preempt inconsistent state regulations *should they arise,* this does not constitute reviewable final action by the agency.[10]

Relying on the foregoing principles governing federal preemption, let us now turn to how these principles have been applied to FCC action.

5.3 PRE-1934 DEVELOPMENTS

Western Union started it. Leaving the Pony Express in the dust as a colorful footnote, the telegraph played a critical role in the Civil War and in the explosive economic growth of the Nation in the decades following. International communications, making adventurous use of undersea telegraph cables, linked the continents.[11] The telegraph quickly became a key element in the formation of modern nations, creating entirely new possibilities for the press, for commercial interests and for governments in time of war and peace.

Telephone service, furnished by the Bell System and unaffiliated competitors, came into this dynamic picture in the last quarter of the Nineteenth Century. By 1900, the essential Bell patents had expired.[12] Non-Bell ("Independent") telephone companies, seeking federal action to require Bell interconnection, supported the Mann-Elkins Act of 1910,[13] which brought interstate communications under regulation by the Interstate Commerce Commission (ICC). The Bell System's aggressive program to acquire Independents was blocked by the King-

---

[8]Jones v. Rath Packing Co., 430 U.S. 519, 526 (1977), *reh'g denied,* 431 U.S. 925 (1977).

[9]Florida Lime & Avocado Growers, Inc., et al. v. Paul, 373 U.S. 132, 142 (1963).

[10]Alascom, Inc. v. FCC, 727 F.2d 1212, 1219 (D.C. Cir. 1984). The FCC often issues a cautionary statement to the effect that preemptive action will be taken if necessary. *See* for example item (ii), *supra,* note 4; and NARUC, 94 F.C.C.2d 409, 416, 53 R.R.2d 1609, 1614 (1983).

[11]For the remnants of early legislation on communications, notably the 1888 Submarine Cable Act (the result of the 1884 International Convention for the Protection of Submarine Cables) *see* 47 U.S.C. §§ 9-17 and 21-39.

[12]*See* J. BROOKS, TELEPHONE: THE FIRST HUNDRED YEARS 102-26 (1976).

[13]Mann-Elkins Act of June 18, 1910, 49 U.S.C. § 1 *et seq.* For a useful review of how federal regulation of telecommunications came to exist, *see* Essential Communications Systems, Inc. v. AT&T, 610 F.2d 1114, 1117-21 (3rd Cir. 1979).

sbury Commitment,[14] so that by the time AT&T was returned to private ownership in 1919 following brief wartime nationalization, the shape of the telephone industry was set. Bell generally controlled the major population centers as of that time. The Independents served primarily rural areas, although some of the then-thinly populated Independent areas have since developed into important communications centers. Starting in the 1880s and by the 1970's embracing all the fifty states, state regulation became an increasingly important factor.[15]

Two pre-1934 developments of special importance were: (i) the *"Shreveport Rate Case"*[16] and (ii) *Smith v. Illinois Bell Tel. Co.*[17]

In *Shreveport*, the Texas commission placed Louisiana railroad shippers at a disadvantage; this was done by establishing a system of intrastate rates under which rates for shipments by interstate carriers eastward from Dallas and Houston to points in Texas were set to undercut ICC-regulated rates for shipment by the same carriers over the same distances westward from Shreveport into Texas. The Supreme Court held that the ICC was not limited to lowering insterstate rates as a remedy for the discrimination against interstate commerce arising from the Texas rate system. The Court held that state power over exclusively local rates was inviolable *only* where local rates, in comparison with interstate rates, did not create unreasonable discriminations against interstate commerce.[18] The ICC issued no *Shreveport*-type decision affecting communications; nonetheless, in 1934, NARUC was to press for a Communications Act that negated the application of the "Shreveport Doctrine."[19]

---

[14]The FCC has linked the Kingsbury Commitment, and the terms of the Act as follows: In the 1913 Kingsbury Commitment AT&T agreed not to acquire any more independent telephone companies without the prior approval of the Interstate Commerce Commission. *Report of FCC Investigation of the Telephone Industry,* Chapter 5, Elimination of Competition, (1939). One year after the Kingsbury Commitment, Congress passed the Clayton Act of 1914, 38 Stat. 734. Section 7 outlawed corporate stock acquisitions which tended to lessen competition. Power to enforce Section 7 against communications common carriers was given to the ICC by Section 11 of the Clayton Act, and transferred to the FCC in 1934. [G.T.E.-Telenet Merger, 72 F.C.C.2d 91, 103, 45 R.R.2d, 1189, 1197 (1979).]

Section 221 (a) was originally enacted as the Willis-Graham Act of 1921 "in response to the need for a mechanism whereby duplicate *local* telephone systems could be merged or consolidated while immunizing the carriers involved from the application of the antitrust laws." *Id.* at 102-03, 45 R.R.2d at 1197.

[15]*See* PAUL ROGERS: THE NARUC WAS THERE: A HISTORY OF THE NATIONAL ASSOCIATION OF REGULATORY UTILITY COMMISSIONERS 1-32 (1979). This article shall refer to the Association simply as "NARUC". The same acronym, in 1934, was used by the same Association, then known as the National Association of Railroad and Utilities Commissioners.

[16]Houston, East and West Texas Ry. Co. v. U.S., 234 U.S. 342 (1914).

[17]Smith v. Illinois Bell Tel. Co., 282 U.S. 133 (1930), *conformed to,* Illinois Bell Tel. Co. v. Gilbert, 3 F. Supp. 595 (D.C. Ill. 1933), *rev'd* Lindheimer v. Illinois Bell Tel. Co., 292 U.S. 151 (1934). *See also* Smyth v. Ames, 169 U.S. 466, 540-42 (1898), *modified,* 171 U.S. 361 (1898); and Minnesota Rate Cases (Simpson v. Shephard), 230 U.S. 352, 435 (1913).

[18]*See* discussion of *Shreveport* in North Carolina II, *infra* note 117, 552 F.2d at 1047: "[I]n enacting the Communications Act, Congress sought to deny the FCC the kind of jurisdiction over local rates approved by the *Shreveport Rate Case." See also* CCIA v. FCC, *infra* note 133, 693 F.2d at 216 n.99: "Congress may well have intended § 2(b) of the Communications Act to prevent . . . [the *Shreveport*] result in the communications area."

[19]*See* THE NARUC WAS THERE *supra* note 15, at 27-28.

Smith v. Illinois Bell is an important case in its treatment of affiliated interests, depreciation[20] and confiscation; but, for purposes of this article, its primary significance lies in its approach to "Jurisdictional Separations." The Illinois commission issued an order prescribing rates for Illinois Bell in the city of Chicago. Illinois Bell then obtained an order from a three-judge Federal District Court enjoining enforcement of the commission's prescription. After years of litigation, a federal court found the state commission's order confiscatory. On appeal to the U.S. Supreme Court, the lower court's decree was set aside for a variety of reasons, and the matter was remanded.

In deciding to remand, the Court noted that neither the state commission nor the federal court made a distinction between the intrastate and the interstate property and business of the company, even though Illinois Bell had introduced evidence making this distinction. Both commission and lower court decisions were issued "on the basis of the total Chicago property of the company."[21] The Court said that Bell's contention that this was improper should not be dismissed simply because of the (small) number of interstate calls "without considering other factors of time and labor entering into the relative use."[22] Stressing the importance of "the appropriate recognition of the competent governmental authority in each field of regulation,"[23] the Court held the interstate service of Illinois Bell to be within ICC jurisdiction and confined state regulation to the intrastate business:

> The proper regulation of rates can be had only by maintaining the limits of state and federal jurisdiction, and this cannot be accomplished unless there are findings of fact underlying the conclusions reached with respect to the exercise of each authority . . . . [T]he validity of the order of the state commission can be suitably tested only by an appropriate determination of the value of the property employed in the intrastate business and of the compensation receivable for the intrastate service under the rates prescribed.[24]

The Court then called for further consideration on remand, which was expected to lead to "some practical method [by which] the different uses of the property may be recognized and the return properly attributable to the intrastate service may be ascertained accordingly." The Court added:

> While the difficulty in making an exact apportionment of the property is apparent, and extreme nicety is not required, only reasonable measures being essential . . . it is quite another matter to ignore altogether the actual uses to which the property is

---

[20]Where the Interstate Commerce Commission had not prescribed depreciation, the Court accepted the authority of the Illinois commission to prescribe depreciation rates in connection with intrastate business. 282 U.S. at 159-160. A similar result applied in Northwestern Bell Tel. Co. v. Nebraska State Ry. Comm'n, 297 U.S. 471, 478 (1936), where the Court explicitly declined to pass on the question of whether an ICC prescription, if issued, would be preemptive. *See also* Lindheimer v. Illinois Tel. Co., *supra* note 17,292 U.S. at 165-82; and Virginia State Corporation Comm'n v. FCC, *infra* note 154.

[21]282 U.S. at 146-47.

[22]*Id.* at 148.

[23]*Id.*

[24]*Id.* at 149.

put. It is obvious that, unless an apportionment is made, the intrastate service to which the exchange property is allocated will bear an undue burden—to what extent is a matter of controversy.[25]

A critical point in the *Smith* case, often overlooked, is that no *federal* action was before the Court; the Court's concern was action by the state in violation of the Commerce Clause of the United States Constitution. The jurisdictional holding of the case is that "interstate tolls are the rates applicable to interstate commerce," and such tolls are not "a matter for the determination either of the Illinois Commission or of the court in dealing with the order of that Commission."[26]

Even today, the *Smith* holding is subject to misinterpretation. The D.C. Circuit, in upholding the jurisdictional premises of the FCC's access charge policy,[27] noted that petitioners opposing the policy "misapprehend the Court's holding" in *Smith*. The court rejected their argument that *Smith* dealt with the manner in which costs are to be recovered:

> *Smith* dealt with jurisdiction; it held that a portion of the costs of local subscriber plant may be recovered only under the authority of a body with interstate regulatory powers.[28]

The court recognized that the "practical effect" of the *Smith* decision was "a system under which subscriber plant costs in the interstate jurisdiction would be recovered on a usage basis," but added "nothing in *Smith* mandated that result;

---

[25]*Id*. at 150-51, footnotes omitted. For a brief review of how Smith v. Illinois Bell eventually led to "interim" acceptance, with no "formal determination on the basis of a hearing record" of the "Separations Manual" and various revisions thereof, *see AT&T*, Docket No. 16258, 3 F.C.C.2d 307, 309-11 (1966), *modified*. Interim Decision and Order, 9 F.C.C.2d 30, 88-94 (1967); Jurisdictional Separations of Telephone Companies, Docket No. 17975, Report and Order, 16 F.C.C.2d 317, 319-323 (1969); and, leading to adoption of the "Ozark" plan, Separations Procedures, Report and Order, Docket No. 18866, 26 F.C.C.2d 247 (1970), Docket closed, 80 F.C.C.2d 230 (1980). *See also supra* note 2.

[26]*Id*. at 148. *See* Lone Star Gas Co. v. Texas, 304 U.S. 224 (1938), *reh'g denied*, 304 U.S. 590 (1938) and *on remand*, 129 S.W.2d 1164 (1939), *aff'd in part and rev'd in part*, 153 S.W.2d 681 (1941), *petition denied*, Ex Parte Texas, 315 U.S. 8 (1942). Characterizing his own opinion in the *Smith* case, Chief Justice Hughes wrote in *Lone Star*: "This [Lone Star] was not a case where the segregation of properties and business was essential in order to confine the exercise of state power to its own proper province [citing *Smith*]." 304 U.S. at 241. Similarly, *see* State Corporation Comm'n of Kansas v. Wichita Gas Co., 290 U.S. 561, 563-64 (1934), where *Smith* is cited to support this conclusion: "But the sale, transportation, and delivery of natural gas by the pipe line company to the distributing companies constitutes interstate commerce, and therefore the state is without power to prescribe rates or prices to be charged therefor." Note that *Wichita Gas* and *Smith* itself (282 U.S. at 148) both couch the *Smith* holding in Commerce Clause terms. In the author's view, the jurisdictional holding of the *Smith* decision is simply that state agencies may not interfere with interstate commerce. This invalidates any reading of *Smith* as limiting federal agency action; references in *Smith* to maintaining the limits of federal jurisdiction are merely *dicta*. *See also* Justice Douglas' opinion in Colorado Interstate Gas Co. v. FPC, 324 U.S. 581, 589 (1945), *reh'g denied*, 325 U.S. 891 (1945), emphasizing flexibility in approaching Jurisdictional Separations.

[27]NARUC v. FCC, 737 F.2d 1095, 1113 (D.C. Cir. 1984).

[28]*Id*. at 1112.

other plans under which those costs were subject to federal, rather than local, regulatory authority might have served as well."[29]

5.4 THE 1934 ACT[30]

In passing the Communications Act,[31] the 1934 Congress created a new federal agency, the FCC, to assume responsibilities previously borne by the Interstate Commerce Commission (ICC)[32] and the Federal Radio Commission (FRC).[33]

Clearly both of the bills introduced in February 1934, S. 2910 and H.R. 8301, were intended to create a scheme of dual regulation that negated the *Shreveport* doctrine. But there followed a complex Congressional process of trade-off and

---

[29]*Id.* at 1112-13 footnotes omitted. The D.C. Circuit rejected arguments (n.19) that petitioners' view of *Smith* became statutory law when Congress enacted Subsection 410(c) of the Act in 1971. The courts have interpreted Congress' 1971 action as reinforcing the FCC's primacy. *See infra* note 44.

[30]The Appendix to this article sets out the jurisdictionally important provisions of the two bills introduced in February 1934, S. 2910 and H.R. 8301, that became the Communications Act of 1934. The jurisdictional provisions were identical in the two bills. With only two exceptions, section numbers are the same in the two bills and in the Act passed in June 1934; these exception are: (a) the two bills placed in Section 210 the important jurisdictional exclusion now contained, with modifications, in Section 2(b) of the Act; and (b) differences between the two bills not relevant to this discussion caused Section 410 of the Act and Section 410 of S. 2910 to be designated Section 310 in H.R. 8301. The various Congressional Committee reports are as follows: (i) S. Rep. No. 781, 73rd Cong., 2d Sess., ("The Senate Report"), *see* PIKE AND FISCHER RADIO REGULATIONS (Pike & Fischer) at 10,221) *et seq.*, and SCHWARTZ, THE ECONOMIC REGULATION OF BUSINESS AND INDUSTRY ("Schwartz") at 2425 *et seq.*; (ii) H.R. Rep. No. 1918, 73rd Cong., 2d Sess. ("The House Report"), *see* Pike & Fischer at 10,241 *et seq.* and Schwartz at 2436 *et seq.*; and (iii) H.R. Rep. No. 1918, 73rd Cong., 2d Sess. ("The Conference Report"), *see* Pike & Fischer at 10,261 *et seq.* and Schwartz at 2513 *et seq.*

[31]Title I of the Communications Act (Section 151 *et seq.*) sets out purposes and jurisdictional provisions. Title II (Section 201 *et seq.*), derived from the Interstate Commerce Act, provides for utility regulation of common carriers engaged in interstate or foreign communications. Title III (Section 301 *et seq.*), derived from the Federal Radio Act, provides for regulation of the radio spectrum; this embraces broadcasting and common carrier activities, as well as other uses of radio. Title IV, Title V and Title VII (respectively, Sections 401 *et seq.*, 501 *et seq.*, and 701 *et seq.*) deal with such matters as procedural requirements and appeals, enforcement, and transfer of powers. Title VI (Section 601 *et seq.*), added to the Act by the 1984 Amendment (P.L.—), deals with cable television.

[32]In interpreting the Communications Act, the Commission and the courts will look to corresponding provisions of the Interstate Commerce Act, and administrative and jurdicial interpretation thereof. *See* for example AT&T v. United States, 14 F. Supp. 121, 125 (S. D.N.Y. 1936), *aff'd,* 299 U.S. 232 (1936), and the Depreciation Preemption Order, *infra* note 154, 92 F.C.C.2d at 870 *et seq.* Cases decided under the Interstate Commerce Act "retain their importance for purposes of determining the scope of the [Act]." Ivy Broadcasting Co. v. AT&T, 391 F.2d 486, 490-91 (2d Cir. 1968).

[33]The Federal Radio Act of 1927, the source of Title III of the Communications Act, was considered the achievement of then-Secretary of Commerce Herbert Hoover. It created the FRC to administer the use of the radio spectrum. The agency was expected to deal with the chaos which had resulted from the explosive growth of radio broadcasting in the 1920s without effective control. *See* Red Lion Broadcasting Co. v. FCC, 395 U.S. 367, 375-77 (1969). Its power to regulate radio communications on a nationwide basis was emphasized in Federal Radio Comm'n v. Nelson Bros. Bond & Mortgage Co., 289 U.S. 266, 279 (1933), often relied on in later decisions: "No state lines divide the radio waves, and national regulation is not only appropriate but essential to the efficient use of radio facilities." *See also* Whitehurst v. Grimes, 21 F.2d 787 (E.D. Ky. 1927); and Fisher's Blend Station, Inc. v. Tax Comm'n of State of Washington, 297 U.S. 650 (1936). To eliminate any

balancing that led to passage of the Act in June 1934.[34] We have the outcome of this process in the words of the statute; sometimes these words clearly reflect intent, but often not.

Perhaps the least ambiguous indication of Congress' intent to ensure that the *Shreveport* result would not apply to communications was the elimination of language, from what would become Subsection 410(b) of the Act, authorizing the Commission "to remove unjust discrimination against interstate commerce caused by State-made intrastate charges or regulations;" the Act as passed contained no such authorization.[35]

Sections 1 and 2 of the 1934 Act, in conjunction with the definitions contained in Subsection 3(e), confined FCC jurisdiction to interstate and foreign communications, and precluded the FCC from regulating intrastate communications.[36] But the problem that bedevilled Congressional draftsmen in 1934, and that the courts ultimately had to resolve, followed from the simple fact that facilities entirely within a single state would be, in modern telephony, employed for *both* interstate and intrastate purposes. This was implicitly recognized by the 1934

---

remaining doubts, Congress modified Section 301 of the Act in 1982, deleting the words "interstate or foreign" from the phrase "to maintain the control of the United States over all the channels of interstate of foreign radio transmission. . . ." *See* 1982 U.S. CODE CONG. & AD. NEWS 2237, 2275-76.

[34]In testimony before Congress in 1934, the principal adversaries on the question of federal/state powers were NARUC and W. S. Gifford, President of AT&T. NARUC supported a more effective federal commission which would be able to aid state regulation through the use of powers not restricted by state borderlines. However, NARUC urged the Congress to reverse the possible effect of the *Shreveport* case insofar as communications were concerned, and to reserve to the states a number of important powers. Gifford of AT&T opposed NARUC's view of the federal agency's role, particularly in terms of accounting requirements and depreciation. Gifford also expressed concern with the excessive reach of the federal agency's jurisdiction under what was to become Section 214 of the Act. *See Regulation of Interstate and Foreign Communications by Wire or Radio: Hearings on S. 2910 before the Committee on Interstate Commerce,* 73rd Cong., 2d Sess. (1934) *("The March Senate Hearings").* Gifford's testimony is at 76 *et seq.*; the testimony of NARUC General Solicitor Benton is at 180 *et seq. See also Regulation of Interstate and Foreign Communications by Wire or Radio, and for Other Purposes: Hearings on H.R. 8301 before the Committee on Interstate and Foreign Commerce,* 73rd Cong. 2d Sess. (1934) ("The April/May House Hearings.") Gifford's testimony is at 167 *et seq.*, Benton's at 70 *et seq.*

[35]Interstate Commerce Act Subsection 13(4), 49 U.S.C. § 13(4), contained the quoted language.

[36]Congress made no Section 1 changes from the original bills of jurisdictional importance. The language of Section 2 of the original bills became Subsection 2(a) of the Act, with the addition of the phrase "and to the licensing and regulating of all radio stations as hereinafter provided. . . ." Section 210 of the original bills became Subsection 2(b) of the Communications Act, with the extensive modifications discussed below. An "Except" clause was added in 1934 referring to Section 301, thus taking Title III out of the jurisdictional disclaimer. Apart from the "Except" clause (and post-1934 amendments), the only difference between the first five lines of Subsection 2(b) of the present Act and the Section 210 language is the 1934 addition of the word "facilities" after "practices, services."

But the last short phrase of bill Section 210, "or to any carrier engaged exclusively in intrastate commerce," was replaced by Subsection 2(b)(2), in which Congress created a special and complex kind of jurisdictional exclusion. In substance, this exclusion means that a telephone company (or other carrier), that is in all other respects engaged only in intrastate communications, is not brought under full Title II regulation merely because such telephone company interconnects with a long distance carrier, *unless* such long distance carrier is an affiliate of that telephone company. The intent was that the Bell System companies, interconnecting directly with AT&T Long Lines, an affiliate, would not come within the Subsection 2(b)(2) exclusion, and would be subject to all of Title II. The companies that came under Subsection 2(b)(2), defined as "connecting carriers" by Subsection 3(u), were made subject only to Sections 201-05 of Title II.

Congress when, for example, it replaced Subsection 214(e) of the original bills ("The authority conferred upon the Commission by this section [214] shall not extend to the construction, operation, or extension of lines or circuits within a single state.") with the first proviso of Subsection 214(a).[37]

There are other provisions of jurisdictional importance. Subsections 4(i) and 4(j) grant broad powers to the commission, and the courts have construed these powers broadly.[38] Subsection 221(b) contains another jurisdictional exclusion— which has been given an interpretation by the courts essentially limiting its scope to metropolitan areas straddling state borderlines.[39] The 1934 Congress modified proposed Subsection 201(a) to give the FCC the power to order physical connections among carriers and the division of charges.[40] Subsection 202(b) brought

---

[37]In 1934, Commissioner McManamy, Chairman of the ICC's Legislative Committee, argued against a simplistic notion of "intrastate" embracing anything connecting points within a single state. McManamy challenged the original version of Section 214 (in S.2910 and H.R. 8301), arguing for the deletion of proposed Subsection 214(e). The 1934 Congress in fact deleted Subsection 214(e), placing in the first proviso of Subsection 214(a) a more limited provision (*e.g.* "No such certificate shall be required . . . unless such line constitutes part of an interstate line. . . ."). Similarly, McManamy challenged the two bills' definition of "interstate;" the 1934 Congress struck from the two bills' Subsection 3(e), defining "interstate communication" or "interstate transmission," the following phrase offensive to McManamy: "if the point of origin and the point of reception are not in the same state." *See* The March Senate Hearings at 200 *et seq.*; The April/May House Hearings at 88 *et seq.* An important clarification of the reach of Section 214 was effected by the 1943 Amendment. *See* 1943 CODE CONG. SERVICE 2-2 and the Commission's interpretation, 10 F.C.C. 315, 318-21 (1944). *See also AT&T,* 91 F.C.C.2d 1, 14 n.10 (1982).

[38]For example, heavy emphasis was placed on the Commission's discretion under Subsection 4(i) in U.S. v. Southwestern Cable Co., *infra* note 76, 392 U.S. at 180-81. And the courts have stressed the FCC's broad discretion under Subsection 4(j) in deciding the procedures which would be appropriate to accomplishing statutory objectives. *See* FCC v. Schreiber, 381 U.S. 279, 289-93 (1965); FCC v. Pottsville Broadcasting Co., 309 U.S. 134, 143-44 (1940); Nader v. FCC, 520 F.2d 182, 195-96, 199 (D.C. Cir. 1981); Western Union Tel. Co. v. FCC, 665 F.2d 1112, 1121 and n.13 (D.C. Cir. 1981); MCI Telecommunications Corp. v. FCC, 712 F.2d 517 (D.C. Cir. 1983).

[39]North Carolina I, *infra* note 108, 537 F.2d at 795; North Carolina II, *infra* note 117, 552 F.2d at 1045; Puerto Rico Tel. Co. v. FCC, 553 F.2d 694, 698-99 (1st Cir. 1977); New York Tel. Co. v. FCC, *infra* note 126, 631 F.2d at 1064; CCIA v. FCC, *infra* note 133, 693 F.2d at 216-17. *But see* cases that continue to refer to Subsection 221(b) in a broader application than "straddling" situations, Department of Defense v. the Chesapeake and Potomac Tel. Co., 69 F.C.C.2d 393, 394-95 (1978), reconsideration 71 F.C.C.2d 1336, 1338-1339 (1979) modified 75 F.C.C.2d 45 (1979) [ ]; General Tel. Co. of the Southwest v. United States, *infra* note 65, 449 F.2d at 855-56 n.5. The FCC clarified this point, in AT&T Co. (F.C.C. Tariff No. 270 1.544 Mbps), Memorandum Opinion and Order (November 8, 1983), *recon. denied,* Memorandum Opinion and Order (April 3, 1984), para. 18, which emphasized that where state borderlines are not straddled, Subsection 221(b) does not apply. The analysis of Subsection 221(b) contained in Kitchen v. FCC, 464 F.2d 801, 803 (D.C. Cir. 1972), was later expressly rejected by the D.C. Circuit and replaced by the North Carolina I and II interpretation, in CCIA v. FCC, *infra* note 133, 693 F.2d at 217.

[40]In 1934, James B. McDonough, general counsel for the Oklahoma-Arkansas Tel. Co., argued for stronger preemptive powers for the new federal agency in terms of requiring carriers to establish physical connections. The March Senate Hearings at 109-16. In fact, the 1934 Congress added to Subsection 201(a) of the original bills the phrase "to establish physical connections with other carriers" and "and the divisions of such charges." *See* Oklahoma-Arkansas Tel. Co. v. Southwestern Bell Tel. Co., 45 F.2d 995 (8th Cir. 1930), *cert. denied,* 283 U.S. 822 (1931). *See also* Oklahoma-Arkansas Tel. Co. v. Southwestern Bell Tel. Co., 6 F.C.C. 809 (1939), where Oklahoma-Arkansas Tel. Co. v. Southwestern Bell Tel. Co., 6 F.C.C. 809 (1939), where Oklahoma-Arkansas failed to convince the FCC to issue an order requiring employment of the company's facilities; and Lavey, *Joint Network Planning in the Telephone Industry,* 34 FED. COMM J. 345, 358-59 (1982).

common carrier services to broadcasters under FCC Title II jurisdiction.[41] Congress included provisions reserving certain decisional powers to the states in Subsection 221(a)[42] and in Subsection 213(h); but declined to include such a provision in Section 220, concerned with accounting and depreciation.[43] The FCC was given the power to determine, after hearing, what carrier property was used in interstate and foreign telephone toll service (Subsection 221(c)). The FCC was also granted the authority to convene Joint Boards and to determine Jurisdictional Separations matters (Section 410).[44]

Based on these various provisions, and the compromises that underlay them, the Commission and the courts would have to define the FCC's preemptive power.

---

[41]Subsection 202(b) had no counterpart in the Interstate Commerce Act. Senator Dill described the provision as "new" and "thought" to be desirable because the charges for the use of wires for chain broadcasting have been without any control whatsoever." 78 CONG. REC. 8823 (1934). Its location in Section 202 is somewhat peculiar, since logically it belongs among the definitional provisions of Section 3. It is a reasonable inference that this provision was inserted in S. 2910 and H.R. 8301 as a reaction to Spriggs v. Bell Tel. Co. of Pennsylvania, 12 Pa. Pub. Serv. Comm'n 512, 3 P.U.R. (N.S.) 42 (1934), where the Bell Company was upheld by the Pennsylvania Public Service Commission in maintaining that jurisdiction over telephone company rates or facilities provided to broadcasters rested exclusively with the federal government. Further, Bell of Pennsylvania maintained that, absent Congressional action, the company would be free to set the rates it deemed appropriate. *Spriggs* was decided just two weeks before S. 2910 was introduced on February 20, 1934. For an application of Subsection 202(b), *see* Capital City Tel. Co., 3 F.C.C. 189 (1936), *infra* note 58. The wording of Subsection 202(b) was modified in 1960. *See* 1960 U.S. CODE CONG. & AD. NEWS 3512.

[42]*See supra* note 14.

[43]S. 2910 and H.R. 4301 contained the NARUC-sponsored version of Subsection 220(j), reserving to the states the power to prescribe depreciation for state purposes. This provision was challenged by McManamy, who said: Paragraph (j) of these new paragraphs should be most carefully considered. It unquestionably directly conflicts with, and destroys the uniformity of systems of accounts and depreciation accounting required by the preceding provisions of the section. That is not true under the present law. In this connection consideration should also be given to the last 4 lines of paragraph (h). The March Senate Hearings at 208-09; *see also* The April/May Hearings at 96. In fact, the 1934 Congress replaced the NARUC-sponsored version of Subsection 220(j), which reserved power to the states, with Subsection 220(j) of the present Act, requiring the FCC to investigate and report to Congress as to the need for legislation to define further or harmonize the powers of the FCC and state commissions. Commissioner McManamy's comments on Subsection 220(j) were given heavy emphasis by the FCC in its Depreciation Preemption Order, *infra* note 154, 92 F.C.C.2d at 871. Notwithstanding McManamy's comments on Subsection 220(h), this provision was enacted without significant alteration.

[44]Section 410 is not part of Title II itself, although it deals with a subject matter directly relevant to Title II action. Its post-1934 history is significant. The 1952 Amendment to Subsection 410(a) gave a joint board, appointed by the Commission, the jurisdiction and powers conferred by law upon the Commission. *See* 1952 U.S. CODE CONG. & AD. NEWS 2234, 2255. In 1956, the Commission was successful in having Congress modify Subsection 410(a) to give joint boards the same powers as conferred on hearing examiners—thus giving the Commission an opportunity to act before a final determination would be made in a particular case. Since reference to a Joint Board under Subsection 410(a) was discretionary, the FCC said it would not be likely to refer any matter to a joint board without such a modification; this would "make the section more usable to the Commission." *See* 1956 U.S. CODE CONG. & AD. NEWS 4134, 4136-39. Subsection 410(c), added in 1971, made joint board reference mandatory for "any proceeding regarding the jurisdictional separation of common carrier property and expenses between interstate and intrastate operations, which [the FCC] institutes pursuant to a notice of proposed rulemaking." The Amendment also established the structure of the joint board (three FCC commissioners, four state commissioners). Joint boards convened under Section 410 are limited to making recommendations, with the power of final decision

5.5 DEVELOPMENTS SINCE 1934

5.5.1 The Good-Bad Old Days and the Opening to Competition

The 1940s and 1950s might be thought of, depending on one's perspective, as either the "good old days" or the "bad old days." For all practical purposes, domestic telecommunications were provided on a non-competitive basis.[45] The Bell System, in association with the Independents, provided domestic telephone service. This included the terminal equipment located at the customer's premises; tariff restrictions prohibited "foreign attachments," *i.e.,* connection to any part of the system of items not furnished by the telephone company. Resale of telephone service was proscribed by tariff restrictions.[46] Western Union provided domestic message telegraph and telex service, facing significant competition only in Bell's TWX system.[47] There was some competition in mobile telephone service, with Radio Common Carriers or "RCCs" competing with telephone companies[48]—but this was still insignificant.

The non-competitive nature of the industry under regulation had been recognized by the United States Supreme Court in what was known as the "Three Circuits" case. This decision rejected the notion of a national policy in communications favoring competition "without careful qualification." Noting the comprehensive regulatory scheme of the Act, the Court said that the FCC, in authorizing a competitor, "must at least warrant, as it were, that competition would serve some beneficial purpose such as maintaining good service and improving it."[49]

resting with the FCC. The state commissioners may participate in deliberations when the Commission considers joint board recommendations, but they may not vote. In effect, then, the 1971 Amendment underscored the power of the FCC—acting in compliance with Subsection 410(c)—to decide Jurisdictional Separations questions. Further, as noted by the D.C. Circuit: Congress has obviously been aware that for nearly forty years the Commission has claimed jurisdiction over some instrastate facilities. Congressional acquiescence in these claims is symbolized by the Joint Federal-State Board procedure of [Subsection] 410(c). Congress would not have created this procedure in 1971 if it had been concerned that the FCC was inappropriately exercising jurisdiction over matters committed to state regulation. The Joint Board procedure actually augmented the Commission's powers in part by recognizing national primacy. [Citing *North Carolina I, infra* note 108, 537 F.2d at 795.] NARUC v. FCC, *infra* note 130.

[45]The last vestiges of competition among local exchange telephone companies were disappearing in the 1940's. *See* New Jersey Bell Tel. Co., 9 F.C.C. 261 (1943).

[46]*See* Ambassador, Inc. v. United States, 325 U.S. 317 (1945), *reh'g denied*, 325 U.S. 896 (1945), upholding tariff restrictions on resale of interstate and foreign service. *See also* Mackay Radio and Telegraph Co., 6 F.C.C. 562 (1938). *Contrast* the 1970's decisions referred to in notes 128-30 *infra*, eliminating such restrictions.

[47]The 1940's saw the disappearance of competition in the domestic telegraph field as the failing Postal Telegraph and Cable System was merged into the Western Union Telegraph Company—under specific authorization by Congress. *See* Section 222 of the Act, as it existed prior to the 1980 Amendment (P.L. 96-590) and the Record Carrier Competition Act of 1981 (P.L. 97-130).

[48]The FCC decided to introduce competition in mobile telephone service in the late 1940's, granting separate frequencies to RCCs. General Mobile Radio Service, 13 F.C.C. 1190, 1218 (1949).

[49]FCC v. RCA Communications, Inc., 346 U.S. 86, 91, 93, 97 (1953). The "warrant, as it were" requirement was met by the FCC in formal terms as it moved towards competition, thereby satisfying the test while evading its spirit. *See,* for example, Above 890, *infra* note 52, 27 F.C.C. at 412; Execunet I, *infra* note 121, 561 F.2d at 380. *But see* Hawaiian Tel. Co. v. FCC, 498 F.2d 771 (D.C. Cir. 1974), which applied the Three Circuits doctrine.

In this environment, the FCC presided over "interstate" and "foreign" communications; the state commissions regulated "intrastate" communications. As a practical matter, the jurisdictional distinction between interstate and intrastate service generally followed the tariffs filed by the industry with either the FCC or state commissions. Separation of investment, revenue and costs for purposes of setting rates within the two jurisdictions was accomplished by procedures worked out by the industry.[50] With competition a minor factor and federal and state attitudes generally in harmony, there was no great pressure for more refined jurisdictional analysis. This rather static picture describes the common carrier world when Don Larsen disposed of 27 Brooklyn Dodgers in October, 1956.

But, in 1956, there were several important indicators of the communications world to come. The D.C. Circuit pried open the "foreign attachments" rule by upholding the subscriber's right to use a cup-like device which snapped onto a telephone instrument; the court's opinion announced the "telephone subscriber's right reasonably to use his telephone in ways which are privately beneficial without being publicly detrimental."[51] The FCC initiated proceedings that were eventually to assign radio frequencies to private users, permitting large users to create systems avoiding the telephone network.[52] And a Consent Decree was entered in *United States v. Western Electric Co.* generally confining the Bell System to regulated activities.[53] FCC preemption of the states was not a factor in these developments, but it was to become a factor in the 1960s as FCC policies affecting cable television and telephone service began to impinge on the states' domain.

5.5.2 Cases Bringing Common Carrier Service Between Points With a State Under Federal Jurisdiction

Soon after passage of the Act in 1934, the Commission was called on to define its jurisdiction in relation to the terms "interstate" and "intrastate" as used in the Act. In requiring Southwestern Bell Telephone Company to obtain authorization under Subsection 214(a) for construction of additional facilities connecting points entirely within the State of Texas, the FCC rejected the notion that the facilities constituted "a line within a single State" since it was conceded that such facilities "are to be used, to an undetermined extent, for the transmission of messages interstate."[54] Further, the Commission rejected a "preponderance of use" test in classifying a carrier's property as interstate or intrastate for the

---

[50]*See supra* notes 2 and 25.

[51]Hush-A-Phone Corp. v. United States, 238 F.2d 266, 269 (D.C. Cir. 1956).

[52]Above 890, 27 F.C.C. 359, 404-405, 18 R.R. 1767, 1785 (1959).

[53]1956 Trade Cas. ¶ 68,246 (D.C.N.J. 1956). The 1956 Consent Decree "precluded AT&T from engaging in any business other than the provision of common carrier communications services: precluded Western Electric from manufacturing equipment other than that used by the Bell System; and required the defendants to license their patents to all applicants upon the payment of appropriate royalties." United States v. AT&T, *supra,* 552 F. Supp. at 137-38. *See* CCIA v. FCC, *infra* note 133, 693 F.2d at 219-20.

[54]Southwestern Bell Tel. Co., 6 F.C.C. 529, 532 (1938).

purpose of determining jurisdiction.[55] The Commission also rejected a test based on "continuity of interstate connection," *i.e.* whether the traffic is switched or not, since this test would leave jurisdictional classification of carrier facilities entirely to company discretion. "[W]e cannot attribute to Congress an intent to leave with the carrier [this] discretion. . . ."[56] Since the services and facilities of Southwestern Bell were *interstate, i.e.* carried some interstate traffic, the Commission rejected arguments that it was invading state jurisdiction.[57] Over the opposition of NARUC as well as Southwestern Bell, the Commission required compliance with Section 214.

The notion of defining "intrastate" communication as simply connecting two (or more) points within the same state was similarly rejected in the context of service to broadcasters, where Subsection 202(b) came into play, and in a broader context. Thus, the holding of *Capital City Telephone Co.,*[58] that the provision of service and facilities to broadcasters would come under FCC regulation, was followed by a series of such cases.[59] The principle was also applied to cases not involving service to broadcasters.[60]

---

[55]*Id.* at 532-533. The Commission observed: We find no authority for the theory advanced by the telephone companies to the effect that this Commission should regard its jurisdiction with respect to the construction of a new line or extension of any line as being limited to such toll facilities as are intended to be used "primarily" for interstate service. Congress provided no such test. It could have done so if it had so desired. Quite probably, one reason for the absence from the Act itself of such a test is that it would be no test. It is doubtful whether the companies themselves, or the Commission, can arbitrarily fix a line to distinguish between that service which is "primary" and that which is "secondary" or "incidental". . . . The result would be complete frustration of whatever purpose the Congress may have had in mind in framing the provision of the Act here involved. *We find no authority of law to support the theory that "preponderance of use" is a proper test for the classification of a carrier's property as interstate or intrastate for the purpose of determining jurisdiction.* [*Id.* at 532, emphasis added.]

[56]*Id.* at 534.

[57]*Id.*

[58]3 F.C.C. 189, 193 (1936). The Commission has also cited Petition of AT&T, 2 F.C.C. 89 (1935), *recon. denied,* 2 F.C.C. 308 (1936), to support the statement that "Section 214 authority has long been required for a telephone company's interstate coaxial cable." National Telephone Cooperative Ass'n, 69 F.C.C.2d 1097, 1099 n.4 (1978). *See also* the Commission's conclusion that Capital City came within the Subsection 2(b)(2) exclusion, nothwithstanding 29% of all its capital securities being held by Southwestern Bell Tel. Co. *Contrast* Rochester Tel. Corp. v. United States, 307 U.S. 125 (1939), where Rochester Tel. was held fully subject to Title II under similar circumstances.

[59]Ward v. Northern Ohio Tel. Co., 300 F.2d 816, 818-20 (6th Cir. 1962), *cert. denied,* 371 U.S. 820 (1962); Pacific Teletronics, Inc., 4 R.R.2d 145 (1964); Idaho Microwave, Inc. v. FCC, 352 F.2d 729 (D.C. Cir. 1965).

[60]*See* United States v. AT&T Co., 57 F. Supp. 451, 454 (S.D.N.Y. 1944), *aff'd sub nom.* Hotel Astor, Inc. v. Unites States, 325 U.S. 837 (1945): "That the Communications Act contemplates the regulation of interstate wire communication from its inception to its completion is confirmed by the language of the statute and by judicial decisions." Section 605 of the Act has been specifically held to apply to both interstate and intrastate communications. Benanti v. U.S., 355 U.S. (96) (1957). *And see* California Interstate Tel. Co. v. FCC, 328 F.2d 556 (D.C. Cir. 1964), where the D.C. Circuit upheld the FCC's jurisdiction over provision of a system communicating between two points located in California—Pasadena and Goldstone—as merely an adjunct to "foreign" communications, *i.e.,* between Pasadena (Jet Propulsion Laboratories) and the spacecraft. *See also* General Tel. Co. of California v. FCC, *infra* note 62, 413 F.2d at 401; and United States Department of Defense v. General Tel. Co. of the Northwest, 38 F.C.C.2d 803, 26 R.R.2d 245 (1973), *review denied,* FCC 73-854 (August 10, 1973), *aff'd without opinion sub nom.* St. Joseph Tel. and Tel. Co. v. FCC, 505

This line of cases would play a significant role in the FCC's extension of regulation to the developing phenomenon of cable television service, including the role of telephone companies (and their affiliates) in providing such service, as discussed in the following paragraphs. These cases would also provide a base for implementing FCC policies opening common carrier services to competition.[61]

In *General Telephone Co. of California v. FCC*,[62] the D.C. Circuit affirmed the FCC's decision to require Section 214 certification where a telephone company sought to construct distribution facilities to provide channel service to cable television firms—even if the telephone company's activities were entirely within a single state. Seen in the context of the FCC's prior assertion of jurisdiction over cable television (discussed below), there is special significance in the language of the D.C. Circuit (Opinion by Warren Burger) that rejected arguments claiming Subsection 2(b)(1) excluded FCC jurisdiction.[63] Stressing the court's concern with fragmentation of regulation, Judge Burger stated that "fifty states and myriad local authorities cannot effectively deal with bits and pieces of what is really a unified system of communication." This underscored the court's focus on the FCC's comprehensive and pervasive responsibilities, on the need for decision-making of national scope, and on Commission action within the broad purposes of the Act:

> The Supreme Court [*United States v. Southwestern Cable, infra*, 392 U.S. at 169] aptly characterized the functional aspect of the CATV [community antenna television] systems as an "essentially uninterrupted and properly indivisible" stream of communication.
>
> * * * * *
>
> The Petitioners [telephone companies] have, by choice, inserted themselves as links in this indivisible stream and have become an integral part of interstate broadcast transmission. They cannot have the economic benefits of such carriage as they perform and be free of the necessarily pervasive jurisdiction of the Commission.[64]

F.2d 476 (D.C. Cir. 1974) ("DRP case"). Cases relied on in the DRP decision included Use of Recording Devices, 11 F.C.C. 1033 (1947); Katz v. AT&T, 8 R.R. 919 (1953); Jordaphone Corp. of America v. AT&T, 18 F.C.C. 644 (1954); AT&T-TWX, 38 F.C.C. 1127 (1965); and Department of Defense v. AT&T, 38 F.C.C.2d 819 (1970) ("COPAN case"). *See also* Tranquilli v. Mississippi Tel & Communications, Inc., 38 F.C.C.2d 192, 196-97, 25 R.R.2d 1060, 1066 (Review Board, 1972); and Department of Defense v. AT&T, 68 F.C.C.2d 40, 42 R.R.2d 1710 (1978), *recon. denied*, 71 F.C.C.2d 1340 (1979), *aff'd* 80 F.C.C.2d 287, 47 R.R.2d 1559 (1980) ("MOB case"), where the FCC refused to require FCC tariffing of the MOB console (*infra* note 146).

[61]*See* for example California v. FCC, *infra* note 122, 567 F.2d at 86, approving the FCC's conclusion that the key issue is the nature of the communications which pass through the facilities, not the physical location of the lines, and citing United States v. Southwestern Cable, *infra* note 76, 392 U.S. at 168-69. On this key issue, *see also* United States v. Midwest Video Corp., *infra* note 82, 406 U.S. at 663 n.21; New York Tel. Co. v. FCC, *infra* note 126, 631 F.2d at 1066; General Tel. Co. of California v. FCC, *infra* note 62, 413 F.2d at 401; and NARUC v. FCC, *infra* note 130.

[62]413 F.2d 390 (D.C. Cir. 1969), *cert. denied*, 396 U.S. 888 (1969).

[63]*Id.* at 398-400.

[64]*Id.* at 401.

In 1971, in *General Telephone Co. of the Southwest v. United States*,[65] the Fifth Circuit affirmed the FCC in prohibiting telephone companies or their affiliates from furnishing cable television service in their telephone service areas. The FCC's concern was that, by reason of their control over utility poles or conduits, the telephone companies were in a position to preclude or substantially delay an unaffiliated cable system from commencing service, thereby eliminating competition.[66] The court upheld the application of the prohibition to parent corporations, whose activities can be imputed to subsidiary telephone companies.[67] Further, the Subsection 2(b)(2) exclusion was treated as inapplicable since it "was meant to protect State jurisdiction over local telephone facilities which could place interstate calls through their connection with major toll lines [where] this interstate facet of the company's operation was incidental to its primary local service. . . ."[68] The court therefore held the Subsection 2(b)(2) exclusion did not bar the FCC's exercise of jurisdiction since the "reach of Section 214 . . . [may embrace] a 'connecting carrier' . . . if an exemption is not otherwise available."[69]

Finally, the court upheld FCC rules requiring telephone companies to offer pole or conduit space to cable firms as a precondition for grant of Section 214 authorization to provide channel service to cable companies.[70]

5.5.3 Assertion of "Ancillary" FCC Jurisdiction Over Cable Television[71]

The foregoing cases involved the exercise of FCC authority under Title II of the Act—dealing with regulation of common carriers. Overlapping in time was a series of cases in which the FCC extended its jurisdiction over non-common carriers, on the theory that such extension was reasonably ancillary to the effective performance of the FCC's responsibilities with respect to television broadcasting; FCC preemptive action would be founded on the jurisdictional base thus established.

In 1968, the United States Supreme Court, in *United States v. Southwestern Cable Co.*, without dissent, upheld the FCC's imposition of signal carriage restrictions on cable television firms.[72] In view of the cases discussed above, it is

---

[65]449 F.2d 846 (5th Cir. 1971).

[66]*Id*. at 851.

[67]*Id*. at 855. For a discussion of the further extension of indirect regulation, *see* Dougherty, *The Use of Section 214 of the Communications Act of 1934 to Control Shifts in Corporate Control over Common Carriers*, 29 CATH. U.L. REV. 891 (1980).

[68]*Id*. at 855, quoting General Tel. Co. of California v. FCC, *supra* note 62, 413 F.2d at 402.

[69]*Id*. at 855, footnote omitted. *See also* GTE Service Corp. v. FCC, *infra* note 132, 474 F.2d at 731-37, where connecting carriers were held subject to a variety of FCC restrictions.

[70]*Id*. at 860.

[71]This article uses the terms "cable television" and "CATV" interchangeably. *See* United States v. Midwest Video Corp., *infra* note 82, 406 U.S. at 651 n.3.

[72]392 U.S. 157 (1968). For a comparison of the restrictions imposed by the FCC on cable firms in 1968, 1972, and 1979, *see infra* note 217.

no surprise that cable companies were treated as interstate even where their facilities were entirely within one state. The Court refused to accept the cable companies' activities as intrastate in character since they were "ordinarily employed in the simultaneous retransmission of communications that have very often originated in other States."[73] Jurisdictional arguments based on Subsection 2(a) of the Act were swept away; stressing the FCC's "unified jurisdiction" and "broad authority," the Court reasoned that the Commission's authority was not limited to those activities and forms of communication specifically described by the Act's other provisions (*i.e.*, broadcasting and common carrier service)[74] and spoke of the need for flexibility in the administrative process, adding:

> Congress in 1934 acted in a field that was demonstrably "both new and dynamic" and it therefore gave the Commission "a comprehensive mandate," with "not niggardly but expansive powers."[75] We have found no reason to believe that [Section] 152 does not, as its terms suggest, confer regulatory authority over "all interstate . . . communication by wire or radio."[76]

The Court said the Commission "has reasonably found that the achievement of . . . [its] purposes [with respect to local broadcasting] is 'placed in jeopardy by the unregulated explosive growth of CATV.'"[77] So the Court "must conclude that there is substantial evidence that the Commission cannot 'discharge its overall responsibilities without authority over . . . [cable television].'"[78] The Commission's jurisidiction was therefore upheld under Subsection 2(a) on an ancillary-to-broadcasting theory—"restricted to that reasonably ancillary to the effective performance of the Commission's various responsibilities for the regulation of television broadcasting."[79] The Court relied on the principle that "we may not, 'in the absence of compelling evidence that such was Congress' intention . . . prohibit administrative action imperative for the achievement of an agency's ultimate purposes.'"[80]

Finally, in upholding the FCC's order limiting further expansion of the cable companies' service pending appropriate hearings, the Court emphasized the broad grant of authority to the Commission under Subsection 4(i) of the Act.[81]

In 1972, *United States v. Midwest Video Corp.*, at a further stage in the FCC's regulation of cable television, went to the Supreme Court, and again the Com-

---

[73]*Id.* at 169.

[74]*Id.* at 172.

[75]Citing National Broadcasting Co. v. United States, 319 U.S. 190, 219 (1943).

[76]United States v. Southwestern Cable Co., 392 U.S. 157, 172-73 (1968), footnotes omitted.

[77]*Id.* at 175 (quoting H.R. Rep. No. 1635, 89th Cong., 2d Sess. 7).

[78]*Id.* at 177 (quoting Staff of Senate Comm. on Interstate and Foreign Commerce, 85th Cong., 2d Sess., The Television Inquiry: The Problem of Television Service for Smaller Communities 19 (Comm. Print 1959).

[79]*Id.* at 178.

[80]*Id.* at 177, quoting Permian Basin Area Rate Cases, 390 U.S. 747, 780 (1968).

[81]*Id.* at 181. *See also* New York State Commission on Cable Television v. FCC, 669 F.2d 58, 64-5 (2d Cir. 1982).

mission was upheld—but this time by a bare plurality.[82] The Commission's program-origination rules were found to be "'reasonably ancillary to the effective performance of . . . [its] various responsibilities for the regulation of television broadcasting.'" The plurality specifically upheld the Commission's concerns not merely with avoiding adverse effects on broadcasting but also with requiring cable companies to act affirmatively in furtherance of statutory policies; thus the Commission made a reasonable determination that compelling cable companies to originate programming would "'further the achievement of long-established regulatory goals in the field of television broadcasting by increasing the number of outlets for community self-expression and augmenting the public's choice of programs and types of services . . . .'"[83]

The Chief Justice concurred in the result while four Justices dissented.[84] As the swing vote, Chief Justice Burger signalled his discomfort with the Commission's jurisdictional position ("[it] strains the outer limits of even the open-ended and pervasive jurisdiction that has evolved . . . .") and his sympathy with the dissenters and the (reversed) Eighth Circuit on the merits; but he voted to affirm the FCC ("until Congress acts, the Commission should be allowed wide latitude . . .").[85] Justice Douglas, writing for the dissenters, distinguished the FCC's program origination rules, requiring new investment, personnel and equipment, from the more limited regulations at issue in *Southwestern Cable*. He regarded as beyond the scope of the Communications Act the notion that the FCC can force cable companies into, in effect, becoming broadcasters. Justice Douglas concluded that the plurality was granting the FCC "ancillary" power over cable firms greater than that which the Commission could exercise over broadcasters themselves.[86]

The misgivings with regard to cable television regulation expressed by five Justices in *United States v. Midwest Video, supra,* foreshadowed heavy going for FCC regulation of the field. The D.C. Circuit, in the 1976 decision *NARUC v. FCC,*[87] set aside FCC action that had sought to preempt state and local regulation of two-way, intrastate, non-video cable transmissions. The grounds upon which Judge Wilkey and Judge Lombard (concurring) agreed were that the the leased access channels providing this kind of service did not fall within the "reasonably ancillary" standard of *United States v. Southwestern Cable, supra.*[88] Judge Wilkey's Opinion found applicable the jurisdictional bar of Subsection 2(b) of the Act since, he concluded, "the substantial bulk of the two-way, non-video communications expected to be carried over leased access bandwidth will be both

---

[82]406 U.S. 649 (1972), *reh'g denied,* 409 U.S. 898 (1972).
[83]*Id.* at 667-78 (quoting CATV, First Report and Order, 20 F.C.C.2d 201, 202, 17 R.R.2d 1570 (1969)).
[84]*Id.* at 675.
[85]*Id.4* at 675-76.
[86]*Id.* at 677-81.
[87]533 F.2d 601 (D.C. Cir. 1976).
[88]*Id.* at 621.

intrastate and common carrier in nature."[89] However, Judge Lombard found it unnecessary to reach the question of a Subsection 2(b) bar, and Judge Wright strenuously dissented, generally and on this point.[90]

In his thoughtful Opinion, Judge Wilkey noted that *"Midwest* rather than *Southwestern* presents the farthest outpost of Commission power. . . ." The distinction was *"Southwestern* involved a regulation of cable whose direct purpose was the protection of broadcasting operations," while "the *Midwest* origination requirement presents a far less direct and more complicated relationship with the broadcasting media."[91] As such, *Midwest* "takes a giant step beyond *Southwestern,* in relaxing the nature of the ancillariness necessary to support an assertion of Commission power over cable." *Midwest* "turns upon a determination that 'ancillary to broadcasting' means not only 'for the protection of broadcasting,' but also embodies any regulation of cable which in its own right serves the purposes pursued by broadcast regulation." Based upon this analysis, Judge Wilkey, in the *NARUC* case, concluded that two-way non-video preemption did not meet the ancillary standard. Judge Lombard said: "I agree with Judge Wilkey that the nature of these services is such that its impact on broadcasting will be minimal."[92]

In the author's view, Judge Wilkey put his finger on the problem—regulation of cable television that focused on protecting broadcasters from cable competition was accepted by the *Southwestern Cable* court without dissent, and at least this came within a plausible concept of ancillariness. But after *Midwest Video,* FCC regulation of cable seemed to take on a life of its own to a point where the relationship to protecting broadcasting became more and more remote.

This remoteness of cable regulation from its ostensible purpose was one of the grounds of Judge Markey's 1978 Opinion in *Midwest Video Corp. v. FCC,*[93] which skewered the Commission's mandatory access and capacity requirements:

---

[89]*Id.* at 611. Judge Wilkey's discussion of the concept of "common carrier" focused on (i) the carrier's quasi-public character and (ii) the carrier's transmission of intelligence of the user's design and choosing (at 609-610). *See* Judge Wilkey's more specific discussion of the common carrier concept in NARUC v. FCC, 525 F.2d 630 (D.C. Cir. 1976), *cert. denied sub nom.* National Ass'n of Radiotelephone Systems v. FCC, 425 U.S. 992 (1976) ("SMRS decision"), where the FCC was upheld in preempting state certification requirements for "SMRS" (Specialized Mobile Radio Systems)—certain non-carrier systems operated for a profit. According to Judge Wilkey, "the quasi-public character implicit in the common carrier concept is that the carrier 'undertakes to carry for all people [or an identified classification] indifferently. . . .'" (At 641.) (quoting Semon v. Royal Indemnity Co., 279 F.2d 737,739 (5th Cir. 1960)' A carrier "will not be a common carrier where its practice is to make individualized decisions, in particular cases, whether and on what terms to deal." (525 F.2d at 641). *See* discussion of cases, n.56 through n.62. *See also* FCC v. Midwest Video Corp., 440 U.S. 689, 700-02 (1979), where the common carrier concept is discussed; Judge Wilkey's words on "individualized decisions" are set out with apparent approval. For further discussion of "common carrier" as this definition has been applied under the Act, *see* 46 ALR Fed. 626 (1980); and CCIA v. FCC, *infra* note 133.

[90]*Id.* at 623-37.

[91]*Id.* at 615.

[92]*Id.* at 622.

[93]571 F.2d 1025 (8th Cir. 1978), *aff'd,* FCC v. Midwest Video Corp., 440 U.S. 689 (1979).

The present [access and capacity] rules are not designed to govern some deleterious interrelationship of cable systems to broadcasting, or to require that cable systems do what broadcasters do, *but relate to cable systems alone,* and are designed to force them into activities not engaged in or sought; *activities having no bearing, adverse or otherwise, on the health and welfare of broadcasting* (emphasis added).[94]

An additional ground for reversal was that the Commission had imposed common carrier obligations on entities that were not common carriers; the court noted that the mandatory construction and access rules may constitute a taking of property without just compensation, in violation of the Fifth Amendment.[95]

Judge Willey and Judge Markey correctly focused on the heart of the problem: where is the outer limit to the "ancillary" standard? What makes this an especially difficult question is that it tends to intermix the jurisdictional issue with consideration of the merits.

On appeal, the Supreme Court did not follow Judge Markey's lead in addressing the outer limit of ancillariness. A far more skeptical attitude was displayed than in 1968 and 1972; and (with three dissenters) the Court struck down the FCC's cable access rules, but on a rather narrow basis:

[W]e are constrained to hold that the Commission exceeded those limits [of Commission authority] in promulgating its access rules. The Commission may not regulate cable systems as common carriers, just as it may not impose such obligations on television broadcasters. We think authority to compel cable operators to provide common carriage of public-originated transmissions must come specifically from Congress.[96]

With three Justices in dissent, perhaps it is not surprising that the Court chose to address only one of the Eighth Circuit's grounds, and to do that in somewhat different terms than Judge Markey's caustic Opinion. One can speculate that it might have been difficult to confine the effects of a broader attack on the Commission's policy. Moreover, three of the Justices were part of the 1972 plurality, including the Chief Justice. Nonetheless, while the Court did not adopt all the Eighth Circuit reasoning, that Circuit's decision was affirmed and can be fairly cited as law of the case.[97]

---

[94]*Id.* at 1038.

[95]*Id.* at 1051.

[96]FCC v. Midwest Video Corp., 440 U.S. 689, 708-9 (1979), footnotes omitted. The dissenters in 1972 were concerned about forcing cable companies to become, in effect, broadcasters. United States v. Midwest Video, 406 U.S. 649, 677-80 (1972). Similarly, the majority in 1979 objected to compelling cable firms to furnish the equivalent of common carriage when broadcasters cannot be forced into common carrier status under Subsection 3(h) of the Act. 440 U.S. at 705.

[97]The Commission departed from its pattern of extending FCC jurisdiction over cable television in 1977 when it concluded that making available pole and conduit arrangements to cable operators is an activity which does not constitute "communication by wire or radio," and is thus beyond the scope of the FCC's [Title II] authority. California Water and Telephone Co., 64 F.C.C.2d 753, 758-59, 40 R.R.2d 419 (1977). This decision was rendered academic when, in 1978, Congress added to the Act (P.L. 95-234; further modified in 1982, P.L. 97-259) Section 224 giving the FCC jurisdiction to regulate pole/duct rates—in the absence of state action assuming jurisdiction. 47 U.S.C. § 224

Notwithstanding these developments, the Second Circuit issued decisions in 1978 and 1982 giving preemptive effect to Commission policies related to cable television. In *Brookhaven Cable TV, Inc. v. Kelly,* the FCC's authority to preempt state and local price regulation of certain pay-cable programming was upheld.[98] The court's brief opinion contains no indication of discomfort with the lengths to which ancillary jurisdiction had reached. In *New York State Commission on Cable Television v. FCC,* the FCC was affirmed in its decision preempting state or local regulation of MATV (Master Antenna Television) systems—normally installed in multi-unit buildings.[99] The FCC, which regulated MDS (Multi-point Distribution Service), concluded that "'the MATV system to which MDS reception equipment is attached is an integral and necessary part of the transmission of . . . programming. . . ;'" and that "'the practical effect of the State's regulation of MATV systems was to interfere with, burden, and limit service provided by MDS.'"[100] The court upheld the FCC's decision to preempt based on the burden the state's regulation would impose on interstate MDS development. It is significant that the FCC chose to base its preemption on exercise of its Title III powers with respect to MDS, rather than Title II jurisdiction.[101] This avoided the question of possible conflict with Subsection 2(b) of the Act.[102]

An especially important point is that the Second Circuit, citing *Brookhaven* and *NARUC v. FCC* (the SMRS decision), stressed a conclusion that would influence the D.C. Circuit in *CCIA v. FCC:*

> [T]he FCC's preemption order is not invalidated by its failure to impose its own regulations directly upon MATV systems which are used to distribute MDS signals.
> . . . *Federal regulation need not be heavy-handed in order to preempt state regulation.*[103]

(1976). But Congress reversed the result of the FCC's *California Water* decision without affecting the decision's underlying rationale, since the FCC's responsibility under Section 224, as a distinct statutory assignment, does not come within the ambit of the Commission's other responsibilities under Title II. While the result, and spirit, of the *California Water* decision seem to be anomalies, it should be emphasized that the Commission did not find exercise of jurisdiction to be reasonably ancillary to attainment of statutory objectives; a supportable finding of this character would have been, in all likelihood, upheld by a reviewing court.

[98]573 F.2d 765 (2d Cir. 1978), *cert. denied sub nom.* NARUC v. Brookhaven Cable TV, Inc., 441 U.S. 904 (1979).

[99]669 F.2d 58 (2d Cir. 1982).

[100]*Id.* at 63 (quoting Orth-O-Vision, Inc., 69 F.C.C.2d 657, 658 (1978)).

[101]*See* Orth-O-Vision, Inc., 69 F.C.C.2d 657, 666, 44 R.R.2d 329, 339 (1978), *recon. denied,* 82 F.C.C.2d 178, 48 R.R.2d 503 (1980), *aff'd sub nom.* New York State Comm'n on Cable Television v. FCC, 669 F.2d 58 (2d Cir. 1982).

[102]*See* United States v. Southwestern Cable Co., *supra* note 76, 392 U.S. 157, 168-69 n.29.

[103]669 F.2d at 66, emphasis added. The D.C. Circuit would adopt the Second Circuit's reasoning that preemptive federal regulation need not be heavy-handed; *see* CCIA v. FCC, *infra* note 133, 693 F.2d at 217. Cf. NARUC v. FCC, *supra* note 87, 533 F.2d 601, 616 (D.C. Cir. 1976), which suggests that the court viewed preemption doubtfully where the effect would be leaving the activities in question regulated by neither federal nor state authorities. In Earth Satellite Communications, Inc., 95 F.C.C.2d 1223 (1983), 55 R.R.2d 1427, *recon. denied,* FCC 84-206 (May 14, 1984), *appeal pending sub nom.* New York State Comm'n on Cable Television v. FCC, No. 83-2160 (D.C. Cir. November 8, 1983), the FCC clarified its preemption policy, affirming that it had previously

In 1984, the Supreme Court in *Capital Cities Cable, Inc. v. Crisp*[104] reversed the Tenth Circuit (which had reversed a district court decision granting summary judgment to the cable firm seeking declaratory and injunctive relief directed against the State of Oklahoma). The Court concluded that Oklahoma's prohibition against cable television firms retransmitting out-of-state commercials for alcoholic beverages conflicts with the FCC's preemptive regulatory scheme which, among other things, requires cable companies to retransmit television signals. The Court reviewed the cable television case law discussed *supra* and applied it to preempt the state.

> [B]y requiring cable television operators to delete commercial advertising contained in signals carried pursuant to federal authority, the State has clearly exceeded that limited jurisdiction [allowed to the state by FCC policy] and interfered with a regulatory area that the [FCC] has explicitly preempted.[105]
>
> * * * * * *
>
> [A]s we have repeatedly explained, when federal officials determine, as the FCC has here, that restrictive regulation of a particular area is not in the public interest, "States are not permitted to use their police power to enact such a regulation."[106]

In summary, the significance of the cable television cases just discussed lies, *first,* in the jurisdictional conclusions of the various courts, and *second,* in the FCC's preemptive action founded on this jurisdictional base. The courts have been willing to find authority within the terms of the Act when persuaded that the FCC's exercise of jurisdiction is either part of, or reasonably ancillary to, the effective performance of the Commission's statutory responsibilities. But where the Commission's action seems to approach the limits of what is "reasonably ancillary," affirmance is hedged with doubts (*United States v. Midwest Video, supra*); where the courts believe that the FCC's action is beyond these limits, the Commission will be reversed (Eighth Circuit 1978 decision in *Midwest Video v. FCC, supra; NARUC v. FCC, supra*). And the courts will not countenance the imposition of common carrier obligations on non-common carriers, *i.e.,* cable television firms, just as it will not permit imposition of such obligations on broadcasters (*FCC v. Midwest Video, supra*). Finally, jurisdiction being upheld, the courts will affirm appropriate preemptive action of the Commission—which action need not be "heavy-handed" (*Brookhaven, supra; New York State Comm'n, supra*).

Let us see how the doctrine of these cable television cases applies with respect to broader common carrier-related issues.

---

preempted the states from exercising jurisdiction over Satellite Master Antenna (SMATV) Systems which normally serve residents of private multi-unit dwellings by receive-only satellite earth stations and a master antenna system picking up over-the-air broadcasts. In Community Cable TV, Inc., 95 F.C.C.2d 1204, 54 R.R.2d 1351 (1983), *recon. denied,* 56 R.R.2d 735 (1984), the FCC refused to limit its preemption of state and local rate regulation of cable television services; an order of the Nevada Commission seeking to regulate all cable television service other than "pay channel services" was preempted.

[104]104 S.Ct. 2694 (1984).
[105]*Id.* at 2703.
[106]*Id.* at 2705.

5.5.4 FCC Preemption of "CPE" Interconnection

In the late 1960s, the FCC started to break with the past. Dissatisfied with the essentially non-competitive nature of domestic telecommunications, the Commission moved to pry open closed doors; the first goal became opening the provision of Customer Premises Equipment ("CPE") to non-telephone company competition. This led to the *Carterfone* decision in 1968.[107] State commission resistance to these FCC policies would yield the keystone preemption cases in the common carrier field.

In 1973, actions by the North Carolina and Nebraska commissions raised the possibility that certain states might prevent interconnection of CPE other than that furnished by telephone companies. The FCC decided to issue a declaratory ruling asserting primacy over the terms and conditions governing the interconnection of CPE to the nationwide telephone network.[108]

On appeal to the Fourth Circuit, the FCC did not have to rely on "ancillary" jurisdiction; the court accepted the agency's position that in preempting the states it was discharging its responsibilities under Sections 201 through 205 of the Act.[109] *"North Carolina I"* therefore upheld the FCC's assertion of preemptive power. The Subsection 2(b) exemption was limited to local services, facilities and disputes "that in their nature and effect are separable from and do not substantially affect the conduct or development of interstate communications."[110] Finding that CPE interconnection necessarily affects interstate as well as intrastate communication, the court emphasized the limited impact of Subsection 2(b):

> [W]e are not persuaded that Section 2(b) sanctions any state regulation, formally restrictive only of intrastate communication, that in effect encroaches substantially upon the Commission's authority under Sections 201 through 205.[111]
>
> * * * * *
>
> [T]he purpose of Section 2(b) is to restrain the Commission from interfering with those essentially local incidents and practices of common carriage by wire that do

---

[107]Carterfone. 13 F.C.C.2d 420, 13 R.R.2d 597 (1968), *recon. denied,* 14 F.C.C.2d 571, 14 R.R.2d 185 (1968). The FCC, building on Hush-A-Phone Corp., *supra* note 51, held unlawful various Bell tariff restrictions which prohibited the use of the Carterfone and other interconnecting devices without regard to actual harm caused to the telephone system. 14 F.C.C.2d at 572. While the holding of Carterfone was narrow, its implications led to a revision of telephone company tariffs, eliminating the prohibition against "foreign attachments." *See also* Mebane Home Tel. Co., 53 F.C.C.2d 473, 33 R.R.2d 1629 (1975), *aff'd sub nom.* Mebane Home Tel. Co. v. FCC, 535 F.2d 1324 (D.C. Cir. 1976), where the Commission recognized the effect of the Carterfone principle to include PBX's, key systems, and other substitutions for telephone system equipment; and Primary Instrument Concept, 68 F.C.C.2d 1157, 43 R.R.2d 1205 (1978), where the Commission refused to curtail the choice available to individual customers.
[108]Telerent Leasing Corp. 45 F.C.C.2d 204, 29 R.R.2d 553 (1974), *aff'd sub nom.* North Carolina Util. Comm'n v. FCC, 537 F.2d 787 (4th Cir. 1976) ("North Carolina I"), *cert. denied,* 429 U.S. 1027 (1976). *See* D. O. Stewart, *Competition in the Telephone Equipment Industry: Beyond Telerent,* 86 Yale L. J. 538 (1977).
[109]North Carolina I, *supra* note 108, 537 F.2d at 792.
[110]*Id.* at 792.
[111]*Id.* at 793-94, footnotes and citations omitted. *See* the reference to Subsection 2(b) as "'merely a perfecting amendment'" in United States v. Southwestern Cable, *supra* note 76, 392 U.S. at 169 n.29.

not substantially encroach upon the administration and development of the interstate telephone network.[112]

In rejecting Subsection 2(b) arguments, the court noted "that for some 30
years FCC had viewed and treated section 2(b)(1) of the Act as imposing no bar
to its exercise of jurisdiction over facilities used in connection with both intrastate
and interstate telephone communications. . . .;"[113] and "Congress cannot have
been unaware" of this fact. In relation to Section 410 of the Act, "Congressional
design" was deemed to conflict "with the present contention that Section 2(b) is
intended to deprive the Commission of jurisdiction over the use of facilities that
necessarily serve both interstate and intrastate communications."[114] Based on
legislative history, the jurisdictional exclusion of Subsection 221(b) was held to
apply only in the case of a service area straddling state borderlines.[115] Finally, the
court noted that "rate making typifies those activities of the telephone industry
which lend themselves to practical separation of the local from the interstate in
such a way that local regulation of one does not interfere with national regulation
of the other."[116]

The next step was the FCC's adoption of its Registration Program (47 C.F.R. §
68.1 *et seq.*) to prescribe the conditions under which CPE may be interconnected
with the telephone network. *"North Carolina II"*[117] followed *North Carolina I,*

---

[112]*Id.* at 794 n.6. The Fourth Circuit's reading of Subsection 2(b) would be followed by the Fourth
Circuit itself, North Carolina II, *infra* note 117, 552 F.2d at 1045-47; by the D.C. Circuit, CCIA v.
FCC, *infra* note 133, 693 F.2d at 215; by the First Circuit, Puerto Rico Tel. Co. v. FCC, 553 F.2d
694, 699-700 (1st Cir. 1977); and by the Second Circuit, New York Tel. Co. v. FCC, *infra* note 126,
631 F.2d at 1066.

[113]*Id.* at 795.

[114]*Id.* at 794.

[115]*Id.* at 795, footnote omitted. *See infra* note 39. Judge Widener's dissent, *Id.* at 796 *et seq.*,
argued against restricting the effect of Subsection 221(b) to a "straddling" situation. North Carolina
II, *infra* note 117, adopted the *North Carolina I* conclusion on Subsection 221(b). 552 F.2d at 1045.

[116]*Id.* at 793 n.6. In CCIA v. FCC, *infra* note 133, the D.C. Circuit rejected the argument that state
ratemaking is not preemptible; the D.C. Circuit saw no distinction between state ratemaking and other
state powers in terms of FCC preemption. 693 F.2d at 216.

[117]North Carolina Util. Comm'n v. FCC, 552 F.2d 1036 (4th Cir. 1977) ("North Carolina II"), *cert.
denied,* 434 U.S. 874 (1977). The Fourth Circuit addressed again the subscriber's right to use his
telephone equipment in ways that are "privately beneficial without being publicly detrimental,"
citing Hush-A-Phone, *supra* note 51, 238 F.2d at 269, in Fort Mill Tel. Co. v. FCC, 719 F.2d 89 (4th
Cir. 1983). The *Fort Mill* decision upheld the subscriber's right to interconnect his PBX with Southern
Bell Tel. Co. in North Carolina, rather than interconnecting with Fort Mill Tel. Co. in South
Carolina, where the subscriber's contiguous property extended across both the state and service area
borderlines. In *Fort Mill,* the Fourth Circuit affirmed Heritage Village Church, 88 F.C.C.2d 1436
(1982).

In a reaffirmation of the *Telerent* principle, the FCC struck down a rule of the Oklahoma
commission requiring vendors of CPE to obtain a certificate of authority from the Oklahoma
commission. Commercial Communications, Inc., 81 F.C.C.2d 106, 48 R.R.2d 616 (1980). Similarly, the FCC concluded that interpretation of an intrastate tariff to prohibit two subscribers in
adjacent buildings from sharing a single customer-provided PBX constitutes unreasonable interference with use of customer-provided CPE. Com. Services, Inc. v. Murraysville Tel. Co., 87
F.C.C.2d 664, 49 R.R.2d 1425 (1981).

The FCC did not preempt state tariff regulation of CPE in Diamond International Corp. v. AT&T,
70 F.C.C.2d 656, 659-60 (1979), *aff'd sub nom.* Diamond International Corp. v. FCC, 627 F.2d 489

supra, on all essential points. Again, the decision was based on an invocation of Title II authority rather than "ancillary" jurisdiction.[118] Of particular interest was the following discussion disposing of arguments that the Registration Program would be an assumption of power similar to the ICC's in *Shreveport*[119]:

> Petitioners correctly point out that in enacting the Communications Act, Congress sought to deny the FCC the kind of jurisdiction over local rates approved by the *Shreveport Rate Case.* . . . Congress' dissatisfaction with the *Shreveport* doctrine was that it permitted the ICC to control the *rates* for exclusively local service because of the relationship between those rates and the interstate rates. But the FCC's registration program in no way purports to prescribe charges for local services; state commissions remain unfettered in their discretion to set rates for all local services and facilities provided by the telephone companies. *Shreveport* dealt specifically with rates for services which were admittedly local in nature; this appeal concerns the definition of what services and facilities are "intrastate" and hence subject to state rather than federal control.[120]

5.5.5 FCC Preemption: Opening Common Carrier Service to Competition

While the foregoing chain of events proceeded, a parallel series of developments, informed by much the same spirit, was occurring on other fronts. The FCC opened to competition the provision of interstate common carrier services, first on a limited scale; then, following the *"Execunet I"* and *"Execunet II"* decisions, the FCC expanded this policy to embrace the full range of services.[121]

In view of the line of cases discussed earlier, it is no surprise that the D.C. Circuit, in *California v. FCC,* concluded the FCC could regulate the provision of "interstate service" by "Other Common Carriers" or "OCCs" even though the facilities were located entirely within a single state.[122] FCC jurisdiction was established when the facilities were found to constitute " 'an integral part of a

---

(D.C. Cir. 1980). Also, the Ninth Circuit affirmed dismissal of a customer's complaint involving state-tariffed CPE in [McDonnell] Douglas Corp. v. General Tel. Co. of California, 594 F.2d 720, 723-25 (1979); but the FCC had made no attempt to assert jurisdiction in the McDonnell Douglas case. State regulation of CPE was later foreclosed by the FCC's decision in *Second Computer Inquiry. See* CCIA v. FCC, *infra* note 133.

[118]*Id.* at 1051-52.

[119]*See supra* note 16.

[120]North Carolina II, 552 F.2d at 1047.

[121]*See* Microwave Communications, Inc., 18 F.C.C.2d 953, 16 R.R.2d 1037 (1969), *reconsideration,* 21 F.C.C.2d 190, 18 R.R.2d 226 (1970); Washington Util. & Transp. Comm'n v. FCC, 513 F.2d 1142, 1155 *et seq.* (9th Cir. 1975), *cert. denied sub nom.* NARUC v. FCC, 423 U.S. 836 (1975); Bell Tel. Co. of Pennsylvania v. FCC, 503 F.2d 1250 (3d Cir. 1974), *Cert. denied sub. hom.* AT&T v. FCC, 422 U.S. 1026 (1975), *reh'g denied,* 423 U.S. 886 (1975); AT&T, Docket 20099, 52 F.C.C.2d 727 (1975); MCI Telecommunications Corp. v. FCC, 561 F.2d 365, 377-80 (D.C. Cir. 1977) ("Execunet I"), *cert. denied sub nom.* USITA v. MCI Telecommunications Corp., 434 U.S. 1040 (1978); *compliance directed,* 580 F.2d 590 (D.C. Cir. 1978) ("Execunet II"), *cert. denied sub nom.* USITA v. MCI Telecommunications Corp., 439 U.S. 980 (1978); MCI Telecommunications Corp. v. FCC, 712 F.2d 517 (D.C. Cir. 1983); MTS and WATS Market Structure, 81 F.C.C.2d 177, 183 (1980).

[122]567 F.2d 84, 86 (D.C. Cir. 1977), *cert. denied,* 434 U.S. 1010 (1978).

dedicated interstate communications network.'"[123] The Court added that the FCC "may regulate facilities used in both inter- and intrastate communications to the extent it proves 'technically and practically difficult' to separate the two types of communications."[124] The effect of this decision was that the pro-competitive policies of the FCC could not be blocked by state commissions, even though, in fact, users could employ the "dedicated" interstate network for essentially intrastate communications.[125]

In relation to the price for interconnection, the Second Circuit upheld FCC action preventing New York Telephone Company from collecting a discriminatory surcharge on users of certain interstate services. These surcharges— which were imposed under directions issued by the New York State Public Service Commission—ranged up to 1600% higher than the charge for comparable services to intrastate users.[126] The question of a definitive FCC policy governing rates and terms of end user interconnection to the interstate network, and governing the rates and terms of interexchange carrier interconnection to exchange facilities, is being addressed in the Commission's CC Docket Nos. 78-72 and 83-1145.[127]

5.5.6 Resale of Service

The resale and shared use of common carrier service was typically prohibited by tariff until the FCC found such restrictions unlawful—first as to interstate private line service[128] and then as to interstate toll and WATS.[129] The FCC later decided that resale or shared-use restrictions may not be lawfully applied to "physically intrastate" WATS used in interstate communication.[130] The Commission stressed

---

[123]Id.

[124]Id. For an indicator of Commission attitude, see AT&T Co. (F.C.C. Tariff No. 270 1.544 Mbps), supra note 39, where the Commission directed provision of a kind of private line service at interstate rates whenever the customer requests such service for interstate use. The ambiguity in the tariffs at issue was to be construed in favor of the customer; meanwhile tariff language was to be revised to remove ambiguity.

[125]See Southern Pacific Communication Co. v. Corporation Comm'n of Oklahoma, 586 P.2d 327 (1978). Letters written to OCCs by the FCC staff in 1978 said the Commission asserted no jurisdiction over "any communications service (voice or non-voice) between any two points within the same state where the charge for such service is made on a usage basis." See infra note 148.

[126]The FCC ruled that New York Tel. Co. must file tariffs with the FCC if the company charges discriminatory rates for interstate users of certain private line services. New York Tel. Co. v. FCC, 631 F.2d 1059, 1067 (2d Cir. 1980). The Second Circuit adopted the Fourth Circuit's interpretation (under North Carolina I, supra note 108 and North Carolina II, supra note 117) of Subsection 221(b), at 1064-65, and Subsection 2(b), at 1066. See also Pacific Tel. & Tel. Co., 88 F.C.C.2d 934 (1981), recon. denied, FCC 82-545 (December 15, 1984).

[127]See supra note 2.

[128]Resale and Shared Use of Common Carrier Services and Facilities, 60 F.C.C.2d 261, 38 R.R.2d 141 (1976), reconsideration, 62 F.C.C.2d 588, 39 R.R.2d 765 (1977), aff'd sub nom. AT&T v. FCC, 572 F.2d 17 (2d Cir. 1978), cert. denied sub nom. IBM v. FCC, 439 U.S. 875 (1978).

[129]Resale and Shared Use of Common Carrier Services and Facilities, 83 F.C.C.2d 167, 48 R.R.2d 1067 (1980).

[130]AT&T Co., 94 F.C.C.2d 1110, 1112 n.4, 53 R.R.2d 112 (1983), aff'd sub nom. NARUC v. FCC, Nos. 83-1354 and 83-1360, slip. op. (D.C. Cir. October 26, 1984).

that "jurisdiction turns on the nature of the communications, rather than the location of the facilities links through which they pass;" and concluded that resale and sharing restrictions contained in intrastate WATS tariffs could not be invoked by telephone companies where the effect is to bar resale and shared use of interstate communications.[131]

5.5.7 The "Computer Inquiry" and the "Second Computer Inquiry": preempting state regulation of "CPE" and "Enhanced Services"

In 1973, the Second Circuit upheld the FCC in its (First) *Computer Inquiry* decision restricting telephone companies, including "connecting carriers," from the provision of data processing services to others except through a fully separated subsidiary; but the court struck down restrictions the Commission would have imposed on any such fully separated, and unregulated, subsidiary.[132]

In 1980, the Commission's *Second Computer Inquiry* found that the furnishing of "CPE" and "enhanced services" by telephone companies should be deregulated, *i.e.*, not subject to regulation at the state or federal levels. In *CCIA v. FCC*,[133] the D.C. Circuit affirmed on all points, specifically rejecting arguments

---

[131]*Id.* at 1114. Upholding the Commission's decision, the D.C. Circuit in NARUC v. FCC, *supra* note 130, limited the effect of the Subsection 2(b) jurisdiction exclusion to "purely intrastate communications." Judge Bork's opinion, citing the consistent holdings of "Every court that has considered the matter," stated that "purely intrastate facilities and services used to complete *even a single interstate call* may become subject to FCC regulation to the extent of their interstate use." (emphasis added.)

Rejecting various theories proposed by NARUC, the court said that "the Commission must be free to strike down the costly and inefficient burdens on interstate communications which are sometimes imposed by state regulation." Noting that the FCC's ruling is specifically limited to WATS connections used to terminate communications originating in other states, so it does not extend to tariff restrictions which pertain solely to intrastate WATS, the D.C. Circuit found the ruling within the FCC's broad powers. "[T]he purpose of the Communications Act would be frustrated by any other conclusion." NARUC v. FCC, *supra* note 130, slip op.

[132]GTE Service Corp. v. FCC, 474 F.2d 724, 731, 733-37 (2d Cir. 1973).

[133]Second Computer Inquiry, Docket 20828, Final Decision, 77 F.C.C.2d 384 (1980), *reconsideration,* 84 F.C.C.2d 50 (1980), *further consideration,* 88 F.C.C.2d 512 (1981), *aff'd sub nom.* Computer and Communications Industry Ass'n v. FCC ("CCIA v. FCC"), 693 F.2d 198, 214-18 (D.C. Cir. 1982), *cert. denied sub nom.* Louisiana Pub. Service Comm'n v. FCC, 103 S. Ct. 2109 (1983); *further recon. denied,*—F.C.C.2d—, 56 R.R.2d 301 (1984). In its *Second Computer Inquiry* decision, the FCC reexamined the rule established in 1971 and modified after GTE Service Corp. v. FCC, *supra* note 132, generally restricting telephone companies from furnishing data processing services except through a fully separated subsidiary. The former rule was replaced by a new rule which required the deregulation of "enhanced service" as well as CPE, and which imposed various restrictions on the Bell System, notably that the Bell System companies could not furnish either enhanced services or CPE, except through fully separated subsidiaries. As with the CPE aspect of the decision, the Commission's decision on enhanced services was affirmed on all points by the D.C. Circuit. For a more detailed discussion of the *Computer Inquiry* and the *Second Computer Inquiry, see* Frieden, *The Computer Inquiries: Mapping the Communications/Information Processing Terrain,* 33 FED. COMM. L.J. 55 (1981). "Enhanced services" were defined to refer to "services, offered over common carrier transmission facilities used in interstate communications, which employ computer processing applications that act on the format, content, code, protocol or similar aspects of the subscriber's transmitted information; provide the subscriber additional, different, or restructured information; or involve subscriber interaction with stored information." (47 CFR § 64.702). In Illinois Bell Tel. Co. v. FCC, 740 F.2d 465 (7th Cir. 1984), the FCC was upheld in continuing to apply the *Second Computer Inquiry* restrictions to the divested Bell Operating Companies.

raised by NARUC and various state commissions based on the Subsection 2(b) and 221(b) exclusions. Since the FCC's preemptive action as to both CPE and enhanced services was this time based on "ancillary" jurisdiction,[134] the decision represents a convergence of the *Southwestern Cable* and the *North Carolina* lines of cases—producing a sweeping result of remarkable implications.

There were two alternative grounds for the Commission's deregulation of CPE and enhanced services: (i) enhanced services and CPE are not common carrier services within the scope of Title II; and (ii) the Commission may forbear from Title II regulation "where . . . it finds that it cannot feasibly separate regulable from nonregulable services." The D.C. Circuit affirmed on both of these grounds.[135]

The court found not irrational the Commission's essential factual conclusion that the only way to give consumers an unfettered choice of CPE was to require that charges for CPE be completely severed from transmission rates on both the federal and state levels. The court upheld FCC primacy, recognizing that consumers use the same CPE in both interstate and intrastate communications and generally wish to purchase both interstate and intrastate transmission services, and based on the FCC's supported findings that state regulation would be "detrimental to both the consumer and the interstate communication system."[136]

On Subsection 221(b), the D.C. Circuit adopted the *North Carolina* interpretation that the provision applies only to jurisdictional questions arising from a metropolitan area straddling a state line; and explicitly rejected the analysis of Subsection 221(b) contained in *Kitchen v. FCC.*[137]

The court disposed of arguments "that the Commission has unlawfully attempted to preempt state regulation of dual use CPE by creating a vacuum of deregulation" and "that preemption can be accomplished only by affirmative regulation that occupies the field," by adopting the "needy-not-be-heavy-

---

[134]The court said that *Southwestern Cable* settled "beyond peradventure that the Commission may assert jurisdiction under [Subsection 2(a)] of the Act over activities that are not within the reach of Title II . . . . [H]owever, the Supreme Court limited the Commission's jurisdiction to that which is 'reasonably ancillary to the effective performance of the Commission's various responsibilities.' One of those responsibilities is to assure a nationwide system of wire communications services at reasonable prices." The court concluded: "In [the *Second Computer Inquiry*] the Commission found that the exercise of ancillary jurisdiction over both enhanced services and CPE was necessary to assure wire communications services at reasonable rates. . . . We believe this conclusion is well founded." 693 F.2d at 213.

[135]*Id.* at 210. The court emphasized "that [its] sanction is a very narrow one, given in light of the peculiar nature of the communications and data processing industries and the alternate regulatory scheme [competition] adopted by the Commission" (at 210). Notwithstanding these reservations, the Commission has, in Competitive Carrier, CC Docket No. 79-252, moved ahead to apply "forbearance" (in the form of eliminating tariff and Section 214 requirements) to such entities as resellers and OCCs. *See* Fourth Report and Order, 95 F.C.C.2d 554, 56 R.R.2d 1219 (1983), *reconsideration,*—F.C.C.2d—, 56 R.R.2d 1204 (1984). The Commission has used the term "forbearance" as equivalent to deference to state authority. *See Common Carrier Services,* Second Report and Order in CC Docket No. 79-252, 91 F.C.C.2d 59, 66-67 (1982), discussing several examples of such forbearance.

[136]*Id.* at 215.

[137]*Id.* at 216-17. *See* Kitchen v. FCC, 464 F.2d at 803.

handed" theme from *Brookhaven* and *New York State Commission on Cable Television:*

> These parties misapprehend the Commission's actions. Although the Commission has discontinued Title II regulation of CPE, it has substituted a different, *affirmative* regulatory scheme [i.e. competition] through its ancillary jurisdiction. . . . It is clear to us that the *Computer II* regulations embody a comprehensive federal regulatory scheme, including rules governing the marketing of CPE by common carriers. We agree with the Second Circuit: "Federal regulation need not be heavy-handed in order to preempt state regulation."[138]

The *CCIA* decision extended the reasoning of *North Carolina I* and *North Carolina II* in finding that Subsection 2(b) does not prohibit preemption of state tariffing of CPE. The court pointed out that the FCC has "neither attempted to set rates for intrastate communications services or facilities nor as [serted] jurisdiction over matters of state concern because of intrastate discrimination against interstate business;" but rather, the Commission has "here exercised its direct authority to determine the regulatory treatment of CPE used for interstate communications."[139] Responding to state commission arguments that continued tariffing of CPE is the best way to protect the interest of consumers, the court concluded that the FCC's decision was neither arbitrary, capricious, nor an abuse of discretion.[140]

Further, the D.C. Circuit saw no distinction between preemption principles applicable to state ratemaking and those applicable to other state powers. The court reasoned that preemption was proper based either on the principles that demanded state preemption in the *North Carolina* cases,[141] or on the wording of the Act itself: "conflicting federal and state regulations regarding dual use of CPE are no more acceptable under the Act when equipment rates are involved, as here, than when interconnection policies are involved, as in the [*North Carolina*] cases."[142]

In the author's view, the court was entirely correct in observing that the same preemption principles apply "to state ratemaking authority and . . . to other state powers."[143] But the *impact* of these principles may be different in the case of ratemaking. *Separability* of interstate and intrastate elements is a key factor in applying the preemption principles discussed in the cases;[144] and in fact there has

---

[138]*Id.* at 217, quoting New York State Comm'n on Cable Television v. FCC, 669 F.2d at 66, *supra* note 99, and citing Brookhaven Cable TV, Inc. v. FCC, *supra* note 98. *Compare* Judge Wilkey's Opinion in NARUC v. FCC, *supra* note 87, 533 F.2d at 616, intimating that the replacement of state regulation by federal non-regulation would be questionable.

[139]*Id.* at 216.

[140]*Id.* at 217.

[141]*Id.* at 216.

[142]*Id.*

[143]*Id.*

[144]*Id.* at 215 (quoting with approval *North Carolina I, supra* note 108, at 793): "[S]ection 2(b) deprives the Commission of power over local services or facilities only where 'their nature and effect are separable from and do not substantially affect the conduct or development of interstate communications.'"

been separate federal and state tariff regulation since 1910.[145] Thus, in *California v. FCC*, the Commission exercised jurisdiction over "facilities used in both inter- and intrastate communications to the extent it proves 'technically and practically difficult' to separate the two types of communications;"[146] but the FCC "refused to assert jurisdiction over those purely local services that could be practically separated from inter-state services supplied through the same facilities . . . leaving any regulation over such service to the appropriate state bodies."[147] Another example is the 1978 notification to OCCs by the FCC staff[148] that the FCC asserted no jurisdiction over "any communications service (voice or non-voice) between any two points within the same state where the charge for such service is made on a usage basis." And in the *MOB* case, the Commission refused to accede to the demands of the Department of Defense that the Main Operating Base (MOB) console—tariffed in part at the state level—should be tariffed entirely at the FCC; the decision relied on the "separate interstate and intrastate functions" performed by components of the console "in an electrically non-integrated manner," which made it "irrelevant that the equipment, for convenience sake, is assembled in a single console."[149]

Even if there is separability in the first instance between interstate and intrastate elements, the second part of the test applied in the *North Carolina* cases and *CCIA v. FCC* may justify FCC preemption—where the local services or facilities "substantially affect the conduct or development of interstate communica-

---

[145]*See supra* note 13.

[146]567 F.2d at 86 (quoting AT&T, 56 F.C.C.2d 14, 19 (1975)).

[147]*Id.*

[148]*See supra* note 125. Thus, the Chief of the FCC's Common Carrier Bureau rejected tariff revisions filed by ITT Corporate Communications Services, Inc. (ITT-CCS) that would have allowed customers for ITT-CCS's Switched Private Network Service (SPNS) to place calls among cities in the same state and within a city, with specific usage charges on a per-minute basis for such intrastate calls. Among the reasons for rejection was the jurisdictional limitation of Subsection 2(b)(1). Relying principally on California v. FCC, the Chief's rejection letter to ITT said:

The Commission has the authority to regulate interstate communication [citing Section 1], but does not have jurisdiction over intrastate communication [citing Section 2(b)]. It is undisputed the ITT-CCS intends to charge for interstate SPNS calls on a per-minute basis, as it already charges for intrastate SPNS calls. *This means that the individual communications over the SPNS network can readily be separated as either interstate or intrastate.*

The nature of the communications which pass through the facilities is the pertinent factor . . . . [citations] . . . . [T]he Commission has jurisdiction over facilities that are an "integral part of the dedicated interstate communications network." [citation.] However, the Commission does not have jurisdiction with respect to "charges, classifications, practices, services, facilities or regulations for or in connection with intrastate communications services. . . ." [citing Subsection 2(b)(1)] Although some tariffs on file with the Commission offer services involving facilities which carry both interstate and intrastate communications, the nature of these tariff offerings is such that the charges are applied on a fulltime basis (e.g., with private line services) rather than on a per-call basis. Therefore, the Commission has ruled that it has jurisdiction over such offerings. [citation.] *In contrast, this tariff filing involves charges on a per-call basis, in which case the intrastate communications are separable from the interstate ones. . . .*

Letter of the Chief, Common Carrier Bureau, dated November 8, 1978, to M.J. Nelligan, ITT-CCS (emphasis added).

[149]68 F.C.C.2d at 42. *See supra* note 60.

tions."[150] Thus, the Second Circuit upheld FCC action preventing the imposition of a discriminatory surcharge on interstate customers imposed by tariffs regulated at the state level.[151] But absent an FCC finding that facilities or services substantially affect interstate communications, there will be no preemption where there is separability of interstate and intrastate elements; and historically the Commission has made no general application of preemptive power preventing the states from tariff regulation of communication service connecting points within a state.[152]

In summary, while the same principles governing preemption under the Act apply to state ratemaking as to other state powers, the practical effect of these principles may be different in view of the long-standing recognition by the FCC of ratemaking separability.

5.5.8 Depreciation Preemption

The FCC recognized that the introduction of competition would dictate fundamental changes in the way telephone companies should be allowed to operate. After an extensive study of depreciation practices, the Commission concluded, over the objections of a number of state commissions, that certain changes in these practices were necessary in light of the new environment of competition and dynamic technology, notwithstanding likely short-term increases in revenue requirements for the companies involved.[153] The Commission also concluded that certain changes should be made in telephone company accounting practices related to "station connections" (which includes wiring and other equipment at the customer's premises apart from CPE) so as to place the burden of costs associated therewith on the cost-causative ratepayer.[154]

In a March, 1981 decision, the Commission ordered telephone companies, among other things, to implement a program of expensing station connection costs, phased in over four years, and to amortize embedded station connection costs over a ten-to-fourteen year period.[155] Responding to petitions filed by NARUC and the California commission, the FCC, in a decision released in April, 1982, reached the remarkable conclusion that "state commissions are not

---

[150]*See supra* note 144.

[151]New York Tel. Co. v. FCC, 631 F.2d 1059, 1066 (2d Cir. 1980); "Even if the local exchange service is separable technologically and in terms of cost assessment . . . , there is no doubt that the . . . surcharge . . . substantially affects the conduct or development of interstate communication and encroaches on FCC authority."

[152]As commented by the Fourth Circuit in *North Carolina I*: "rate making typifies those activities of the telephone industry which lend themselves to practical separation of the local from the interstate in such a way that local regulation of one does not interfere with national regulation of the other." 537 F.2d at 793 n.6.

[153]Property Depreciation, 83 F.C.C.2d 267, 281-84 (1980), *reconsideration,* 87 F.C.C.2d 916, *Supplemental Opinion and Order,* 87 F.C.C.2d 1112 (1981).

[154]Amendment of Part 31, 85 F.C.C.2d 818 (1981); *reconsideration,* 89 F.C.C.2d 1094 (1982); *further reconsideration,* 92 F.C.C.2d 864 (1983) (herein the "Depreciation Preemption Order"), *aff'd sub nom.* Virginia State Corporation Comm'n v. FCC, 737 F.2d 388 (4th Cir. 1984).

[155]85 F.C.C.2d at 828-30.

precluded from using their own accounting and depreciation procedures for intrastate ratemaking purpose[s]."[156] Petitions were then filed by AT&T and the GTE telephone companies; the *Depreciation Preemption Order* reversed the prior decision on all points. This order concluded that "this Commission's depreciation policies and rates, including the expensing of inside wiring, preempt inconsistent state depreciation policies and rates."[157]

The stated rationale for the *Depreciation Preemption Order* started with the conclusion that the Commission's decision on expensing station connections involved questions of depreciation policy, since "the decision to expense is a determination that there is no category of asset for which depreciation expense will be allowed."[158] The Commission concluded: "The legislative history . . . supports the actual language of Section 220(b) and indicates that Congress intended to preempt state commission jurisdiction over depreciation rates for subject carriers when it recodified the language from the Interstate Commerce Act."[159]

The Commission noted that the "setting of depreciation rates is not an essentially local incident or practice" and has substantial effects upon the "administration and development of the interstate telephone network."[160] The Commission therefore concluded that preemption would be justified "to avoid frustration of validly adopted federal policies," even absent automatic preemption under Subsection 220(b) of the Act.[161] Here the Commission stressed its conclusion that inadequate capital recovery at the state level would frustrate accomplishment of FCC policy.[162] Further, the FCC reasoned that state action preventing carriers from utilizing the FCC's depreciation prescriptions for all purposes could undermine "the Commission's objective to develop policies that will engender a dynamic, efficient telecommunications marketplace with services being provided at reasonable prices."[163] Finally, the Commission found further support for preemption in Section 410 of the Act, stressing the need for uniformity and equity for ratepayers and carriers.[164]

In the Fourth Circuit's decision affirming the Commission, Judge Murnaghan's Opinion agrees that the FCC's order "preempts state regulation of the depreciation rates and methods here involved [and] that 'FCC regulations must preempt any contrary state regulations where the efficiency . . . of the national communications network is at stake. . . .'"[165] Relying on the *North Carolina* line of cases, the court found it "unnecessary to decide whether, as a matter of law, the

[156]89 F.C.C.2d at 1095.
[157]92 F.C.C.2d at 880.
[158]*Id.* at 868.
[159]*Id.* at 873.
[160]*Id.* at 875, footnote omitted.
[161]*Id.*
[162]*Id.* at 876.
[163]*Id.* at 877.
[164]*Id.* at 878.
[165]*Virginia State Corporation Comm'n v. FCC, supra* note 154, 737 F.2d at 389-90.

language of the Act itself requires preemption."[166] The majority reasoned that "it cannot be said that depreciation policies are 'separable from' interstate communications. Indeed, the conduct and development of interstate communication would undoubtedly be affected by the states' imposition of depreciation policies that slowed capital recovery and innovation."[167] The court noted that "physical impossibility is but one ground for preemption; frustration of federal objectives provides a rationale at least equally valid."[168]

Judge Widener, who was the dissenter in the two *North Carolina* cases, dissented again. His underlying concern is reflected in the closing sentences of his Dissent: local ratepayers, as he sees it, will be required to finance the "benefits of competition."[169] Judge Widener's essential argument is grounded on the proposition that "communication carrier accounting has until now retained a clear division between its intrastate and interstate components, and this because of the Communications Act itself."[170] On this basis, Judge Widener argues that Subsection 220(b) does not require preemption and that the FCC has no *North Carolina*-type preemptive authority in this area.[171] Judge Widener exclaims:

> [I]f the FCC can achieve preemption of state-prescribed depreciation methods by reciting the shibboleth of encouraging competition with as little showing of federal-state conflict as it has made here, it has effectively written 47 U.S.C. §§ 152(b) and 221(b) out of the Communications Act. . . . The logical result of this decision is to permit the FCC to abrogate completely the state regulation of intrastate ratemaking for the carriers' intrastate operations in violation of the Communications Act.[172]

---

[166]*Id.* at 392.

[167]*Id.* at 395.

[168]*Id.* at 396.

[169]*Id.* at 399.

[170]*Id.* at 397.

[171]*Id.*

[172]*Id.* at 398. The Dissent refers to Subsection 221(b) without acknowledging the judicial limitation of that subsection to straddling cases. *See supra* note 39. A number of federal courts directed, on an interim basis, state commission compliance with FCC depreciation prescriptions.

See The Chesapeake and Potomac Tel. Co. of Maryland v. Maryland Public Service Comm'n, 560 F. Supp. 844 (D. Md. 1983), *petition for review pending,* No, 83-1403 (4th Cir. filed May 3, 1983); South Central Bell Tel. Co. v. Louisiana Public Service Comm'n, 570 F. Supp. 227 (D.C.M.D. La. 1983), *aff'd sub nom.* South Central Bell Tel. Co. v. Louisiana Public Service Comm'n, No. 83-3494, slip. op. (5th Cir. October 11, 1984); Southwestern Bell Tel. Co. v. Arkansas Public Service Comm'n, [] 738 F.2d 901, (8th Cir. 1984), *petition for certiorari pending,* No. 84-483, October Term, 1984; Northwestern Bell Tel. Co. v. Iowa State Commerce Comm'n, No. 83-688-A, slip. op. (S.D. Iowa September 27, 1984; Pacific Northwest Bell Tel. Co. v. Washington Util. and Transp. Comm'n, 565 F. Supp. 17 (W.D. Wash. 1983), *petition for review pending,* No. 83-3746 (9th Cir. filed April 7, 1983); Southwestern Bell Tel. Co. v. State Corporation Comm'n of Kansas, No. 83-4090, slip. op. (D. Kan. April 8, 1983).

Requests for similar injunctive relief have been denied in New England Tel. and Tel. Co. v. Public Util. Comm'n of Maine, No. 83-1779, slip. op. (1st Cir. June 29, 1984), *reversing* New England Tel. and Tel. Co. v. Public Util. Comm'n of Maine, 570 F. Supp. 1558 (C.D. Maine 1983); and New England Tel. and Tel. Co. v. Public Service Board of Vermont, 576 F. Supp. 490 (D. Vt. 1984), *petition for review pending.*, No. 84-7051 (2d Cir. filed June 27, 1984).

5.5.9 Preemption Concerning Interstate Toll Settlements

In 1983, the FCC granted a petition for declaratory ruling filed by Southern Bell Telephone and Telegraph Company (Southern Bell) with respect to an order issued by the Florida Public Service Commission that Southern Bell should make certain retroactive and prospective *interstate* toll settlement payments to an independent, General Telephone Company of Florida.[173] These payments would have resulted from the employment of seven calendar-day studies, rather than five-day studies, to calculate holding time minutes of use—a key factor in settlement calculations. Even though the Florida Commission had reconsidered its order, the FCC found that "recent and potential State actions have tended to create uncertainty regarding the scope of State authority," and, accordingly, that the FCC should address the issue.[174]

The FCC decided to preempt the Florida Commission's action, but limited its preemption to the specific type of actions taken by the Florida PSC.[175] The FCC said:

> [T]his Order preempts two types of State action. First, any action that requires the use of a particular time period in connections with actual use measurements for interstate toll settlements. Second, any action that requires the use of a particular time period in connection with such measurements for purposes of cost allocations between the interstate and intrastate jurisdictions.[176]

The FCC based its preemptive action on its broad plenary authority, particularly in the specific area in dispute:

> Acting in accordance with our statutory authority, we have established in the *Separations Manual* a comprehensive and pervasive regulatory scheme in the separations and settlements areas. The absence of specific provisions in the *Separations Manual* regarding time periods for actual use measurements does not open the way for the States to establish these time period requirements and impose them upon carriers.[177]

In addition, the FCC found a unique requirement with respect to the issue raised by Southern Bell's petition:

> We find that the specific subject matter of this proceeding, the jurisdictional allocation of common carrier costs and the subsequent division of interstate toll revenues, uniquely requires a uniform, nationwide regulatory scheme.[178]

---

[173]*Southern Bell Tel. and Tel. Co.,* 93 F.C.C.2d 1287, 53 R.R.2d 1649 (1983), *recon. denied,*— F.C.C.2d,—56 R.R.2d 605 (1984), *petition for review pending sub nom.* State Corporation Comm'n of the State of Kansas v. FCC, No. 84-2259 (10th Cir. September 13, 1984). *See also* Illinois Bell Tel Co. v. Illinois Commerce Comm'n, 740 F.2d 566 (7th Cir. 1984), where the district court was affirmed on the issuance of a preliminary injunction requiring the Illinois Commission to conform to the FCC's decision.
[174]*Id.* at 1290.
[175]*Id.* at 1306.
[176]*Id.* n.20.
[177]*Id.* at 1305-06.
[178]*Id.* at 1306.

And the FCC found that the Florida Commission's action would upset the FCC's decision on CC Docket No. 80-286 fixing a certain element in the allocation formula for Jurisdictional Separations.[179] However, the Commission declined to give a "broader sweep" to its preemptive authority in the separations and settlements areas.[180]

5.5.10 Implementation of CPE Deregulation

In granting approval of certain elements of AT&T's capitalization plan for its subsidiary, American Bell, Inc. (later known as AT&T Information Systems), under the requirements adopted in the *Second Computer Inquiry,* the FCC preempted state commission action that would prevent or delay the transfer of assets necessary for compliance with the FCC's policy effective January 1, 1983:

> The issue before us is whether individual state regulatory commissions should be permitted to disapprove those asset transfers which AT&T deems necessary for commencement of AmBell's provision of new CPE consistent with our Computer II policies. . . . [W]e authorize the transfer to AmBell of those assets that AT&T has earmarked for capitalization of AmBell as of January 1, 1983. In so doing, we preempt state action that would preclude the transfer of assets or delay the transfer of assets pending a state determination as to the apropriate transfer value.[181]

While not foreclosing the states from using alternative valuation methodologies for state ratemaking purposes, the FCC said that "state commissions may not condition approval of the January 1, 1983 asset transfers to AmBell on AT&T's use of a different valuation methodology," *i.e.,* different from the valuation methodology (adjusted net book) approved by the FCC on an interim basis pending the FCC's resolution of valuation questions.[182]

5.5.11 The United Telephone Case and Subsection 201(a) Jurisdiction

The United Telephone case represents a puzzling departure from the general pattern of expansive judicial reading of FCC powers in the telephone field.[183] When two Independents sought FCC action to require a Bell System company to provide a more favorable settlement reflecting the higher cost of capital typical of Independent companies, the FCC declined.[184] Rather than simply affirming on

---

[179]Amendment of Part 67; *see supra* note 2.

[180]93 F.C.C.2d at 1306.

[181]AT&T Co., 91 F.C.C.2d 578, 586, 52 R.R.2d 881, 888 (1982) (footnote omitted), *clarification and recon. denied,* 95 F.C.C.2d 167 (1983).

[182]91 F.C.C.2d at 588.

[183]United Tel. Co. of the Carolinas, 54 F.C.C.2d 289 (1975), *aff'd sub nom.* United Tel. Co. of the Carolinas v. FCC, 559 F.2d 720 (D.C. Cir. 1977) (Judge Wilkey dissenting without Opinion.)

[184]54 F.C.C.2d at 290. The FCC decision refers to the *United* case as essentially a division-of-charges matter and simply finds an insufficient showing to justify discretionary action, with no suggestion of jurisdictional limits:

> While Section 201 (a) empowers the Commission to prescribe divisions of charges, after opportunity for hearing, where it finds such action necessary or desirable in the public interest, no carrier is entitled to such prescription of hearing as a matter of right. In the

the basis of the FCC's action, the court, without citing legislative history or case law, or relating its pronouncement to the words of the statute, said:

> The obligations of section 201(a) run directly and unavoidably only to interstate carriers like Southern Bell. As connecting carriers, United and Carolina are only subject to such requirements tangentially because they have chosen to interconnect with interstate carriers. Section 201(a) does not give the Federal Communications Commission power to order purely intrastate communications companies to join with interstate companies in providing through route services. United and Carolina are free to remove their interconnection with Southern Bell and thereby also remove themselves completely from the jurisdiction of the . . . [FCC].[185]

The D.C. Circuit's use of "connecting carrier" and "purely intrastate communications companies" as synonymous terms conflicts with the whole range of FCC and court decisions, and is inconsistent with a careful reading of Subsection 2(b) and Subsection 3(u). The words of the statute do not define the interstate as intrastate; rather Subsection 2(b)(2) applies a limited jurisdictional exclusion as to Title II (except for Sections 201-205), such exclusion coming into play where a carrier is engaged in interstate communications only through interconnection with non-affiliated companies. Nothing in the Act suggests that a connecting carrier is a "purely intrastate communications company;" on the contrary, the Act contemplates expressly that connecting carriers *do* provide interstate services but only through non-affiliate facilities.

Moreover, connecting carriers are subject to Sections 201-205 of the Act; and the issue in the *United* case discussed by the court involved specifically Subsection 201(a). The D.C. Circuit, however, relied on the connecting carrier status of the companies to deny the FCC authority under Subsection 201(a)—citing no case law or supporting logic.

But the D.C. Circuit hedged its statement of no authority:

> We do not intend to imply that the Commission lacks the authority to hold a hearing on the issues raised by United's and Carolina's petitions and to prescribe a just and reasonable division of charges if it so chooses. We simply hold that it was not an abuse of discretion for the Commission to dismiss their petitions without an evidentiary hearing on the grounds that United and Carolina had not sufficiently challenged the reasonableness of the existing division of joint revenues.[186]

The "issues raised" included the very issues as to which the court said the FCC had no authority; but the court also said it did not mean to imply that the FCC lacks authority to hold a hearing and to issue a prescription as to such issues. Struggling to find logic in this, the author can only guess that the court intended to say that the FCC could not order connecting carriers to join with interstate carriers in providing through route services; but could order "a just and

---

exercise of our discretion we have determined here that no sufficient basis has been shown for concluding that the public interest would be served here by instituting proceedings looking forward to modification of the present divisions. [*Id.*]

[185]559 F.2d at 724.

[186]*Id.* at 725.

reasonable division of charges." But the same provision, Subsection 201(a), sets out both sets of FCC powers—requiring interconnection and prescribing divisions of charges—in similar terms, with no hint of a jurisdictional distinction.[187] Why would the Commission have the power to do one and not the other, and that in relation to connecting carriers which are subject to the FCC's Section 201 authority?

Furthermore, the last sentence quoted above ("We simply hold. . . .") characterizes the D.C. Circuit's own decision as a more limited holding than the earlier denial-of-jurisdiction language, and may justify regarding this language as *dictum*.[188] In terms of the *United* decision itself, therefore, one can question whether the decision should be considered a denial of FCC jurisdiction over connecting carriers under Subsection 201(a), even in the D.C. Circuit.

This point is given further emphasis when *United* is viewed in the context of subsequent D.C. Circuit decisions. Judge Tamm, who wrote the Opinion in *United*, also wrote the Opinion in *CCIA v. FCC, supra,* giving the broadest recognition to the FCC's preemptive authority over fully subject carriers and connecting carriers, with no mention of a jurisdictional limit as to Subsection 201(a). Similarly, the D.C. Circuit's June, 1984, affirmance of the FCC's access charge policy decision,[189] specifically concerned with Subsection 201(a) matters (carrier interconnection and compensation), suggests no jurisdictional limit; such a jurisdictional limit would certainly have been relevant since the FCC was in that case addressing and prescribing the technical and financial terms of carrier interconnection for "exchange carriers"—a classification necessarily embracing hundreds of connecting carriers.

In summary, the *United* decision is doubtful authority for any jurisdictional limit on the FCC in view of the ambivalence of the decision itself, its lack of supporting authority, and the weight of case law to the contrary.

5.5.12 Summary

Jurisdictional and preemptive theory, developed in early common carrier cases and in cable television cases, was applied and extended by the Commission and the courts to overcome state commission resistance to pro-competitive FCC policies affecting the domestic telephone industry. The Fourth Circuit in the *North Carolina* cases, *supra,* the D.C. Circuit in *CCIA v. FCC, supra,* the First Circuit in *Puerto Rico Tel. Co. v. FCC, supra,* and the Second Circuit in *New*

---

[187]The court's *United* decision cites no legislative history to support the notion that there is a difference in jurisdictional terms between the FCC's power to order carrier interconnection and 16 FD's power to order a division of charges, both under Subsection 201(a). *See id.* n.7 at 724. Recourse to the legislative history throws such a notion still further in doubt. The 1934 Congress modified the words of proposed Subsection 201(a) contained in the original bills by adding language which granted the FCC the two powers in question (interconnection and division of charges). *See supra* note 40.

[188]Ample non-jurisidictional grounds for affirming the FCC are cited by the D.C. Circuit, including agency discretion and reasoned analysis (at 723) and the companies' failure to make necessary allegations (at 725-26).

[189]NARUC v. FCC, *supra* note 2, 737 F.2d at 1095.

York Tel. Co. v. FCC, supra, all reached the same conclusions as to somewhat different facts and circumstances: (i) limiting the Subsection 221(b) exclusion to state-borderline-straddling cases; (ii) limiting the Subsection 2(b) exclusion to matters that in their nature and effect are separable from and do not substantially affect the conduct or development of interstate communications; (iii) therefore finding these exclusions inapplicable; and (iv) finding jurisdiction in the FCC and authority within the terms of the Act for FCC preemption. In the cases just cited and a number of subsequent cases, these four Circuits were persuaded that the actions of the FCC (1) were consistent with the statutory scheme, coming either within explicit responsibilities of the FCC under the Act or within the ancillary concept, and therefore (2) would be preemptive as to conflicting state actions. A successful defense of FCC decisions now on appeal will depend on the reviewing courts' being similarly persuaded.[190]

5.6 WHERE FCC PREEMPTION STANDS

5.6.1 Review of Legal Principles

Let us here pause to take stock of what principles have been firmly established in respect of FCC preemption—as reflected in the cases discussed in Section 5.5. The following points can be considered settled law by virtue of decision by the United States Supreme Court and/or United States Court(s) of Appeal:

First, Congress gave the Commission "'unified jurisdiction,'" "'broad authority,'"[191] and a "'comprehensive mandate,' with 'not niggardly but expansive powers;'"[192] Section 2 of the Act confers on the Commission regulatory authority over *all* interstate communication by wire or radio;[193] the Commission's authority is not limited to the activities specifically described in the Act or to the forms of communication specifically described, *i.e.* broadcasting and common carrier service.[194]

Second, the Commission's authority embraces not only its statutory responsibilities, but also that which is reasonably ancillary to the effective performance of its statutory responsibilities.[195]

---

[190]*See supra,* note 4 on pending appeals of FCC decisions.

[191]United States v. Southwestern Cable Co., *supra* note 76, 392 U.S. at 172.

[192]*Id.* at 173, citing National Broadcasting Co. v. United States, *supra,* 319 U.S. at 219. *See also* General Tel. Co. of the Southwest v. United States, *supra* note 65, 449 F.2d at 853.

[193]*Id.* at 173.

[194]United States v. Southwestern Cable, *supra* note 76, 392 U.S. at [172]. *See also* General Tel. Co. of the Southwest v. United States, *supra* note 65, 449 F.2d at 854: "[E]ven though CATV systems are neither common carriers nor broadcasters, they do not, by that fact alone, fall beyond the purview of the Act."

[195]United States v. Midwest Video, *supra* note 82, 406 U.S. at 663; United States v. Southwestern Cable, *supra* note 76, 392 U.S. at 177-78; Permian Basin Area Rate Cases, 390 U.S. 747, 780 (1968). *"[W]e may not,* 'in the absence of compelling evidence that such was Congress' intention . . . prohibit administrative action imperative for the achievement of an agency's ultimate purpose.'" Southwestern (at 177) citing Permian Basin (at 780) (emphasis added).

Third, the nature of the communication itself rather than the physical location of the technology determines whether interstate or intrastate communication is involved.[196]

Fourth, under Section 1 and Subsections 2(a) and 3(a) of the Act, FCC authority extends to facilities used for both interstate and intrastate communication; and Subsection 2(b)(1) does not withdraw FCC jurisdiction *except* as to facilities "separable from and . . . not substantially affect[ing] the conduct or development of interstate communications;"[197] the purpose of Subsection 2(b) is merely "to restrain the . . . [FCC] from interfering with those essentially local incidents and practices of common carriage by wire that do not substantially encroach upon the administration and development of the interstate telephone network."[198]

Fifth, Subsection 221(b) of the act is intended to do no more than to prevent an enlargement of FCC jurisdiction over the business and facilities of a telephone exchange that serves an area including parts of more than one state; thus, Subsection 221(b) is merely to enable state commissions to regulate local exchange service in metropolitan areas which extend across state boundaries, and has no application to other facilities.[199]

Sixth, the FCC has the jurisdiction necessary to impose requirements even on "connecting carriers," *i.e.,* carriers subject only to Sections 201-205 of the Act by virtue of Subsection 2(b)(2). The FCC's "overall responsibility and broadly construed authority to insure adequate and efficient telephone service at reasonable rates" and "jurisdiction over the connecting carrier's services, charges and practices which are a part of the uninterrupted and indivisible national system of telephone service" provide authority for the FCC's imposition, on connecting carriers as well as fully subject carriers, of such requirements as (i) maximum separation (separate subsidiary),[200] and (ii) deregulation of CPE and enhanced services.[201]

Seventh, an affirmative regulatory scheme (*e.g.,* competitive provision of CPE) may replace state regulation; "Federal regulation need not be heavy-handed in order to preempt state regulation."[202]

What limits to the exercise of FCC jurisdiction have been recognized by the courts or the Commission? Apart from those constraints implicit in the foregoing jurisdictional principles, the recognized limits to FCC preemption are as follows:

First Limit: The relationship between intrastate tariff charges and intrastate costs has been said by the Commission to be "entirely within the purview of individual state commissions." But the FCC requires acceptance by the states,

---

[196]*See supra* note 61.
[197]North Carolina I, 537 F.2d at 793; *see supra* notes 108-112.
[198]*Id.* at 794 n.6.
[199]*See supra* note 39.
[200]GTE Service Corp. v. FCC, *supra* note 132, 474 F.2d at 736-37.
[201]CCIA v. FCC, *supra* note 133, 693 F.2d at 214-17.
[202]*See supra* note 103.

for intrastate ratemaking purposes, of FCC depreciation prescriptions, under the express mandate of Section 220 of the Act and because state action causing inadequate capital recovery for telephone company investors would frustrate validly adopted FCC policies.[203]

Second Limit: The function or regulating rates for CPE furnished by telephone companies is to be left to state commissions—absent a "record reveal[ing] a very clear need" for an exercise of FCC jurisdiction "in such a way as to preclude exercise of jurisdiction by state or local bodies;"[204] but subsequently the Commission's affirmative regulatory scheme for CPE (*i.e.* competition) precluded regulation by the states.[205]

Third Limit: Jurisdiction under Subsection 214(a) does not attach to the construction of a telephone exchange building—challenged by local area residents on environmental grounds.[206]

Fourth Limit: In a decision the author regards as doubtful authority, it was stated, with qualifications, that the FCC lacks jurisdiction necessary to order two connecting carriers to interconnect with Southern Bell Tel. Co. "[T]he Commission does not have the jurisdiction necessary to order United [Tel. Co. of the

---

[203]*See* text accompanying notes 154-172. Responding to the argument that federal preemption of depreciation practices would constitute intrastate ratemaking which might run afoul of Subsection 2(b), the Commission said: "Section 220(b) . . . . does not require that any particular tariff for intrastate service be accepted by the state commissions. The setting of depreciation rates and classes of depreciable property only resolves a single issue impacting the ratemaking process. It does not restrict the state commission's broad discretion in setting charges for individual services." Depreciation Preemption Order, *supra* note 154, 92 F.C.C.2d at 874. In CCIA v. FCC, *supra* note 133, the court saw no distinction between preemption principles applicable to state ratemaking or applicable to other state powers (693 F.2d at 216). But while state ratemaking as such may be preemptible, the author would be surprised if the FCC chose to involve itself in state ratemaking any more than it deemed necessary to protect federal policies. *See infra* note 216 for a discussion of various instances where the FCC has declined to exercise preemptive power.

[204]Diamond International Corp. v. FCC, *supra* note 117, 627 F.2d at 493. The court noted that nothing in the record suggested the FCC's decision to refrain from exercising jurisdiction will substantially affect the conduct or development of interstate communications; and emphasized, citing North Carolina II, *supra* note 108, 552 F.2d at 1049-50, that "this is not to say that the . . . [FCC] could never exercise its primary jurisdiction over PBX terminal equipment 'should the need for federal action arise.'"

[205]*See supra,* note 133.

[206]Kitchen v. FCC, 464 F.2d 801 (D.C. Cir. 1972). But note that *Kitchen's* analysis of Subsection 221(b), at 803, was rejected by the D.C. Circuit in CCIA v. FCC, *supra* note 133, 693 F.2d at 217. Stripped of the Subsection 221(b) rationale, *Kitchen's* holding becomes difficult to identify in statutory terms: "[W]e have not heretofore asserted or found that we could assert jurisdiction to require prior approval for construction of what is essentially a local exchange building. . . . Nothing . . . persuades us that we should intervene to consider the questions that are the substance of the subject complaint and disturb their resolution by appropriate local agencies." (At 803.) The basis of the holding might be deference to "local agencies" or perhaps, by implication, that a switching building does not come within the "extension of lines" language of Subsection 214(a). If *Kitchen* arose today the Commission would be likely to use the "forebearance" rationale to avoid involvement in questions of this kind that are dealt with at the state level. See AT&T, 91 F.C.C.2d 1, 14, 52 R.R.2d 287, 296, n.10 (1982), for a discussion of the "extension of lines" concept.

Carolinas] and Carolina [Tel. and Tel. Co.] to continue their interconnection with Southern Bell."[207] But the court hedged on this denial of jurisdiction.[208]

Fifth Limit: The Commission may not impose common carrier obligations on non-common carriers, *i.e.* cable television systems.[209]

5.6.2 Analysis

There is not a neat fit of the two lists just discussed (authority recognized and limits recognized) as against each other or even among the items on each list. The decisions in question arose over a period exceeding twenty years, in varying contexts as the telecommunications industry went through dramatic changes. Some of the later decisions might be deemed to supersede the earlier decisions, although this may not be evident in their text. Perhaps the "forbearance" theory might have been employed at an earlier stage instead of jurisdictional principles, if that theory had then been generally accepted. This could be a way for the FCC to control its regulatory responsibilities and burdens without establishing inflexible jurisdictional limits, and FCC draftsmen would have been likely to make use of the theory for this purpose.[210] However, for the sake of this analysis, let us put aside these hypotheticals and read the decisions just as they were written.

Considering the sweep of all these decisions, and particularly the two *North Carolina* cases, *CCIA v. FCC,* and *Virginia State Corporation Commission v.*

---

[207]United Tel. Co. of the Carolinas, Inc. v. FCC, *supra* note 183, 559 F.2d at 724.

[208]*Id.* at 725.

[209]FCC v. Midwest Video Corp., *supra* note 93, 440 U.S. at 701-09.

[210]It should be understood that the FCC historically has sought to avoid involvement in many subjects traditionally handled by state commissions—perhaps for reasons of comity, but also presumably to avoid expending scarce FCC resources in largely duplicating state commission activities. It seems that the Commission staff characteristically tries to write decisions so as to avoid committing the FCC to activities considered unproductive, while making sure the Commission's jurisdiction would be available if needed. Thus, Commission draftsmen have preferred to avoid drawing clear jurisdictional limits. Following are some examples: (i) The FCC instituted a requirement for a *prima facie* showing of predatory pricing before the Commission would initiate an investigation of such allegations in the context of Title III applications. Commonwealth Tel. Co., 88 F.C.C.2d 782 (1981). This *prima facie* requirement, while drawing no jurisdictional lines, serves to avoid the need for the FCC to re-investigate rate questions dealt with at the state level. (ii) In Eastex Tel. Cooperative, Inc. 45 F.C.C.2d 464 (1974), the FCC refused to become involved in a dispute between Eastex and Lake Tel. Co. over which company would interconnect directly with Southwestern Bell Tel. Co. The FCC avoided setting a jurisdictional limit, saying it "will not act in cases of this nature unless it is clearly shown that the efficacy of interstate communication is being impaired to a significant degree and that attempts to remedy the situation at the local level have failed or would prove futile." 45 F.C.C.2d at 469-70. (iii) The FCC used to require entrants into mobile telephone service to obtain any necessary state authorization before filing an FCC application. This requirement encouraged adversaries, who may have delayed the new entry in the course of proceedings at the state level, to attempt to create still another litigated proceeding at the federal level. Initially, the FCC invoked the jurisdictional limits of Subsection 221(b) (Souris River Tel. Mutual Aid Corp., 28 F.C.C. 275 (1960)). But a better way was found that avoided drawing limits to FCC jurisdiction and also avoided reiteration of the proceeding at the FCC. The FCC invoked the principle that it may accord "great weight" to the results of state proceedings even though such results are not binding on the Commission. *See,* for example, Bay Springs Tel. Co., 25 R.R. 662, 665 (1963), citing Wisconsin Tel. Co., 27 F.C.C. 1, 23 (1959); Mobile Tel., Inc., 92 F.C.C.2d 97, 101-02 (1983).

FCC, supra, one must ask: What is left for the states? A possible answer to this question is a "residual" theory: There is left to the states those responsibilities and powers that have *not* been preempted by the FCC either (i) on the basis of powers explicitly granted by the Act, or (ii) on the basis of an appropriately supported finding of the FCC that preemptive action is necessary to make effective the intent of Congress as properly interpreted and applied.

But did not the 1934 Congress intend to limit the powers of the FCC vis-a-vis the states? Certainly the statute contains unmistakable words of limitation, and the legislative history reflects an intent to impose limitations on FCC powers. We must therefore explore the problem beyond the residual theory.

Today, as in 1934, the core problem is that there is a high degree of overlap in the real world between the interstate, and the intrastate. And yet the jurisdictional provisions in Sections 1, 2 and 3 were constructed around the distinction between "interstate" and "intrastate." The 1934 Congress was told about this problem time and again—by Commissioner McManamy, among others.[211] Important wording changes were made by the 1934 Congress recognizing that "intrastate" communications did not necessarily embrace any communications link connecting points within the same state; and the cases are uniform in rejecting any such simplistic notion of what comprises intrastate communications.[212] The Act, however, defines "intrastate" and "interstate" in unhelpful, circular fashion, and then proceeds to employ the terms as if they were known quantities. Congress met the requirement to produce a statute as requested by President Roosevelt, but it was left to the Commission and the courts to sort out what the Act's scheme of dual regulation meant and how it would work.

Nothing in the Act or its legislative history establishes congressional intent that a concept of predominance should prevail, *i.e.* that there must be left to the states that which is predominantly intrastate. It was well known in Congress in 1934 that interstate (and foreign) communications represented a very small percentage of traffic at the exchange level;[213] a predominance test would then (as now) have produced absolute domination by the states. While it seems clear that there was an intent in Congress in 1934 to negate the "Shreveport Doctrine,"[214] there is nothing in the Act to support the notion of a predominance test, and the Commission and the courts have rejected the concept.[215]

---

[211]*See supra* note 37.

[212]*See supra* note 61.

[213]*See* North Carolina II, 552 F.2d at 1044 n.7, stating that about 97 percent of telephone calls are intrastate. About 98 percent were intrastate in 1934. *See* 78 Cong. Rec. 10316 (1934).

[214]*See* North Carolina I, *supra* note 108, 537 F.2d at 793 n.6.

[215]*See* the 1938 decision, Southwestern Bell Tel. Co., *supra* note 54, rejecting the "preponderance of use" argument. 6 F.C.C. at 533-34. Commission rejection of a predominant use theory has thus been a matter of record for 46 of the 50 years of the Act, and Congress has taken no action to reverse this holding—despite addressing jurisdictional issues a number of times (for example, the 1954 Amendment, modifying Subsections 2(b), 3(e)(3) and 221(b) "to make certain the use of radio will not subject to Federal regulation companies engaged primarily in intrastate operations"; *see* 1954 U.S. CODE CONG. & AD. NEWS 2133.) *See also,* North Carolina II, *supra* note 114, 552 F.2d at 1046:

Putting aside, then, the notion of predominant use as well as the residual theory, is there another theory based on which the Subsection 2(b) reservation of state power could be given practical effect? The author has found no coherent alternative theory in briefs submitted to support state commission arguments.

We are left with this situation: The courts have adopted a definition of intrastate that, as a practical matter, extends *potential* FCC jurisdiction (*i.e.* if there is no forbearance) over all common carrier communications facilities. Even where separability of the interstate and the intrastate can be demonstrated, the "substantially affect" test may bring a matter within the FCC's preemptive power. So long as the FCC establishes its jurisdictional claim on one of the two grounds mentioned earlier (explicit grant of authority or necessity for making congressional intent effective), the statutory language precluding the FCC from the intrastate domain can be negated, for all practical purposes. Putting aside a case falling within the *Shreveport* decision,[216] given that the same systems and companies furnish both intrastate service and interstate service, given the interrelationship of virtually all matters affecting the furnishing of intra- and interstate service, and given a supportable FCC finding, the author is unable to visualize any likely regulatory question or legal issue of any importance affecting telephone companies that could be shown to be separable from and not substantially affecting the conduct or development of interstate communications.

This is not to say that active FCC regulation will necessarily supersede state regulation across the board. As noted above, long-standing institutional patterns of FCC behavior suggest the agency would not wish to regulate most of the subjects traditionally regulated at the state level.[217] But in view of the policy of

---

Petitioners confuse the fact that almost all terminal equipment is and has been used predominantly for local communication with the statutory division of decisionmaking power. We find it difficult to credit an argument which amounts to an assertion that Congress depended on a regulatory scheme that depends on the calling habits of telephone subscribers to determine the jurisdictional competence of the FCC versus state utility commissions.

[216]*See supra* notes 16, 18, 34-35 with accompanying text. Compare N.Y. Telco v. FCC, *supra* note 126 where the FCC was upheld in preventing New York Telephone Company from collecting discriminatory surcharges on interstate customers.

[217]Examples of instances where the FCC has declined to exercise preemptive power, completely or in part, include: (i) Curtin Call Communications, Inc., 62 F.C.C.2d 211, 217, 39 R.R.2d 282, 288 (1976) (The FCC chose to rely on a state court's determination:

We note that the Supreme Court of the State of Nebraska carefully considered the facts and issues raised herein when it reviewed the order of the . . . [Nebraska commission] and upheld . . . [its] jurisdiction . . . to order Curtin Call to cease and desist from offering paging service to customers in Nebraska. . . . Because the Nebraska Court has had the opportunity to rule on issues raised herein and has demonstrated a sensitivity to the complex issues implicit in federal and state regulatory jurisdictional matters, we shall rely on that court's determination in this matter. [Footnote omitted.]);

(ii) Amtel Communications, Inc., 89 F.C.C.2d 562 (1982), *remanded by Court at Appeals of FCC's request to permit reconsideration* ("Commission policies favoring the competitive provision of various telecommunications services and products, however, have not compelled a telephone carrier to open the doors of its central office to equipment of other service vendors. . . . A record has not been compiled to date that would warrant the exercise of federal jurisdiction in this matter." (At 567-68, footnote omitted.)); (iii) Earth Satellite Communications, Inc., *supra* note 103 (limited preemption).

the present Commission favoring deregulation, it is possible, even likely, that we will see more extensive action by the FCC foreclosing state regulation—preemption analogous to that upheld in *CCIA v. FCC, supra,* and *Brookhaven, supra.* Under the cases, this kind of preemption would be upheld provided the Circuit involved were satisfied that the FCC was acting within its delegated authority, that continued state regulation would impede a validly adopted federal policy, and that the decision was not arbitrary, capricious or an abuse of discretion.

Is there a point at which a United States Court of Appeals would come to believe that the agency is departing from the statutory scheme of dual regulation, thereby offending the court's sense of consistency with congressional intent? This must be a matter of speculation since no such point has been reached in any of the telephone industry cases decided by the courts—perhaps apart from the very dubious *United* case, *supra.*

Perhaps we might find some guidance in the judicial progression discussed earlier in the cable television cases: from total acceptance of FCC policy and affirmance of its jurisdictional premises in 1968, to reluctant affirmance in 1972, to reversal in 1979. Of course, different regulatory programs were before the Supreme Court in each case.[218] As the FCC's rules moved beyond the protection of broadcasting to enhancement of cable service itself, judicial resistance increased at the Court of Appeals and the Supreme Court. But other factors seemed to be at work as well.

As the years went by, as the deficiencies of FCC execution of its cable policies became clear in the course of numerous appeals, as the FCC itself abandoned some of its original concepts, and as the general environment changed, the attitude of the courts changed. Theoretically, the same test was applied in 1968, 1972 and 1979—did the agency action come within the "reasonably ancillary" standard? But a shift in attitude is detectable in the cases, changing from willingness-to-accept to skepticism. Reading Judge Markey's devastating Opinion in the Eighth Circuit's decision in 1978[219] convinces the author that the practical and logical infirmities of the FCC's cable regulation program heavily influenced rejection of its jurisdictional premises. In fact, the "reasonably ancillary" standard necessarily leads to intermixture of merits and jurisdiction, making it immensely difficult to judge the outcome of any controversy ostensibly concerned with jurisdiction alone.

---

[218]In 1968, it was FCC rules that cable firms had to transmit to their subscribers the signals of any television station into whose service area the cable firms brought competing signals, and that restricted cable firms so as to minimize duplication of television station programming. United States v. Southwestern Cable Co., *supra* note 76, 392 U.S. at 166. In 1972, it was FCC rules requiring cable firms to originate programming, other than simply showing films and tapes. Unites States v. Midwest Video Corp., *supra* note 82, 406 U.S. at 653-54. In 1979, it was FCC rules requiring cable firms to create surplus capacity and then to make that capacity available, at no charge, with necessary equipment and facitlities, to public, educational, local governmental and leased access users. FCC v. Midwest Video Corp., *supra* note 93, 440 U.S. at 689-90.

[219]*See* Midwest Video Corp. v. FCC, *supra* note 93, 571 F.2d 1025.

In the *North Carolina* cases, and *a fortiori* in *CCIA v. FCC,* where the jurisdictional theory was "ancillary," the courts accorded immense deference to the agency. As a result, it is difficult even to approach identifying a theoretical outer limit to potential FCC jurisdiction. One is tempted to think the courts are at the *Southwestern Cable* stage. Can we expect a more critical stage, where a more rigorous test will be applied?

Even assuming a more critical stage, it appears unlikely that the general thrust of FCC preemptive power will be turned back from the point where it now stands. No sustainable alternative for clearly dividing federal and state power within the framework of the present Act has been presented. Any approach to dual regulation under the present Act must involve an overlap of functions; and, to comport with congressional intent as construed by the courts, the states must yield where they would obstruct realization of congressional objectives. This does not mean that the FCC cannot be reversed on a preemptive strike. But it does mean that the jurisdictional base exists for the FCC to sustain preemptive jurisidiction at its present stage or even beyond—so long as the agency is careful to establish a plausible case that preemptive action is necessary for the implementation of congressional objectives.

APPENDIX

73rd Congress 2d Session
H.R. 8301

TITLE I—GENERAL PROVISIONS
Purposes of Act; Creation of Federal Communications Commission

SECTION 1. For the purpose of regulating interstate and foreign commerce in communication by wire and radio so as to make available, so far as possible, to all the people of the United States a rapid, efficient, nation-wide, and world-wide wire and radio communication service with adequate facilities at reasonable charges, and for the purpose of securing a more effective execution of this policy by centralizing authority heretofore granted by law to several agencies and by granting additional authority with respect to interstate and foreign commerce in wire and radio communication, there is hereby created a commission to be known as the "Federal Communications Commission", which shall be constituted as hereinafter provided.

APPLICATION OF ACT

SEC. 2. The provisions of this Act shall apply to all interstate and foreign communication by wire or radio and all interstate and foreign transmission of energy by radio, which originates and/or is received within the United States, and to all persons engaged within the United States in such communication or such transmission of energy by radio; but it shall not apply to persons engaged in wire or radio communication of transmission in the Philippine Islands or the Canal Zone, or to wire or radio communication or transmission wholly within the Philippine Islands or the Canal Zone.

DEFINITIONS

SEC. 3. For the purposes of this Act—

(a) "Wire communication" or "communication by wire" means the transmission of writing, signs, signals, pictures, and sounds of all kinds by aid of wire, cable, or other like connection between the points of origin and reception of such transmission, including all instrumentalities, facilities, and services incidental to such transmission.

(b) "Radio communication" or "communication by radio" means the transmission by radio of writing, signs, signals, pictures, and sounds of all kinds, including all instrumentalities, facilities, and services incidental to such transmission.
* * * * *

(e) "Interstate communication" or "interstate transmission" means communication or transmission (1) from any State, Territory, or possession of the United States (including the Philippine Islands and the Canal Zone), or from the District of Columbia to any other State, Territory, possession of the United States (including the Philippine Islands and the Canal Zone), or to the District of Columbia; or (2) between points within the same Territory, or possession (except the Philippine Islands and the Canal Zone), or the District of Columbia; or (3) between points within the United States but through a foreign country if the point of origin and the point of reception are not in the same State.
* * * * *

(h) "Common carrier" or "carrier" means any person engaged in communication by wire or radio, as a common carrier for hire, except where reference is made to common carriers not subject to this Act; but a person engaged in radio broadcasting shall not, insofar as such person is so engaged, be deemed a common carrier.

* * * * *

(k)　Two or more persons shall be deemed to be affiliated if they are members of a group, composed of a parent and its subsidiary or subsidiaries, or of a parent, its subsidiary or subsidiaries, and other corporations, of which each member except the parent is a subsidiary of some other member.

* * * * *

(t)　"Telephone exchange service" means service within a telephone exchange, or within a connected system of telephone exchanges within the same exchange area operated to furnish to subscribers intercommunicating service of the character ordinarily furnished by a single exchange.

(u)　"Telephone toll service" means telephone service between stations in different exchange areas for which there is made a separate charge not included in contracts with subscribers for exchange service.

(v)　"State commission" means the commission, board, or official (by whatever name designated by the laws of a State) which under the laws of such State has regulatory jurisdiction with respect to intrastate operations of carriers.

PROVISIONS RELATING TO THE COMMISSION

* * * * *

[SEC. 4.] (i) The Commission may perform any and all acts, make such rules and regulations, and issue such orders, not inconsistent with this Act, as may be necessary in the execution of its functions.

(j)　The Commission may conduct its proceedings in such manner as will best conduce to the proper dispatch of business and to the ends of justice. No commissioner shall participate in any hearing or proceeding in which he has a pecuniary interest. Any party may appear before the Commission and be heard in person or by attorney. Every vote and official act of the Commission shall be entered of record, and its proceedings shall be public upon the request of any party interested.

* * * * *

TITLE II—COMMON CARRIERS SERVICE AND CHARGES

SEC. 201. (a)　It shall be the duty of every common carrier engaged in interstate or foreign communication by wire or radio to furnish such communication service upon reasonable request therefor; and, in accordance with the orders of the Commission, to establish through routes and charges applicable thereto, and to establish and provide facilities and regulations for operating such through routes, in cases where the Commission, after opportunity for hearing, find such action necessary or desirable in the public interest.

(b)　All charges, practices, classifications, and regulations for and in connection with much communication service, shall be just and reasonable, and any such charge, practice, classification, or regulation that is unjust or unreasonable is hereby declared to be unlawful: *Provided,* That messages by wire or radio subject to this Act may be classified into day, night, repeated, unrepeated, letter, commercial, press, Government, and such other classes as the Commission may decide to be just and reasonable, and different charges may be made for the different classes of messages: *Provided further,* That nothing in this Act shall be construed to prevent a common carrier subject to this Act from entering into any contract with any common carrier not subject to this Act, for the exchange of their services, if the Commission is of the opinion that such contract is not contrary to the public interest.

DISCRIMINATION AND PREFERENCES

* * * * *

SEC. 202. (b)   Charges or service, whenever referred to in this Act, include charges for, or service in connection with, the use of wires in chain broadcasting or incidental to radio communication of any kind.

* * * * *

ACT NOT TO APPLY TO COMMUNICATION IN INTRASTATE COMMERCE

SEC. 210.   Nothing in this Act shall be construed to apply, or to give the Commission jurisdiction, with respect to charges, classifications, practices, or regulations for or in connection with intrastate communication service of any carrier, or to any carrier engaged exclusively in intrastate commerce.

VALUATION OF CARRIER PROPERTY

SEC. 213. (a)   The Commission may from time to time, as may be necessary for the proper administration of this Act, make a valuation of all or of any part of the property owned or used by any carrier subject to this Act, which is used and useful in the public service, as of such date as the Commission may fix.

(b)   The Commission may at any time require any such carrier to file with the Commission an inventory of all or of any part of the property owned or used by said carrier, which is used and useful in the public service, which inventory shall show the units of said property classified in such detail, and in such manner, as the Commission shall direct, and shall show the estimated cost of reproduction new of said units, and their reproduction cost new less depreciation, as of such date as the Commission may direct; and such carrier shall file such inventory within such reasonable time as the Commission by order shall require.

(c)   The Commission may at any time require any such carrier to file with the Commission a statement showing the original cost of all or of any part of the property owned or used by said carrier, which is used and useful in the public service. For the showing of such original cost said property shall be classified, and the original cost shall be defined, in such manner as the Commission may prescribe; and if any part of such cost cannot be determined from accounting or other records, the portion of the property for which such cost cannot be determined shall be reported to the Commission; and, if the Commission shall so direct, the original cost thereof shall be estimated in such manner as the Commission may prescribe. If the carrier owning the property at the time such original cost is reported shall have paid more or less than the original cost to acquire the same, the amount of such cost of acquisition, and any facts which the Commission may require in connection therewith, shall be reported with such original cost. The report made by a carrier under this paragraph shall show the source or sources from which the original cost reported was obtained, and such other information as to the manner in which the report was prepared, as the Commission shall require.

(d)   Nothing shall be included in the original cost reported for the property of any carrier under paragraph (c) of this section on account of any easement, license, or franchise granted by the United States or by any State or political subdivision thereof, beyond the reasonable necessary expense lawfully incurred in obtaining such easement, license, or franchise from the public authority aforesaid, which expense shall be reported separately from all other costs in such detail as the Commission may require; and nothing shall be included in any valuation of the property of any carrier made by the Commission on account of any such easement, license, or franchise, beyond such reasonable necessary expense lawfully incurred as aforesaid.

(e)   For the purpose of enabling the Commission to make a valuation of any of the property of any such carrier, or to find the original cost of such property, or to find any other facts concerning the same which are required for use by the Commission, the Commission may exercise all of the powers and authority conferred upon the Interstate Commerce Commission in its administration of section 19a of the Interstate Commerce Act, as amended, and it shall be the duty of each such carrier to furnish to the Commission, within such reasonable time as the Commission may order, any information with respect thereto which the Commission may by order require, including copies of maps, contracts, reports of engineers, and other data, records, and papers. The Commission, in making any such valuation shall be free to adopt any method of valuation which shall be lawful.

EXTENSION OF LINES AND CIRCUITS

SEC. 214.   (a)   No carrier shall undertake the extension of its line or circuits, or the construction of a new line or circuit, or shall acquire or operate any line or circuit, or extension thereof, or shall engage in transmission over or by means of such additional or extended line or circuit, unless and until there shall first have been obtained from the Commission a certificate that the present or future public convenience and necessity require or will require the construction, or operation, or construction and operation, of such additional or extended line or circuit.

(b)   Upon receipt of an application for any such certificate the Commission shall cause notice thereof to be given to and a copy filed with the Governor of each State in which such additional or extended line or circuit is proposed to be constructed or operated, with the right to be heard as provided with respect to the hearing of complaints; and said notice shall also be published for three consecutive weeks in some newspaper of general circulation in each county which said line or circuit will serve.

(c)   The Commission shall have power to issue such certificate as prayed for, or to refuse to issue it, or to issue it for a portion or portions of a line or circuit, or extension thereof, described in the application, or for the partial exercise only of such right or privilege, and may attach to the issuance of the certificate such terms and conditions as in its judgment the public convenience and necessity may require. After issuance of such certificate, and not before, the carrier may, without securing approval other than such certificate, comply with the terms and conditions contained in or attached to the issuance of such certificate and proceed with the construction, operation, or extension covered thereby. Any construction, operation, or extension contrary to the provisions of this section may be enjoined by any court of competent jurisdiction at the suit of the United States, the Commission, the State commission, any State affected, or any party in interest.

(d)   The Commission may, after full opportunity for hearing, in a proceeding upon complaint or upon its own initiative without complaint, authorize or require by order any carrier, party to such proceeding, to provide itself with adequate facilities for performing its service as a common carrier and to extend its line or circuits; but no such authorization or order shall be made unless the Commission finds, as to such extension, that it is reasonably required in the interest of public convenience and necessity, or as to such extension or facilities that the expense involved therein will not impair the ability of the carrier to perform its duty to the public. Any carrier which refuses or neglects to comply with any order of the Commission made in pursuance of this paragraph shall forfeit to the United States $100 for each day during which such refusal or neglect continues.

(e)   The authority conferred upon the Commission by this section shall not extend to the construction, operation, or extension of lines or circuits within a single State.

* * * * *

ACCOUNTS, RECORDS, AND MEMORANDA; DEPRECIATION CHARGES

SEC. 220.   (a)   The Commission may, in its discretion, prescribe the forms of any and all accounts, records, and memoranda to be kept by carriers subject to this Act, including the accounts, records, and memoranda of the movement of traffic, as well as of the receipts and expenditures of moneys.

(b)   The Commission shall, as soon as practicable, prescribe for such carriers the classes of property for which depreciation charges may be properly included under operating expenses, and the percentages of depreciation which shall be charged with respect to each of such classes of property, classifying the carriers as it may deem proper for this purpose. The Commission may, when it deems necessary, modify the classes and percentages so prescribed. Such carriers shall not, after the Commission has prescribed the classes of property for which depreciation charges may be included, charge to operating expenses any depreciation charges on classes of property other than those prescribed by the Commission, or, after the Commission has prescribed percentages of depreciation, charge with respect to any class of property a percentage of depreciation other than that prescribed therefor by the Commission. No such carrier shall in any case include in any form under its operating or other expenses any depreciation or other charge or expenditure included elsewhere as a depreciation charge or otherwise under its operating or other expenses.

(c)   The Commission shall at all times have access to and the right of inspection and examination of all accounts, records, and memoranda, including all documents, papers, and correspondence now or hereafter existing, and kept or required to be kept by such carriers, and the provisions of this section respecting the preservation and destruction of books, papers, and documents shall apply thereto. The burden of proof to justify every accounting entry questioned by the Commission shall be on the person making such entry and the Commission may suspend a charge or credit pending submission of proof by such person. Any provision of law prohibiting the disclosure of the contents of messages or communications shall not be deemed to prohibit the disclosure of any matter in accordance with the provisions of this section.

(d)   In case of failure or refusal on the part of any such carrier to keep such accounts, records, and memoranda on the books and in the manner prescribed by the Commission, or to submit such accounts, records, and memoranda as are kept to the inspection of the Commission or any of its authorized agents, such carrier or other person shall forfeit to the United States the sum of $500 for each day of the continuance of such offense.

(e)   Any person who shall willfully make any false entry in the accounts of any book of accounts or in any record or memoranda kept by any such carrier, or who shall willfully destroy, mutilate, alter, or by any other means or device falsify any such account, record, or memoranda, or who shall willfully neglect or fail to make full, true, and correct entries in such accounts, records, or memoranda of all facts and transactions appertaining to the business of the carrier, shall be deemed guilty of a misdemeanor, and shall be subject, upon conviction, to a fine not less than

$1,000 nor more than $5,000 or imprisonment for a term of not less than one year nor more than three years, or both such fine and imprisonment: *Provided*, That the Commission may in its discretion issue orders specifying such operating, accounting, or financial papers, records, books, blanks, or documents which may, after a reasonable time, be destroyed, and prescribing the length of time such books, papers, or documents shall be preserved.

(f)   No member, officer, or employee of the Commission shall divulge any fact or information which may come to his knowledge during the course of examination of books or other accounts as hereinbefore provided except insofar as he may be directed by the Commission or by a court.

(g)   After the Commission has prescribed the form and manner of keeping of accounts, records, and memoranda to be kept by any person as herein provided, it shall be unlawful for such person to keep any other accounts, records, or memoranda than those so prescribed or such as may be approved by the Commission or to keep the accounts in any other manner than that prescribed or approved by the Commission. Notice of alterations by the Commission in the required manner or form of keeping accounts shall be given to such persons by the Commission at least six months before the same are to take effect.

(h)   The Commission may classify carriers subject to this Act and prescribe different requirements under this section for different classes of carriers, and may, if it deems such action consistent with the public interest, except the carriers of any particular class in any State from any of the requirements under this section in cases where such carriers are subject to State commission regulation with respect to matters to which this section relates.

(i)   The Commission, before prescribing any requirements as to accounts, records, or memoranda, shall notify each State commission having jurisdiction with respect to any carrier involved, and shall give reasonable opportunity to each such commission to present its views, and shall receive and consider such views and recommendations.

(j)   Nothing in this section shall (1) limit the power of a State commission to prescribe, for the purposes of the exercise of its jurisdiction with respect to any carrier, the percentage rate of depreciation to be charged to any class of property of such carrier, or the composite depreciation rate, for the purpose of determining charges, accounts, records, or practices, or (2) relieve any carrier from keeping any accounts, records, or memoranda which may be required to be kept by any State commission in pursuance of authority granted under State law.

SPECIAL PROVISIONS RELATING TO TELEPHONE COMPANIES

* * * * *

[SEC. 221.] (b)   Nothing in this Act shall be construed to apply, or to give the Commission jurisdiction, with respect to charges, classifications, practices, or regulations for or in connection with wire telephone exchange service, even though a portion of such exchange service constitutes interstate or foreign communication, in any case where such matters are subject to regulation by a State commission.

(c)   For the purpose of administering this Act as to carriers engaged in wire telephone communication, the Commission may classify the property of any such carrier used for wire telephone communication, and determine what property of said carrier shall be considered as used in telephone service. Such classification shall be made after hearing, upon notice to the carrier, the State commission (or the Governor, if the State has no State commission) of any State in which the property of said carrier is located, and such other persons as the Commission may prescribe.

USE OF JOINT BOARDS—COOPERATION WITH STATE COMMISSIONS

[*]SEC. 310 (a)   The Commission may refer any matter arising in the administration of this Act to a joint board to be composed of a member, or of an equal number of members, as determined by the Commission, from each of the States in which the wire or radio communication affected by or involved in the proceeding takes place or is proposed, and any such board shall be vested with the same powers and be subject to the same duties and liabilities as in the case of a member of the Commission when designated by the Commission to hold a hearing as hereinbefore authorized. The action of a joint board shall have such force and effect and its proceedings shall be conducted in such manner as the Commission shall by regulations prescribe. The joint board member or members for each State shall be nominated by the State commission of the State or by the Governor if there is no State commission, and appointed by the Federal Communications Commission. The Commission shall have discretion to reject any nominee. Joint board members shall receive such allowances for expenses as the Commission shall provide.

(b)   The Commission may confer with any State commission having regulatory jurisdiction with respect to carriers, regarding the relationship between rate structures, accounts, charges, practices, classifications, and regulations of carriers subject to the jurisdiction of such State commission and of the Commission; and the Commission is authorized under such rules and regulations as it shall prescribe to hold joint hearings with any State commission in connection with any matter with respect to which the Commission is authorized to act. The Commission is authorized in the administration of this Act to avail itself of such cooperation, services, records, and facilities as may be afforded by any State commission.

---

[*]   Designated Section 410 in S.2910.

Chapter 6

AT&T Consent Decree: Trial Excerpts*

UNITED STATES DISTRICT COURT
FOR THE DISTRICT OF COLUMBIA

UNITED STATES OF AMERICA,	)	
Plaintiff,	)	
v.	)	
AMERICAN TELEPHONE AND TELEGRAPH	)	
COMPANY; WESTERN ELECTRIC	)	Civil Action No.
COMPANY, INC.; AND BELL TELEPHONE	)	74-1698
LABORATORIES, INC.,	)	
Defendants.	)	
———————————————————	)	
UNITED STATES OF AMERICA,	)	
Plaintiff,	)	
v.	)	Civil Action No.
WESTERN ELECTRIC COMPANY AND	)	82-0192
TELEGRAPH COMPANY,	)	
Defendants.	)	
———————————————————	)	
UNITED STATES OF AMERICA,	)	
Plaintiff,	)	
v.	)	Misc. No.
AMERICAN TELEPHONE AND TELEGRAPH	)	82-0025 (PI)
COMPANY, et al.,	)	
Defendants.	)	

Wednesday, June 20, 1982
Washington, D.C.
VOLUME 136 (A.M. Session)

---

*Reprinted courtesy of Nicholas Sokal, Official Court Reporter, 4800-F U.S. Courthouse, Washington, DC 20001.

The above-entitled matter came on for continued trial before the Honorable HAROLD GREENE, United States District Judge, Courtroom 20, commencing at approximately 9:45 a.m.

—   —   —   —   —

Reported by: Alfred A. Betz
    Hallock & Betz Reporters, Inc.

Nicholas Sokal
Official Court Reporter
4800-F U.S. Courthouse
Washington, D.C. 20001

APPEARANCES

—   —   —   —   —

ON BEHALF OF THE DEPARTMENT OF JUSTICE:
    James P. Denvir, Esquire

ON BEHALF OF THE AMERICAN TELEPHONE & TELEGRAPH CO.:
    Howard J. Trienens, Esquire

ON BEHALF OF SATELLITE BUSINESS SYSTEMS:
    William E. Willis, Esquire

ON BEHALF OF SAN/BAR, et al.:
    Stanley R. Jones, Esquire

ON BEHALF OF INDEPENDENT DATA COMMUNICATIONS MANUFAC-
TURERS ASSO:
    Herbert E. Marks, Esquire

ON BEHALF OF AMERICAN NEWSPAPER PUBLISHERS ASSOCIATION,
et al.:
    Richard E. Wiley, Esquire

ON BEHALF OF NATIONAL CABLE TELEVISION ASSOCIATION, et al.:
    Jay E. Ricks, Esquire

MR. MARKS: May it please the Court, my name is Herbert E. Marks, I appear here today on behalf of the Independent Data Communications Manufacturers Association. IDCMA is comprised of manufacturers of data communications equipment. That is sometimes denominated as customer premises equipment or CPE. These companies are competitors of Western Electric.

We urge the Court, with respect to this issue of the absence of restrictions on AT&T, to take two steps. First, condition approval of the proposed modification on AT&T offering all aspects of the CPE through a separate subsidiary and two, reject that portion of the proposed modification which would eliminate the patent licensing provisions of the 1956 decree.

The first recommendation is grounded on an evaluation of AT&T's position in the market after divestiture. You have heard from counsel for SBS about how that market power will be retained, a market power grounded in its monopoly position historically and which can give rise to such things as cross-subsidy, denial of interconnection, etcetera. I want to focus on a somewhat different aspect but an aspect that must be weighed in terms of the total picture.

Historically, the telephone network has been operated as an interactive interdependent unit, as AT&T reminds us and reminds us in the briefs in this proceeding. After divestiture, AT&T will continue to set technical standards for the interexchange telephone network. AT&T will continue to dictate standards for the BOCs. Since they must connect to the interexchange core network operated by AT&T, and the entire network must work together, the Government has recognized that AT&T will have a dominant role to this process.

Further, as we have discussed in our brief, AT&T will in certain instances be able to directly set interface standards for a customer even where the customer interconnects first through a BOC. There will also be direct interconnection with AT&T at a number of situations. As for carriers, private networks, the bypass situations, they will still have Cincinnati Bell and Southern New England Tel as subsidiaries.

First, what can AT&T do from this position as what we will describe as a standard set—I would like to preface this by saying I would like you to keep this issue in mind also when we talk about patent policy. I'll try and respond to just a few issues on that when I get done here.

First, AT&T can provide its affiliated manufacturer advance information on network changes, thereby permitting Western to design CPE which optimizes on this information. The same can be done as Western learns of operational data of a network, and finally AT&T can make changes in the network independent of the BOCs that affect the operation of customer premises equipment.

Next, AT&T can introduce a change in regulated services to advance the sales of its equipment or of its enhanced subsidiary services.

THE COURT: Well, I know that and I heard that for many months last year. But what exactly do you want me to do about that at this juncture?

MR. MARKS: What we would like you to do, Your Honor, is recognizing the residual power of AT&T which still has monopoly aspects, what we are asking you to do is prescribe a separate subsidiary for AT&T's customer premises equipment activities. This would be grounded on the step that the FCC took in the second computer inquiry. But there are—I'll anticipate a question, if I may, that, why not rely on the FCC? the answer to that is two points.

First of all, this Court is the court responsible for the consent decree and the modification of the 1956 consent decree. You're asked to modify the line of business restrictions in the '56 decree by eliminating them and eliminating the requirement that AT&T generally be regulated; in other words, structural type provisions. It is up to you to be satisfied that what is in place is an effective servant. In the Court of Appeals on the computer rules issues the Government, the FCC and AT&T and all said wait a minute. There is a responsibility of this Court to determine that what is replacing the old provisions is appropriate.

Now, secondly, as to the specific framework, that adopted by the FCC is inadequate with respect to CPE. What they did in the customer premises equipment business is require a separate subsidiary. The separate subsidiary will only have to do retail marketing and product specific advertising. The FCC rules do not require any separation of research, development, manufacturing.

THE COURT: So you're talking about divesting Western Electric and Bell Laboratories?

MR. MARKS: We are talking about putting them into American Bell, Inc. American Bell, Inc. is the separate subsidiary established pursuant to Computer II. It is briefly, or soon will be, offering an enhanced service. On January 1 it can do marketing of CPE and we're suggesting that the operational aspects of CPE other than just marketing ought to be added to American Bell, Inc.

I would like to respond now to a few comments on patents. First of all, AT&T in its brief attempts to utilize the monopoly revenue funding of their research and development. They noted that only 18 percent of the Bell System patents have been funded by the BOCs under the license contract. Assuming arguendo that that's appropriate, what they miss is, of course, the funding that comes through the captive sales of central office equipment and other equipment to both Long Lines and BOCs.

I would like to respond to a question you asked Mr. Jones about what patents are we talking about. We're talking about any patent that, A, hasn't been licensed as of the date the '56 decree is abandoned, or any new patent that comes on line because once the decree goes, as we understand it, you can't go to Bell for a license. So, anyone who doesn't have a patent or who doesn't have a patent as of the day of the change is out of luck, and with respect to new patents they are out of luck.

With respect to new patents, you have at least three categories that I think are worthy of attention. First, there are pipeline patents that—the patent will be the result of research in the pipeline. You have probably, oh, I would say probably up to a four—or five-year—and it could be more—lead time from the time you funded the research until the time you apply for your patent and you get a patent issued. So when you cut off the licensing provision, and let's say you do it tomorrow and approve the decree, well then, a whole raft of research that will result in patents that was funded under the old license contract escapes licensing requirements. Of course, even the licensing requirement is going to be around for at least 18 months. So there is a long lead time to sort of flush the system with respect to license contract funding.

Secondly, we are very concerned in this standards area. The effect of AT&T setting network standards is that it will be able to compel the BOCs as a practical matter to procure equipment from Western Electric or to procure equipment that is compatible with Western Electric. This, then, means that a patent license may be needed so that nonWestern equipment is compatible. This license could be for telecommunications network equipment or for CPE. Given this situation, it is very important that compulsory nondiscriminatory licensing at reasonable royalties be retained.

THE COURT: For how long? Forever?

MR. MARKS: Your Honor, I think the point is it will be there as long as AT&T retains its standard setting role for the integrated . . .

THE COURT: Forever.

MR. MARKS: It may or may not be forever. If the predictions of competition come to pass, we will be at some point looking at it differently. Secondly, this issue can be revisited through the modification procedures at any point in time. Thirdly, there may be, again, two classes of patents to consider: Patents generally and patents that relate to use of the telephone network. With respect to those, as long as we are talking about interoperative and integrated networks, then they take on a specially crucial role. The AT&T publications to date—and we have one attached to our brief—still talk about AT&T setting standards for the entire network and that those standards affect the way you communicate with that network.

I would like to respond just to one point in . . .

THE COURT: Well, you don't—do you object to the standards setting role of AT&T as such in principle?

MR. MARKS: It has to work together. It's a . . .

THE COURT: So you don't object to it.

MR. MARKS: . . . of their having been there first.

THE COURT: They have to—somebody has to set that role.

MR. MARKS: Having assumed that role growing out of . . . what we're asking for is that they, very naturally having maintained that role, that they retain the responsibilities that go along with it, and we think patent licensing is an important function of that responsibility.

I would like to reply to one issue in the AT&T reply brief. They suggested as to our point that with respect to people who don't have licenses now, well, they won't really be cut off even if the worst happens, because if you license one competitor you have to license all competitors. We would commend your attention to this issue. We agree in principle, but the problem is when the courts get this issue they talk about not making arbitrary restrictions, what is a competitor, and you have a situation that can lead to extensive litigation and in effect—effectively no patent through the process.

We would call to your attention in the response to the case they cite, a case at

438 F.2d 733. We think that the better way to proceed is to maintain the current patent licensing provisions of the 1956 decree in effect if and until the power of AT&T is documented to be dissipated.

THE COURT: Let me, before you finish, let me ask you a somewhat broader question than what you have addressed, which is somewhat similar but more concrete, what I asked somebody else yesterday, I think Ms. Dupont, namely this: We have a proposed decree here that's a result of negotiation between the Justice Department and AT&T. AT&T gives up the 22 operating companies and in return for which, in effect, the Justice Department assures them, to the extent that it can, that they will be able to compete relatively freely in other markets. Now, you and your colleagues and the ones that are going to talk a little later this morning about information services are saying that AT&T should have more onerous interconnection requirements than they have now. They should be required to license patents for the indefinite future, they should, in effect, be required to divest or to put in a separate subsidiary Western Electric and Bell Laboratories and the information services. There should be restrictions placed on them, in information services and perhaps some enhanced services.

Now, what is left of the bargain and can the Court—aren't you really saying when you're saying all of that that the Court should disapprove the entire decree and forget about it and continue with the trial and see what happens?

MR. MARKS: No sir. I think we have to qualify that kind of question. Obviously, you would have to make individual determinations as to which components of this . . .

THE COURT: Assuming that all of those demands and requests and recommendations were adopted, what would be left of the bargain, of the basic bargain?

MR. MARKS: Can I quibble on one item and I'll answer the question? I think the question on Western Electric and Bell Labs is not a total—is neither a divestiture nor is it total. It is a separation of certain functions in the case of ours, CPE, which would allow them still to retain the profit levels as if it were independent, untainted by the advantages of running the regulated service. I think that's far from divestiture. They have offered that in the legislative arena on several occasions. They have taken steps to implement it. I'm not so sure that's a big deal.

But talking more philosophically about deals, you have to go look at the privotal pieces and see how good it is, I think you have to keep in mind that Bell is being let out of the 1956 consent decree with the constraints on the line of business and constraints on being regulated. That is awfully nice to get. And the question really is what price. I think what we're asking this Court is to, A, put this in perspective, the legal perspective as one has to look at the '56 deal as being modified and the problems there. I think in terms of another speaker, this is the time to do the job right.

Thirdly, when it comes to the equation, I think one would have to say there is a great deal left for the Bell System and I feel uncomfortable either representing what a good deal it is for them or—but I think a fair analysis . . .

THE COURT: No, that's what—in all of these questions I'm not trying to tell you what I think the answer should be. I'm trying to get information. What are you saying would be left in terms of basic—as the *quid pro quo?*

MR. MARKS: The ability, Your Honor, to go into the data processing services business, the information business, exclusive of electronic publishing is a vast business. There are endless information services. They can go into any other business they want.

THE COURT: The American Newspaper Publishers are going to be here in half an hour telling us that they shouldn't be able to go into electronic publishing.

MR. MARKS: I'm not arguing their case. I prefer to just argue my case. But assuming we take a broad view which is that let's assume that you exclude that, you have—they still have all the rest of data processing that they get that they didn't have before. They get any number of other businesses that are unlisted and not appearing here that they get that they were excluded from. They get a clear path out of regulation for customer premise equipment and certain kinds of what used to be called communications—they are now called enhanced services—so that's a pretty good deal.

In terms of price ratios, the characterization of that business versus what they are leaving, I think they'll do quite well. I disclaim under the Investment Advisors Act any advice, etcetera.

THE COURT: I'm not going to invest in them.

MR. MARKS: I just conclude with the fact that I would like to suggest a perspective, Your Honor. The parties propose that no restrictions be imposed on AT&T even for a transition period. They propose an elimination of all restrictions embodied in the 1956 consent decree. Thus, on the day that the modification of final judgment would be entered, AT&T on that day is free from the prior restrictions and incurs no new restrictions. This assumes that magically that while AT&T monopolizes the market on Wednesday that this will immediately disappear without even a transition. I suggest this is inherently incredible for several reasons.

First, no preorganization plan need even be filed for six months. Second, divestiture need not be effected for 18 months. Third, and license contracts and supply contracts need not be terminated for one month. Fourth, until September 1, 1987, you have this special relationship between AT&T, Western, the labs, and the BOCs. Fifth, phased-in BOC provision of equal access to other common carriers which the Government says is one of the touchstones of getting a competitive market will not be completed under the decree's terms until September 1, 1986 and the FCC is talking about a 1990 timeframe, if ever, for achieving this.

Thus, on the face of the decree, of the proposed decree, there is significant evidence of an absence of effective competition of the type described by the Government and AT&T for a significant period of time. Then you add to that the analyses of the commentators which at a minimum very serious consideration about whether you are likely to get this type of competition for significant periods due to all sorts of problems, the residual bottlenecks in the interexchange market, the ability to close subsidies there, the standard setting as we have described it. Therefore, we just suggest that the total absence of any restrictions even for a transitional period renders the proposed settlement not in the public interest.

Thank you, sir.

THE COURT: Thank you.

Chapter 7

Economic Goals and Remedies of the AT&T Modified Final Judgment*

WARREN G. LAVEY and DENNIS W. CARLTON

The consent degree leading to the forthcoming divestiture of AT&T has set the stage for the future development of the telecommunications industry in the United States. Yet, the full impact of the settlement between the Department of Justice and AT&T upon consumers and the telecommunications-services and telecommunications-equipment industries remains uncertain. In this article, Mr. Lavey and Professor Carlton analyze the antitrust policies upon which the agreement is based and conclude that there are some anomalies in the application of these policies in the agreement. The authors then discuss the settlement agreement as a response to imperfect regulation of cross-subsidies. Finally, the authors discuss the problem of raising sufficient revenue to cover the costs of telephone companies after the divestiture.

7.1 INTRODUCTION

An antitrust consent decree, commonly referred to as the Modified Final Judgment (MFJ), was entered into by the American Telephone & Telegraph Company[1] and the United States Department of Justice and approved by District of Columbia District Court Judge Harold Greene in 1982.[2] The judgment has

---

[1] American Telephone & Telegraph Company (AT&T) included Western Electric (an equipment manufacturer), the Bell Operating Companies (providers of telecommunications services and equipment within franchised areas), AT&T Lone Lines (a provider of toll telecommunications services), and Bell Laboratories (a research center). United States v. American Tel. & Tel. Co., 461 F. Supp. 1314, 1317 n.1 (D.D.C. 1978).

[2] United States v. Western Elec. Co. (American Tel. & Tel. Co.), 552 F. Supp. 131, 226-34 (D.D.C. 1982), *aff'd sub nom.* Maryland v. United States, 103 S. Ct. 1240 (1983). The full details of compliance with the MFJ were approved on August 5, 1983, by order of Judge Greene. United States v. Western Electric Co., No. 82-0192 (D.D.C. Aug. 5, 1983) (memorandum and order). The term "Modified Final Judgment" reflects the relationship between this consent decree and the original consent decree that resolved the 1949 antitrust suit brought by the United States to break up AT&T. *See* United States v. Western Elec. Co., 1956 Trade Cas. (CCH) ¶ 68,246 (D.N.J. 1956) (original consent decree).

become a landmark in the development of the telecommunications industry in the United States and its effects on the structure and operation of the telecommunications industry will be extensive. For example, the Bell Operating Companies (BOCs) will be divested from AT&T, new exchange areas, known as "LATAs," have been approved,[3] property is being valued and transferred between the BOCs and AT&T, new channels for marketing Western Electric's equipment are being opened, and access charges are being developed. The number of technical details involved in these changes is monumental, as are the range and complexity of the legal issues.

In assessing the impact of these changes, it is important to remember that the MFJ is the settlement of an antitrust case. The assumption underlying the MFJ from the Department of Justice's (DOJ's) perspective is that the infusion of competition will enhance consumers' welfare, and thereby realize a fundamental goal of the antitrust laws.[4] Simply stated, the DOJ's theory was that ineffective regulation allowed AT&T to abuse its monopoly power in telecommunications services and equipment, and resulted in certain products and services being offered at prices that were above competitive levels.[5] Pricing a product above the competitive level is inefficient because it causes consumers to purchase less of the product than they would at the competitive price.

This article has two principal objectives. First, it evaluates the goals and remedies of the MFJ through application of the economic criteria of efficiency and consumers' welfare. In addition, the article seeks to establish an economic framework that will be useful to courts and regulators in interpreting and applying the MFJ, to business and government in pursuing legal remedies related to the MFJ, and to legislators and regulators in developing new regulatory regimes.

Sections 7.2 and 7.3 of this article examine two concerns of the MFJ: (1) abuse of monopoly power, and (2) cross-subsidization from an imperfectly regulated monopoly market to a competitive market. Each section initially addresses the relevant economic and legal theories underlying antitrust enforcement and then

---

[3] United States v. Western Elec. Co., No. 82-0192, slip op. at 104-116 (D.D.C. July 8, 1983); United States v. Western Elec. Co., 1983-1 Trade Cas. (CCH) ¶ 65,333 (D.D.C. 1983). Under the MFJ, the BOCs cannot provide inter-LATA services. Among the relevant factors in establishing LATAs are "the minimization of service disruption to telephone subscribers, the avoidance of costly network management; and the establishment of LATAs of sufficient size to attract several interexchange carriers." Id. at 69,972 n.27.
[4] A central goal of the antitrust laws is to promote economic efficency and consumers' welfare through increases in the quantity and quality of products available to consumers. See Reiter v. Sonotone, 442 U.S. 330, 343 (1979); Broadcast Music, Inc. v. Columbia Broadcasting Sys., Inc., 441 U.S. 1, generally R. Posner & F. Easterbrook, Antitrust Cases, Economic Notes and Other Materials 152-70 (2d ed. 1981) (discussing procompetitive policy designed to maximize consumers' welfare and economic efficiency as goals of antitrust laws); 1 P. Areeda & D. Turner, Antitrust Law 7-31 (1978) (same).
[5] The Department of Justice reasoned that AT&T, as a rate base/rate of return regulated monopolist, had "both the incentive and the ability, through cross-subsidization and discriminatory actions, to leverage the power it enjoys in its regulated monopoly markets to foreclose or impede the development of competition in related, potentially competitive markets." Department of Justice, Competitive Impact Statement, Daily Exec. Rep. (BNA) B-1, B-2 (Feb. 11, 1982).

analyzes the application of these theories in the MFJ. Section 7.4 considers an important economic problem that is affected by, but largely beyond the scope of, the MFJ: Raising sufficient revenue to cover the costs of a regulated firm.

7.2 ABUSE OF MONOPOLY POWER

7.2.1 Economic Framework

Monopoly power is defined as the ability of a firm (or group of firms acting jointly) to raise its price above the competitive level without driving away so many customers as to make the price increase unprofitable.[6] The price a firm may charge for its product is constrained by the availability of close substitutes for the product and, provided that there are sufficient close substitutes, its price remains no higher than that which will give it a competitive rate of return. If a firm attempts to charge a higher price—a supracompetitive price—customers will turn to other firms able to supply substitute products at competitive prices. These firms in turn will expand their production to meet the increased demand for their products. If a firm provides a large percentage of the substitutable products actually or potentially available, however, customers may find it more difficult to buy from alternative suppliers when the firm increases its price. Consequently, a firm with a large share of the relevant market of substitutable products may be able to raise its price without losing many customers.[7] For this reason, courts often use market share as a rough indicator of monopoly power.[8]

Supracompetitive prices are associated with a loss of consumers' welfare because such prices force buyers to consume a mix of products that is different from, and less attractive to them than, what their choices would have been if

---

[6] Landes & Posner, *Market Power in Antitrust Cases,* 94 Harv. L. Rev. 937,937 (1981). *See* United States v. Grinnell Corp., 384 U.S. 563, 570 (1966) (monopoly power is power to control prices or exclude competition); *Valley Liquors,* 678 F.2d at 745 (monopoly power is power of firm to raise prices above competitive levels profitably). *See generally* 2 P. Areeda & D. Turner, *supra* note 4, at 322 (discussing necessary elements of monopoly power).

[7] Technically stated, the elasticity of demand facing a firm increases with the availability of close demand and supply substitutes. *See* Landes & Posner, *supra* note 6, at 945. A relevant market is defined as an "area of effective competition," has product and geographic dimensions, and includes the demand and supply substitutes. *See* United States v. E.I. du Pont de Nemours & Co., 351 U.S. 377,395 (1956); Standard Oil Co. v. United States, 337 U.S. 293, 299-300 n.5 (1949).

[8] *See Grinnell,* 384 U.S. at 571; Broadway Delivery Corp. v. United Parcel Serv. of Am., Inc., 651 F.2d 122, 129 (2d Cir.) (market share below 50% rarely evidence of monopoly power; share between 50% and 70% usually strong evidence of monopoly power); *cert. denied,* 455 U.S. 943 (1981); Landes & Posner, *supra* note 6, at 938 (market share common indicium of market power). Recent research, however, indicates that the links between concentration and market power may be quite weak. *See, e.g.,* Ravenscraft, *Structure-Profit Relationships at the Line of Business and Industry Level,* 65 Rev. Econ. & Stat. 22, 29 (1983); Peltzman, *The Gains and Losses from Industrial Concentration,* 20 J.L. & Econ. 229 (1977). The DOJ, in the 1982 Merger Guidelines of the Department of Justice, 2 Trade Reg. Rptr. (CCH) ¶ 4500, 6881-11, June 4, 1982), uses the Herfindahl-Hirschman Index to measure the competitiveness of a market. This index is calculated by adding the squared shares of the firms in the market. *Id.* ¶ 4503 at 6881-11-6881-12.

firms supplied all goods and services at competitive prices.[9] Antitrust laws, however, do not attempt to counter the mere existence of monopoly power, or even the use of monopoly power to extract supracompetitive profits. Some firms, by virtue of their superior skill, foresight, efficiency, or luck, can offer better products and lower prices than their rivals and still earn supracompetitive profits.[10] If the antitrust laws posed disincentives to the existence and growth of such firms, the laws could impair consumers' welfare.[11] For example, a firm enjoying economies of scale—as AT&T alleges that it does in interexchange telecommunications services[12]—does not violate the antitrust laws when it obtains a large market share by charging prices that are profitable to it but so law that its smaller rivals cannot survive.

Some antitrust prohibitions focus on abuses of monopoly power that exclude competition in the monopolized market or involve leverage—the use of power in one market to restrain competition in another market.[13] An illustration of such a forbidden practice is a tying arrangement, whereby a monopolist conditions the sale of a product in one market on the buyer's purchase of another product in a different market.[14] A firm may also attempt vertical foreclosure, another prohibited practice, by monopolizing a key stage of an industry's operations.[15] A

---

[9] See, e.g., J. Gould & C. Ferguson, Microeconomic Theory 9-88 (5th ed. 1980); T. Scitovsky, Welfare and Competition 55-85 (1971); Lavey, Patents, Copyrights, and Trademarks as Sources of Market Power in Antitrust Cases, 27 Antitrust Bull. 433, 436 (1982).

[10] See United States v. Aluminum Co. of Am., 148 F.2d 416, 430 (2d Cir. 1945) (L. Hand, J.).

[11] See, e.g., 2 P. Areeda & D. Turner, supra note 4, at 331-41 (excess profits may be result of lower production costs or innovation in product design); Schmalensee, Another Look at Market Power, 95 Harv. L. Rev. 1789, 1805 (1982) (excess profits may provide signals to guide flow of investment funds).

[12] The Design and Cost Characteristics of Telecommunications Networks 1-4 (R. Skoog ed. 1980). See also J. Meyer, The Economics of Competition in the Telecommunications Industry 181-213, Appendix D (1979).

[13] See, e.g., Northeastern Tel. Co. v. American Tel. & Tel. Co., 651 F.2d 76, 93 (2d Cir. 1981), cert. denied, 455 U.S. 943 (1982); California Computer Prods. v. International Business Machs. Corp., 613 F.2d 727, 744 (9th Cir. 1979); Berkey Photo, Inc. v. Eastman Kodak Co., 603 F.2d 263, 284 (2d Cir. 1979), cert. denied, 444 U.S. 1093 (1980). See generally Landes & Posner, supra note 6; Lavey, supra note 9.

[14] See, e.g., United States Steel v. Fortner Enters., 429 U.S. 610, 620 (1977); Times-Picayune Publishing Co. v. United States, 345 U.S. 594, 611 (1953). Some economists and lawyers have questioned the rationale for antitrust liability for tie-in arrangements made by unregulated firms. See R. Posner & F. Easterbrook, supra note 4, at 802-10. A firm that is capable of earning monopoly profits on one product can gain no additional profits by tying a second, related product. Even when tying increases a monopolist's profits, consumers are not necessarily harmed. A firm subject to regulatory restraint on profits from its monopolized product, however, may seek to leverage or engage in tying to earn supracompetitive profits on a related product. See 1 A. Kahn, Economics of Regulation 28 (1970). The DOJ recognized that AT&T's incentive for leverage grew out of its status as a rate base/rate of return regulated monopolist. See supra note 5 (quoting DOJ). See generally Bowman, Tying Arrangements and the Leverage Problem, 67 Yale L.J. 19, 20 (1957); Burstein, A Theory of Full-Line Forcing, 55 Nw. U.L. Rev. 62 (1960); Markovitz, Tie-ins, Reciprocity, and the Leverage Theory, 76 Yale L.J. 1397, 1398 (1967).

[15] Many economists and lawyers have criticized the proposition that an unregulated monopolist would find it profitable to abuse its monopoly power by curtailing competition in related markets through vertical foreclosure. These authorities argue that it is often unlikely that a monopolist will

vertically-integrated firm may discriminate against competitors by denying access to a facility that is essential to the sale of a product and that cannot be duplicated by competitors readily or at a similar cost, and thereby may exclude more efficient rivals.[16]

To summarize, two elements of certain antitrust violations are relevant to an analysis of the MFJ.[17] First, a firm must be shown to possess monopoly power. Second, that power must have been used to exclude competition in the monopolized market or related markets. The possible effects of regulation on the existence and abuses of monopoly power will be discussed in the next section.

7.2.2 Analysis of the Modified Final Judgment

The MFJ reflects concerns about four types of abuses of monopoly power. This section discusses these abuses and examines the MFJ's response to them.

1. Interexchange Services

The MFJ clearly regards the BOCs as present monopolists in local telecommunications, even though there is currently some bypass of the BOC's exchange facilities and bypass technologies are becoming increasingly attractive.[18] The MFJ further assumes that the use of the BOCs' exchange (local) facilities is essential to competitors providing interexchange (toll) services,[19] raising a concern that the BOCs could confer a competitive advantage on AT&T's interex-

---

obtain a second source of monopoly profits from such arrangements. *See, e.g.,* 3 P. Areeda & D. Turner, *supra* note 4, at 199; R. Bork, The Antitrust Paradox 225-45, 365-81 (1978); E. Singer, Antitrust Economics: Selected Legal Cases and Economic Models 206-23 (1968); Bork, *Vertical Integration and the Sherman Act: The Legal History of an Economic Misconception,* 22 U. Chi. L. Rev. 157 (1954); McGee & Bassett, *Vertical Integration Revisited,* 19 J. L. & Econ. 17 (1976); Posner, *The Chicago School of Antitrust Analysis,* 127 U. Pa. L. Rev. 925, 926 (1979). Tying sometimes can increase a monopolist's profits, but may or may not harm consumers. Carlton, Notes on Tie-In Sales, Vertical Foreclosure (unpublished paper 1982) (copy on file at *Georgetown Law Journal*). The DOJ noted that the fact that some of AT&T's services and equipment offerings were regulated could give it the economic incentive to engage in vertical foreclosure (or refusal to purchase from outside suppliers). *See supra* note 5. The 1982 Merger Guidelines of the Department of Justice, 2 Trade Reg. Rptr. (CCH) ¶ 4500 (June 4, 1982), recognized certain competitive problems possibly arising from vertical mergers, including evasion of rate regulation. *Id* ¶ 4504, at 6881-17 - 6881-19.

[16] *See, e.g.,* United States v. Terminal R.R. Ass'n, 224 U.S. 383, 409-10 (1912): Hecht v. Pro-Football, Inc., 570 F.2d 982, 992-93 (D.C. Cir. 1977), *cert. denied,* 436 U.S. 956 (1978); United States v. Otter Tail Power Co., 331 F. Supp. 54, 61 (D. Minn. 1971), *aff'd in relevant part,* 410 U.S. 366 (1973).

[17] *See supra* note 13 and cases cited therein.

[18] *American Tel. & Tel. Co.,* 552 F. Supp. at 187; United States v. Western Elec. Co., 1983-1 Trade Cas. (CCH) ¶ 65,333, at 69,974 n.38 (D.D.C. 1983).

[19] *American Tel. & Tel. Co.,* 552 F. Supp. at 188. The Department of Justice noted that AT&T's control over the local exchange monopolies . . . has given it the power—and its concomitant control of Long Lines has given it the economic incentive—to impede competition in intercity services. The United States alleged that AT&T, after having failed to persuade regulators and courts to prevent new entry, attempted to exercise this power. Competitive Impact Statement, *supra* note 5, at B-6. *See generally* Lavey, *Joint Network Planning in the Telephone Industry,* 34 Fed. Com. L.J. 345 (1982).

change services over the services of its competitors by denying exchange access[20] to other common carriers, providing them with inferior exchange access, or charging them a higher price than what AT&T pays for equal exchange access.

The MFJ is not directed at eliminating the BOCs' monopoly control of local facilities. Rather, it seeks to prevent the abuse of this power to impair interexchange services. Thus, the MFJ does not prevent the BOCs from providing exchange services and exchange access by cable, optical fiber, cellular radio, or other new technologies,[21] all of which could compete with their present exchange facilities. Instead, the MFJ attempts to constrain the BOCs' ability to use their monopoly position to engage in leverage.

The MFJ tries to achieve this objective by requiring that the BOCs not discriminate in providing current and future facilities to other interexchange carriers. Under the MFJ, the BOCs must provide to all interexchange carriers exchange access to an unbundled, tariffed basis that is equal in type, quality, and price to that provided to AT&T.[22] The BOCs also may not discriminate in establishing and disseminating interconnection standards and in planning for new exchange-access facilities.[23] These requirements of nondiscrimination are fortified by the ordered divestiture of the BOCs from AT&T and the elimination of joint ownership of facilities.[24] Such actions are intended to decrease the likelihood that the BOCs will have an incentive to favor AT&T. In addition, the BOCs cannot provide interexchange telecommunications services on their own.[25]

By fostering interexchange competition, these provisions aim at decreasing the prices and increasing the quantity, quality, and diversity of services available to

---

[20] The MFJ defines 'exchange access" as, *inter alia,* "the provision of exchange services for the purpose of originating or terminating interexchange telecommunications." *American Tel. & Tel. Co.,* 552 F. Supp. at 288. The MFJ sets forth criteria for the establishment of exchange areaas by the BOCs. *Id. See also* United States v. Western Elec. Co., 1983-1 Trade Cas. (CCH) ¶ 65,333, at 69,980 (D.D.C. 1983) (requiring BOCs to provide equal access to all interexchange carriers on nondiscriminatory basis for intra-LATA as well as inter-LATA traffic); United States v. Western Elec. Co., No. 82-0192, slip op.

[21] *American Tel. & Tel. Co.,* 552 F. Supp. at 228.

[22] *Id.* at 227. Provision of equal exchange access by BOCs will be phased-in. *Id.* at 232-34.

[23] *Id.* at 227.

[24] *Id.* at 226-27. The Federal Communications Commission has ordered structural separation between a firm's multiple ventures in several cases, requiring separate books of account, facilities, and personnel. *See* Final Decision, *In re* Amendment of Section 64.702 of the Commission's Rules and Regulations [hereinafter *Second Computer Inquiry*], 77 F.C.C.2d 384, *reconsid.,* 84 F.C.C.2d 50, 71-75 (1980), *further reconsid.,* 88 F.C.C.2d 512 (1981), *aff'd sub nom.* Computer and Communications Indus. Ass'n v. FCC, 693 F.2d 198 (D.C. Cir. 1982), *cert. denied,* 103 S. Ct. 2109 (1983); Application of Gen. Tel. and Elecs. to Acquire Control of Telenet Corp., 72 F.C.C.2d 111 (1979); Satellite Business Sys., 62 F.C.C.2d 977, *mod.,* 72 F.C.C.2d 609 (1977), *aff'd en banc sub nom.* United States V. FCC, 652 F.2d 72 (D.C. Cir. 1980); Regulatory Policies Concerning Resale and Shared Use of Common Carrier Services, 62 F.C.C.2d 945 (1975), *aff'd sub nom.* National Ass'n of Regulatory Utility Comm'rs v. FCC, 525 F.2d 630 (D.C. Cir. 1976). Structural separation, unlike structural divestiture, does not eliminate a firm's incentives for discrimination because profits from separate subsidiaries go to the same parent.

[25] *American Tel. & Tel. Co.,* 552 F. Supp. at 227.

consumers making interexchange calls.[26] Unfortunately, it is possible that the combination of nondiscrimination requirements and divestiture will go beyond preventing abuses of monopoly power, to the detriment of competition and consumers' welfare. Divestiture alone would eliminate any incentive for the BOCs to favor one provider of interexchange services.[27] The BOCs will have the incentive to make utilization of their facilities attractive to interexchange carriers[28] and to potential users of interexchange services.[29]

The BOCs may require flexibility in developing interconnection arrangements and prices.[30] The MFJ's restrictions on the BOCs' prices, terms of offering services, and planning activities for interconnections may force the BOCs to justify differences in arrangements and prices as nondiscriminatory. The costs of proving nondiscrimination may be substantial, possibly increasing exchange access charges. In addition, fear of possible liability for discrimination may lead the BOCs to offer only a few interconnection arrangements and prices. Such a limited range of options may be suboptimal in terms of innovation, completion among interexchange carriers, and consumers' welfare.[31]

---

[26] Competition in interexchange services can prevent "supracompetitive price pressures that the [Federal Communications] Commission might not be able to perceive or control" and spur "greater technological advances and more efficient operations." United States v. FCC, 652 F.2d 72, 104 (D.C. Cir. 1980).

[27] Of course, it is possible that the injunctive provisions will be beneficial even after divestiture if, in light of the history of close ties between AT&T and the BOCs, the BOCs would have chosen to favor AT&T.

[28] Interexchange carriers can bypass the BOCs' exchange facilities for originating and terminating traffic. See infra footnotes 96-99 and accompanying text. Some interexchange carriers will bypass even if treated discriminatorily and others will not bypass even if subject to substantial discriminatory disadvantages. Still, the threat of greater bypass by any interexchange carrier gives the BOCs an incentive to proivde low-cost, high-quality interconnections.

[29] If an interexchange carrier can provide a service at a price and with qualities that will increase demand for interexchange services and, thereby, exchange access, the BOCs have no incentive to disadvantage that carrier in interconnection arrangements and prices.

[30] The MFJ recognizes that in some exchange areas with small, mechanical switches, non-discriminatory access arrangements would not promote consumers' welfare because the cost of the necessary equipment changes would raise access fees and cause a decline in interexchange traffic, and allows an exception for these areas from the nondiscrimination requirement. American Tel. & Tel. Co., 552 F. Supp. at 233. The MFJ's requirement that exchange access be provided on an unbundled basis, id., at 227, recognizes that interexchange carriers differ in their demands for interconnections and willingness to pay for certain arrangements, reflecting differences in their customers, services, and facilities. An optimal price/quality combination for one carrier's customers may be suboptimal for those of another carrier.

[31] The Robinson-Patman Act, 15 U.S.C. §§ 13-13b, 21a (1976), prohibits charging different prices to different buyers for products of like grade and quality where the price difference may lessen competition. A number of scholars have criticized the Act as inducing price uniformity, discouraging efficient distribution schemes, and, thereby, lessening competition and damaging consumers' welfare. See R. Bork, supra note 15, at 384-91, 398-401; R. Posner, The Robinson-Patman Act: Federal Regulation of Price Differences 49-53 (1976); R. Posner & F. Easterbrook, supra note 4, at 951-54. 968-89; 1 American Bar Association Section of Antitrust Law, The Robinson-Patman Act: Policy and Law 27-37 (1980); Cooper, Price Discrimination Law and Economic Efficiency, 75 Mich. L. Rev. 962 (1977). While the Robinson-Patman Act is limited to price differences for products "of like grade and quality," the MFJ's prohibitions are broader. Though "discrimination" is not defined in the MFJ, it may be that the "term 'price discrimination' describes a pattern of pricing that yields different net

2. Information Services

The MFJ treats the use of the BOCs' exchange facilities as essential to providers of information services.[32] The concern arises as to the treatment of rival information-service providers by the BOCs in terms of design of, access to, and charges for use of the BOCs' facilities. That is, how can the BOCs be prevented from abusing their monopoly power in exchange telecommunications to exclude competition in information services?

Under the MFJ, the BOCs can expand the quantity, quality, and range of exchange facilities that they offer to providers of information services, but cannot discriminate among such providers or provide information services themselves.[33] The BOCs must charge equal access fees to all providers of information services making equal use of the BOCs' facilities. Before the MFJ, the vertical integration of the BOCs with AT&T could have provided the incentive for the BOCs to favor AT&T if AT&T competed against other suppliers of information services. The divestiture of the BOCs from AT&T and the requirement that the BOCs provide equal access to exchange facilities to all information services are aimed at eliminating the BOCs' ability and incentives to impair development of the information-services industry as a competitive, efficient market.[34]

A related question addressed by the MFJ deals with the ability of AT&T itself to provide information services. The MFJ, as modified by Judge Greene, prohibits AT&T from engaging in electronic publishing over its own transmission facilities.[35] This prohibition reflects concerns that these faciltiies are essential to

---

returns from the sale or lease of the same or different products to different customers." 2 P. Areeda & D. Turner, *supra* note 4, at 341-42. Prohibition of price discrimination in this broad sense creates enormous uncertainties and costs of compliance. In addition, it is not clear whether a meeting-competition defense, explicit in the Robinson-Patman Act, will be implied for the MFJ.

Another approach to discrimination in charges and practices is evident in the cases interpreting section 202(a) of the Communications Act of 1934, 47 U.S.C. § 202(a) (1976). *See, e.g.,* American Tel. & Tel. Co. (TELPAK), 38 F.C.C.2d 370 (1964), *aff'd sub nom.* American Trucking Ass'ns v. FCC, 377 F.2d 121 (D.C. Cir. 1966), *cert. denied,* 386 U.S. 943 (1966); American Tel. & Tel. Co. Private Line Services, 61 F.C.C.2d 587, 656 (1976), *reconsid.,* 64 F.C.C.2d 971 (1977), *further reconsid.,* 67 F.C.C.2d 1441 (1978), *rev'd in part sub nom.* Aeronautical Radio, Inc. v. FCC, 642 F.2d 1221 (D.C. Cir. 1980).

[32] *American Tel. & Tel. Co.,* 554 F. Supp. at 227. The court expressed this view by compelling the BOCs to provide all interexchange carriers and information service providers exchange access, information access, and exchange services on an equal basis. *Id.* The MFJ defined "information services" as (with some exceptions) "the offering of a capability for generating, acquiring, storing, transforming, processing, retrieving, utilizing, or making available inforamtion which may be conveyed via telecommunications." *Id.* at 229. *See also id.* at 189-90 (free access to BOC exchange facilities will encourage competition in information services).

[33] *Id.* at 227. The limitation on the BOCs' provision of information services and divestiture seems to make the nondiscrimination restrictions unnecessary to prevent abuses of monopoly power. Consequently, the nondiscrimination restrictions may cause a loss of consumers' welfare. *See supra* text accompanying notes 28-31.

[34] *See id.* at 189-90 (revenues from access fees will encourage BOCs to design network to accommodate information-service providers).

[35] *Id.* at 225. The court defined electronic publishing as the provision of any information that AT&T or one of its affiliates "has, or has caused to be, originated, authored, compiled, corrected, or edited, or in which it has a direct or indirect financial or proprietary interest, and which is disseminated to an unaffiliated person through some electronic means." *Id.*

providers of information services[36] and that, if AT&T entered into electronic publishing, it would abuse its power to exclude competition.[37] Judge Greene viewed electronic publishing as an infant industry populated by a small number of firms unable to fend for themselves in competition with AT&T.[38] The prohibition on AT&T providing electronic publishing removes the economic incentives for AT&T to discriminate against providers of these services.

In contrast, AT&T is not prohibited from engaging in remote-access data processing services, based on the view that other large corporations are already established in this field, making it unlikely that AT&T would or could exclude competition through discrimination.[39] Judge Greene treated AT&T entry into this field as likely to stimulate competition.[40] He viewed the facilities of AT&T as less essential than those of the BOCs to providers of data processing services. Supposedly, if AT&T tried to cripple well-established competitors in remote-access data processing by discriminating against them in the price and quality of interexchange services, these competitors would have sufficient alternate transmission facilities available, such as microwave and satellite common carriers or private networks, to survive. Yet, anomalously, these alternatives are basically the same as those available to providers of information services, which are assumed in the MFJ to be subject to AT&T's monopoly power.

Under the 1980 decision of the Federal Communications Commission (FCC) in *Second Computer Inquiry*,[41] AT&T, through a separate subsidiary, is not prohibited from providing any "enhanced service," including both electronic publishing and remote-access data processing, on an unregulated basis.[42] The

---

[36] An implicit assumption here is that divestiture and nondiscriminatory exchange access will not result in a competitive market structure in interexchange services for at least a few years. *See id.* at 171 (AT&T conceded that as late as 1981 its share of interexchange revenue was about 77%). *But see id.* at 172 (after divestiture, competitive entry in interexchange telecommunications is likely to increase and AT&T should be unable to engage in monopoly pricing in any market). If providers of information services have competitive alternatives for interexchange services, this prohibition on AT&T is unnecessary for competition in information services and may cause a loss of consumers' welfare by eliminating an efficient supplier.

[37] Judge Greene recognized that AT&T could discriminate against competing electronic publishers by giving priority to traffic from its own publishing operations, gaining proprietary information about its competitors' publishing services, developing technology, facilities, and services that favor its own publishing operations and areas served, or providing competitors with inferior or more costly interconnections and maintenance. *Id.* at 181.

[38] *Id.* at 182.

[39] *Id.* at 179-80.

[40] *See id.* at 180 (inclusion of AT&T will result in further technological advances, new products, and better services).

[41] 77 F.C.C.2d 384, *reconsid.*, 84 F.C.C.2d 50 (1980), *further reconsid.*, 88 F.C.C.2d 512 (1981), *aff'd sub nom.* Computer and Communications Indus. Ass'n v. FCC, 693 F.2d 198 (D.C. Cir. 1982), *cert. denied*, 103 S. Ct. 2109 (1983).

[42] The FCC defined basic service as a "pure transmission capability over a communications path that is virtually transparent in terms of its interaction with customer supplied information." *Second Computer Inquiry*, 77 F.C.C.2d at 420. Enhanced service "combines basic service with computer processing applications that act on the format, content, code, protocol or similar aspects of the subscriber's transmitted information, or provide the subscriber additional, different, or restructure information, or involve subscriber interaction with stored information." *Id.* at 387.

FCC found that the market for enhanced services is "truly competitive"[43] and believed that market forces would protect the public interest in reasonable rates and availability of efficient enhanced services. Judge Greene, and to a lesser extend the DOJ, showed more concern than did the FCC about abuses of monopoly power by the BOCs and AT&T affecting competition in enhanced services and about the inability of regulators to prevent discrimination. The MFJ's more restrictive requirements on AT&T will limit the range of its activities that are not prohibited under the FCC's order in *Second Computer Inquiry*.

3. Terminal Equipment

Competition in the manufacturing and distribution of terminal equipment is a third concern of the MFJ. Before the MFJ, the BOCs distributed and installed terminal equipment manufactured largely by its corporate affiliate, Western Electric.[44] A BOC also could exclude competing manufacturers or distributors of terminal equipment from selling in its franchise area if it denied, delayed, or charged a higher price for interconnection of terminal equipment made or distributed by its rivals.[45] The vertical integration of the BOCs with Western Electric could have provided the BOCs with the incentive to favor Western Electric in their purchases and installation practices.

Three provisions of the MFJ affect this possible abuse of the BOCs' monopoly power.[46] First, the MFJ prohibits discrimination by the BOCs among suppliers and products in interconnection with, use of, and charges for the BOCs' service and facilities.[47] The obligation of nondiscrimination extends to the establishment and dissemination of interconnection standards.[48] Next, the corporate affiliation between the BOCs and Western Electric is severed.[49] Finally, the BOCs may not engage in the manufacture of telecommunications equipment.[50] These provisions are aimed at lowering the prices and raising the quality of terminal equipment available to consumers.[51]

---

[43] *Id*. at 433.

[44] *American Tel. & Tel. Co.*, 552 F. Supp. at 190. Western Electric was unregulated, though its dealings with AT&T Long Links and the BOCs were subject to regulatory scrutiny.

[45] The DOJ alleged that "protective connecting arrangement" required by AT&T for interconnection of customer-provided terminal equipment "erected an unreasonably restrictive barrier to use of competitive terminal equipment." Competitive Impact Statement, *supra* note 5, at B-7. *See also* Litton Systems, Inc. v. American Tel. & Tel. Co., 700 F.2d 785, 794-802 (2d Cir. 1985), *petition for cert. filed*, 52 U.S.L.W. 3001 (U.S. July 5, 1983).

[46] *American Tel. & Tel. Co.*, 552 F. Supp. at 227.

[47] *Id*.

[48] *Id*.

[49] *Id*. at 226-27. The MFJ also requires termination of the standard supply contract between Western Electric and the BOCs and other subsidiaries. *Id*. at 227.

[50] *Id*.

[51] Again, the nondiscrimination restrictions may be unnecessary or even counterproductive in light of the divestiture. *See supra* text accompanying notes 28-31 and note 33.

The MFJ, however, was revised by Judge Greene to allow the BOCs to distribute new terminal equipment.[52] This revision supposedly would aid manufacturers of terminal equipment by expanding sales if the BOCs become efficient distribution channels.[53] Moreover, the end of the BOCs' affiliation with Western Electric suggests that the BOCs would lose the incentive to discriminate in their choices of which manufacturers' equipment to distribute.[54] Yet, allowing the BOCs to distribute terminal equipment may give them the incentive to discriminate against rival distributors. This revision means that the MFJ's prohibition of discrimination by the BOCs will be relied upon to prevent the BOCs from abusing their market powerrto exclude competition in the distribution of terminal equipment.

Under this revision, BOCs are allowed to distribute, but not manufacture, terminal equipment. The explanation for this treatment does not lie in a difference in the possibility of anticompetitive discrimination. It does not seem that rival distributors could fend for themselves against discriminatory interconnecting by BOCs much better than rival manufacturers could, that consumers would be harmed less by discrimination against distributors, or that the rewards to the BOCs would be less when such conduct is directed against distributors. Instead, the court's reasoning is that distribution is an existing business of the BOCs, and continued participation by the BOCs may promote competition in distribution.[55] Conversely, manufacturing is not an existing business of the BOCs and, supposedly, participation by the BOCs in manufacturing would create a greater risk of loss to consumers via anticompetitive leveraging than the likelihood that consumers would benefit from the BOCs as the most efficient suppliers.

4. Switching and transmission equipment

Procurements by the BOCs represent a large portion of total sales of switching and transmission equipment in the United States. Assuming that the corporate affiliation between Western Electric and the BOCs lessened the degree to which price and quality considerations formed the basis for the BOCs' procurement practices or the ability of other manufacturers to make equipment satisfying the

---

[52] *American Tel. & Tel. CO.*, 52 F. Supp. at 231. The DOJ opposed this revision. *See infra* note 82 (DOJ reasoning that distribution for terminal equipment by BOCs would pose competitive dangers). Under the decree, AT&T will retain both the embedded terminal equipment and the existing network of retail outlets. 552 F.Supp. at 192.

[53] *Id.* at 191-92.

[54] *Id.* at 191.

[55] "The [BOCs], with their existing relationship to telephone users, are more likely than any other competitive entity to provide an effective counterbalance to AT&T's market strength [in distributing terminal equipment]." *Id.* at 192. Moreover, Judge Greene observed that the BOCs are likely to serve as outlets for many small equipment manufacturers, stimulating both price competition and innovative design and manufacturing. *Id.* at 192 n.249.

BOCs' needs, the BOCs' procurement practices would have foreclosed competition in manufacturing switching and transmission equipment.[56]

The MFJ provides that the BOCs must make nondiscriminatory procurements, nondiscriminatorily establish and disseminate technical information, sever their affiliation with Western Electric, and neither nor provide any switching or transmission equipment.[57] These provisions seek to promote consumers' welfare by increasing competition in manufacturing such equipment and lessening incentives for inefficient purchases.[58]

5. Summary

The preceding discussion of the goals and remedies of the MFJ indicates the skepticism of the DOJ and the court about the effectiveness of state and federal regulators in limiting the ability of the BOCs and AT&T to abuse their market power. The MFJ assumes that the precompetitive policies set forth in the antitrust laws have not been and, without the MFJ's remedies, would not be implemented effectively by regulators.[59] Underlying the MFJ is the supposition that AT&T is not immune from the antitrust laws by reason of pervasive regulation.[60] Accord-

---

[56] Competitive Impact Statement, *supra* note 5, at B-8. Judge Greene noted that the DOJ's procurement case was "not extremely strong." *American Tel. & Tel. Co.*, 552 F. Supp. at 163 n.137, and dismissed the part of the case dealing with the pricing of equipment sold by Western Electric. 524F. Supp. 1336, 1380-81 (D.D.C. 1981).

[57] *American Tel. & Tel. Co.*, 552 F. Supp. at 227.

[58] The nondiscrimination provisions may be unnecessary to prevent abuses of market power and may actually be detrimental to consumers' welfare. *See supra* notes 28-31 and accompanying text. The requirement under the Communications Act of 1934 that the FCC approve investments in transmission lines was designed to prevent carriers from inflating their rate basis, such as by inefficient purchases. *See* 47 U.S.C. §214(a) (1976); 78 Cong. Rec. 10,314 (1934); AT&T: Construction and Operation of Carrier Systems, 10 F.C.C. 315, 321 (1944). The FCC found that competition in supplying equipment to the BOCs benefits consumers. AT&T: Charges for Interstate Telephone Service, 64 F.C.C.2d 1, 26 (1977), and that there was some inefficiency in the BOCs' equipment procurements because of the close relationship between Western Electric and the BOCs. *Id.* at 41. At times, the FCC has monitored closely AT&T's equipment procurement practices. *See, e.g.*, AT&T: Northeast Corridor Lightguide Cable, 84 F.C.C.2d 303, 316 (1981). *See also* AT&T: Charges for Interstate Telephone Service, 64 F.C.C.2d 1, 51-52 (1977) (chronic forecasting errors by AT&T and ineffective regulatory review led to overbuilding and network underutilization); Competitive Carrier Rulemaking, 77 F.C.C.2d 308, 344-47 (1979) (FCC's frustration in reviewing AT&T's construction and purchase plans too late in planning cycle reasonable to require major changes).

[59] The FCC is not limited in its pursuit of the public interest to the policies of the antitrust laws. United States v. FCC, 652 F.2d 72, 88 (D.C. Cir. 1980).

[60] The court in *American Tel. & Tel. Co.* noted that "the Bell System has been neither effectively regulated nor fully objected to true competition." 552 F. Supp. at 170. *See also* MCI Communications Corp. v. American Tel. & Tel. Co., 1982-83 Trade Cas. (CCH) ¶ 65,137, at .71,363-72 (7th Cir. 1983) (denying AT&T antitrust immunity for involuntarily initiated interconnection practices neither controlled nor supervised by FCC), *petitions for cert. filed,* 52 U.S.L.W. 3011 (U.S. July 11, 1983); Phonetele Inc. v. American Tel. & Tel. Co., 664 F.2d 716, 727-38 (9th Cir. 1981) (AT&T claim of implied antitrust immunity due to pervasive regulation denied; noting limited authority of FCC to approve proposed tariffs before they go into effect), *cert. denied*, 103 S. Ct. 785 (1983); Northeastern Tel. Co. v. American Tel. & Tel. Co., 651 F.2d 76, 82-84 (2d Cir. 1981) (denying antitrust immunity to AT&T; noting compatability and effectiveness of FCC regulation under Federal Communications

ing to the MFJ, drastic structural remedies, limitations on the scope of firms' activities, and clear prohibitions against discrimination are necessary to prevent future exclusionary conduct by these regulated firms.

7.3 CROSS-SUBSIDIZATION

7.3.1 Economic Framework

This section discusses economic harms that can arise from a firm's use of profits earned in a regulated monopoly market to help cover its costs in a competitive market. Cross-subsidization enables a firm to price one of its products below its directly-attributable costs and still survive.[61] It thereby may be able to drive out efficient rivals in supplying the subsidized product. It then could use actual or potential cross-subsidization to prevent potential competitors from electing to enter the market for the subsidized product, leaving the firm with the ability to extract monopoly profits for that product and impair consumers' welfare. In addition, cross-subsidization will incresae the price charged for the regulated, subsidizing product.[62]

An integrated firm that has a regulated monopoly in one market and faces competition in another is difficult to regulate because regulators cannot possibly detect all instances of cross-subsidization.[63] One form of regulation involves limiting the rates charged by a firm so that it covers its costs in providing a

---

Act and antitrust actions under Sherman Act), *cert. denied,* 455 U.S. 943 (1982); Sound, Inc. v. American Tel. & Tel. Co., 631 F.2d 1324, 1327-35 (8th Cir. 1980) (implied antitrust immunity based on tension between FCC regulation and antitrust principles denied); Mid-Texas Communications Sys., Inc. v. American Tel. & Tel. Co., 615 F.2d 1372, 1377-82 (5th Cir.) (implied antitrust immunity denied; FCC's mandate not centered upon competitive effects of regulation so inquiry into antitrust concerns obscured), *cert. denied,* 449 U.S. 912 (1980); Essential Communications Sys., Inc. v. American Tel. & Tel. Co., 610 F.2d 1114, 1121-26 (3d Cir. 1979) (FCC action not level of agency approval required for grant of implied antitrust immunity); Southern Pac. Communications Co. v. American Tel. & Tel. Co., 556 F. Supp. 825, 1095-97 (D.D.C. 1982) (denying antitrust immunity to AT&T; noting FCC's uncertainty and delay in regulating competition); United States v. American Tel. & Tel. Co., 524 F. Supp. 1336, 1357-60 (D.D.C. 1981) (no Congressional intent that FCC regulatory authority override antitrust considerations).

[61] The courts in MCI Communications Corp. v. American Tel. & Tel. Co., 1982-83 Trade Cas. (CCH) ¶ 65,137 (7th Cir. 1983), *petitions for cert. filed,* 52 U.S.L.W. 3011 (U.S. July 11, 1983), and Northeastern Tel. Co. v. American Tel. & Tel. Co., 651 F.2d 76 (2d Cir. 1981), *cert. denied,* 455 U.S. 943 (1982), rejected the claim that pricing below fully-distributed costs but above directly-attributable (long-run incremental or average marginal) costs constitutes predatory pricing. *MCI,* 1982-83 Trade Cas. (CCH) at 71,383-84; *Northeastern Tel. Co.,* 651 F.2d at 89-90. The courts held that pricing above directly-attributable costs does not involve cross-subsidies. *MCI,* 1982-83 Trade Cas. (CCH) at 71,383-84; *Northeastern Tel. Co.,* 651 F.2d at 88. *See* W. Sharkey, The Theory of Natural Monopoly 40-42 (1982) (cross-subsidization is the failure of the price charged for a service or product to cover the cost of producing it).

[62] Perfect competition and perfect regulation in the competitve and regulated markets, respectively, would protect consumers from the harms of cross-subsidization. The danger of harmful cross-subsidization arises only when regulation in imperfect.

[63] The FCC has at times attempted to improve its ability to detect and thereby to limit cross-subsidies by requiring the formation of separate subsidiaries for certain activities. *See infra* note 73.

regulated product and earns no more than a competitive rate of return on its investment for that product.[64]

Problems exist with cost-based regulation because cost accounting for a multiproduct firm is often inadequate. Under the basic principles of cost accounting, firms should assign costs and investment to the specific activities that caused them.[65] It may be difficult, if not impossible, to allocate some categories of costs and investment, such as executives' salaries, research and development expenditures, and the expenses of production facilities used to manufacture several products, to particular products on the basis of cost causation. Even if it is possible to arrive at a sound cost-causation-based allocation of a firm's costs and investment by product, it may be hard for regulators to detect instances of cross-subsidization in which the firm misallocated its costs and investment across its products. The FCC's failure to develop effective cost-accounting procedures for AT&T's interstate services is a classic example of these difficulties.[66]

The main issue is why a firm would have an incentive to cross-subsidize. One concern is that cross-subsidization may foster predatory pricing. Predatory pricing is the temporary reduction of price by one firm in an attempt to drive out rivals or to discourage new competitors from entering the market. Once the rival firms are eliminated, the predator may raise its prices above the competitive level in order to recoup its short-term losses and realize supracompetitive profits.[67] Successful predatory pricing thus decreases consumers' welfare in the long run, although there is a short-run benefit from the temporarily lower prices.

---

[64] *See, e.g.,* S. Breyer, Regulation and its Reform 36-59 (1982); P. Garfield & W. Lovejoy, Public Utility Economics 44-45 (1964); 1 A. Kahn. The Economics of Regulation 25-54 (1970); F. Scherer, Industrial Market Structure and Economic Performance 481-86 (2d ed. 1980); Averch & Johnson, *Behavior of the Firm Under Regulatory Constraint,* 52 Am. Econ. Rev. 1053 (1962); Joskow & Hall, *Regulation in Theory and Practice: An Overview,* in Studies in Public Regulation 1 (G. Fromm ed. 1981).

[65] *See generally* S. Davidson, Fundamentals of Accounting 621-39 (5th ed. 1975); E. Hendricksen, Accounting Theory 28-31 (1965); 1 A. Kahn, *supra* note 64, at 63-158; F. Scherer, *supra* note 64, at 483-86.

[66] *See* American Tel. & Tel. Co. Private Line Rate Cases (TELPAK), 61 F.C.C.2d 587, 589-90 (9176) (FCC adopted fully distributed costs as the ratemaking standard for multiservice carriers; chose FDC-7, a cost-causation based method), *reconsid.,* 64 F.C.C.2d 971 (1977), *further reconsid.,* 67 FC.C.2d 1441 (1978), *rev'd in part sub nom.* Aeronautical Radio, Inc. v. FCC, 642 F.2d 1221 (D.C. Cir. 1980); American Tel. & Tel. Co. (Interim Cost Allocation Manual), 84 F.C.C.2d 384, 385, 397 (1981) (FDC-7 unworkable for AT&T ratemaking because historical cost-causation data lacking; lack of a proper and manageable methodology for the allocation of investment and expenses to AT&T's individual services or service elements; interim cost allocation methodology adopted), *aff'd sub nom.* MCI Telecommunications Corp. v. FCC, 675 F.2d 408 (D.C. Cir. 1982).

[67] *See, e.g.,* 3 P. Areeda & D. Turner, *supra* note 4, at 151; R. Bork, *supra* note 15, at 144-59; R. Posner, Antitrust Law 188 (1976); Areeda & Turner, *Predatory Pricing and Related Practices Under Section 2 of the Sherman Act,* 88 Harv. L. Rev. 697, 698 (1975); Baumol, *Quasi-Permanence of Price Reductions: A Policy for Prevention of Predatory Pricing,* 89 Yale L.J. 1, 26 n.50 (1979); Brodley & Hay, *Predatory Pricing: Competing Economic Theories and the Evolution of Legal Standards,* 66 Cornell L. Rev. 738, 741 (1981); Easterbrook, *Predatory Strategies and Counterstrategies,* 48 U. Chi. L. Rev. 263, 265 (1981); Hurwitz & Kovacic, *Judicial Analysis of Predation: The Emerging Trends,* 35 Vanderbilt L. Rev. 63, 67 (1982); Joskow & Klevorick, *A Framework for Analyzing Predatory Pricing Policy,* 89 Yale L.J. 213, 219-20 (1979).

Courts view predatory pricing as an attempt to monopolize in violation of the antitrust laws.[68] Many legal and economic scholars believe that unregulated firms have no incentive to engage in predatory pricing and rarely do so. A predator's success depends upon both the successful and permanent elimination of rivals and the ability to charge supracompetitive prices in the rivals' absence to regain lost profits. In reality, however, fulfillment of such conditions is unlikely. Evidence of successful predators is scarce because predation is often more costly to the predatory firm than it is to its rivals.[69]

The incentives for predatory pricing may be the same for a multi-product firm possessing a regulated monopoly in some products and facing competition in others as for unregulated firms. Under the assumptions of profit maximization and poor regulatory scrutiny of cost allocations, such a firm could shift some of its costs and investment attributable to the competitive product into the rate base for a regulated product to maximize its overall profits on the regulated and competitive products. Thus the firm may earn apparently supracompetitive profits on the unregulated product even though it charges a competitive price. If the firm attempts predation by pricing below the competitive level in the unregulated market, it will incur lost profits in the short run. It will sacrifice these profits only on the hope of excluding competition and recouping its losses. The regulated firm may differ from an unregulated firm in that, during predation, the former might appear to earn competitive or supracompetitive profits on the product subject to predation through cost shifting. Yet under these assumptions, regulated and unregulated firms actually would face similar incentives regarding the decision whether to engage in predation. Any theory that predicts why predatory pricing is not attractive to unregulated firms would apply equally to regulated firms.[70]

A second concern about cross-subsidization involves economic efficiency. Rate-base regulation seeks to limit rates such that a firm's total revenues from a service cover the costs and yield a fair (*i.e.,* competitive) rate of return on the investment allocated to the service. If rate-base regulation permits improper shifting of costs toward the regulated service, the price of the regulated service will be higher than is justified under efficient pricing principles. This result may

---

[68] *See, e.g.,* MCI Communications Corp. v. American Tel. & Tel. Co., 1982-83 Trade Cas. (CCH) ¶ 65,137 at 71,372-84 (7th Cir. 1983), *petitions for cert. filed,* 52 U.S.L.W. 3011 (U.S. July 11, 1983); William Inglis & Sons Baking Co. v. ITT Continental Baking Co., 668 F.2d 1014, 1030 (9th Cir. 1981), *cert. denied,* 103 S. Ct. 58 (1982); Northeastern Tel. Co. v. American Tel. & Tel. Co., 651 F.2d 76, 86 (2d Cir. 1981), *cert. denied,* 455 U.S. 943 (1982).

[69] *See, e.g.,* 3 P. Areeda & D. Turner, *supra* note 4, at 150-52; R. Bork, *supra* note 15, at 154, Federal Trade Comm'n, Strategic Predation and Antitrust Analysis 9-12 (S. Salop ed. 1981); Easterbrook, *supra* note 67, at 312-18; McGee, *Predatory Pricing Revisted,* 23 J.L. & Econ. 289, 292-300 (1980).

[70] *See* R. Posner & F. Easterbrook, *surpa* note 4, at 994-95 (discussing Otter Tail Power Co. v. United States, 410 U.S. 366 (1973)). If managers in regulated firms do not profit maximize, but instead pursue other goals such as maximizing their job security, while managers in unregulated firms do profit maximize, it is possible to conceive of cases in which predation is more likely to occur in the multi-product regulated firm than in the multi-product unregulated firm.

increase the firm's profits but will generally be detrimental to consumers' welfare.

7.3.2 Analysis of the MFJ

The DOJ recognized the potential for AT&T to engage in cross-subsidization.[71] Likewise, the court acknowledged the possibility for cross-subsidization if the divested BOCs were permitted to engage in particular activities.[72] The MFJ manifests this awareness in two ways.

1. Divestiture

On several occasions the FCC has required that the competitive activities of a regulated monopolist be carried out through a separate subsidiary.[73] This structural separation reduces the monopoly's ability to cross-subsidize by promoting detection and prevention of cross-subsidization attempts.[74] The MFJ achieves structural separation of the BOCs from AT&T and Western Electric through total divestiture, a more drastic remedy than separate subsidiaries. Two reasons underly the MFJ's approach.

First, the court reasoned that neither the FCC nor a "judicially-created bureaucracy"[75] to oversee an injunction decree possesses the ability to police effectively AT&T's cost accounting and conduct,[76] perhaps even with separate subsidiaries.

---

[71] The Department of Justice reasoned that because AT&T's aggregate earnings may not exceed a specified rate of return, when it faces competition for some but not all of its services AT&T has an incentive to reduce prices for its competitive services and raise prices for its monopoly services. Competitive Impact Statement, *supra* note 5, at B-7. The DOJ reasoned that consequently, when faced with competitive entry in certain intercity services, AT&T lowered its prices on those services, without regard to the costs of providing them and with the effect of impeding new intercity competition. *Id.*

[72] *American Tel. & Tel. Co.*, 552 F. Supp. at 188-94 (restrictions imposed on divested BOCs prohibiting them from manufacturing terminal equipment and providing interexchange or information services; no restrictions placed on marketing terminal equipment or on directory advertising because no danger of cross-subsidization from regulated to unregulated products in these areas).

[73] *See* Application of Gen. Tel. and Elecs. to Acquire Control of Telenet Corp., 72 F.C.C.2d 111, 137 (1979) (in approving acquisition FCC required that Telenet operate as separate subsidiary; structural separation necessary to avoid cross-subsidization), *mod.*, 84 F.C.C.2d 18, 32-37 (1979); *Second Computer Inquiry*, 77 F.C.C.2d at 457-87, *reconsid.*, 84 F.C.C.2d at 71-75 (amendment of §64,702 of FCC's Rules and Regulations to require AT&T to offer customer-premises equipment and enhanced services through separate subsidiary); Land Mobile Services, 51 F.C.C.2d 945, 951 (1975) (wireline telephone companies must establish separate corporations for the operation of cellular mobile radio communication systems), *aff'd sub nom.* National Ass'n of Regulatory Util. Comm'rs v. FCC, 525 F.2d 630, 637 (D.C. Cir. 1976), *cert. denied*, 425 U.S. 992 (1976).

[74] *See Second Computer Inquiry*, 77 F.C.C.2d at 462 (principal mechanisms employed include reduction in extent of joint and common costs between affiliated firms, requirement that transactions move from one set of corporate books to another, and publication of rates, terms, and conditions on which services will be available to all potential purchasers).

[75] *American Tel. & Tel. Co.*, 552 F. Supp. at 168. *See also* Byars v. Bluff City News Co., 609 F.2d 843, 863-64 (6th Cir., 1979) (courts should consider feasiblity of forming final decrees; injunction ordering monopolist to deal might enmesh court in difficult problems of price regulation).

[76] Competitive Impact Statement, *supra* note 5, at B-27; *American Tel. & Tel. Co.*, 552 F. Supp. at 167-68.

The court viewed divestiture as a more effective enforcement mechanism than structural separation. Although the separate subsidiary approach provides a means for revealing intra-company transactions so that regulators may better detect and prevent cross-subsidization, it does not eliminate the economic incentives, to the extent they exist, for anticompetitive conduct.[77] The parent company still has the same incentive to use a regulated-monopoly subsidiary to provide a competitive advantage to another of its subsidiaries through cross-subsidization or discrimination. In contrast, a monopolist has no incentive to favor a separately-owned company over its rivals.

Second, the court viewed separate subsidiaries essentially as a regulatory device and therefore not an appropriate antitrust remedy.[78] The nature of the action against AT&T, and not just the goal of economic efficiency, thus dictated certain aspects of the final order.

2. Opportunities for Cross-Subsidization

Under the MFJ, the BOCs will be allowed to continue engaging in certain unregulated activities, specifically the sale of directory advertising (Yellow Pages) and the distribution of terminal equipment.[79] The court did not require separate subsidiaries for these activities, but recognized that regulators may want to impose this requirement to help detect cross-subsidies.[80] Cross-subsidization considerations entered into the court's treatment of these activities in two ways.

First, the court reasoned that cross-subsidization affecting the distribution of terminal equipment was unlikely since the risk of detection were high and the possibility of successful predation low.[81] Nevertheless, the DOJ viewed a ban on the BOCs engaging in the distribution of terminal equipment as necessary for efficient competition in that market because the BOCs might have the incentive to cross-subsidize or leverage through discriminatory interconnections.[82]

On the other hand, cross-subsidization from directory advertising to regulated services was both expected and encouraged.[83] The court treated directory advertising as a source of profits that could be used to subsidize local telephone rates. The court believed that having the BOCs provide directory advertising instead of AT&T would have no anticompetitive effect on the market for advertising.

[77] *American Tel. & Tel. Co.*, 552 F. Supp. at 193 n.251.
[78] *Id.*
[79] *Id.* at 231.
[80] *Id.* at 193 n.251.
[81] *Id.* at 191-92.
[82] *District Court Accepts Government's, AT&T's Assent to Changes in Settlement*, 43 Antitrust & Trade Reg. Rep. (BNA) No. 1079, at 380-381 (Aug. 26, 1982) (DOJ reasoning that "provision by the BOCs of more complex customer premises equipment, which necessarily involves a high degree of coordination between the equipment provider or customer and the local exchange carrier with respect to such matters as installation, maintenance, testing and restoration, would pose substantial competitive dangers. *See supra* notes 14 and 15 (discussing tie-in and foreclosure arrangements).
[83] *American Tel. & Tel. Co.*, 552 F. Supp. at 193-94.

Rather, the court saw the cross-subsidies to local telephone service as promoting the federal policy of making telephone service available at reasonable rates.[84]

In the absence of structural separation of directory advertising from the BOCs' exchange and exchange access services, the court expected cross-subsidization. It is not clear, however, whether the court expected the revenues or, possibly, losses from the BOCs' distribution of terminal equipment to affect the amount of revenue required to provide services.

7.4 RAISING SUFFICIENT REVENUE

7.4.1 Economic Framework

The historical rationale for telephone regulation was that because the provision of local telephone service was a natural monopoly, output could be provided most efficiently by one firm.[85] The provision of telephone service is characterized by high fixed costs, and the incremental (marginal) cost of serving an additional subscriber is less than the average cost (the total cost of providing telephone service in the specified area divided by the total number of subscribers). Charging a price per subscriber equal to the marginal cost of serving him would not produce sufficient revenues to cover a telephone company's total costs. Consequently, the prices for some products or services must be set above their marginal costs. The difficulty facing regulators is how to set the price of each service so as to cover total costs.

There are well-established economic pricing principles for raising the necessary revenue in such circumstances, assuming that the goal is to minimize the unavoidable economic inefficiency that results from charging prices in excess of marginal cost.[86] The extent of the economic inefficiency or distortion will depend on the degree to which the demand for a product is reduced by an increase in its price and to what extent the price of a product exceeds its marginal cost. The greater the disparity between product demand at the elevated price level and product demand at marginal cost, the greater tends to be the economic distortion. The distortion is minimized if (1) products whose demand is less price sensitive

---

[84] *Id. See also* United States v. Western Elec. Co., No. 82-0192, slip op. at 150-54 (D.D.C. July 8, 1983); United States v. Western Elec. Co., 1983-1 Trade Cas. (CCH) ¶ 65,333 at 69,973 (D.D.C. 1983) (continued viability of BOCs in public interest in light of goal of universal telephone service); *infra* note 113.

[85] *See, e.g.,* 1 A. Kahn, *surpa* note 64, at 125-26; W. Lavey, Factors Influencing Investments, Costs, and Revenues of REA Telephone Companies (Harvard Program on Information Resources Policy 1982).

[86] *See generally* Baumol & Bradford, *Optimal Departures from Marginal Cost Pricing,* 60 Am. Econ. Rev. 265 (1970); Braeutigam, *An Analysis of Fully Distributed Cost Pricing in Regulated Industries,* 11 Bell J. Econ. 182 (1980); Ng & Weisser, *Optimal Pricing with a Budget Constraint— The Case of the Two-Part Tariff,* 41 Rev. Econ. Stud. 337 (1974); Ordover & Panzar, *On the Existence of Pareto Superior Outlay Schedules,* 11 Bell J. Econ. 351 (1980); Ramsey, *A Contribution to the Theory of Taxation,* 37 Econ. J. 47 (1927); Willig, *Pareto Superior Nonlinear Outlay Schedules,* 9 Bell J. Econ. 56 (1978). We are assuming no lump-sum taxes.

bear the brunt of the financing burden, and (2) there are many products whose prices can be raised above marginal cost. If there are many products, the amount by which any of one product's price exceeds its marginal cost can be less while raising the same amount of revenue.[87]

Consider the situation in which regulators have the option of raising the prices of many products above their marginal costs in order to cover the costs of providing telephone exchange services. This occurs when the regulated monopolist is permitted to sell multiple products and is protected from competitive entry. Suppose that the BOCs were allowed to sell salt and tried to do so at a price above its marginal cost in order to contribute to the revenue requirement of their telephone exchange facilities.[88] They would be unable to sell salt at a supracompetitive price because salt buyers would turn to rival sellers of salt. Only if the BOCs were granted a monopoly in salt and the entry of rivals was forbidden would it be possible for them to earn revenue in the salt market to help pay for the costs of the telephone facilities.[89] The benefit to consumers from granting the BOCs a monopoly in salt is the resulting drop in the distortionary effects of raising sufficient revenue to cover costs. Consumers, however, would not be protected from resulting inefficiencies in salt production. That task would fall on regulators as ancillary to the regulation of exchange telephone service.[90] The restraint on competition in the production and sale of salt involved in this situation is antithetical to the antitrust laws.

An alternative method for efficiently raising revenue is to allow free entry into a market but subject sales to a government charge or "tax" used to help finance the costs of providing telephone service. For example, there may be free entry into the salt market but all sales of salt would bear a charge to help offset the costs of providing telephone service. This would raise revenue that could be used to help cover costs regardless of whether the BOCs could compete in selling salt. The effect on salt buyers would be similar to the existence of a monopolist in salt in that the price would be above the competitive level, causing some decline in salt demand. Consumers, however, would be protected from inefficiencies in the

---

[87] *If demands for products are interrelated, the principles for optimal pricing must be modified somewhat. See* Baumol & Bradford, *supra* note 86, at 266-67.

[88] The principles described in this section apply as well to exchange facilities owned by independent telephone companies and to interexchange plant owned by AT&T.

[89] For a discussion of instances in which a natural monopolist of several products must be protected from entry for efficiency reasons, see Panzar & Willig, *Free Entry and the Sustainability of Natural Monopoly,* 8 Bell J. Econ. 1 (1977).

[90] *Cf.* United States v. Southwestern Cable Co., 392 U.S. 157, 167-68 (1968) (broad construction of agency power to enable it to exercise comprehensive regulatory authority); National Broadcasting Co. v. United States, 319 U.S. 190, 219 (1943) (regulatory powers of FCC include oversight of affiliations between broadcast stations and networks); General Tel. Co. of Southwest v. United States, 449 F.2d 846, 853 (5th Cir. 1971) (FCC endowed with broad authority to accommodate new developments in field of communications such as CATV systems). *But cf.* Home Box Office, Inc. v. FCC, 567 F.2d 9, 13-14 (D.C. Cir.) (ancillary jurisdiction of FCC over CATV more limited than jurisdiction over broadcast services), *cert. denied,* 434 U.S. 829 (1977). Of course, we are not suggested that the FCC's jurisdiction under the Communications Act of 1934 extends to the production and sale of salt.

production of salt because the pre-tax price would still reflect a competitive market, the disparity between the regulated market price and a purely competitive price being the result of the government-imposed tax. If the level of the tax on salt is determined according to economic principles, there would be a net gain in social welfare over the alternative proposal of covering all telephone exchange costs through telephone rates alone. In short, a general tax to raise revenue is superior to licensing monopolies in otherwise competitive industries; the former forces firms to produce efficiently while the latter does not.

7.4.2 Analysis of the MFJ

The MFJ recognized the need for the BOCs to raise sufficient revenue to cover their costs.[91] The MFJ's primary concern, however, is with remedying restraints on competition that might violate the antitrust laws.[92] The MFJ is not a blueprint for raising revenue for the BOCs and AT&T, despite the relationship of this problem to economic efficiency and competition in the telecommunications industry and other industries. Rather, the MFJ left to the federal and state regulators and legislatures the problem of raising revenue to recover the costs of providing telephone service.[93]

1. Free Entry

The MFJ firmly rejected the proposition that economic efficiency justifies a lack of competition within the telecommunications industry. The additional efficiency in raising revenue from protected markets was judged to be small relative to the potential inefficiency that may result from insulating potentially competitive markets from competition. The court saw no reason to exempt this industry from the antitrust laws[94] and did not believe that the antitrust remedies of the MFJ— divestiture and prohibitions on the BOCs' entry into certain activities—endangered the BOCs' viability.

---

[91] *American Tel. & Tel. Co.*, 552 F. Supp. at 169, 187-88.

[92] The court noted that

Many persons . . . claim that [the MFJ's] restrictions [on the BOCs] would have adverse consequences in that they would either undermine the financial viability of the divested [BOCs], or produce substantial increase in the rates for local telephone service, thus eroding the statutory goal of universal telephone service for all Americans . . . This factor, to be sure, cannot preclude the imposition of a restriction necessary to preclude the anticompetitive activity, but to the extent that a restriction does not have a procompetitive effect, it may not be imposed if it infringes upon other important public policies.

Id. at 187-88 (footnotes omitted). However, in a later opinion, Judge Greene noted that "[o]ne of the Court's principal aims throughout the public interest process has been to ensure that divestiture would not bring about or contribute to local telephone rate increases." United States v. Western Elec. Co., No. 82-0192, slip op. at 153 (D.D.C. July 8, 1983).

[93] *American Tel. & Tel. Co.*, 552 F. Supp. at 169 n.161.

[94] *Id.* at 170 (history teaches that fair competition is more likely to benefit consumers than monopoly; telecommunication industry is no exception). *See also supra* note 60 and cases cited therein.

[95] *American Tel. & Tel. Co.*, 552 F. Supp. at 189-91.

The court considered the proposal that AT&T should be prevented from using new local distribution technologies that would allow it to originate and terminate interexchange traffic by bypassing the BOCs' exchange plant.[96] Entry by AT&T into exchange access service would deprive the BOCs of revenue that otherwise would be used to help cover the BOCs' costs. The court rejected this proposal, reasoning that other interexchange carriers have the ability to bypass the BOCs and that to prohibit AT&T from bypassing would restrict competition and thus be antithetical to the antitrust laws.

In addition, development of competitive bypass facilities would further the purpose of the antitrust laws by increasing the quantity and quality of exchange access services and decreasing their price and the potential for their use in exclusionary conduct.[97] According to the court, a legislative program of subsidies, special charges, or other regulatory means ultimately may have to be developed in order to maintain affordable local rates as the growth of bypass services decrease the number of customers upon which the BOCs must depend to recover their costs.[98] The potential for such problems did not warrant preventing bypass by AT&T in this antitrust consent decree.[99]

The court removed two of the restrictions on the BOCs' activities that were previously agreed to by the DOJ and AT&T. The MFJ permitted the BOCs to continue to publish local Yellow Pages advertising and to distribute customer-premises equipment.[100] The court noted that there were profits derived from local directory advertising,[101] making these activities an attractive source of revenue to help cover the BOCs' costs. This factor played a large role in the court's decision to remove these restrictions. Raising revenue to cover the BOCs exchange plant, however, was not a major consideration in the court's decision to allow them to distribute terminal equipment. According to the court, competition in this activity makes it unlikely that the BOCs will be able to extract much revenue from it for that purpose. Rather, the decision seems to have been made in the hope of promoting efficient distribution.[102] In addition, the court allowed the BOCs to raise revenues by sublicensing AT&T's patents on customer-premises equipment to manufacturers.[103]

The DOJ and the court rejected arguments that the BOCs should be allowed to enter into interexchange and information services because of potential abuses of monopoly power. Those who favored allowing the BOCs to provide interexchange services argued that the operating companies would provide additional

---

[96] *Id.* at 175-76.

[97] *Id.* at 175. *See also* Staff Report, FCC Policy on Cable Ownership 141, 159-60 (1981).

[98] *American Tel. & Tel. Co.*, 552 F. Supp. at 175-76.

[99] *Id.* at 176.

[100] *Id.* at 186-91. If there is no realistic possibility of abuse of monopoly power, the court would grant a BOC's petition to engage in an unrelated industry. *Id.* at 195 n.267.

[101] *Id.* at 193-94.

[102] *Id.* at 192 n.249. *See also supra* note 55 (discussing competition between AT&T and BOCs in terminal equipment distribution).

[103] United States v. Western Elec. Co., No. 82-0192, slip op. at 68-69 (D.D.C. July 8, 1983).

competition in the interexchange market and that the resulting revenues to the BOCs would increase their viability and reduce the need for local rate increases to cover their costs.[104]

2. Access Charges

The MFJ requires the BOCs to establish charges for exchange access provided to interexchange carriers and information-service suppliers.[105] While access charges are to be "cost justified," the MFJ leaves to regulators the decision as to what costs should be included in this calculation and what costs should be covered by exchange service.[106] Regulators could retain the cost allocation presently used in telephone separations and settlements procedures, providing a large allocation of plant costs to interexchange services. In addition, regulators could choose to make access charges for carriers and subscribers usage sensitive or flat fees per line.[107] Finally, Judge Greene referred to the possibility of using state or federal tax revenues to subsidize exchange and exchange access services.[108]

Though the MFJ is silent on the optimal methodology for covering the cost of providing telephone service, economic theory is not. The cost should be covered by pricing services above their marginal costs according to the inverse of the elasticities of demand for the services.[109] Studies have shown that the demand for interexchange service is more elastic (price sensitive) than the demand for connection to exchange facilities.[110] A five-percent increase in a BOC's price for using each unit of exchange access for interexchange service will cause a decline in demand for such exchange access because of a drop in interexchange traffic or possibly-inefficient bypass of the BOC's exchange facilities. This percentage decline is larger than the percentage decline in subscribers resulting from a five-percent increase in the flat cost of connection to the BOC's exchange facilities. A similar result may be expected for usage-sensitive charges on exchange access for information services. It therefore would be more efficient to cover costs primarily

---

[104] *American Tel. & Tel. Co.*, 552 F. Supp. at 186-87.

[105] *Id.* at 232-34.

[106] *Id.* at 169 n.161. *See also* Access Charges; MTS and WATS Market Structure (Third Report and Order) (Dkt. No. 78-72, Phase 1), 48 Fed. Reg. 10,319 (1983) (codified at 47 C.F.R. §69).

[107] The court criticized the FCC's decision to adopt flat fees per line as running "directly" counter to one of the decree's principal assumptions and purposes—that the fostering of competition in the telecommunications field need not and should not be the cause of increases in local telephone rates." United States v. Western Elec. Co., 1983-1 Trade Cas. (CCH) ¶ 65,333 at 69,973. The court seemed to be more concerned about "the protection of rates which will permit all segments of the population to enjoy telephone service" than about economically-efficient pricing. *Id.* at 69,975. *See also* United States v. Western Elec. Co., No. 82-0192, slip op. at 74-76 (D.D.C. July 8, 1983).

[108] *American Tel. & Tel. Co.*, 552 F. Supp. at 169 n.161.

[109] *See supra* notes 86-87 and accompanying text (discussing effect of elasticities of demand on optimal pricing structure).

[110] *See, e.g.*, J. Meyer, *supra* note 12, at Appendix C; B. Mitchell, Pricing Subscriber Access to the Telephone Network (1982); Griffin, *The Welfare Implications of Externalities and Price Elasticities for Telecommunications Pricing*, 64 Rev. Econ. & Stat., 59, 66 (1982).

through flat fees or surcharges on subscriber connections than through usage-sensitive charges that greatly exceed marginal cost.[111]

3. Achieving Social Goals

The reason economists use prices to allocate goods and require firms to be self-financing is to make sure that those who consume the firm's, product benefit enough to justify the cost of providing the product.[112] In a competitive market, consumers of a good must be willing to pay for the cost of its production. Attempts to cross-subsidize by charging a supracompetitive price would not succeed in a competitive environment because the first group would turn to alternative suppliers ready to supply them profitably at the competitive price.

The MFJ encourages competition in interexchange services and terminal equipment. These developments make it more difficult for AT&T and the BOCs to charge rates exceeding the costs of supplying some users. For example, under current nationwide toll rate averaging, supracompetitive toll rates charged by AT&T for traffic between some low-cost (typically densely-populated) areas generate revenues (cross-subsidies) that make it possible to charge subcompetitive rates on traffic between some high-cost (typically rural) areas. Competition in interexchange service between densely-populated areas undercuts the ability of AT&T to continue such pricing.

If the United States continues to pursue public policy goals like universal[113] and toll-rate averaging, someone must ultimately bear the costs of providing these services. When a public policy decision is made to provide a service to those who are unable or unwilling to pay its cost, the economic rationale that the telecommunications industry must be self-financing and competitive can no longer apply. The MFJ promotes competition within the industry and restricts the products and services that the BOCs and AT&T can provide. Therefore, requiring the BOCs and AT&T to set prices to achieve certain social goals and yet be self-financing could seriously distort the pricing of the products and services that are monopolized. Such distortions would cause inefficiencies, such as the suppression of usage of certain services, construction of inefficient bypass facilities, and development of arrangements to take advantage of underpriced services (e.g.,

---

[111] The FCC's adoption of end-user, flat access charges to recover non-traffic sensitive common line costs—replacing in part usage-sensitive charges—is a move to more efficient pricing. See Access Charges; MTS/WATS Market Structure Inquiry (Third Report and Order) (Dkt. No. 78-72, Phase 1), 48 Fed. Reg. 10,319 (1983) (codified at 47 C.F.R. §69).

[112] See A. Kahn, supra note 64, at 65-66; Coase, The Marginal Cost Controversy, 13 Economica 169, 173 (1946).

[113] The policy of universal service is commonly trced to the goal stated in the Communications Act of 1934: "[T]o make available, so far as possible, to all the people of the United States a rapid, efficient, Nation-wide, and world-wide wire and radio communication service with adequate facilities at reasonable charges." 47 U.S.C. §151 (1976). See also 7 U.S.C. §§921 et seq., 941 et seq. (1976 & Supp. V 1981) (legislation creating and funding the Rural Electrification Administration's telephone loan programs).

arbitrage).[114] As a matter of economic theory, general tax revenues are the most appropriate source of revenue to achieve social goals in telephone service pricing.[115]

7.5 CONCLUSION

The primary economic goals of the MFJ involve promotion of competition in interexchange services, information services, manufacture and distribution of terminal equipment, and manufacture of switching and transmission equipment. The MFJ attempts to prevent abuses of monopoly power by the BOCs and AT&T as well as anticompetitive cross-subsidization by the BOCs. The corresponding remedies aimed at eliminating incentives for anticompetitive conduct require divestiture of the BOCs from AT&T and restrictions on the activities of the BOCs and AT&T. Any remaining incentive to discriminate or cross-subsidize is discouraged by equal-access requirements on the BOCs. Certain anomalies appear in these restrictions.

The competitive structure of the telecommunications industry is only one aspect of its economic efficiency. Another aspect is how revenue is raised to cover the costs of providing telephone service and achieve certain social policy goals in pricing telephone services. The MFJ affects this issue by promoting competition, making it more difficult to raise revenues for these purposes. The MFJ leaves for regulatory and legislative action the development of cost allocations, surcharges, taxes, and subsidies. The resolution of these issues will have a major impact on the efficiency of the post-MFJ telecommunications industry.

---

[114] *See, e.g.*, Resale and Shared Use, 60 F.C.C.2d 261 (1976), *aff'd sub nom.* AT&T v. FCC, 572 F.2d 17 (2d Cir.), *cert. denied*, 439 U.S. 875 (1978); Resale and Shared Use (MTS/WATS), 83 F.C.C.2d 167 (1980).

[115] Political realities may prevent the use of the most economically-efficient methods of raising revenue.

Chapter 8

Equal Access—The View of a Competing Carrier

KENNETH A. COX*

I have been asked to discuss the aftermath of the AT&T consent decree[1]—in particular the implementation of its command that all interexchange carriers be provided equal access—from the standpoint of a carrier competing with AT&T. One way to approach this is by first considering the promise we thought it held for us, and then looking at four sets of problems which MCI and the other competing carriers have encountered on the way to that promised land.

First, the promise of equal access. It certainly seemed to portend the solution of the central problem we faced. At last we were to get the same kind of connections to the local exchanges as AT&T has always enjoyed.[2] This would allow us to provide a service of the same quality as AT&T—and one that would be as convenient for our customers to use, without the need for them to dial access numbers and authorization codes. This would make it easier for us to attract and hold customers.

This article is based on a paper presented on January 14, 1985 to the Third Annual Advanced Computer Law Invitational: Computer and Communications.

[1] *United States* v. *American Telephone and Telegraph Co.*, 552 F. Supp. 731, (D.D.C. 1982), aff'd sub nom. *Maryland* v. *United States,* 460 U.S. 1001, 103 S. Ct. 1240, 75 L. Ed. 2d 472 (1983).

[2] Par. II A of the consent decree—called by the parties the Modification of Final Judgment—reads as follows:

> "Subject to Appendix B, each BOC [Bell Operating Company] shall provide to all interexchange carriers and information service providers exchange access, information access, and exchange services for such access on an unbundled, tariffed basis, that is equal in type, quality, and price to that provided to AT&T and its affiliates."

Par. A.1 of Appendix B specified that each BOC should begin to offer such equal access no later than September 1, 1984, and that, "upon bona fide request, every end office shall offer such access by September 1, 1986."

True, we would have to pay the same price for access as AT&T, and that would force us to reduce the savings margin over AT&T that we could offer the public. But since MCI believes it can build and operate its transmission and switching systems more efficiently than its competitors, it felt sure it would be able to make a growing place for itself in the market even with the higher costs that improved access would entail.

Well, how have things worked out? We knew from the terms of the consent decree that it would be September 1, 1986 before we were to get full equal access—and even before the transition began we were told that exchanges with some 25% or more of the Bell System's telephones would not be converted by then, if ever.[3]

We've also found that equal access won't be exactly equal even when it arrives. It will be a big improvement, but the so-called Feature Group D facilities we will get will not be quite equal to the Feature Group C connections that AT&T now enjoys, even though this seems contrary to the direct command of the consent decree. In the long run this difference may be eliminated as AT&T loses the more efficient transmission of dial pulses which it now enjoys, especially in connection with rotary dial phones. For the next several years, however, it will still have somewhat superior access even after conversion.

But, there have been more serious problems along the way. The first of these is that we are saddled with the legacy of 30 to 35 years of misallocation of costs through the so-called separations process. This has resulted in the transfer to the interstate side of the jurisidictional separations line of billions of dollars worth of local subscriber plant—telephones, inside wiring, local hoops to the subscribers' serving central offices, and the little pieces of the switches there which are

---

[3] In a letter dated December 12, 1983, William R. Stump of AT&T responded to a request by FCC Commissioner Mimi Dawson for information as to "expected equal access penetration." He reported that 53.6 per cent of AT&T's 9,720 switches were "Not Planned To Be Capable of Equal Access" by January 1, 1987, which will be four months after every end office is supposed to offer equal access. Mr. Stump tried to suggest that a substantial number of these unconverted offices would be in rural areas, but in a response dated January 4, 1984, Robert S. Jackson, MCI's Director of Federal Policy, reported:

"Our analysis of information supplied to us by the Bell Operating Companies shows clearly that these 'nonconforming' switches, for which no equal access is proposed, are everywhere: In the heart of existing MCI service areas; in urban, suburban, and rural locations; in the same buildings with 'equal access' switches, which bifurcates neighborhoods into equal and unequal situations.

For example, in the New York City Metro LATA, according to information attached as an appendix to this letter, we count 274 end offices, of which 193, or 70 per cent, are proposed by NYNEX to remain 'nonconforming' through 1986. In the case of 177 of these nonconforming switches—92 per cent of them—MCI presently has revenue-producing service.

So it was clear that the Bell Operating Companies (BOCs) did not intend to provide equal access in a timely way in all the exchanges where the Other Common Carriers (OCCs) need the access the consent decree was thought to insure. MCI has made bona fide requests for conversion in more than 1,300 end offices with over 14 million lines. In some cases the BCOs say these offices will not be converted until 1987 or 1988—or, in some areas served by NYNEX and U.S. West, for five or six years. MCI is seeking a ruling from Judge Harold Greene, of the U.S. District Court for the District of Columbia, who signed the MFJ on August 24, 1982, which would fix a reasonable schedule of dates for completing the transition to equal access.

dedicated to the subscribers' service. This is plant used *only* when a subscriber calls someone, or is called by someone. It is never used to handle traffic between other users of the communications network, because it was dedicated to the individual subscriber's use when he or she first subscribed to local exchange service.

It has cost the exchange companies all those billions of dollars just to give their customers dial tone—that is, just to put them in a position to use the telephone system. This is termed non-traffic sensitive (NTS) plant and is dedicated to the individual customer. That is, its cost to the local exchange company is the same each month whether the customer places many calls, or a few, or none at all— and it remains exactly the same whether the customer's calls are all local, or include some intrastate toll calls, or go across the country or around the world.

Beyond this dedicated subscriber access plant lies the common switching and trunking plant of the local exchange companies—and beyond that, the common facilities of the carriers who provide interexchange service. These transmission and switching facilities may seem to be the more impressive portions of our nationwide telephone network, but all the billions of dollars invested in this plant are of no value to an individual customer until he or she is given the subscriber plant which serves as the critical link to the network.

In a rational system, each subscriber should pay all the costs of his or her dedicated access and then, in addition, should pay for his or her proportional use of the local exchange's switches and trunks, and of the switches and microwave, satellite, fiber optic, or other transmission facilities of whatever interexchange carrier he or she chooses to use. All this plant is used in common (i.e., is not dedicated to individual customers, except in the case of private line service). Also, it is traffic sensitive; that is, the quantity required—and, therefore, the amount that a carrier must invest—depends on the aggregate demands of all those who use the common switching and transmission facilities. Since individual demands vary, individual customrs should pay in proportion to the use they make of such common plant.

We don't have a rational system, however. It has been distorted by the shifting of subscribers' costs to others thorugh a series of changes in the jurisdictional separations. This was done for reasons of political expedience, because there was a mistaken belief that the price of local telephone services (alone of all the prices the public pays) could be kept nearly constant, and because state regulatory commissioners perceived it to be their primary duty to hold down residential rates.

Another contributing factor was that this shifting of costs made no real difference to AT&T, as long as it had no competition. The costs shifted to the interstate jurisdiction could be recovered through artificially high prices for interstate services because there were no competitors to offer such services for less. The result has been that over some 35 years a great part of the cost of the subscribers' access plant has been shifted from them to the users of interstate telephone service. The latter have paid not only for the interstate facilities of the interexchange carriers they use, but have also been required to pay for the portion of subscriber plant costs which has been transferred to interstate—not just their own subscriber costs, but also those of others who make few or no interstate calls. In other words, the interstate callers have been required to subsidize the costs of others—even though the Federal Communications Commission (FCC) and the courts have said this is improper and illegal.[4]

Because of criticism of the results of its jurisdictional separation policies, the FCC undertook to begin developing a new system of access charges in 1979,[5] but did nothing really significant until May 1982. Then between February 1983 and February 1984 it issued three separate rulemaking orders defining how such charges are to be structured.[6] Also, since October 1, 1983 it has been engaged in reviewing an ever changing array of access tariffs implementing those orders.[7]

To its credit, the Commission indicated, at the outset, that it wished to initiate

---

[4] The FCC first authorized general competitive entry into the long distance market in *Specialized Common Carrier Services* (Docket No. 18920), 20 FCC 2d870 (1971). In petitions for reconsideration, the National Association of Regulatory Utility Commissioners (NARUC) and the Utilities & Transportation Commission of the State of Washington (UTCW) argued that the only way to minimize the impact of new competition on the rates for local service would be "to generate excess earnings in interstate operations and to 'flow through' these earnings for the benefit of local users by allocating more of the cost of our national communications system to interstate operations and thereby affording relief in local operations." Quoted in *Specialized Common Carrier Services,* 31 FCC 2d 1106, at 1108. The agency rejected this effort to "subsidize the revenue requirements applicable to local exchange services subject to state regulatory jurisdiction." *Id.* The Commission denied the various petitions for reconsideration, and its rulings were affirmed *sub. nom. Washington Utilities & Transportation Commission* v. *FCC,* 513 F.2d 1142 (9th Cir.), *cert. denied,* 423 U.S.836 (1975).

Long established basis for this Commission ruling is found in *Smith* v. *Illinois Bell,* 282 U.S.133 (1930) and its progeny. In *Smith* the Supreme Court held that jointly used telephone property must be separated between the interstate and state jurisdictions in order to assess the reasonableness of state-imposed rates. It indicated that the separations process, however, must not be intended as, or result in, a subsidy of either of the jurisdictions. See the discussion of *Smith* and related cases at pages 51 to 57 of MCI's brief as petitioner filed on May 27, 1986 in *Rural Telephone Coalition and MCI Telecommunications Corporation* v. *FCC,* Consolidated Case Nos. 84-1110, 84-1139, and 85-1152, before the U.S. Court of Appeals for the District of Columbia Circuit.

[5] *Exchange Network Facilities for Interstate Access* (ENFIA), 71 FCC 2d 440 (1979). When AT&T filed its so-called ENFIA tariff in 1978, the FCC supervised the negotiation of a settlement agreement among the parties, which was accepted by the agency in the cited ruling. The agreement recited (Pars. 4 and 5) that there were other entities which accessed local exchanges in the same way and urged the Commission to proceed expeditiously to resolve this situation by developing policies applicable to these other parties. In its order accepting the agreement, the FCC said it would "study the existing compensation mechanisms for local telephone companies whose facilities are used in connection with the 'other services' discussed in the agreement" so that it could "determine whether, and under what procedures, any changes should be made." 72 FCC 2d at 457.

[6] *MTS and WATS Market Structure* (CC Docket No. 78-72), *Third Report and Order,* 93 FCC 2d 241 (1983), *reconsideration,* 97 FCC 2d 682 (1983), *further reconsideration,* 97 FCC 2d 834 (1984), *aff'd sub nom. National Association of Regulatory Utility Commissioners* v. *FCC,* 737 F. 2d 1095 (D.C. Cir. 1984), *cert. denied,* 105 S Ct. 1225 (1985).

[7] See, for example, *Investigation of Access and Divestiture Related Tariffs* (CC Docket No. 85-1145, Phase I), FCC 83-470, released October 19, 1983; FCC 84-51 released February 17, 1984 (*ECA Tariff Order*); Mimeo No. 2802, released March 7, 1984; Mimeo No. 2964, released March 16, 1984; FCC 84-104, released March 27, 1984; FCC 84-106, released March 28, 1984; FCC 84-201, released May 15, 1984; Mimeo No. 4453, rleased May 25, 1984; Mimeo No. 4741, released June 8, 1984. The consideration of access issues has spread to other dockets, the parties hve been required to file new tariffs every fall, and they have also made so-called mid-course corrections. The result has been a maze of filings and rulings with respect to charges for access to the local exchanges.

significant end user charges which would begin to shift subscriber plant costs back onto those responsible for them.[8] But Congress intervened to challenge such charges for residential and single line business customers.[9] However, a compromise was developed which permitted the FCC to impose a $1 per month charge on such small users beginning June 1, 1985.[10] That resulted in significant reductions in interstate rates by AT&T, which were followed by similar rate cuts by its competitors. On June 1, 1986 this Customer Access Line Charge was increased to $2 per month, with another ensuing round of reductions in rates for interstate long distance.[11]

Despite these shifts of part of the NTS subscriber plant costs to individual subscribers, the interexchange carriers (AT&T and the OCCs) are continuing to pay a great part of those costs. MCI and the other OCCs have been getting a discount of 55 percent below what AT&T pays for local access for interstate calling because we continue to have materially inferior connections until we get nationwide equal access. But this differential will disappear in time—perhaps before equal access has been achieved. However, until the bulk of the subscriber plant costs are shifted back to the subscribers, those costs will continue to distort price relationships. That is, they are so large—for both AT&T and its competitors—that they mask the advantages the OCCs enjoy because of their lower transmission and operational costs. And this effect is compounded because the access charges for Feature Group D connections are now usage sensitive, so that

---

[8] *MTS and WATS Market Structure* (CC Docket No. 78-72, Phase I), 93 FCC 2d 241, at 243, 279, 290-292, 349 (1983).

[9] See letter dated January 17, 1984 to the FCC from Senator Robert Dole and 31 other senators which dealt with this and other aspects of the Commission's earlier orders in *MTS and WATS Market Structure, supra*.

[10] See FCC News Release dated January 19, 1984, "FCC Delays Two Dollar Charge"; Report No. 17839 released January 25, 1984; *MTS and WATS Market Structure (Further Reconsideration), supra* at Pars. 4 to 30.

[11] Congress and the FCC have been cautious about imposing subscriber line costs on individual end users because of fears that the higher rates may force some poor people on fixed incomes to drop telephone service, thereby interfering with achievement of the goal of universal service. In its access charge proceedings, the FCC has imposed upon the interexchange carriers the burden of supporting a so-called high-cost fund. This is designed to impose higher charges on long distance users in order to cross-subsidize the rates of telephone companies in areas with costs substantially above the national average—anotehr case of requiring one class of telephone users to pay the costs imposed on the network by others. MCI has challenged the Commission order on the grounds that the agency's access charge plan—and especially its high cost fund—constitutes unlawful taxation and a taking of property without due process of law. Appeal pending in *Rural Telephone Construction and MCI Telecommunications Corporation* v. *FCC, supra* Note 4.

In a speech delivered during the conference where this paper was originally presented, Judge Harold Greene, who signed the consent decree and has been doing a fine job of administering it, expressed concern about preserving universal service. MCI understands his concern, which is shared by many others. However, it is MCI's position that the solution is not to artificially hold down local exchange costs for everyone—in other words, subsidizing *everyone's* local service, since that is wasteful and enormously costly. Instead, any subsidy should be carefully targeted to serve only those who really need help in maintaining their telephone service. And the burden of the program should not be imposed on other categories of telephone users, but should be borne by the taxpaying public.

the more efficiently a carrier uses its local lines, the more it will have to pay for them.[12]

To put it another way, what MCI pays for exchange access is far and away its heaviest expense. It is, furthermore, an expense which it cannot control, and one which is not determined by the cost of the telephone company lines it actually uses to connect its switches to the local telephone central offices that provide access to the local exchanges. Instead, the charges it pays are determined by the access costs of the mass of all telephone subscribers, many of whom are not, and may never be, customers of MCI. The on-going problem is that these rates are uneconomic and inefficient, they give false economic signals to telephone users, and they grossly distort the market. The results appear in MCI's operating statements in the form of increased access charges each month. MCI and the other OCCs must bend ever more intensive efforts toward offsetting this rising curve of access charges by rigorous control of other costs, and especially, by cutting back their dependence on facilities leased from other carriers, primarily AT&T.

In addition to these problems with the FCC and its access charges, the competing carriers have had difficulties with state regulators. After having confined itself for years to interstate operations, in 1982 MCI began seeking intrastate authorizations as well. This was due in part to pressure from some of the state commissions, but also to our realization that, in seeking to take advantage of the introduction of equal access, we would have to offer service geographically coextensive with AT&T's. In other words, MCI recognized it would be impossible to persuade telephone users to choose MCI as their primary long distance carrier if we could not handle the intrastate calls that AT&T can carry, as well as the interstate calls MCI has been handling all along.

Things went pretty well in the states at the start. New York, Ohio, Maryland, and Florida authorized MCI to provide statewide service,[13] and California said

---

[12] This represents a change which seriously disadvantages AT&T's competitors. Under the ENFIA Agreement, as well as the initial access charges set by the Commission, the OCCs paid a flat rate per line for access. This permitted them to reduce the impact of the charges they paid by making very efficient use of each line.

[13] The first three granted MCI authority to provide both interLATA and intraLATA service. LATAs (Local Access and Transport Areas) are the areas within which the MFJ permits the local Bell Operating Company to provide service. The proposed consent decree, when it was made public in January 1982, seemed to restrict them to providing local exchange service (and local exchange access), specifically barring them from interexchange service. See MFJ Sections I.A.1 and 2 and II.D The concepts of "local exchange service" and "interexchange service" were well understood, and in those conventional terms would have barred the BOCs from providing any toll service. But in Section IV.G. of the MFJ the parties inserted a definition of "exchange area" which was based on concepts that AT&T had advanced, for entirely different reasons, in connection with legislation that had been pending earlier in Congress. The four criteria in the definition could have been interpreted in line with the established concept of local exchange service, but the parties to the decree persuaded Judge Greene to acept a much more expansive scheme—primarily, I believe, because he was afraid the BOCs would need the revenues from the short-haul toll (i.e., "interexchange" service in the conventional sense) in order to keep them financially healthy. The result is that nine states contain only one LATA (Idaho, Maine, Nevada, New Hampshire, New Mexico, Rhode Island, Utah, Vermont, and Wyoming) and Delaware is simply an appendage to the Philadelphia LATA. Similarly,

we could offer interLATA communications, with the possibility of broader authority later. All these states were willing to give MCI the reduced level of regulation that the FCC has prescribed for nondominant carriers.[14] After that encouraging beginning, however, the going got tougher.

Many of the other state commissions are dubious about the desirability of competition in the first place, and are suspicious of the new carriers that are disrupting the old ways of doing things. Some are inclined to impose on us all the regulation they have traditionally applied to AT&T—including, in a few cases, pressure to provide universal origination service throughout the state. They demand state-specific information for which they have no need, in view of the OCCs' lack of market power, and which, in many cases, MCI simply does not have. Many of them have granted MCI only interim interLATA authority. In some cases we are only allowed to provide intrastate service from the few exchanges in which we have been provided equal access. They have acted slowly (in some cases waiting months), and then issued their orders just a day or two before the date for conversion to equal access. Some are so concerned about the welfare of the local exchange companies that they penalize us for the incidental intraLATA traffic which we handle because of our lack of equal access,through so-called "block or pay" requirements.[15] They have generally imposed very high intrastate access charges, denying us adequate differentials *vis a vis* AT&T[16]—even though many of them have claimed to be mirroring the access charge rulings of the FCC. And one state, Virginia, went to the other extreme; its commission granted a

---

thirteen states (Arizona, Colorado, Kansas, Massachusetts, Mississippi, Montana, Nebraska, North Dakota, Oklahoma, Oregon, South Dakota, Washington, and West Virginia) contain only two LATAs. In view of the size of these states, it is obvious that there are many, many cases where the BOCs provide toll service for 300 miles or more, within the grossly distorted "exchange areas" they have been allowed to serve. Although Judge Greene expressed the hope that there would be competition within the LATAs, he left the matter to the state commissions. *U.S. v. AT&T,* 569 F. Supp. 990, 1005-6 (D.C. 1983). However, most of those agencies have given the BOCs monopoly status throughout the LATAS. Florida, the fourth state referred to in the text, authorized MCI to provide service throughout the state except within areas designated by the state commission as Equal Access Exchange Areas. These are larger than conventional exchanges but smaller than the Florida LATAs. MCI can provide service within the EAEEs only on a resale basis.

[14] *Policy and Rules Concerning Rates for Competitive Common Carrier Services and Facilities Authorizations Therefore, First Report and Order,* 85 F.C.C. 2d 1(1980).

[15] See, for example, *Re: SouthernTel of Virginia, Inc,* 62 P.U.R. 4th 245 (1984), in which the Virginia Supreme Court affirmed such an order by the Virginia Commerce Commission. These orders result from the fact that in unconverted exchanges where MCI still has Feature Group A connections, its customer access MCI's terminals by calling seven digit local business numbers. Since these are local rather than toll calls, the local exchange companies' switches do not capture the short haul toll calls which the exchange carrier is authorized to handle. Since MCI cannot be sure that the calls may not have originated outside the LATA, it does not block completion of these intraLATA calls—though it is very careful not to advertise or promote in any way the use of MCI facilities for intraLATA calling. In some cases, state commissions have tried to compel MCI to pay over to the local carrier the amount the latter would have charged for each call—without giving us credit for the access charges we paid on such traffic or taking any account of the fact that MCI's facilities were used to complete the call, thereby reducing the local company's own costs.

[16] See, for example, The California Public Utilities Commission's *Phase I Access Charge Opinion,* Decision No. 83-12-0241 released December 7, 1983.

number of OCCs' applications for intrastate authority and immediately turned around and totally deregulated AT&T.[17] This not only exposes the people of the state to potentially exorbitant rates, but erodes the state commission's power to deal with predatory practices by AT&T and leaves the competing carriers without recourse to the normal procedural safeguards. So all in all, our experiences with the states, en route to equal access, have been costly, exhausting, and frustrating.

There have also been a few problems with the BOCs. While our mailings to the public in the equal access exchanges say that this great improvement in our services is coming to them with the cooperation of their local telephone companies, the degree of that cooperation varies. Northwestern Bell was perhaps the most helpful in the earlier days. It offered conversion from the outset in the larger cities in its area where MCI originates service, while some other operating companies started their conversion in less convenient areas, including some which have no service from any OCC. Northwestern Bell also mailed out a ballot, asking its subscribers to report their choice of interexchange carrier back to Northwestern Bell. While we weren't enthusiastic about this at first, as administered by Northwestern Bell, it worked well and it produced, in the early months of equal access conversion, the country's highest percentage of actual customer predesignation of long distance carriers.

Unfortunately, Northwestern Bell didn't do so well in regard to supplying us the names and telephone numbers of its subscribers. Like some other BOCs, it demanded prices so high we had to buy lists elsewhere, getting a lot of misinformation in the process. But it allowed us to give it the lists of those who chose MCI as their long distance carrier in convenient tape form, convenient to us, while others required us to work with unwieldy paper lists.[18] In many cases when

---

[17] See decision on appeal, *Re: SouthernTel. of Virginia, Inc.*, 62 P.O.R. 4th 245 (1984). This result was apparently premised on the Commission's belief that AT&T was subject to competition in Virginia and therefore did not need to be regulated. But at that time AT&T faced no competition in the state, because it had been the only carrier authorized to provide intrastate long distance service. And MCI proposed to offer service initially only from eight Virginia cities. More recently Nebraska has enacted legislation which completely deregulates AT&T and the local telephone companies of that state—as well as the OCCs. Other states are being urged to enact similar legislation by the BOCs and AT&T.

[18] Northwestern Bell also allocated those who did not return their ballots among the participating interexchange carriers in proportion to the numbers of people who had chosen the various carriers. This was in sharp contrast to the practice of the other BOCs which assigned all those who did not designate a primary long distance carrier to AT&T by default. In response to protests by MCI and others, the FCC adopted a plan for handling equal access which was based substantially on the practices of Northwestern Bell. *Investigation of Access and Divestiture Related Tariffs,* CC Docket No. 83-1145, Phase I, FCC 85-293-35875, released June 12, 1985; *reconsideration,* released August 20, 1985. That has improved things in the later stages of the transition to equal access, but the OCCs have continued to have problems. In a number of cases, AT&T has "appropriated" tens of thousands of customers who had actually chosen MCI another OCC—blaming such developments on "computer error." And it has been necessary for MCI to go back to the Department of Justice and to Judge Greene again and again to force the BOCs to speedup and improve the process of transferring those who have chosen a competing carrier in place of AT&T. Finally, as noted above, there are millions of telephone lines not yet available for equal access in BOC territories even though the date for completion of the equal access process has come and gone.

we promised our subscribers they would get equal access as of the announced conversion date, we would then find that a significant percentage of them were not converted on time. As a result they continued to be billed at AT&T's rates, and looked to us for reimbursement since they had expected their long distance calls tobe priced at MCI's lower rates.This whole process has been enormously costly—though obviously much of that burden can't be blamed on the BOCs, except in the sense that they were part of the conspiracy which prevented us from getting equal access years ago.

Finally, there is the matter of AT&T's reaction to this whole process. It has certainly not been passive about these matters. It has not sought to block our requests for intrastate authorizations, but has used them as the basis for seeking complete or partial intrastate deregulation for itself. As indicated above, at least one state freed AT&T of all regulation months ago, and a number of others have acted to lighten or eliminate regulation of its operations more recently. But most have recognized that AT&T's continued dominance of the market requires on-going regulation. Unfortunately some of them want to apply the same rules to the OCCs as well, despite their lack of market power.

AT&T, for the first time in its history, is competing very hard in the marketplace. It is spending unprecedented sums on a television campaign to hold onto its interstate customers. It is having a good deal of success—in part, I believe, because substantial elements of the message it is presenting are deceptive. It is also engaging in selective price cutting, as with its Reach Out America and PRO America programs. The former involves the offering of an hour of calling in the night and weekend period for a flat monthly fee, originally $10 but now reduced to $8.95. If the customer had actually used 60 minutes of calling, his per minute cost under the original rate would have been 16-2/3 cents, which was less than AT&T was then paying for local access. Thus even without allocating any of the other costs of the business to this offering, it seemed clear that it was being provided at below cost. It is hard to imagine a more predatory pricing scheme, but the FCC refused to reject or suspend the tariff.[19]

AT&T then offered its Preferred Rate Option, or PRO plan, beginning in the states at first, but now in its interstate tariff as well. This provides a bulk discount to large users. In return for a monthly payment ($15 in the FCC tariff) they get a discount on their calling of 10 percent below AT&T's tariffed rates. Since AT&T cannot provide any cost justification for allowing its large customers to get service for less than others pay for the very same calls, the scheme is clearly

---

[19] After the FCC had denied our petition to reject or suspend the tariff which implemented this plan, MCI filed a formal complaint, *MCI Telecommunications Corporation v. AT&T,* E-85-111. The Commission, after some delay, denied the complaint. FCC 86-30-36755, issued July 2, 1986. An appeal is pending *sub nom. MCI v. FCC,* D.C. Cir.Case No. 86-1483.

discriminatory. A number of states, however, allowed it to go into effect, and the FCC, after first rejecting the concept, has now followed suit.[20]

AT&T is taking full advantage of its long dominance of the market. It is a known quantity, and many people continue to do business with it because it is regarded as familiar and safe. Since it knows the calling patterns of all its customers, it knows just which ones to concentrate on in equal access communities. This is information the OCCs can't buy anywhere, and it gives AT&T a great competitive advantage. Also, its huge resources in money and people allow it to do things its competitors simply can't come close to matching. As a consequence, AT&T has held onto a very high percentage of the people in the areas that have been converted to equal access thus far.

But with it all, we are making progress. Has equal access been an easy path to riches for the OCCs? No, not at all.[21] But it is an essential step toward a competitive marketplace, and we have welcomed it and would like to see it fully implemented as intended by the MFJ.

---

[20] *AT&T Communications Corp, Revisions to Tariff F.C.C. No. 1. ("PRO™ America)*, FCC 86-240-36690, released May 14, 1986, appeal pending *sub nom. U.S. Sprint v. F.C.C.*, D.C. Cir. Case No. 86-1413. As a preliminary to its second ruling on PRO America, the Commission adopted so-called guidelines for such optional calling plans. *Guidelines for Dominant Carriers' MTS Rates and Rate Structure Plans,* FCC 85-540, released October 17, 1985. MCI is also participating in an appeal of that ruling *sub nom. GTE Corp. v. F.C.C.*, D.C. Cir. Case No. 85-1828. Motions to dismiss have bee filed against these two appeals.

[21] For another MCI perspective on the equal access process, see remarks of William G. McGowan, Chairman of MCI Communications Corporation, during a seminar at Communications Networks '85, Washington, D.C., on January 29, 1985.

NOTE: There have been some changes, since this paper was submitted, in the status of regulation in certain states and of various court appeals, but none that affect the substance of the article.

Chapter 9

The AT&T Divestiture, the FCC, and the Structure of CPE Markets*

ALBERT H. KRAMER

The AT&T divestiture has been described as the most important single regulatory event in the history of telecommunications. Undoubtedly there are many respects in which this will prove to be the case. But for vendors and users of customer premises equipment (CPE)—particularly vendors and users of business equipment (or systems)—the post-divestiture world is troubling, not least of all because the Federal Communications Commission seems to have accepted the divestiture court's vision of the post-divestiture marketplace.

9.1 THE CPE INDUSTRY UNDER THE F.C.C.

The landmark event for the CPE industry was the adoption and implementation of the F.C.C.'s Part 68 registration program.[1] That program allowed the interconnection to the public switched network of all CPE that incorporated technical safeguards against harm to the network, and led to an outpouring of technological advances and sophisticated equipment that were eagerly received by a growing market.

---

[1]47 C.F.R. Part 68; *Docket No. 19528, First Report and Order,* 56 F.C.C.2d 593 (1975); *on reconsideration,* 57 F.C.C.2d 1216, 58 F.C.C.2d 716, and 59 F.C.C.2d 83 (1976); *Second Report and Order,* 58 F.C.C.2d 736 (1976); *on reconsideration,* 61 F.C.C.2d 396 (1976); *aff'd sub nom. North Carolina Utilities Commission v. F.C.C.,* 552 F.2d 1036 (4th Cir.), *cert. denied.* 434 U.S. 874 (1977).

Shortly after the Registration Program came the F.C.C.'s decision in *Computer II*.[2] In that proceeding, the Commission deregulated the offering of new CPE[3] effective January 1, 1983. The Commission also required that any new CPE from the then integrated Bell System be offered through a separated subsidiary or affiliate. Eventually, AT&T decided that all CPE marketing would be done through what is now called AT&T Information Systems (AT&T-IS), and not by multiple subsidiaries or affiliates of the Bell Operating Companies.

The Registration Program and *Computer II* decision seemed, to independent CPE manufacturers, to represent an attempt to create a "level playing field" for CPE competition. The Commission had created a federal right to interconnect to the public switched network, and had imposed structural separation requirements on the dominant carrier's (AT&T's) provision of CPE. Structural separation shielded ratepayers and competitors from the burden of cross-subsidizing CPE costs with monopoly revenues. Structural separation also made such anticompetitive conduct as unequal treatment regarding interconnection to the network and advance notice of changes to the network to the carriers of CPE affiliate more difficult.

The competition the Commission attempted to foster in *Computer II* was the provision of CPE by an independent interconnect industry. At that time the BOCs were part of AT&T, and the only competition to the Bell System's provision of CPE came from the independent interconnect industry.

9.2 THE VIEW FROM THE COURT

It was in this posture that the United States District Court for the District of Columbia entered the Modified Final Judgment (MFJ) that resulted in the breakup of the Bell System.[4] The divestiture court ignored the independent CPE sector and the competitive CPE market that the Commission sought to foster in *Computer II*. Despite arguments to the contrary by the Department of Justice, the

---

[2]*Amendment of Section 64.702 of the Commission's Rules and Regulations (Second Computer Inquiry)*, 77 F.C.C.2d 384 *(Final Decision), on reconsideration*, 84 F.C.C.2d 50 (1980) *(Reconsideration), on further reconsideration*, 88 F.C.C.2d 512 *(1981) (Further Reconsideration), aff'd sub nom. Computer and Communications Industry Association v. Federal Communications Commission*, 693 F.2d 198 (D.C. Cir. 1982), *cert. denied sub nom., Louisiana Public Service Commission v. Federal Communications Commission*, 103 S. Ct. 2109 (1983).

[3]Deregulation of embedded CPE was handled in a separate proceeding. *Procedures for Implementing the Detariffing of Customer Premises Equipment and Enhanced Services, (Second Computer Inquiry)*, 95 F.C.C.2d 1276 (1983).

[4]*United States v. American Telephone and Telegraph Co.*, 552 F. Supp. 131 (D.D.C. 1982), *aff'd sub nom. Maryland v. United States*, 460 U.S. 1001 (1983). The decree in that suit is referred to as the Modified Final Judgment because technically it modified a decree settling a 1956 government suit against AT&T.

court permitted the BOCs to "provide, but not manufacture" CPE.[5] The court saw the BOCs as "more likely than any other competitive entity to provide an effective counterbalance to AT&T's market strength and thereby to promote a genuinely competitive market."[6]

The court envisioned a CPE market dominated by carriers; it did not share the Commission's original *Computer II* view of a market that included not only carriers but also an independent sector to spur innovation and technological advances. In contrast, the Commission saw a carrier-dominated industry—even one subject to structural separation—as consisting of enterprises that could potentially cross-subsidize their CPE activities, and might lack the innovative vigor of an independent CPE sector. The court did not accept the Commission's view that the interconnect industry would provide effective competition to carrier dominated segments of the industry.[7]

9.3 THE COMMISSION'S NEW VISION

Had the Commission adhered to its view, the independent CPE industry probably would survive. The Commission did, after all, impose the separate subsidiary requirement on the divested BOCs.[8] But the court's decision has not been the end of the matter, and a series of developments indicate that the Commission may be coming around to the court's view of the CPE industry as a playing field for giants.

Primary among these developments has been a series of steps the F.C.C. has taken to remove the safeguards it erected in *Computer II* to prevent AT&T from exploiting its dominance in the CPE market. The first of these steps occurred shortly after divestiture. Under *Computer II*, the offering of unregulated CPE and regulated long-distance services by a dominant carrier subject to the separate subsidiary requirement was prohibited because of the risks of cross-subsidy or favorable treatment by the carrier in providing common carrier service to its affiliate. In response to an AT&T request, the Commission allowed AT&T-IS to

---

[5]*United States v. American Telephone and Telegraph Co., supra,* 552 F. Supp. at 225. The F.C.C. too endorsed the re-entry of the BOCs into CPE markets. But the Commission did so with full recognition of the need to reconcile that re-entry with the independent competition contemplated by *Computer II.* Thus, the Commission allowed the BOCs to re-enter the CPE market only through CPE affiliates that were structurally separate from the providers of basic network services. *Policy and Rules Concerning the Furnishing of Customer Premises Equipment, Enhanced Services and the Cellular Communications Services by the Bell Operating Companies, Report and Order,* 95 F.C.C.2d 1117, *on reconsideration, Memorandum Opinion and Order on Reconsideration,* CC Dkt. 83-115, F.C.C. 84-252, 49 Fed. Reg. 26056 (June 26, 1984).

[6]*United States v. American Telephone and Telegraph Co., supra,* 552 F. Supp. at 192.

[7]For purposes of this discussion, AT&T-IS is regarded as part of the carrier segment of the industry, even though the post-divestiture AT&T is no longer a "carrier" as that term is often used.

[8]*See* note 11, *supra.*

resell AT&T's long-distance services,[9] subject to certain conditions designed to reduce the risks of anticompetitive conduct. The ruling enabled AT&T-IS to provide a form of one-stop shopping for CPE and long-distance service. AT&T-IS may also act as a customer's agent in dealing with the local phone company.

Earlier this year, the F.C.C. responded to an AT&T request by initiating a proceeding to determine whether to eliminate the requirement that AT&T conduct its CPE operations through a separate subsidiary.[10] After a preliminary round of comments, the Commission issued a tentative statement of its intention to dispense with some of the structural requirements at issue.[11] At the same time, the Commission relieved AT&T of the "software rule"[12] portion of *Computer II*, which had been designed to prevent AT&T from cross-subsidizing its CPE affiliates by making the results of research and development done for AT&T's regulated operations available to its CPE affiliate at reduced rates. It prohibited AT&T Technologies, Inc. (formerly Western Electric) and Bell Labs from developing software for AT&T-IS unless it was generic and available off the shelf on the same basis to any other vendor. In place of the software rule, the F.C.C. accepted accounting guidelines intended to ensure that R&D for AT&T-IS is done on a compensatory basis.[13] The F.C.C., however, has not in the past shown great skill in allocating and monitoring costs through accounting guidelines. The Commission is pressing ahead with the remainder of the proceeding, which many believe was designed to relieve AT&T of other separate subsidiary requirements and replace these, too, with accounting guidelines.

The F.C.C. has also been active on the BOC front. As mentioned, the F.C.C. had applied its *Computer II* rationale to require separated CPE affiliates for the divested BOCs. In so doing, however, the Commission undertook to revisit within two years the question of whether the BOCs should be required to maintain the separated affiliates. In adopting the proposal to relieve AT&T of the competitive safeguards of *Computer II*, the Commission recommitted itself to that re-examination. Coming, as it did, with the Commission's proposal to relieve AT&T of *Computer II* safeguards, that affirmation fueled speculation that the F.C.C. would revisit this issue sooner rather than later.

Moreover, the F.C.C., in requiring the divested BOCs to establish separate CPE affiliates, indicated that it felt somewhat tentative about the decision. The Commission has allowed four exceptions to the separate subsidiary requirement. One allows each BOC to refer customers seeking telephone service to the BOC's

[9]*In re American Telephone and Telegraph Co.; Provision of Basic Services Via Resale Via Separate Subsidiary, Report and Order,* CC Dkt. No. 83-1375, 49 Fed. Reg. 28835 (July 17, 1984).

[10]*In re Policy and Rules Concerning the Furnishing of Customer Premises Equipment and Enhanced Services by American Telephone and Telegraph Company and Related Waiver Requests, Memorandum Opinion and Order and Notice of Proposed Rulemaking,* CC Dkt. 85-26, F.C.C. 85-56, 50 Fed. Reg. 9060 (March 6, 1985).

[11]*Id.*

[12]*Id.* at 9067.

[13]At the same time, the Commission granted AT&T a waiver to provide certain personnel related services to AT&T-IS, subject to accounting guidelines.

CPE affiliate for equipment.[14] Another allows the BOCs to provide billing services to their respective CPE affiliates. The third exception allows the regulated monopoly telephone company and its unregulated competitive CPE affiliate to use the same installation and maintenance personnel for one and two line equipment. The last exception allows the BOCs to share certain administrative services with their respective CPE affiliates.

The F.C.C.'s attitude was sufficiently clear to bring the BOCs back to the Commission to seek exceptions. The BOCs sought and obtained a waiver to allow their separated, unregulated CPE affiliates to market Centrex service.[15] Centrex raises a host of competitive issues for CPE vendors. The service utilizes the same central office switch and cable between the central office and the customer's premises (i.e., the loop) that are used to provide access to the public switched network. As a central office based substitute for customer premises switches that provide the feature enhancements of office telephone systems, Centrex offers the telephone companies opportunities to cross-subsidize from jointly used plant and personnel. While the F.C.C. is aware of the competitive threat posed by Centrex, it has been unwilling thus far to check Centrex's anticompetitive potential. Thus, while the Commission applied access charges to each Centrex loop,[16] it also allowed the telephone companies to offset the increased charges by applying to state regulatory commissions for rate reductions. Similarly, the Commission has recently ruled that the feature enhancements offered through Centrex are an adjunct of telephone service rather than unregulated enhanced services that must be offered through a BOC's separate affiliate.[17] Yet these enhancements require sophisticated data storage and computer processing in the same manner as enhanced services.

All of this seems to indicate that the F.C.C. has abandoned its own view of a CPE industry characterized by competition between an independent sector and a carrier sector in favor of the divestiture Court's view—an industry structure dominated by carriers. To be sure, a few large independent manufacturers will survive by selling equipment to the BOCs. But the mainstay of the independent

---

[14]Again there has been an attempt to prevent abuse. BOC customer service representatives must tell a customer that equipment is available elsewhere—even as the service representative transfers the call to the BOC's CPE affiliate.

[15]In the Matter of Ameritech, BellSouth, NYNEX, Ameritech Capitalization Plans for the Furnishing of Customer Premises Equipment and Enhanced Services; NYNEX Petition for Waiver of Section 64.702 of the Commission's Rules to Allow Marketing of Network Services by Separate Subsidiary, ENF File Nos. 84-10, 84-18, Memorandum Opinion and Order, FCC 84-290 (released July 11, 1984).

[16]In re MTS & WATS Market Structure, Memorandum Opinion & Order, 97 F.C.C.2d 682 (1983) (Reconsideration Order), 49 Fed. Reg. 7810 (1984) (Further Reconsideration Order), aff'd sub nom. National Assn. of Regulatory Utility Commissioners v. Federal Communications Commission, 737 F.2d 1095 (D.C. Cir. 1984), cert. denied No. 84-95 (Feb. 19, 1985).

[17]In the Matter of North American Telecommunications Association, Petition for Declaratory Ruling Under Section 64.702 of the Commission's Rules Regarding the Integration of Centrex, Enhanced Services, and Customer Premises Equipment, Memorandum Opinion & Order, F.C.C. 85-248 (released May 29, 1985).

CPE sector has been the multitude of the independent CPE vendors that provided a ready distribution outlet for new manufacturing entrants. These vendors, and even all but a handful of the very largest manufacturers, are unlikely to survive from the BOCs and AT&T. An industry structure dominated by the carriers and AT&T is likely to emerge.

If that is the result of divestiture, it is worth pausing to consider whether the game was worth the candle. Prior to the divestiture and *Computer II*, the CPE industry was dominated by carriers, each confined to its own service area, with fringe competition that inspired some technological innovation. CPE was, for the most part, a regulated and tariffed offering. While there was little competition, there were also regulatory checks on excesses in pricing and practices.

In the post-divestiture, post-*Computer II* world, there are no regulatory restraints to prevent abuse. Competition is supposed to supplant regulation to prevent abuse and bring efficiency and technological innovation. But competition cannot carry this burden if the industry is carrier-dominated with competition only at the fringes, *i.e.*, remarkably similar to its predivestiture, pre-*Computer II* configuration.

The picture painted here is a simplified one. There will, of course, be *some* differences between the pre- and post-divestiture and *Computer II* worlds even if the same industry structure were to emerge. But the movement toward a return to a carrier-dominated industry is reason to pause and examine the full implications of regulatory action. If one of the purposes of *Computer II* and the divestiture was to make the CPE market fully competitive, recent regulatory actions may have frustrated that goal by paving the way for a carrier-dominated market. It is not inevitable that the industry be dominated by a handful of carriers and large manufacturers. Rather than acquiescing in that structure, the F.C.C. and the divestiture court, along with the Department of Justice (which is responsible for enforcing the divestiture decree) should be considering the steps necessary to preserve vigorous (albeit fragile) competitive balance in the CPE market.

Chapter 10

Defining Local Exchange Service: For Whom May Only Bell Toll?*

HENRY D. LEVINE

Not long ago virtually everyone in the telecommunications industry knew what was meant by "local exchange service." Over the past five years, however, the phrase has come to have different meanings, depending upon the context and who is using it. The choice among these definitions could have profound implications for the development of competition in the industry and, conceivably, on such overarching issues as universal service and the pace of innovation in telecommunications. This article describes the various definitions currently in use, how and why they were promulgated, and the issues that underlie them. It closes with some thoughts on the use of labels as a substitute for analysis in a rapidly evolving industry.

At the outset, it is worth asking why anyone should care about the definition of local exchange service. The answer is that definitions are a means of grouping things or ideas in a way that includes some and excludes others. A faulty definition—one that is over- or under-inclusive—can cause confusion and become a barrier to understanding.

10.1 THE RANGE OF DEFINITIONS

Of the many definitions of local exchange service, the narrowest is plain old voice telephone service—known in the industry as POTS—inside local calling areas within which subscribers may place calls without paying an extra charge. The court in *MCI Communications v. American Tel. & Tel.* had this definition in

---

*Reprinted with permission from *Telematics,* Vol. 2, No. 5, May 1985. Copyright 1985, Law & Business, Inc. All rights reserved.

mind when it described local exchange telephone service as "the ordinary service provided in nearly all homes and businesses."[1]

At the other extreme is the definition put forward by Southwestern Bell Telephone in proceedings that it recently initiated in Texas, Oklahoma, Arkansas, Kansas, and Missouri, seeking to limit the scope of shared tenant services provided by real estate developers to their tenants.[2] Southwestern Bell has sought to define local exchange service to include any direct or addressable electronic communication between distinct customers within its service area. The company has made it clear that the definition was drafted to cover not only voice communication over ordinary, unaugmented telephone lines, but also all forms of low and high speed data transmission, however transmitted, that have not been expressly declared open to competition by the FCC or state authorities. The only telecommunications excluded from Southwestern Bell's definition is transmission that is neither directed nor addressable, such as conversation over walkie-talkies.[3]

POTS and the Southwestern Bell definition are not unambiguous. In some states, e.g., New York, the distinction between local and toll calls has been blurred to requirements that customers pay on a time-and-distance basis for "long haul local calls," and any remaining bright line will disappear if and when local measured service becomes compulsory. Similarly, Southwestern Bell's definition requires a clear understanding of when two parties constitute separate customers, and no one (including Southwestern Bell) has to date come up with a definition of "customer" that satisfactorily answers the questions raised by independent professionals sharing offices, affiliated companies with common space, etc.

It is a long way from POTS to all directed or addressable electronic transmissions, and between them one may find other alternatives. Some have proposed, for example, that local exchange service be defined as "POTS Plus," where the "Plus" refers to low speed data transmission and local voice grade private lines—anything that can (and normally is) carried over the unaugmented public switched network. Then there is the Modified Final Judgement (MFJ) in *U.S. v. AT&T,* which limited the divested Bell Operating Companies to the provision of "exchange telecommunications" and local "exchange access." Judge Greene

---

[1] 708 F.2d 1081, 1093 n.8 (7th Cir. 1983).

[2] Shared tenant service (STS) refers to the provision of telecommunication services to tenants by their landlord, on his own or through a service provider. Typically, the landlord or his franchisee places an advanced PBX in the basement of a high rise office building (or somewhere in a large office park) and then offers Centrex-like features, along with access to local and discounted long distance service, equipment, and enhanced services like voice mail or video teleconferencing to tenants. *See* Levine, "Smart Buildings Come of Age," *TELEMATICS,* Vol. 1, No. 2, June 1984. The features of STS that local companies find objectionable are the sharing of local access trunks and "behind the switch" calling, which involves using the developer's switch to complete calls between "unrelated" tenants without use of the public switched network.

[3] Conversations between unrelated parties over wire-connected devices, such as a Radio Shack intercom system, *would* be covered by Southwestern Bell's proposed definition, according to the company.

defined exchange telecommunications to include all "electromagnetic transmission" of information within the bounds of newly constructed territories called Local Access and Transport Areas or LATAs. As the judge acknowledged, LATAs are much larger than traditional local exchange territories.[4] Indeed, one of the principal controversies before state regulatory commissions for the past year has been whether competition would be allowed in the provision of intra-LATA *toll* service, which would not exist if LATAs were coextensive with local exchange areas in the classic sense.

While the phrase "local exchange service" is clearly of geographic origin, the distinctions among the definitions described above (and variations upon them) make it clear that far more than territory is at issue. The definitions differ, for example, in the services they encompass—some are confined to voice, while others would include all forms of data transmission. They also differ in the transmission media covered, which may be limited to ordinary twisted copper wire or extended to include carrier-on-cable, coaxial cable, optical fiber, and (at least in theory) advanced forms of digital microwave transmission.

There is also debate as to how public a service must be in order to be viewed as local exchange. Traditional common carriers—companies that hold themselves out to serve all members of the public indifferently on a non-discriminatory, tariffed basis—are clearly covered. But there is disagreement about the inclusion of "uncommon" carriage, which can range from a private offering that is distinguishable from common carriage largely in that contracts are entered into on an individual basis and the provider reserves the right to refuse service, through offerings aimed at narrowly defined groups (e.g., the tenants of a particular building or complex) and even to the mere non-profit sharing of a service by two otherwise unrelated entities. Some jurisdictions, e.g., Arkansas and Florida, would treat all of these as local exchange service or a regulatable substitute for it. Others—like New York—appear to draw the line at services sold to others for a profit, and do not try to reach private networks or non-profit sharing. Still others, like Illinois, recognize a jurisdictional distinction between common and private carriage and regulate only the former.

10.2 WHY ARE THERE DIFFERENT DEFINITIONS?

The different definitions of local exchange service can be traced in part to conflicts in the telecommunications industry. The Bell Operating Companies and other local telephone companies seek the broadest possible definition of local exchange service because it is the area in which state regulatory bodies are most likely to permit competition and most likely to preserve the local companies' monopoly franchise. Other participants in the industry—notably the AT&T

---

[4] *See United States v. Western Electric Co.*, 569 F. Supp. 992, 993-995 (1983).

OCCs—want local exchange service defined as narrowly as possible, for much the same reason.

There are arguments to be made on both sides. Those who favor a broad definition of local exchange service, including the Bell Operating Companies and the more conservative state commissions, fear that the introduction of competition threatens a system (based on cross-subsidies) that has kept rates for basic residential service low. These parties fear that allowing competition in the provision of telecommunications services will force rates to cost, reducing the revenues available for cross-subsidization and spurring geographic deaveraging (i.e., higher local service rates in rural areas).

The proponents of a narrower definition of local exchange service include pro-competitive state commissions, like those in New York, Illinois, and Texas, and the newer entrants into the telecommunications business, like MCI and GTE-Sprint. Broadening the definition of local exchange service reduces the size and number of markets that they are allowed to enter, and they argue that this causes prices to exceed cost, to the detriment of total consumer welfare; prevents efficient use of facilities; and retards the innovation characteristic of competitive markets.

Policy differences are only part of the story, however, since many of the suggested definitions don't conflict as much as they just miss each other—as though they were designed with different agendas in mind. Thus, the classic definition of local exchange service is service inside an area within which calls may be placed without incurring charges other than the basic monthly service charge. That purpose, however useful in an industry that chooses to charge for some calls (but not others) on a time or distance basis, has little to do with the task that faced Judge Greene early in 1983. He, and the parties before him, were using the term local exchange service to divide the assets and revenues of the old Bell System, and to limit the activities of the Bell Operating Companies in order to prevent the misuse of their monopoly power in competitive or potentially competitive markets.

And neither free calling areas nor the goals of the MFJ are uppermost in the minds of state regulators. They, too, use the term local exchange service to divide monopoly services from those to be offered on a competitive basis, but the reasons have less to do with fostering competition than with protecting the public from monopoly abuses, avoiding waste and, more recently, preserving their ability to maintain cross-subsidies among services.

The traditional role of utility regulation has been to protect the public from price gouging and other evils associated with the provision of essential services that are assumed to be "natural monopolies." the prevention of wasteful (i.e., inefficient) competition in markets that constitute natural monopolies has also played a role. Since the end of World War II, however, and particularly in the last 15 years, state telephone regulators have increasingly sought to *preserve* both natural and unnatural monopolies in the face of nascent competition. A large part of the transition can be traced to the post-War development of pricing structures under which toll revenues are allegedly used to subsidize basic local service. The stated goal of that redistribution is the maintenance of "universal service." Because public utility commissions do not have the power to make general appropriations or levy taxes, they cannot implement this income transfer like other welfare programs. Instead, they must rely upon their authority to approve—and adjust—rates.

Control over pricing requires control over market entry and competition. Monopolists (and those who regulate them) need not fear that if prices are too high customers will go elsewhere, because the only alternatives to buying from the monopolist is to do without. Unregulated competition, in contrast, forces companies to price their services close to cost lest they be underpriced by—and lose customers to—new or lean entrants. Cross-subsidization is, therefore, sustainable only in an environment in which prices are administered and each provider offers a full range of services so that providers can charge above-cost prices for some services in order to generate revenues that can be internally transferred by charging below cost prices for other services. Monopoly (or at least a well organized cartel) is no longer the regulator's curse; it becomes his cause.

10.3   THE IMPLICATIONS

Local exchange service (along with intraLATA toll in some states) is the last bastion of monopoly telecommunications, and one of the few areas in which state communications regulators retain substantial authority. Its definition and limits are therefore important to the consuming public, regulators, local telephone companies, and their potential competitors.

Leaving aside the traditional "free calling area" function, the common purpose of the various definitions of local exchange service is the separation of *de facto* or *de jure* monopoly markets from competitive ones. But classifying by definition requires clean, bright lines and a kind of mutuality that is arguably inappropriate in telecommunications. Judge Greene and the Department of Justice have often observed that because of the Bell Operating Companies' monopoly power in local exchange markets or sub-markets, the scope of their activities in other markets must be curtailed to protect competition. They have also observed, however, that these conditions do *not* require that the monopoly markets be protected from competition by companies that lack comparable market power, and have in fact encouraged the states to open these markets to new entrants. Using local exchange service as a kind of shorthand to divide the communications world into monopoly and competitive spheres frustrates these efforts by fostering a kind of compartmentalization in which the divisions between markets are seen as impenetrable walls rather than one-way doors.

Moreover, as noted above, the phrase local exchange service has been used to distinguish both geographic and product markets, although it is obviously of geographic origin. If the only natural monopoly in telecommunications is public switched voice service within relatively small geographic areas, sweeping other communications products and media (including those that can efficiently be provided on a competitive basis) within the definition is neither analytically sound nor likely to lead to good policy.

Questions of what is a natural monopoly and whether cross-subsidization is appropriate are, of course, far broader than the definition of local exchange service. But because it is a more or less common ground that local exchange service is and (for the time being) should be a monopoly offering of the local telephone companies, the definitional struggle has important substantive consequences. One need look no further than the battle over whether competition should be allowed in the provision of intraLATA toll to see that, even without the blinders of a definition, the scope of the local company monopoly is a major issue.

In short, the definition of local exchange service makes a difference because how we label something profoundly affects how we think about it. In college anthropology one learns of Eskimos that have seventeen different words for what corresponds to the English word "snow," and therefore literally *see* many different kinds of solid precipitation, whereas those who live in more temperate climates see one. Given the mindset of most of the industry (and its regulators), defining a product as part of local exchange service cuts off the debate about whether it should be competitively offered, preventing a hard look at the appropriate questions of whether the product has the characteristics of a natural monopoly and, if not, whether it should nevertheless be provided on a monopoly basis.

10.4 A SOLUTION

One obvious solution is to abjure the label altogether except for use in the universally accepted sense of switched calls inside a free calling area. If that seems too radical a step, we might at least make an effort to distinguish monopoly local service from competitively provided local service. Indeed, to the extent that the FCC has expressly authorized competition in the provision of certain kinds of local telecommunications services and pre-empted state regulation of those services,[5] that distinction is already a reality.

It can (and undoubtedly will) be argued that this is mere semantics, form rather than substance. If everyone knows that local exchange service is a synonym for the monopoly offerings of the local telephone companies, it shouldn't matter that the phrasing is a bit arcane or imprecise. It is all a bit reminiscent of Fred Kahn, who made people nervous when he was chairman of President Carter's Council on Wage and Price Stability by talking often and in public about the threat of a

---

[5] Examples include Digital Termination Service (DTS), FM subcarrier and, most recently, resale of private operational fixed microwave.

recession. Kahn was not about to cut his beliefs to fit the fashion of the times, so he responded to criticism by changing vocabulary, announcing that thenceforth he would refer to a significant slowdown in the economy as as "banana," and opining that if the polices he favored were not implemented a severe banana was likely.

There is a grain of truth in the view that it matters not what you call something as long as everyone knows what you mean, but it's a small grain. In the case of local exchange service, however, everyone *doesn't* necessarily know what you mean, which gives rise to a real danger that authoritative pronouncements will be quoted out of context because they were made with one definition in mind but are being used by someone who means something else.

More importantly, a debate over whether a particular service is or is not local exchange service differs in important ways from a debate over whether or not it should be offered on a monopoly basis, even if the two "amount to the same thing." Deciding whether an offering falls within the scope of a defined or definable term tends to be an exercise in semantics and legislative/administrative history.

Most state public utility statutes say nothing about local exchange services or even telecommunications. They speak instead of telephones or telephone service, or telephone corporations. Did the legislature that wrote such a law in 1911 (or 1906, or 1923) intend to include digital microwave or local area networks? (Of course not—but neither did it intend to exclude them; they were unheard of.) Can we read into a statue's distinction between telegraph and telephone service an intent to separate record/data and voice transmission and to restrict local telephone monopolies to the latter? (Maybe.) Is offering service to the residents of one small village an offer to "the public"? How about offering service to tenants of one large building? Policy arguments frequently become secondary to strained interpretations and extrapolations of cases decided a generation or two ago. By contrast, when the question is posed as one of policy—whether the public interest is best served if a given service is provided by one carrier—the debate tends to focus directly on the pros and cons of the issue at hand. Decisionmakers receive much more useful information and a fuller explication of what is at stake.

Precisely for that reason, the abandonment or restricted use of the phrase local exchange service may well be an idea whose time has not yet come. It would force local telephone companies to go beyond labels to justify their desire to offer services on a monopoly basis, especially when the services in question cannot easily be offered over the unenhanced public network and are not now a substantial source of revenue that is used to support local service. The local companies tend to be influential in the states—they are large employers, substantial taxpayers, and the vessels of universal service. Given a choice between proving that new services are natural monopolies (or should be) and judicious application of a dispositive label, they usually prefer to define and conquer.

Chapter 11

Ending Structural Separation For Telephone Companies

WARREN G. LAVEY

The Federal Communications Commission (FCC), some state regulatory commissions, and two recent antitrust consent decrees cumulatively require the American Telephone and Telegraph Company (AT&T), the Bell Operating Companies (BOCs), GTE Corporation, and some other exchange telephone companies to establish separate subsidiaries for some of their unregulated activities. Although the details of these requirements vary, they force some telephone companies to compete in certain offerings only through organizations separate from their telephone operations—separate in personnel, facilities, equipment, marketing, operations, and capitalization. In addition, these regulations and decrees restrict information flows between some telephone operations and the state subsidiaries, and limit some subsidiaries' revenues.

There is intense dispute over whether these requirements serve the public interest.[1] Regulators and courts have recognized that separate-subsidiary requirements may impede innovative offerings, create operating inefficiencies, cause higher rates for regulated and unregulated services, inconvenience consumers, and stifle the ability of certain carriers to compete. On the other hand, some regulators and courts have found that such requirements limit anticompetitive discrimination and cross-subsidies from monopoly to competitive services, and thereby encourage technological innovations and lower rates.

---

[1] *See* National Telecommunications and Information Administration (NTIA), Comprehensive Study of the Structure and Regulation of the U.S. Telecommunications Industry, 50 Fed. Reg. 5657 (Feb. 11, 1985) (inquiry into future governmental policies affecting the telecommunications industry); Comments to NTIA filed by parties in response to the NTIA Comprehensive Study (Mar. 29, 1985); U.S. DEP'T COMMERCE, ISSUES IN DOMESTIC TELECOMMUNICATIONS: DIRECTIONS FOR NATIONAL POLICY 59-82 (July 1985) (report recommending end of structural separation requirements).

This article examines the analytic framework upon which these separate-subsidiary requirements are based. Section 11.1 describes the structural separation requirements imposed by three sources: the FCC, state regulatory commissions, and antitrust consent decrees. It discusses seven decisions in which regulators or courts imposed structural separation, two orders in which the FCC lifted a separation requirement, and one order in which the FCC refused to impose separation. This discussion establishes the basis for Section 11.2, which describes four fallacies underlying the analytic framework of separation requirements. One fallacy is that regulators and judges can develop a reasonably exact cost-benefit analysis to guide the imposition of structural separation. Another is that structural separation is necessary to achieve reasonable regulated rates. A third fallacy is that structural separation makes a critical contribution to effective competition. Finally, a fourth false belief is that regulators and courts can craft viable definitions of the activities subject to structural separation.

After examining these weaknesses in the rationale for the separation decisions, the article concludes with a recommendation to end all structural separation requirements for telephone companies.

11.1 THREE SOURCES OF STRUCTURAL SEPARATION REQUIREMENTS FOR TELEPHONE COMPANIES

11.1.1 FCC Orders

It is not necessary for the purposes of this article to describe fully or even catalogue all instances in which the FCC imposed or considered structural separation requirements.[2] Rather, this discussion simply outlines one line of cases where the FCC did require separation and another order where the FCC rejected a

---

[2] *See also* Proposed Modification of the Commission's Authorized User Policy Concerning Access to the Int'l Satellite Servs. of the Communications Satellite Corp., 90 F.C.C.2d 1394 (1982), *vacated and remanded sub nom.* ITT World Communications, Inc. v. Federal Communications Comm'n, 725 F.2d 732 (D.C. Cir. 1984), *on remand,* 50 Fed. Reg. 2552 (Jan. 17, 1985) (requiring Communications Satellite Corp. (Comsat) to provide competitive offerings through separate subsidiary); Blanket Section 214 Authorization for Provision by a Tel. Common Carrier of Lines for its Cable Television and other Non-Common Carrier Servs. Outside Its Tel. Serv. Area. 98 F.C.C.2d 354.359 (1984) (requiring separate books of account, but not structural separation, for exchange telephone companies' cable television operations); Concord Tel. Exch., 78 F.C.C.2d 676.682 (1980) (same); Chesapeake & Potomac Tel. Co. of Va., 98 F.C.C.2d 238, 244-48 (1984) (rejecting structural separation and separate books of account for an exchange telephone company's Digital Termination System); Southern Bell Tel. Co., F.C.C. Mimeo No. 4472 (released May 10, 1985) (same); Application of Gen. Tel. and Elecs. Corp. to Acquire Control of Telenet Corp., 72 F.C.C.2d 111. 137 (1979) (requiring that Telenet operate as a separate subsidiary), *modified,* 84 F.C.C.2d 18, 26-36 (1979); Land Mobile Serv., 51 F.C.C.2d 945, 951 (1975) (requiring that exchange telephone companies operate cellular mobile radio systems through separate subsidiaries); Detariffing the Installation and Maintenance of Inside Wiring, 50 Fed. Reg. 13,991 (Apr. 9, 1985) (notice of proposed rulemaking asking whether separation should apply to a deregulated offering); Detariffing of Billing and Collection Services, 50 Fed. Reg. 15,191 (Apr. 17, 1985) (same).

separation request. The line of cases involves the interrelationship between telecommunications and data processing services and equipment. The order deals with competition in interexchange telecommunications services.

1. Four Orders Requiring Separation for Data Processing

Communications services are used to connect people and computers to remotely-located computers. As demand for remote-access data processing grew in the mid-1960's, common carriers were well-positioned to provide computer equipment and specialized transmission services that would interconnect with telephone lines for high-speed, low-error data communications. Common carriers had technical expertise in computers used in telephone switching and billing, and the ability to provide end-to-end integration of equipment and services. They also had established distribution systems and economies in providing telephone operations and data processing services using the same computers.[3]

These developments caused regulators and data processing firms to become concerned that telephone companies would shift some of the costs of their data processing equipment and services into their revenue requirements for regulated communications services. If undetected by regulators, this cost-shifting (cross-subsidizing) would enable telephone companies to justify unreasonably high rates for their regulated communications services,[4] and encourage them to charge below-cost, anticompetitive rates for their unregulated data processing equipment and services.[5]

Regulators and data processing firms also worried that telephone companies might leverage their monopolies in communications services to impede competition in data processing.[6] Telephone companies might "bundle" or tie their communications and data processing offerings, or they might discriminate in access to, design of, and disclosure of information about their communications services. To further complicate these problems, it was unclear which aspects of

---

[3] See S. Mathison & P. Walker, Computers and Telecommunications in Issues in Public Policy (1970); Berman, *Computer or Communications? Allocation of Functions and the Role of the Federal Communications Commission*, in High and Low Politics Information Resources for the 80s 147-94 (1977); Baer, *Telecommunications Technology in the 1980s*, in Communications for Tomorrow: Policy Perspectives for the 198   (G. Robinson ed. 1978).

[4] See generally S. Breyer, Regulation and Its Reform 36-59 (1982); F. Scherer, Industrial Market Structure and Economic Performance 481-86 (2d ed. 1980); 1 A. Kahn, The Economics of Regulation 25-54 (1970).

[5] See Lavey & Carlton, *Economic Goals and Remedies of the AT&T Modified Final Judgment*, 71 Geo L.J. 1497, 1509-10 (1983) (discussing predatory pricing by regulated firms).

[6] For some leading antitrust cases on anticompetitive leverage, see Jefferson Parish Hosp. Dist. No. 2 v. Hyde, 104 S. Ct. 1551, 1558 (1984); United States Steel v. Fortner Enters., 429 U.S. 610, 620 (1977); Northeastern Tel. Co. v. American Tel. & Tel. Co., 651 F.2d 76.93 (2d Cir. 1981), cert. denied, 455 U.S. 943 (1982); California Computer Prods. v. International Business Mach Corp., 613 F.2d 727, 744 (9th Cir. 1979); Berkey Photo, Inc. v. Eastman Kodak Co., 603 F.2d 263, 284 (2d Cir. 1979), cert. denied, 444 U.S. 1093 (1980).

the computer-communications interdependence should be regulated as common carrier offerings under the Communications Act of 1934.[7]

Consequently, the FCC began to address the need for structural separation in the growing interdependence of computers and communications. It conducted proceedings to determine what services telephone companies could provide in computer-communications, and what regulations, including structural-separation requirements, would apply to such services. This section describes four landmarks in those proceedings.

a. FCC Orders Separation for Data Processing: *First Computer Inquiry*

In the *First Computer Inquiry*,[8] the FCC adopted rules that attempted to distinguish common carriers' use of computers for unregulated data processing from their use of computers for integral components of regulated communications services. The FCC decided not to prohibit absolutely carriers from providing data processing services. Instead, the FCC restricted common carriers with annual revenues exceeding one million dollars from engaging in unregulated data processing except through a separate subsidiary.[9]

Three aspects of this 1971 decision warrant particular attention. First, the requirement of structural separation for data processing was *ad hoc*.[10] The *First Computer Inquiry* grew out of certain technological developments that attracted public attention. But there was no showing that the harms of cross-subsidies and anticompetitive leverage caused by these activities were greater than those caused by other unregulated activities of telephone companies. Nor was there any

---

[7] 47 U.S.C. § § 151-156, 201-224 (1982).

[8] Regulatory and Policy Problems Presented by the Interdependence of Computer and Communication Services and Facilities (First Computer Inquiry), 28 F.C.C.2d 267 (1971). *affd in part and rev'd inpart sub nom.* GTE Serv. Corp. v. Federal Communications Comm'n, 474 F.2d 724 (2d Cir. 1973), *decision on remand*, 40 F.C.C.2d 293 (1973).

[9] The subsidiaries had to utilize separate books of account, personnel, equipment, and facilities; all agreements between the carriers and subsidiaries had to be filed with the FCC; and the carriers could not sell or promote the subsidiaries' data processing services. An appellate court struck down two additional FCC prohibitions requiring that the subsidiaries could neither use the carriers' names nor provide services to the carriers. The court held that these restrictions reflected the FCC's concerns about competition in data processing, which exceeded its statutory authority to regulate communications services. GTE Serv. Corp. v. Federal Communications Comm'n, 474 F.2d 724, 732-35 (2d Cir. 1973).

[10] It was not until 1984 that the FCC addressed carriers' unregulated activities generally, in Procedures for Implementing the Detariffing of Customer Premises Equipment and Enhanced Services (Second Computer Inquiry); and Amendment of the Commission's Rules to Provide for Nonregulated Activities of Telephone Carriers, 49 Fed. Reg. 46,378 (Nov. 26, 1984) (requiring separate books of account utilizing a fully-allocated-costs methodology without structural separation). Concerns about cross-subsidies and anticompetitive leverage also apply to carriers' multiple regulated offerings. It was not until 1981 that the FCC adopted an accounting plan for allocating costs among carriers' regulated services. American Tel. & Tel. Co. (Interim Cost Allocation Manual), 84 F.C.C.2d 384 (1981) (lack of a proper and manageable methodology for allocating investment and expenses to AT&T's individual services and service elements), *aff'd sub nom.* MCI Telecommunications Corp. v. Federal Communications Comm'n. 675 F.2d 408 (D.C. Cir. 1982).

comparison of the inefficiencies caused by separation in data processing with the potential inefficiencies from separation in other areas of telephone company operations.

Second, while the FCC ostensibly based its *First Computer Inquiry* decision on a weighing of costs and benefits, the decision was devoid of any empirical analysis. The FCC did not produce or cite any evidence of actual cross-subsidies or anticompetitive leveraging.[11] For example, although the FCC recognized that restricting the carriers' sales of excess computer capability would raise their costs for regulated services, it did not estimate the impact of separation on these rates.[12] Similarly, the FCC made no attempt to quantify the amount of data processing costs that might "leak" through regulatory audits into regulated revenue requirements absent separation, even though it viewed this concern as an important reason to impose separation.[13]

Finally, the FCC adopted an unworkable functional approach for identifying data processing activities that would be both unregulated and separated. Explaining that communications services included computerized message switching and that data processing services included other uses of computers such as storing, retrieving, sorting, merging, and calculating data, the FCC concluded that "hybrid" offerings combining communications with data processing would be difficult to categorize broadly.[14] The FCC decided to use a case-by-case approach to characterize hybrid services and equipment as either communications or data processing.[15] This approach spawned uncertainty and long, costly regulatory proceedings.[16] As technological changes increased the interdependence of communications and data processing, the FCC's case-by-case method of defining unregulated activities subject to separation deprived consumers of new technologies and impeded corporate planning for new products and services.

---

[11] *See First Computer Inquiry*, 28 F.C.C.2d at 290 (separate statement of Chairman Burch: "on the record, there is no showing of abuse"). Without any actual instances of harm, the FCC relied on the following:

Our experiences with attempting to allocate investment and costs between and among communication services provided by fungible plant and operated by the same personnel of a common carrier convince us of the great difficulties which could be involved in allocation procedures between communications and data processing activities.

Id. at 271. This reference to potential for abuse hardly constitutes a cost-benefit analysis.

[12] *Id.* at 271.

[13] The FCC's chairman described the decision as following "simply from some visceral reaction to the 'possibility of harm.' " *Id.* at 290 (separate statement of Chairman Burch). No empirical analysis supported the specification of certain data processing activities as subject to separation, or the exception from separation of carriers with annual revenues under one million dollars.

[14] *Id.* at 277-81, 287-88.

[15] In making this judgment, the FCC intended to "look to the essential substance of a service in terms of its principal orientation," to determine whether the communication was merely incidental to the data processing, or vice versa. *Id.* at 280.

[16] In one case, the FCC took two years to decide that AT&T could market as a communications service a terminal with communications and data processing capabilities. American Tel. & Tel. Co., 62 F.C.C.2d 21, 30-31 (1977) (Dataspeed 40/4), *aff'd sub nom.* International Business Machs. v. Federal Communications Comm'n, 570 F.2d 452 (2d Cir. 1978).

b. FCC Orders Separation for Certain Services and Equipment: *Second Computer Inquiry*

In 1980, in the *Second Computer Inquiry*,[17] the FCC redrew the line between regulated and unregulated activities, and changed the coverage of the structural-separation requirement. In an attempt to provide greater certainty and predictability of regulation for companies, and to stimulate competition in communications and data processing,[18] the FCC rejected its earlier case-by-case approach to characterizing hybrid equipment and services. Instead, the FCC deregulated all customer-premises equipment (CPE)[19] and all "enhanced" services.[20]

Under the FCC's new rules, AT&T was the only carrier that had to have structural separation for its enhanced services and CPE distribution.[21] Although all other carriers had to establish separate books of account for their enhanced services and CPE distribution, they could have integrated operations for regulated and unregulated offerings.[22] All carriers had to make separately available (unbundle) their regulated offerings from those that were unregulated. To protect against cross-subsidies and discrimination, all carriers had to acquire regulated services at tariffed rates as inputs to their enhanced services.[23]

One important aspect of the *Second Computer Inquiry* decision is the different treatment accorded to AT&T. All exchange telephone companies had local monopolies[24] and any costs they could shift from unregulated to regulated

---

[17] Amendment of Section 64.702 of the Commission's Rules and Regulations (Second Computer Inquiry), 77 F.C.C.2d 384, *reconsidered*, 84 F.C.C.2d 50 (1980), *further reconsidered*, 88 F.C.C.2d 512 (1981), *aff'd sub nom.* Computer and Communications Indus. Ass'n v. Federal Communications Comm'n, 693 F.2d 198 (D.C. Cir. 1982), *cert. denied*, 461 U.S. 938 (1983).

[18] 77 F.C.C.2d at 423, 428-30.

[19] CPE includes such equipment connected to telephone lines as telephone sets, private branch exchanges (PBXs), and computer terminals.

[20] Enhanced services combine clear-channel transmissions or "basic" services with certain specified data processing applications, *See* C.F.R. § 64.702(a) (1984), which defines "enhanced services" as:

> [S]ervices, offered over common carrier transmission facilities used in interstate communications, which employ computer processing applications that act on the format, content, code, protocol or similar aspects of the subscriber's transmitted information; provide the subscriber additional, different, or restructured information; or involve subscriber interaction with stored information.

In the *Second Computer Inquiry*, the FCC defined "basic service" as the offering of "a pure transmission capability over a communications path that is virtually transparent in terms of its interaction with customer supplied information." 77 F.C.C.2d at 419-20.

[21] The FCC reversed its original decision (*Second Computer Inquiry* at 77 F.C.C.2d at 474) to impose structural separation on GTE. 84 F.C.C.2d at 72. Structural separation for AT&T required separate personnel, facilities, equipment, operations, and marketing; limited joint software development; and restrictions on information flows between AT&T's telephone operations and its subsidiary. 47 C.F.R. § 64.702 (1984).

[22] 77 F.C.C.2d at 474. The FCC stated its commitment to the minimum necessary degree of separation: "To the extent there may be efficiencies within [carriers'] structures they should not be precluded from capitalizing on them where countervailing regulatory considerations do not demand stringent separation." *Id.* at 476.

[23] 77 F.C.C.2d at 474-75; 47 C.F.R. § 64.702(c)(1) (1984).

[24] *See* Illinois Bell Tel. Co. v. Federal Communications Comm'n, 740 F.2d 465, 473, 476 (7th Cir. 1984).

services without regulatory detection would increase their regulated service rates.[25] Because they all have bottle-neck control over local exchange facilities, any of these companies could use discriminatory interconnections to impede competition in supplying CPE and enhanced services to its subscribers. Yet the FCC decided that the costs of structural separation outweighed the benefits for all carriers except AT&T. Despite its claims of careful consideration,[26] the FCC never attempted to quantify the costs and benefits of structural separation for any carrier.[27] The FCC merely found that AT&T was the only carrier having "sufficient market power to engage in effective anticompetitive activity on a national scale and . . . sufficient resources to enter the competitive market through a separate subsidiary."[28]

The separation requirement for AT&T's enhanced services and CPE distribution became even more questionable after AT&T divested the BOCs in 1984.[29] AT&T no longer controls nationwide bottleneck exchange facilities, and competition has grown substantially since 1980 in interexchange services, enhanced services, and CPE.[30] Moreover, the divestiture decree allows AT&T to engage in

---

[25] Because all these carriers originate and terminate interstate transmissions, an increase in their costs would raise interstate rates under the FCC's jurisdiction.

[26] 77 F.C.C.2d at 502 (separate statement of Chairman Ferris).

[27] Even a serious attempt to analyze the costs and benefits of structural separation for AT&T would have encountered large areas of speculation. Technology, demand and competition were changing rapidly. A quantitative cost-benefit analysis would have been confounded with uncertainties: How much similar software would there be for the future generations of central-office switches and CPE, and how much higher would the development and maintenance costs be if the telephone company could only work on switches and the subsidiary could only work on CPE? What new services would customers demand, how much more wout it cost AT&T to supply them under separation, and what would be the effects on the U.S. economy if separation raises the costs and delays introduction of these services? Would AT&T impair competition under the antitrust laws absent separation, and how much would prices decline and services improve if this anticompetitive conduct were prevented by separation?

Even in its retrospective evaluation of the costs and benefits of the *Second Computer Inquiry*, NTIA failed to quantify any impacts of separation. U.S. DEP'T OF COMMERCE, ISSUES IN DOMESTIC TELECOMMUNICATIONS: DIRECTIONS FOR NATIONAL POLICY 72 (1985). AT&T estimated in 1984 that structural-separation requirements caused it to incur costs exceeding one billion dollars annually. *Id.* at 69.

[28] 77 F.C.C.2d at 389. There has been no evidence brought to the FCC that failure to require structural separation for non-AT&T carriers caused substantial cost shifting or anticompetitive practices.

[29] *See* Furnishing of Customer Premises Equipment and Enhanced Services by American Tel. & Tel. Co., 50 Fed. Reg. 9060 (Mar. 6, 1985); AT&T Petition for Relief from Structural Separation Requirements, F.C.C. ENF 84-17 (filed Apr. 30, 1984); MacAvoy & Robinson, *Losing by Judicial Policymaking: The First Year of the AT&T Divestiture*, in 2 YALE J. REG. 225, 259-60 (1985). The antirust consent decree ordering the AT&T divestiture was entered in United States v. American Tel. & Tel. Co., 552 F. Supp. 131 (D.D.C. 1982), *aff'd sub nom.* Maryland v. United States, 460 U.S. 1001 (1983).

[30] For discussions of such competition, see e.g., Procedures for Implementing the Detariffing of Customer Premises Equipment and Enhanced Services, F.C.C. 85-220 at 19-20 (released May 15, 1985); Furnishing of Customer Premises Equipment and Enhanced Services by American Tel. & Tel. Co., 50 Fed. Reg. 9060 at 9064 (Mar. 6, 1985); American Tel. & Tel. Co.: Provision of Basic Services via Resale by Separate Subsidiary, 98 F.C.C.2d 478 (1984); Long-Run Regulation of AT&T's Basic Domestic Interstate Services, 95 F.C.C.2d 510 (1983); Baumol & Willig, *Telephones and Computers: The Costs of Artificial Separation*, REGULATION, Mar.-Apr. 1985, at 23.

new, unregulated activities not covered by a separation requirement.[31] In February 1985, the FCC denied an AT&T petition to lift separation entirely, granted some limited exceptions to separation, and began proceedings on further relief.[32] In a major order in September 1985, the FCC removed the separation requirement for AT&T's CPE.[33] The FCC concluded that non-structural alternatives for checking cross-subsidies and anticompetitive conduct[34] served the public interest better than separation. Without empirical analysis, the FCC justified the switch in regulatory tools by pointing to changed conditions that increased the costs and decreased the benefits of separation.[35]

As in the *First Computer Inquiry*, the definitional approach adopted by the FCC in the *Second Computer Inquiry*—enhanced versus basic services, and CPE versus other telephone equipment—proved to be unworkable. Again, the march of technology blurred distinctions as telephone companies increasingly used data processing applications to improve their efficiency in transmitting calls.[36] Be-

---

[31] The 1982 consent decree lifted restrictions on AT&T's lines of business established by an earlier consent decree that ended the 1949 antitrust suit brought by the United States to break up AT&T *See* United States v. Western Elec. Co., 1956 Trade Cas. (CCH) ¶ 68,246 (D.N.J. 1956). Now, for example, no structural separation prevents AT&T from shifting costs from its manufacturing and distribution of computers into its regulated revenue requirement. There has been no evidence brought to the FCC or U.S. Department of Justice that AT&T has engaged in substantial cross-subsidization or discrimination regarding these activities.

[32] *See* Furnishing of Customer Premises Equipment and Enhanced Services by American Tel. & Tel. Co., 50 Fed. Reg. 9060 (Mar. 6, 1985); AT&T Information Systems Inc.: Petition for Waivers in Connection with AT&T's Line of Business Reorganization, F.C.C. Mimeo No. 3925 (released Apr. 18, 1985); AT&T: Compliance Plan Regarding Network Information and Accounting Submitted in Response to Conditional Waiver of Computer II Software Rules, F.C.C. Mimeo No. 5607 (released July 9, 1985).

[33] Furnishing of Customer Premises Equipment and Enhanced Services, 50 Fed. Reg. 40.379 (Oct. 3, 1985). Separation requirements for the enhanced services of AT&T and the BOCs continue, but the FCC has proposed to eliminate or revise them. Amendment of section 64.702 of the Commission's Rules and Regulations (Third Computer Inquiry), 50 Fed. Reg. 33.581 (Aug. 20, 1985). The FCC has not proposed to eliminate the separation imposed on the BOCs' CPE.

[34] Furnishing of Customer Premises Equipment and Enhanced Services, 50 Fed. Reg. 40.379, at 40.385, 40.389, 40.391-94 (Oct. 3, 1985) (regulatory comparisons of transfer prices to marketplace prices; network and customer information disclosure obligations; monthly reports to FCC of installation and maintenance practices; accounting procedures).

[35] *Id.* at 40.385-87.

[36] Consequently, the FCC confronted the question of what interactions between a subscriber and a stored database are simply extensions of historic message switching practices, and what interactions are enhanced services. *See* Custom Calling II, 88 F.C.C.2d 1 (1981); American Tel. & Tel.Co.: Revision to Tariff F.C.C. No. 259 (WATS) for Advanced 800 Service, F.C.C. 84-562 (released Nov. 30, 1984). Other proceedings drawing lines between basic and enhanced services dealt with providing information about calls to customers, screening and routing calls for customers, packet switching, converting the protocol of data transmissions, and teleconferencing with terminal resolution capability. *See* Applied Spectrum Technologies: Petition for Declaratory Ruling Under Section 64.702 of the Commission's Rules Regarding the Status of "Spread Spectrum" Transmission Services, F.C.C. Mimeo No. 5532 (released July 3, 1985); North American Telecommunications Ass'n.: Petition for Declatory Ruling Under Section 64.702 of the Commission's Rules Regarding the Integration of Centrex, Enhanced Services, and Customer Premises Equipment, F.C.C. 85-248 (released May 29, 1985); American Tel. & Tel. Co. (BPSS), 91 F.C.C.2d 1 (1982); American Tel. & Tel. Co., 94 F.C.C.2d 48 (1983); Petitions for Waiver of § 64.702 of the Commission's Rules (Second Computer Inquiry), 50 Fed. Reg. 13,573 (Apr. 5, 1985); Communications Protocols Inquiry, 95

cause all activities subject to structural separation were unregulated, interpretations of definitions and waiver decisions turned on technological factors as well as on evaluations of the public interest in regulating the service or equipment. The market analysis involved in assessing the likely strength of competition and the effects of deregulation on consumers increased the uncertainty of regulation and the complexity and length of proceedings.[37]

c. FCC Orders Separation for the BOCs' Enhanced Services and CPE

After the BOCs were divested from AT&T, the FCC examined whether the structural separation imposed on AT&T by the *Second Computer Inquiry* should similarly be imposed on the BOCs. In 1983, the FCC ordered that the BOCs could not provide enhanced services or distribute CPE except through separate subsidiaries.[38] The order provided limited exceptions from full separation and

---

F.C.C.2d 584 (1983); AT&T Communications: Revisions to Tariff F.C.C. No. 263 Introducing Audiographics Teleconferencing Bridge, F.C.C. Mimeo No. 642 (released Nov. 6, 1984).

Technological developments also affected the definition of CPE. The FCC was called upon to characterize satellite earth stations that transmit, receive and perform network control functions in American Tel. & Tel. Co.: Request for Clarification of Computer II Requirements Concerning Earth Stations, F.C.C. 83-603 (adopted Dec. 22, 1983); coinless pay telephones in Petition for Declaratory Ruling of Tonka Tools, 50 Fed. Reg. 24,694 (June 12, 1985); network channel terminating equipment that interacts with central-office switches for digital transmissions in Amendment of Part 68 of the Commission's Rules Concerning Connection of Telephone Equipment, System and Protective Apparatus to the Telephone Network, 94 F.C.C.2d 5 (1983), F.C.C. 84-145 (released Apr. 27, 1984), 49 Fed. Reg. 48,714 (Dec. 14, 1984); interfaces for a data transport service in International Business Machs. (Local Area Data Transport Service), F.C.C. 85-292 (released June 11, 1985); and the baseband unit associated with Digital Termination System subscriber stations, Status of Certain Equipment Necessary to Provide Digital Termination Systems, F.C.C. Mimeo No. 6577 (released Aug. 22, 1985).

In its recent notice of proposed rulemaking that started the *Third Computer Inquiry*, the FCC proposed to move from definitional demarcations based on the function performed by equipment to analysis of the need for regulation based on market power. Under this proposal, the FCC would not require structural separation. However, the FCC also stated proposals that would modify the definition of enhanced services and continue to require structural separation. Amendment of Section 64.702 of the Commission's Rules and Regulations (Third Computer Inquiry), 50 Fed. Reg. 33,581, at 33,589 (Aug. 20, 1985).

[37] In light of the range of considerations, the FCC's recent order granting in part the BOCs' requests for waiver of the structural-separation requirement for offerings of protocol conversion services created an intricate interweaving of regulated with unregulated components, and of components provided by a telephone company with components provided by a separate subsidiary. *See* Petitions for Waiver of § 64.702 of the Commission's Rules (Second Computer Inquiry), 50 Fed. Reg. 13,573 (Apr. 5, 1985); *See also* Applied Spectrum Technologies: Petition for Declaratory Ruling Under Section 64.702 of the Commission's Rules Regarding the Status of "Spread Spectrum" Transmission Services, F.C.C. Mimeo No. 5532 (released July 3, 1985). Although these proceedings dealt with the separation requirement imposed on the BOCs, *see infra*, notes 38-47 and accompanying text, the definitions were those established in the *Second Computer Inquiry*.

[38] Policy and Rules Concerning the Furnishing of Customer Premises Equipment, Enhanced Services and Cellular Communications Services by the Bell Operating Companies, 95 F.C.C.2d 1117 (1983), *aff'd sub nom.* Illinois Bell Tel. Co. v. Federal Communications Comm'n., 740 F.2d 465 (7th Cir. 1984) (Posner, J.), *reconsidered*, 49 Fed. Reg. 26,056 (June 26, 1984), *aff'd sub nom.* North American Telecommunications Ass'n v. Federal Communications Comm'n. No. 84-2216 (7th Cir. Aug. 27, 1985) (Posner, J.)

committed the FCC to reexamination of the separation requirement after two years.[39]

Although this order ostensibly relied on cost-benefit analysis, it lacked empirical support for each of three major issues that it determined. First, the FCC found that separation provided substantial benefits in preventing anticompetitive discrimination and cross-subsidies. Yet the BOCs did not satisfy the *Second Computer Inquiry's* criteria for requiring structural separation.[40] Furthermore, each BOC faced more competition in enhanced services and distributing CPE than had confronted AT&T in 1980. Nevertheless, without any quantitative analysis, the FCC found that these benefits outweighed the costs of lost economies of joint operations and delay in introducing new products and services.[41]

Next, the FCC carved out some exceptions to full structural separation for the BOCs. The FCC's visceral calculus showed that the costs of restrictions in these areas would outweigh their benefits. The decision pointed to a low probability of substantial anticompetitive effects or cost shifting from these joint activities, and to a high probability of substantial efficiencies and consumer convenience. However, none of this discussion reflected empirical estimates, market studies, or operations analyses.[42]

Third, the FCC required separation for the BOCs but not for other exchange telephone companies. In particular, the FCC did not require GTE to separate its enhanced services and CPE distribution, even though GTE served approximately as many subscribers as each Bell Regional Holding Company.[43] Again, the FCC

---

[39] 95 F.C.C.2d at 1140-45, 49 Fed. Reg. at 26,057. The permissible joint operations include (1) limited referrals of customers from a BOC's telephone company to its separate subsidiary; (2) installation and maintenance for single-line CPE; and (3) billing services. *See also* American Information Technologies Corp., 98 F.C.C.2d 943 (1984) (permitting separate subsidiaries to act as sales agents for basic services).

[40] No BOC had nationwide control of bottleneck exchange facilities, and none was vertically integrated in manufacturing, *See* 77 F.C.C.2d at 467-68; 84 F.C.C.2d at 72.

[41] In affirming the FCC order, the Seventh Circuit observed:

Although the sacrifice of these economies [of joint provision of services and customer-premises equipment] is the principal cost of the Commission's approach, neither the Commission nor any party made an effort to estimate them. The complete absence of quantitative data gives rather a hollow ring to the Commission's claim to have based its order on a comparison of the "costs" and "benefits" of the separate subsidiary approach.

740 F.2d at 474.

The Seventh Circuit elaborated on this view in affirming the FCC's reconsideration order: No effort to set a price tag on this disadvantage was made, however, and we do not think that the Commission was required to give weight to an argument left in so highly speculative a posture. . .Everyone is making guesses; the principles of judicial review of administrative action require deference to the agency's guesses. . .[A]n agency has, in the nature of things, a particularly broad discretion when balancing considerations left formless and unmeasured because of the parties' failure to present empirical evidence.

North American Telecommunications Ass'n v. Federal Communications Comm'n. No. 84-2216, slip op. at 9, 10, 11 (7th Cir. Aug. 27, 1985) (Posner, J.)

In fact, during the six months from divestiture to the effective data for the separation requirement, there was no evidence brought to the FCC that the BOCs engaged in substantial discrimination or cross-subsidization.

[42] Even if such estimates and studies were performed, they would be quite unreliable in light of uncertainties regarding what the BOCs would market, by what means, and with what success.

[43] The BOCs are organized in seven Bell Regional Holding Companies of similar size.

invoked the language of cost-benefit analysis to support this treatment without performing any empirical analysis.[44] Although the appellate court recognized serious flaws in the FCC's analysis of the non-Bell exchange carrier monopolists and its cost-benefit comparisons, the court deferred to the agency's discretion to address the need for structural separation for different carriers in different proceedings.[45]

Since its 1983 BOC separation order, the FCC's application of full structural separation has become increasingly spotty and lacking in underlying cost-benefit support. The BOCs have been authorized under the antitrust consent decree to engage in new, unregulated activities.[46] Even though these activities are not subject to the same separation requirements as are the BOCs' enhanced services and CPE distribution,[47] no party has brought to the FCC or Justice Department a showing of substantial cross-subsidization or discrimination regarding any of these unregulated activities.

d. FCC Reverses Some Separation Requirements for Satellite Business Systems

The FCC's 1977 certification of a new carrier, Satellite Business Systems (SBS), evidenced another application of structural separation in the communications-data processing area.[48] Formed as a joint venture of International Business Machines Corporation (IBM) and two other companies, SBS proposed to use satellites to provide the first digital system integrating voice, data, and video transmissions.

The FCC was concerned that IBM would use its market power in data processing to impair competition in data communications services. The 1977 order reflected fears that IBM and SBS would make bundled, end-to-end offerings of IBM equipment and SBS services, that IBM would design equipment to be compatible only with SBS's services, and that SBS would design services to

---

[44] The FCC pointed out that the costs of separating GTE's ongoing operations would be higher than the costs of establishing subsidiaries for the newly-formed, divested BOCs. Also, the order discussed the likely concentration of demand for enhanced services in urban areas. The FCC reasoned that because the BOCs serve more urban areas than does GTE, GTE is less likely to impair competition in enhanced services, 95 F.C.C.2d at 1138-39. On the other hand, GTE manufacturers equipment, an activity that can encourage a telephone company to grant anticompetitive preferences in interconnection of an affiliate's equipment to its exchange lines, while the BOCs are barred from this practice by the antitrust consent decree.

[45] 740 F.2d at 475-77.

[46] See infra notes 75-81 and accompanying text; United States v. Western Elec. Co., 592 F. Supp. 846, 870-72 (D.D.C. 1984): Capitalization Plans for the Furnishing of Customer Premises Equipment and Enhanced Services, F.C.C. 85-28 at 13 n.18 (released Feb. 4, 1985).

[47] Although the antitrust court imposed some separation requirements on the BOCs' new lines of business, neither the court nor the FCC prescribed full separation of personnel, equipment, facilities and operations, or prohibitions on sharing proprietary information such as customer lists or engaging in joint marketing presentations. United States v. Western Elec. Co., 592 F. Supp. 846, 872 n.110, 873 n.116 (D.D.C. 1984) See infra notes 75-81 and accompanying text.

[48] CML Satellite Corp., 51 F.C.C.2d 14 (1975); Satellite Business Sys., 62 F.C.C.2d 997 (1977), aff'd sub nom. United States v. Federal Communications Comm'n, 652 F.2d 72 (D.C. Cir. 1980) (en banc). The FCC authorized a restructuring of SBS's ownership in Application for Approval of Certain Changes in the Ownership Structure of Satellite Business Systems, F.C.C. 84-589 (released Nov. 28, 1984).

be compatible only with IBM's products.[69] Consequently, the FCC required IBM to create a separate corporate entity to operate the satellite carrier.[50] The FCC concluded that SBS's entry into interexchange services under these restrictions would have benefits in new services and greater competition that would outweigh the costs of potential anticompetitive effects.[51]

Had the FCC attempted to support this judgment with empirical analysis, any rigorous assessment of costs and benefits would have been extremely difficult. SBS estimated that it would need about three years after certification to build its system and begin offering its innovative services.[52] The FCC was forced to speculate on the future strength of competition for those services as well as for data processing equipment and services. To further complicate this analysis, SBS's technology was new and largely untested; domestic satellite communications were just emerging with uncertain capacity, demand, and competition; and other new transmission technologies such as fiber optics systems were on the horizon.

Seven years after certification, the FCC lifted the IBM-SBS joint marketing restriction.[53] The FCC found that as market conditions actually developed, this aspect of separation was an impediment to competition. SBS, which never earned a profit, faced strong competition from other satellite and terrestrial carriers. The FCC concluded that competition would be more intense with IBM-SBS joint marketing because SBS would have more flexibility to meet consumer needs and lower marketing costs. Finally, the FCC noted that other regulatory requirements and procedures under the Communications Act of 1934 would provide continued protection against anticompetitive practices.[54]

2. Order Rejecting Separate Subsidiaries for Interchange Services

A 1984 decision by the FCC in the *Competitive Carrier Rulemaking*[55] illustrates the FCC's alternatives to imposing structural separation. This decision ordered, inter alia, the substantial deregulation of competitive interstate, interexchange

---

[49] 62 F.C.C.2d at 1046.

[50] Under the FCC's restrictions, IBM and SBS could not share employees, sell or promote each other's products, or give joint marketing presentations. Also, SBS was required to provide interconnections for its customers' data processing systems without discrimination. *Id.* at 1044-51.

[51] *Id.* at 1099-100.

[52] *Id.* at 1023.

[53] Satellite Business Systems: Petition to Modify Conditions of Authorization, 98 F.C.C.2d 762 (1984).

[54] 98 F.C.C.2d at 771-72, See 47 U.S.C. § 203 (1982) (common carriers must make nondiscriminatory service offerings); 47 U.S.C. § 208 (1982) (remedies are available through the FCC's complaint process); and 47 U.S.C. § 218 (1982) (the FCC can require reports on common carriers' marketing practices).

[55] Policy and Rules Concerning Rates for Competitive Common Carrier Services and Facilities Authorizations Therefor (*Competitive Carrier Rulemaking*), 98 F.C.C.2d 1191 (1984) (Fifth Report and Order). A subsequent order in this proceeding was reversed, but the court did not rule on the Fifth Report and Order. MCI Telecommunications Corp. v. Federal Communications Comm'n, 765 F.2d 1186 (D.C. Cir. 1985). *See also* United Telecommunications, Inc. and U.S. Telephone, Inc., 98 F.C.C.2d 1306 (1984).

services provided by exchange telephone companies. One party to the proceeding argued that the FCC should protect against cross-subsidization from exchange telephone companies' monopoly services to their interexchange services. This party proposed that the FCC prohibit all exchange telephone companies from offering interexchange services. Alternatively, this party requested structural separation between all exchange telephone companies and their interexchange affiliates, and full regulation of the interexchange affiliates.[56]

The FCC rejected these proposals. Without attempting to estimate empirically the costs and benefits of separation or other restrictions, the FCC determined that the requested requirements would decrease efficiency, impose unnecessary costs on consumers, and impair competition.[57]

The decision cited the restrictions in antitrust consent decrees on interexchange offerings by the BOCs and the GTE exchange telephone companies.[58] However, in declining to impose structural separation on smaller exchange telephone companies, the FCC did not rely on its previous weak rationale that such companies were either too small to bear the costs of separation or too rural to have separation benefit competition.[59] Instead, the FCC reasoned that other regulatory tools short of structural separation would sufficiently inhibit cost-shifting and anticompetitive conduct. As established in earlier FCC orders, all common carriers must interconnect with all other carriers and private systems on just, reasonable, and nondiscriminatory terms.[60] The FCC stated that even without structural separation, its review of interstate exchange access tariffs should prevent substantial cost shifting or discrimination.[61] Furthermore, the FCC noted that its complaint process was a remedy for and deterrent to discrimination and anticompetitive conduct.[62]

In addition to these regulatory protections, the FCC established two other conditions for substantial deregulation of an exchange telephone company's interstate, interexchange services. To deter cost shifting, these services must be offered by an affiliated carrier using separate books of account.[63] Also, as further protection against cost shifting and discrimnation, the affiliate must acquire use of the exchange telephone company's transmission and switching facilities via its tariffs.[64] These conditions are similar to the *Second Computer Inquiry's* require-

---

[56] 98 F.C.C.2d at 1195.

[57] *Id.* at 1199-200.

[58] *Id.* at 1197-98. *See infra* notes 75-85 and accompanying text.

[59] *See* 77 F.C.C.2d at 467-68; 640 F.2d at 475-77.

[60] 98 F.C.C.2d at 1195 n.12, 1196 n.14. Specifically, the FCC cited orders prohibiting unreasonable bundling of exchange and interexchange services.

[61] *Id.* at 1196. The FCC also stated that it reviews interstate exchange access tariffs with the goals of achieving reasonable revenue requirements, cost-based rates, and just, reasonable, and nondiscriminatory terms and conditions.

[62] *Id.* at 1196.

[63] *Id.* at 1198.

[64] *Id.* Although there can be joint use of these facilities, there can be no joint ownership of them. The FCC did not restrict co-ownership of other facilities and equipment, joint marketing and operations, shared personnel, information flows, or capitalization of the affiliate. These conditions should neither cause substantial lost economies nor impose competitive handicaps.

ments for carriers other than AT&T, and are much less burdensome than structural separation.

11.1.2 State Regulatory Orders

Structural separation has been imposed on telephone companies by state public utility commissions as well as by the FCC. These state decisions are important not only for their current impact, but also because they indicate how states may respond to any FCC order lifting separation requirements. Some state regulators may impose separation requirements if they conclude that state regulatory concerns about cross-subsidies and discrimination warrant such action.[65]

In 1984 the California Public Utilities Commission issued a leading order in this area.[66] California required a GTE exchange telephone company to utilize a separate subsidiary for its unregulated marketing of CPE. This decision was aimed primarily at controlling the telephone company's regulated revenue requirement. The commission observed that it lacked the staff resources to audit the accounting and cost allocations for this unseparated activity. Moreover, although it expressed no concern about lost efficiencies caused by separation, the commission's staff concluded that the regulated revenue requirement would probably not be lowered by the joint use of assets and personnel.[67]

There are two reasons why this decision gives a false sense of the contribution of separation to the state commission's control of regulated revenue requirements. First, assuming economies of joint operation, the commission could adjust the cost allocators so that regulated costs were lower under integrated operations than under separation. Allocators within the range of reasonableness could assign to an unregulated product somewhat more than its direct (incremental) costs, but

---

[65] In the past, the FCC explicitly did not preempt state commissions from imposing structural separation to promote state regulatory goals. *See* Amendment of Section 64.702 of the Commission's Rules and Regulations (Second Computer Inquiry), 88 F.C.C.2d 512, 523, 542 (1981). Along the same lines, the FCC's proposals in the *Third Computer Inquiry* would not preempt state requirements of structural separation. Amendment of Section 64.702 of the Commission's Rules and Regulations (Third Computer Inquiry), 50 Fed. Reg. 33.581 (Aug. 20, 1985).

[66] Application of General Tel. Co. of Cal. for Authority to Increase Certain Intrastate Rates and Charges for Telephone Servs., Cal. Pub. Util. Comm'n Decision 84-07-108 at 82-93 (July 18, 1984). *See also* General Tel. Co. of the Northwest v. Mont. Dept. of Public Service Regulation, 58 P.U.R. 4th 543 (1984) (reversing a state commission's order requiring a separate subsidiary for distributing CPE); Petition of Central Tel. Co. of Fla. for Waiver of Rule 25-4.345, Fla. Pub. Serv. Comm'n Order No. 13863 (Nov. 19, 1984) (denying requested waiver of rule requiring telephone companies to offer new CPE only through separate subsidiary), *modified*, Order No. 14231 (March 25, 1985) (installation and maintenance of old CPE does not necessitate use of separate subsidiary but accounting allocation procedures must be used); Petition of General Tel. of Fla. for Approval of the Transfer of Embedded Customer Premises Equipment and Maintenance and Installation of Inside Wire to a Separate Subsidiary, Fla. Pub. Serv. Comm'n Order No. 14237 (Mar. 25, 1985) (approving transfers to separate subsidiary); SNETCO Petition for a Generic Hearing to Consider Guidelines and Procedures for SNETCO's Diversification into Unregulated Businesses, Conn. Dep't Pub. Util. Control, Docket No. 83-12-15 (Mar. 26, 1985) (requiring Southern New England Telescope Co. to establish separation between its regulated and unregulated operations).

[67] Application of General Tel. Co. of Cal. for Authority to Increase Certain Intrastate Rates and Charges for Telephone Services, Cal. Pub. Util. Comm'n Decision 84-07-108 at 84 (July 18, 1984).

less than its costs under separation. This would leave the costs assigned to regulated services below their costs under separation.[68]

Second, although it seems correct that a thorough audit of costs and allocators is beyond a commission's capabilities, this problem extends to many aspects of regulated revenue requirements and is not cured by separation. Regulators cannot effectively delve into the details of a carrier's operations.[69] In addition, regulators simply do not know enough about the telephone business to develop the revenue requirements for a hypothetical, perfectly-efficient carrier for use in ratemaking. Regulators typically use certain rough indicators to control overstated revenue requirements, such as comparing changes in a cost category over time with inflation, growth in subscribers, and a reasonable adjustment for productivity changes.[70] Such indicators can be used to control cost shifting from unregulated activities in the same way that they are used to identify other unreasonable cost increases.[71]

The California commission could have detected, without separation, unreasonable rates filed by GTE. The commission had GTE's historic costs and rates, and could have made reasonable assumptions about how they would change over time

---

[68] As explained *infra* at notes 96-100 and accompanying text, the derivation of reasonable (albeit not precise) allocators should be a manageable regulatory task. Use of these allocators, once established, would not overwhelm the commission with audit burdens. *See* Joint Plan for Deregulation, Iowa State Commerce Comm'n Docket RPU-84-8 (Apr. 1, 1985) (methods for accounting separation between regulated and deregulated services and facilities). The National Telecommunications and Information Administration recently concluded:

> Granted, it may be difficult, given the current state of the telephone accounting system, to devise unambiguous tests for cross-subsidy. That fact should not, however, drive regulatory policy to embrace increasingly costly solutions which reduce the potential to zero. We believe any additional risks are fully justified by the opportunity to advance other policy goals.

U.S. DEP'T OF COMMERCE, ISSUES IN DOMESTIC TELECOMMUNICATIONS: DIRECTIONS FOR NATIONAL POLICY 75-76 (July 1985).

[69] Professor (now Judge) Breyer explains that:

> [E]fforts to obtain economic precision in the regulatory process . . . are unlikely to be worth the effort expended. The standard to which such efforts implicitly appeal is that of overcoming "distortions" produced by competitive market failure—the standard of trying to replicate what would occur without such a failure. Yet in trying to overcome such failures the regulatory process introduces so many distortions of its own, that one should be satisfied with gross estimates and not insist upon refined economic calculations.

S. BREYER, REGULATION AND ITS REFORM 58-59 (1982).

[70] *See e.g.* Cal. Pub. Util. Comm'n Decision 84-07-108 at 57 (applying five percent productivity gain as reasonable; comparison of General Telephone of California to Pacific Bell), at 69 (six percent escalation factor for expenses from 1983-84), at 73 (construction budget adjustments based on estimated subscriber growth); Investigation of Access and Divestiture Related Tariffs and MTS and WATS Market Structure, 49 Fed. Reg. 23,924, 23.934 (June 8, 1984) (allowing nine percent growth in exchange carriers' switched access revenue requirement from 1983 to 1984); Investigation of Access and Divestiture Related Tariffs, 50 Fed. Reg. 11,440 (Mar. 21, 1985) (applying adjustment factors to exchange carriers' special access revenue requirements); Investigation of Special Access Tariffs of Local Exchange Carriers, F.C.C. Mimeo No. 4726 (released May 24, 1985) (investigation into rate variations across exchange carriers).

[71] When regulators do audit cost studies, the standard of reasonableness replaces hopes of exactness; regulators can always find fault with carriers' cost studies, but cannot develop their own precise analyses. *See* Long-Run Regulation of AT&T's Basic Domestic Interstate Services, 95 F.C.C.2d 510, 517-21 (1983); Private Line Rate Structure and Volume Discount Practices, 97 F.C.C.2d 923 (1984).

absent cross-subsidies. The commission conducted this type of analysis for other regulated costs and rates where a precise audit was not possible.[72] Furthermore, the commission had available its cost analysis of Pacific Bell, which was subject to the FCC's separation requirement and should have provided a baseline of regulated revenue requirements free from concerns about CPE cross-subsidies.[73] The commission could have used the Pacific Bell cost analysis to estimate certain indices, such as installation and maintenance costs per subscriber line, or change in advertising budget over time. Then it could have applied these indices, perhaps with some adjustments, to GTE to prevent substantial cross-subsidies without the lost economies from separation.[74]

11.1.3 Antitrust Consent Decrees

Two recent antitrust consent decrees produced additional structural separation from the BOCs and GTE. These two decrees illustrate sharp differences in the roles and features of structural separation.

1. Separation for the BOCs' New Lines of Business

In a 1982 antitrust consent decree between AT&T and the U.S. Department of Justice divesting the BOCs from AT&T,[75] the Justice Department and the court rejected the notion that some structural separation short of total divestiture could be an adequate remedy for AT&T's allegedly monopolistic practices.[76] They were concerned that, without divestiture, the parent company would have the incentive and the opportunity to use a regulated-monopoly subsidiary to give a competitive advantage to another of its subsidiaries through cross-subsidies or discrimination. In contrast, a carrier generally has no incentive to favor a separately owned company over its rivals.

In a later ruling on petitions for waiver of decree restrictions on the BOCs' lines of business, the same court required the BOCs to utilize separate subsidiaries for their new ventures.[77] The court reasoned that separate subsidiaries would make intercompany transactions more apparent; thus, cross-subsidies and anti-

---

[72] *See supra* note 70.

[73] Pacific Bell is subject to the FCC's structural separation order for BOCs discussed *supra* at notes 38-47 and accompanying text. *See supra* note 70 (comparison of General Telephone of California to Pacific Bell).

[74] In fact, it would be reasonable for the commission to limit GTE's regulated cost indices to less than Pacific Bell's on the assumption of economies from joint operations.

[75] United States v. American Tel. & Tel. Co., 552 F. Supp. 131 (D.D.C. 1982), *aff'd sub nom.* Maryland v. United States, 460 U.S. 1001 (1983). Judge Harold H. Greene entered the consent decree.

[76] 552 F. Supp. at 167-68, 193 n.251. Furthermore, the court viewed the imposition of separate subsidiaries essentially as a regulatory device and not an appropriate antitrust remedy. *See generally* Lavey & Carlton, *supra* note 5, at 1511.

[77] United States v. Western Elec. Co., 592 F. Supp. 846, 870-73 (D.D.C. 1984). This article does not deal with whether there should be restrictions on the BOCs' lines of business. Rather, it focuses on the separation requirement that applies after a line-of-business waiver has been granted.

competitive conduct could be more easily prevented.[78] In addition, the court established "guidelines" to reduce the potential for cross-subsidizing, jeopardizing the financial soundness of the BOCs' telephone operations, and diverting the BOCs' attention away from telephone services. One guideline is that the new subsidiaries must obtain their own debt financing without recourse against the parent. A second guideline is that the total estimated net revenues of a Bell Regional Holding Company's new subsidiaries should not exceed ten percent of the parent's total estimated net revenues.[79]

In imposing separation on the BOCs' new ventures, the court prevented a means of decreasing the BOCs' regulated revenue requirements. Absent full separation, telephone operations could share fixed common costs with unregulated activities, regulators could allocate some of these costs to the unregulated activities, and the new ventures could thereby lower regulated revenue requirements. Yet the court was skeptical that accounting measures would protect against shifting unregulated costs into telephone rates. Instead, it placed a size limitation on the new ventures that constrained another potential contribution to lower telephone rates through decreased capital costs.[80]

It is difficult to identify the purposes behind the court's guidelines on debt financing and net revenues. The guidelines do not limit the parent's capitalization of the subsidiary. Nor do they address the adverse consequences of a subsidiary's failure on the parent's cost of capital, even if the subsidiary had its own debt financing. Moreover, the net-revenue test does not limit the BOCs' involvement in initially unprofitable ventures, but would force them to curtail such ventures at a point of high profits under the limitation to ten percent of net revenues.[81] The telephone ratepayer does not benefit by this limitation on a telephone company's unregulated ventures.

Finally, the court did not impose on the BOCs' new subsidiaries certain restrictions that the FCC believed would increase competition and limit cross-subsidies. For example, the court did not restrict flows of proprietary information, such as customer lists, between the BOCs' telephone operations and subsidiaries. In addition, the court did not prohibit joint marketing presentations. Again, the separation was spotty, and there was no cost-benefit analysis of the restrictions or lack thereof.

---

[78] Although the court sought to ensure against improper cost shifting, it did not go so far as to prescribe full separation of personnel, equipment, facilities, and operations. *Id.* at 872 n.110, 873 n.116.

[79] *Id.* at 870-72.

[80] *See, e.g.* Central Ill. Light Co., Ill. Commerce Comm'n Docket No. 84-0413 (Jan. 9, 1985) (authorizing utility to form holding company and diversify); Ferrar, *Business Diversification: An Option Worth Considering*, 109 Pub. Util. Fort. 13 (1982); Joint Plan for Deregulation, Iowa State Commerce Comm'n Docket RPU-84-8 at 3 (Apr. 1, 1985) (as telephone companies' deregulated activities grow, more assets are removed from regulated rate base).

[81] 592 F. Supp. at 871-72.

2. Separation for GTE's Interexchange Services

In 1984, the Justice Department challenged on antitrust grounds the acquisition by GTE of Southern Pacific Company's interexchange telecommunications enterprises. The complaint alleged that GTE could use its exchange telephone companies to favor its interexchange services and thereby lessen competition. The consent decree[82] provided, inter alia, that GTE's exchange telephone companies must be kept separate from its interexchange operations and information services, and the companies must provide equal access to all interexchange carriers and information services providers. The court distinguished this authorization of an acquisition subject to separation conditions from the AT&T divestiture primarily by GTE's smaller size.[83] The court found that the GTE decree's provisions adequately guarded against cross-subsidies and discrimination.

The decree required GTE subsidiaries providing interexchange and information services to have separate personnel, facilities, assets, marketing, and research and development. It also prohibited the transfer of any proprietary information from the exchange telephone companies to these separate subsidiaries.[84] In the context of approving the consent decree, the court neither considered the costs of separation in terms of lost efficiencies nor evaluated less restrictive alternatives. Apparently, the Justice Department was unwilling to rely on the regulatory tools cited by the FCC in the *Competitive Carrier Rulemaking* as adequate controls against an exchange carrier favoring its affiliate's interexchange services without full separation.[85]

11.2 FOUR FALLACIES IN THE ANALYSIS UNDERLYING STRUCTURAL SEPARATION REQUIREMENTS

11.2.1 Failure of Cost-Benefit Analysis

One fallacy in the analysis underlying structural separation requirements is the use of cost-benefit analysis in deciding whether to require separation. Ideally, cost-benefit analysis would indicate which separation requirements serve the public interest. Separation's costs to the public should include any impacts on prices for regulated and unregulated products caused by lost economies of joint production. Cost analysis must therefore reflect forecasts about the products that will be offered by the carrier and its subsidiary, including how they will be produced, marketed, installed, and maintained. Changing technology, market conditions, and business plans can make these forecasts speculative.[86]

---

[82] United States v. GTE Corp., 1985-1 Trade Cas. (CCH) ¶ 66.354 (D.D.C. 1984). This consent decree was entered by Judge Harold H. Greene, who also entered the AT&T divestiture consent decree. *See supra* note 75.

[83] United States v. GTE Corp., 1985-1 Trade Cas. (CCH) ¶ 66.354 at 64, 755-57 (D.D.C. 1984).

[84] *Id.* at 64,774.

[85] *See supra* notes 60-62 and accompanying text.

[86] For discussion of how courts and regulators have dealt with this problem, see *supra* notes 26-28 (*Second Computer Inquiry*); notes 41-45 (separation of BOCs); note 52 (orders on SBS) and accompanying text.

Separation also has more subtle costs to the public. There will be some customer inconvenience in not having the carrier as a single source of supply for integrated regulated and unregulated products.[87] There will be some delay in introducing products caused by the inefficiencies of separation and ineffective regulatory waiver processes.[88] Moreover, separation may cripple the telephone company as a supplier of certain regulated and unregulated products, and thereby lessen competition. Cost analysis should forecast such harms, and their effects on consumers, in terms of higher prices and lower quality products.[89]

Quantifying most of the benefits of separation is even more elusive. Benefit analysis must compare the amount of cost shifting that would leak through regulatory audits with separation to the amount that would leak without separation.[90] Separation's benefits to the public appear in terms of lower rates for consumers of regulated services. For consumers of unregulated services and products, the benefits depend on the likelihood of attempts at predatory pricing, the consequences of such attempts, and the deterrent effects of separation on cost shifting.

Separation supposedly confers additional benefits in terms of less discrimination in access to the services and information of the telephone company. Again, it is difficult to quantify these competitive consequences and the resulting benefits to consumers. Problems arise in estimating the degree to which the antitrust laws and regulatory prohibitions short of separation can deter discriminatory conduct, and in assessing the extent to which certain possible preferences will indeed impair competition.[91]

Even assuming that an ideal cost-benefit analysis is far beyond the reach of regulators and courts in determining separation requirements, this does not explain why separation decisions were generally devoid of any empirical analyses of costs and benefits. In many of these proceedings, the parties submitted no

---

[87] Allowing the subsidiary to be a sales agent for the telephone company's regulated services can lessen this problem. See American Information Technologies, 98 F.C.C.2d 943 (1984) (authorizing the BOCs' subsidiaries to be sales agents for the BOCs' intrastate services, subject to certain conditions). See also American Tel. & Co.: Provision of Basic Services Via Resale by Separate Subsidiary, 98 F.C.C.2d 478, 482-84 (1984); Satellite Business Systems; Petition to Modify Conditions of Authorization, 98 F.C.C.2d 762, 770-71 (1984).

[88] See e.g. American Tel. & Tel. Co., 62 F.C.C.2d 21 (1977) (Dataspeed 40/4), aff'd sub nom. International Business Machs v. Federal Communications Comm'n, 570 F.2d 452 (2d Cir. 1978); Petitions for Waiver of § 64.702 of the Commission's Rules (Second Computer Inquiry), 50 Fed. Reg. 13,573) (Apr. 5, 1985) (protocol conversion); U.S. DEP'T OF COMMERCE, ISSUES IN DOMESTIC TELECOMMUNICATIONS: DIRECTIONS FOR NATIONAL POLICY 67-75 (July 1985).

[89] See e.g., Satellite Business Systems: Petition to Modify Conditions of Authorization, 98 F.C.C.2d 762, 770-71 (1984); American Tel. & Tel. Co.: Provision of Basic Services Via Resale by Separate Subsidiary, 98 F.C.C.2d 478, 486-87 (1984).

[90] See supra note 61 (tariff review to detect cost shifting from interexchange services); notes 66-74 (California's imposition of separation on GTE); notes 75-81 (requirement under antitrust consent decree of separation for BOCs' new ventures), and accompanying text.

[91] See Illinois Bell Tel. Co. v. Federal Communications Comm'n, 740 F.2d 465, 474 (7th Cir. 1984), where Judge Posner wrote, "It is no doubt true that data on the expected benefits to consumers of making it harder for the operating companies to avoid regulatory and antitrust constraints would be unobtainable in even a remotely reliable form and must therefore be left largely to the Commission's judgment." See also BREYER, REGULATION AND ITS REFORM 147-53 (1982) (examples of regulatory problems in assessing costs and benefits in other industries).

empirical estimates of costs and benefits.[92] Perhaps they were intimidated by the problems in conducting a sound cost-benefit analysis, and feared that whatever numbers they submitted would be undermined as partial or speculative. More likely, however, the parties saw that regulators and courts often invoke the language of costs and benefits without insisting on or utilizing empirical estimates. Because it is expensive to develop empirical estimates through market and operations research, parties welcome the prospect of persuading a decision-maker with vague claims of costs and benefits. When parties do not generate empirical estimates themselves, decision-makers usually lack the resources and expertise to prepare their own figures.

This exploration of the shortcomings of cost-benefit analysis is not intended to deprive regulators and courts of a vocabulary and a way of thinking about a decision. Clearly, any decision has advantages and disadvantages that must be considered and, in some sense, weighed. Rather, the discussion attempts to remove from the separation decision the illusion of careful study involving a sophisticated weighing of costs and benefits. The visceral, political calculus underlying decisions that the benefits of separation outweigh its costs is built upon vague horrors recited by parties and general impressions or guesses formed by decision-makers.

If this is the best that government decisions about telephone companies can produce, then so be it. However, given the rough cost-benefit analysis, neither courts nor regulators[93] should feel bound to past uninformed decisions. Furthermore, the rough analysis, together with changing technology, new market conditions, and regulatory experiences, could easily support a conclusion that the balance has shifted.[94]

11.2.2 Cost-Based Rate Regulation Without Separation

A second fallacy underlying the structural separation requirements is that separation contributes to effective cost-based rate regulation. To a limited degree, this is

---

[92] *See* Illinois Bell Tel. Co. v. Federal Communications Comm'n, 740 F.2d 465, 474 (7th Cir. 1984); North American Telecommunications Ass'n v. Federal Communications Comm'n, No. 84-2216, slip op. at 9-11 (7th Cir. Aug. 27, 1985).

[93] *See generally* Garland, *Deregulation and Judicial Review*, 98 HARV. L. REV. 507 (1985); Heckler v. Chaney, 105 S. Ct. 1649 (1985) (an agency's decision not to take enforcement action is presumed immune from judicial review under the Administrative Procedure Act); North American Telecommunications Ass'n v. Federal Communications Comm'n, No. 84-2216 (7th Cir. Aug. 27, 1985) (deference of reviewing court to agency's judgment about costs and benefits of separation); Quincy Cable Television, Inc. v. Federal Communications Comm'n, 768 F.2d 1434 (D.C. Cir. July 19, 1985) (overturning FCC's "must-carry" restrictions for cable television that were based on FCC's "collective instinct" and "intuition").

[94] Ideally, the argument for ending structural separation would include a reliable cost-benefit analysis of each separation requirement to demonstrate that ending separation serves the public interest. The above discussion describes the weaknesses in a cost-benefit analysis. It is unrealistic to expect such analysis, and no such analysis is attempted here. Rather, this article's recommendation to end separation requirements relies on the assumption that separation causes substantial diseconomies from the bar on joint operations, delays in introducing new offerings, impediments to competition by telephone companies, and customer inconvenience. While these assumptions appear reasonable, even partial empirical support would be helpful.

true. Clearly, separation reduces opportunities for shifting costs from unregulated activities into regulated revenue requirements without detection by regulators. But this does not mean that regulated rates under separation are likely to be just and reasonable, or that regulated rates without separation are likely to be unjust and unreasonable.

The goal of rate regulation is not only to limit rates to the actual costs of providing regulated services, but also to keep the rates from exceeding the costs of *efficiently supplied* regulated services. Assuming that separation causes lost economies of joint operations, it therefore creates costs.[95] The real issue is not whether the amount of unregulated costs in regulated revenue requirements will be less with separation, but whether regulators and telephone companies can develop a set of cost allocators that will make regulate revenue requirements lower under joint operations than under separation without imposing excessive costs on a company's unregulated activities. This seems to be a manageable task.

A telephone company should be allowed to choose to operate with a separate subsidiary as a check on cost allocations. A company could reduce the common costs allocated to its unregulated activities by operating through structural separation and thereby reducing total common costs. This choice would be attractive to companies if the allocated costs exceeded the costs of operating under separation. It does not require burdensome regulatory audits, and it is an answer to carriers' complaints that too much of a company's common costs are allocated to unregulated activities.

Neither separation nor detailed audits of a telephone company should be necessary to protect against cost allocations that excessively burden regulated rates. Generally, regulators rely heavily on cost patterns and indices to detect unreasonable cost increases.[96] Using baseline (historic) costs and assumptions about reasonable changes, they develop a prima facie case for disallowances from regulated revenue requirements. In deciding to disallow certain costs claimed by a telephone company, a commission can cite factors such as inefficiencies, unreasonable plans for construction and equipment acquisition, unreasonable forecasts for operating costs, and possible cost shifting.[97]

---

[95] *See supra* notes 66-68 and accompanying text (California's imposition of separation on GTE). The FCC recently observed in the notice for the *Third Computer Inquiry*:

> While [elimination of common costs through separation] has been a relatively "clean" regulatory result, it has not been an efficient one. The sum of separately incurred costs of this nature often (if not usually) is higher than the total cost that would result if they were incurred jointly or in common. The public pays the difference, a difference that might not be there absent structural separation.

Amendment of Section 64.702 of the Commission's Rules and Regulations (Third Computer Inquiry), 50 Fed. Reg. 33,581, at 33,590 (Aug. 20, 1985).

[96] These indices include increases in one category of costs that are faster than inflation and subscriber growth, or cost increases for one company that are higher than for others. *See supra* notes 69-74 and accompanying text.

[97] Of course, commissions can examine companies' cost studies in analyzing rates that are prima facie reasonable or unreasonable. The opportunities for *some* undetected cost shifting without separation, however, cannot support the claim that separation is essential for *reasonable* cost-based rate regulation. *See supra* note 61 and accompanying text (tariff review to detect cost shifting from interexchange to exchange services).

Proponents of separation frequently cite an example of cost-allocation difficulties involving a telephone company's purchase of trucks for maintenance of its telephone lines and delivery of its unregulated products. Regulators and competitors fear that such a telephone company will claim that ninety percent of the truck costs are for regulated services, while in fact the company uses the trucks primarily to deliver unregulated products. If regulators have no indicators based on historic growth or the experience of other companies, extensive regulatory audits would be necessary to determine an exact cost allocation.[98]

The situation becomes somewhat easier with baseline costs and assumptions about reasonable changes. Regulators should then be able to find that a prima facie reasonable range of truck purchases just for a given company's regulated services would be, for example, thirty-five to forty-five trucks. Similarly, with some economies of joint operations, a prima facie reasonable range of jointly-used new trucks allocated to the company's regulated services would be twenty to forty. Although the company could present operations studies attempting to show that ninety percent of the seventy trucks it purchased should be allocated to regulated services, the burden of proof would be on the company to support the reasonableness of its studies, and regulators would have baseline estimates to use in evaluating the studies.

For some unregulated activities, separation has provided regulators with a set of regulated costs—both total and in specific categories—that is substantially free of cost shifting. Assuming there is no inflation or subscriber growth, these baseline regulated costs should not rise when companies are released from separation requirements or when they enter new unregulated ventures.[99] On the contrary, regulators could use anticipated economies of joint operation to offset the effects of inflation and growth, or even to justify reductions in regulated costs. Regulators could also apply these baseline costs to prevent substantial cost shifting by companies not subject to separation for these unregulated activities. The necessary adjustments for differences across companies, such as variations in subscriber density and growth, are similar to those often made by regulators in intercompany cost comparisons.[100]

A similar analysis applies to other unregulated activities, including regulated activities that will become unregulated and unregulated activities not subject to separation requirements. Regulatory cost allocations among regulated services

---

[98] Certainly regulators would have some sense of whether a company that only provides regulated services has purchased trucks far in excess of its needs, with the trucks sitting on a lot or used for frolics by company employees. Audits alone are not relied on to identify such inefficiences. Rather, a sharp increase in purchases may indicate an unreasonable expenditure, and the costs of such trucks would then be disallowed from the company's revenue requirement.

[99] *See supra* notes 75-81 and accompanying text (requirement under antitrust consent decree of separation for BOCs' new ventures).

[100] *See e.g.*, W. LAVEY, FACTORS INFLUENCING INVESTMENT, COSTS, AND REVENUES OF REA TELEPHONE COMPANIES, HARVARD PROGRAM ON INFORMATION RESOURCES POLICY, PUB. No. P-82-6 (1982); Investigation of Special Access Tariffs of Local Exchange Carriers, F.C.C. Mimeo No. 4726 (released May 24, 1985) (investigation into rate variations across exchange carriers).

and unbundling requirements[101] establish baseline costs and rates for most regulated offerings. Regulators do not require structural separation between two regulated offerings in order to derive a reasonable rate for each offering. In most cases, baseline costs for regulated services should not rise when other services are deregulated. Claims for substantial increases above these baseline costs could be subject to disallowances based, in part, on suspected cost shifting.

An exception to this application of baseline costs may occur when a regulated activity becomes deregulated because of rising competition.[102] Regulated cost allocations employing a fully-distributed-costs methodology may assign a level of costs to that activity that a company cannot sustain under competition.[103] Some cost allocations must shift so that while the competitive activity at least covers its direct (marginal or incremental) costs, the company can meet competition given the allocated costs.[104] This adjustment to baseline costs should be identical whether or not the activity is deregulated, and whether or not it is subject to structural separation.

The argument against separation's contribution to cost-based rate regulation does not depend on the degree to which a company faces competition (its market power) in its regulated services. When a company faces strong competition in a service, it cannot profitably cross-subsidize other services with revenues from that service and still attract customers. Competition can then supplement, or supplant, cost-based rate regulation in checking unreasonably high rates for that regulated service.[105] Regulatory tools for rate regulation, including separation, are unnecessary when a company faces strong competition in all its regulated services. Even if a telephone company faces no competition in a regulated service, separation may increase the service's regulated costs because of lost

---

[101] See supra notes 60-64 and accompanying text. The FCC tentatively concluded that, if it eliminates structural separation requirements, it should establish certain non-structural conditions on pricing, unbundling, and making available comparably efficient access arrangements. Amendment of Section 64.702 of the Commission's Rules and Regulations (Third Computer Inquiry), 50 Fed. Reg. 33,581, at 33,591-93 (Aug. 20, 1985). Similarly, the National Telecommunications and Information Administration recommended that structural separation requirements be replaced by requirements of unbundled services, equal access, and tariffing unbundled building blocks. U.S. DEP'T OF COMMERCE, ISSUES IN DOMESTIC TELECOMMUNICATIONS: DIRECTIONS FOR NATIONAL POLICY 76 (July 1985).

[102] See e.g., Detariffing of Billing and Collection Services, 50 Fed. Reg. 15,191 (Apr. 17, 1985).

[103] For example, if the competitive price is below the allocated costs, there would be little or no demand for the telephone company's product at a price covering those costs.

[104] This assumes that the company is an efficient provider of the competitive activity. If not, cost allocations that mask the company's inefficiency are anticompetitive and reduce consumers' welfare. In this case, cost allocations cannot cover the direct costs of the companies' competitive activity *and* allow it to meet competition. The first standard should not be compromised for the second. See MCI Communications Corp. v. American Tel. & Tel. Co., 708 F.2d 1081, 1123-25 (7th Cir. 1983), cert. denied, 464 U.S. 891 (1983); Private Line Rate Structure and Volume Discount Practices, 97 F.C.C.2d 923, 945 (1984).

[105] See e.g., Policy and Rules Concerning Rates for Competitive Common Carrier Services and Facilities Authorizations Therefor, 95 F.C.C.2d 554, 557 (1983) (Fourth Report and Order); *supra* notes 53 and 54 and accompanying text.

economies of joint operations, and regulators can use baseline costs to control cross-subsidies without separation or extensive audits.[106]

In addition to applying trend analyses and intercompany cost comparisons, requiring separate books of account may help to control cross-subsidies. This tool may make more visible certain cost allocations and transactions, and thereby deter cross-subsidies. Separate books cannot prevent all opportunities for cross-subsidies, because regulated and unregulated activities would still share facilities, personnel, and equipment. As described above, however, full structural separation is not the only regulatory tool that protects against substantial cross-subsidies. Moreover, economies of joint operations can exist with separate books but not with structural separation.[107]

11.2.3 Deterring Anticompetitive Conduct Without Separation

A third false belief underlying separation is that it makes a critical contribution to deterring anticompetitive abuses by telephone companies of their monopoly services. This section considers three types of anticompetitive abuses: (1) bundling of regulated and unregulated services; (2) discrimination in providing regulated services; and (3) discrimination in providing information about regulated services.[108]

Bundling or tying is an anticompetitive abuse of monopoly services whereby a telephone company supplies one (monopoly) service to a customer only if that customer also obtains a second, perhaps unregulated, product from the telephone company. This conduct can lessen competition for the second product.[109] Under separation, companies cannot supply certain unregulated products through their regulated operations, and therefore cannot bundle regulated and unregulated offerings.

Yet unbundling can also occur without separation. In the *Second Computer Inquiry*, the FCC ordered all carriers, including those not subject to separation requirements, to unbundle their regulated offerings from their CPE distribution and enhanced services.[110] Although there is no requirement of structural separation among regulated services, in other proceedings the FCC ordered all carriers to unbundle their regulated services so that customers could choose the compo-

---

[106] *See supra* note 61 and accompanying text (tariff review to detect cost shifting from interexchange to exchange services).

[107] *See* recommendation for separate books of account in U.S. DEP'T OF COMMERCE, ISSUES IN DOMESTIC TELECOMMUNICATIONS: DIRECTIONS FOR NATIONAL POLICY 76 (July 1985). *See also* Amendment of Section 64.702 of the Commission's Rules and Regulations (Third Computer Inquiry), 50 Fed. Reg. 33,581, at 33,591 (Aug. 20, 1985) (proposing accounting approach to cost separation).

[108] The preceding discussion of cost-based rate regulation should be sufficient to expose another false claim about separation's contribution to preventing anticompetitive abuses: that absent separation, telephone companies could shift substantial costs of their unregulated activities into their regulated revenue requirements, and thereby engage in predatory pricing in the unregulated activities. Even if the incentives for such predation existed, however, rate regulation does not require separation to prevent substantial cost shifting.

[109] *See e.g., supra* note 6; Private Line Rate Structure and Volume Discount Practices, 97 F.C.C.2d 923, 934-35 (1984).

[110] *See Second Computer Inquiry*, 77 F.C.C.2d at 442-45.

nents from various carriers and private systems that best meet their needs.[111] Furthermore, separation may carry unbundling too far. Restrictions on joint marketing, installation, and maintenance may cause customer inconvenience and confusion.[112]

Another type of possible anticompetitive abuse involves discrimination in the provision of regulated services. A company might lessen competition by giving customers who purchase its unregulated product regulated services with faster installation and maintenance, lower prices, and better transmission quality. Regulators and courts can impose prohibitions against such discrimination that would apply with or without separation.[113]

Separation's contribution in this area is limited. By restricting certain marketing, installation, and maintenance personnel to regulated services, separation can encourage a company's telephone operations to treat orders from its unregulated operations in the same way as it treats orders from other suppliers. Yet separation does not remove a company's incentives to have its regulated operations favor its unregulated activities. Even without separation, opportunities for discrimination can be restricted by: (1) requiring companies to implement certain procedures for their regulated operations, such as similar order processing for all requests with early masking of the customer's identity;[114] (2) requiring companies to report certain information about their operations, such as comparisons of delays in installation and maintenance for various customers;[115] and (3) maintaining an

---

[111] *See* Private Line Rate Structure and Volume Discount Practices, 97 F.C.C.2d 923, 934-35 (1984); Policy and Rules Concerning Rates for Competitive Common Carrier Services and Facilities Authorizations Therefor, 98 F.C.C.2d 1191 (1984) (Fifth Report and Order).

[112] *See* Satellite Business Systems: Petition to Modify Conditions of Authorization, 98 F.C.C.2d 762 (1984); American Tel. & Tel. Co.: Provision of Basic Services Via Resale by Separate Subsidiary, 98 F.C.C.2d 478 (1984) (allowing AT&T Information Systems to resell basic services); American Information Technologies, 98 F.C.C.2d 943 (1984) (permitting separate subsidiaries to act as sales agents for basic services); Policy and Rules Concerning the Furnishing of Customer Premises Equipment; Enhanced Services and Cellular Communications Services by the Bell Operating Companies, 50 Fed. Reg. 10,029 (Mar. 13, 1985) (allowing joint provisions of cellular services and cellular CPE); Pacific Bell: Petition for Declaratory Ruling or Waiver of Section 64.702 of the Commission's Rules to Enable Pacific Bell to Offer Network Services Through a Joint Venture, F.C.C. Mimeo No. 5568 (released July 8, 1985) (allowing joint venture with CPE suppliers for single response to customers' requests for proposals).

[113] *See e.g.* United States v. American Tel. & Tel. Co., 552 F. Supp. 131, 227 (D.D.C. 1982), *aff'd sub nom.* Maryland v. United States, 460 U.S. 1001 (1983); *Second Computer Inquiry*, 77 F.C.C.2d at 475; Satellite Business Systems: Petition to Modify Conditions of Authorization, 98 F.C.C.2d 762 (1984); United Telecommunications, Inc. and U.S. Telephone, Inc., 98 F.C.C.2d 1306 (1984).

[114] Pursuant to an antitrust settlement agreement between AT&T and some CPE vendors, Jarvis v. American Tel. & Tel. Co., Civ. Action No. 74-1674 (D.D.C. Aug. 19, 1980), each BOC established a Centralized Operations Group (COG) as a point of contact for customers and CPE vendors. The COGs process orders for BOC services relating to CPE interconnection. To ensure the non-discriminatory provision of services, the FCC later required the BOCs to implement COG-like systems in addition to structural separation in North American Telecommunications Ass'n, Petition for Emergency Relief, F.C.C. 84-132 (released Apr. 11, 1984) *corrected in* North American Telecommunications Ass'n, Petition for Emergency Relief Requiring Non-discriminatory CPE Interconnection, F.C.C. 84-132 (released Apr. 24, 1984).

[115] *See e.g.,* American Tel. & Tel. Co.: Provision of Basic Services Via Resale by Separate Subsidiary, 98 F.C.C.2d at 492 (1984) (order on petition for stay); Capitalization Plans for the Furnishing of Customer Premises Equipment and Enhanced Services, F.C.C. 85-28 at 30 (released Feb. 4, 1985).

efficient regulatory complaint process. These measures can substantially deter anticompetitive discrimination without the diseconomies of separation.

A third type of possible anticompetitive discrimination involves access to information about regulated services. Information that may be valuable to suppliers of unregulated services ranges from lists of customers using certain regultaed services to technical specifications and dates of availability for new regulated offerings. A telephone company could favor its own unregulated activities by denying this information to rival suppliers.

Separation can restrict such discrimination in information flows by imposing limitations on joint research, development, and marketing. In addition, separation can require equal dissemination of information to all competitors; when a telephone company discloses information about its regulated services to its unregulated subsidiary, it must make the information equally available to all suppliers.[116]

Nevertheless, disclosure requirements can substitute for separation with little or no increase in anticompetitive effects. Disclosure requirements can ameliorate any headstart that a telephone company's unregulated activities may gain over other suppliers. The timing of some mandatory disclosures about new services can be based on when a telephone company decides to acquire the equipment necessary to offer the services,[117] or it can be required some fixed number of months before the telephone company files tariffs for the services. Regulators or courts can also impose periodic disclosure requirements if they decide that other types of information, such as customer lists, should be available to all unregulated operations.

Separation does not make a critical contribution to deterring any of the anticompetitive conduct discussed above. Antitrust laws plus other regulatory tools should therefore suffice to deter such conduct without separation. In fact, ending structural separation may spur competition on the basis of relative efficiency. Telephone companies would be able to utilize the economies of joint operations to develop, provide, and market unregulated offerings.[118] If telephone

---

[116] *See e.g.*, 47 C.F.R. § 64.702(d)(2)-(3) (1984).

[117] The FCC's rules require disclosure of network changes at the time of a carrier's decision to "make or buy" equipment or software to implement or take advantage of proposed network changes or new network services. 47 C.F.R. § 64.702(d)(2) (1984); Computer & Business Equipment Mfrs. Ass'n, 93 F.C.C.2d (1983) (discount order). This rule would remain workable absent separation.

[118] *See* Foremost Pro Color v. Eastman Kodak, 703 F.2d 534, 546 (9th Cir. 1983) ("That the dominant firm in any market may through technological innovation expand its market share, increase consumer brand identification, or create demand for new products is perfectly consistent with the competitive forces that the Sherman Act was intended to foster.") The following antitrust decisions resulted in similar opposing anticompetitive restrictions on firms with large market shares: Hirsh v. Martindale-Hubbell, 674 F.2d 1343, 1348 (9th Cir. 1982); Northeastern Tel. Co. v. American Tel. & Tel. Co., 651 F.2d 76, 93 (2d Cir. 1981), *cert. denied*, 455 U.S. 943 (1982); California Computer Prods v. International Business Machs., 613 F.2d 727, 744 (9th Cir. 1979); Berkey Photo, Inc. v. Eastman Kodak, 603 F.2d 263, 284 (2d Cir. 1979), *cert. denied*, 444 U.S. 1093 (1980); Telex Corp. v. International Business Machs., 510 F.2d 894, 926 (10th Cir. 1975), *cert. dismissed*, 423 U.S. 802 (1975).

companies become stronger competitors in more unregulated products, the result should be a decline in prices and rise in quality.[119]

11.2.4 Failure of Definitions

A fourth fallacy surrounding structural-separation requirements is the belief that regulators or courts can craft viable definitions of activities subject to structural separation. The experience of the FCC has shown that changes in technologies and marketplace conditions make definitions of separated activities unworkable.[120] The FCC struggled with the definition of communications and data processing and with the characterization of hybrid activities after the *First Computer Inquiry*. Later, the FCC struggled to distinguish basic services from CPE and enhanced services after the *Second Computer Inquiry*.

Part of the problem is that because the scope of regulated services has been changing with new features and technologies (e.g., call forwarding, packet switching, and teleconferencing with terminal resolution capability), regulators have not viewed their responsibilities as confined to a clear set of well-established offerings. Consequently, it has been impossible to list some historically regulated offerings as subject to continuing regulation, or to define all other offerings as unregulated and subject to separation. It is similarly difficult to predict what new offerings should be subject to tariff regulation in the future.

Another part of the problem is that these definitions reflected both regulatory *and* separation requirements.[121] Courts and regulators applied these definitions to determine the technical characteristics of, competition for, and economies of joint operations for the offerings. The stakes of such decisions were high for telephone companies, their competitors, and the public. They did not just determine whether tariff filings would be required; rather, some decisions determined whether telephone companies would compete in certain offerings, what their costs would be, and whether the offerings would be available to customers.[122]

---

[119] If market competition allows a telephone company to monopolize an unregulated activity that is within the jurisdiction of regulators, and if future potential competition is weak, regulators could reimpose cost-based rate regulation on the company. Consumers would not be harmed by re-monopolization (absent anticompetitive practices), and consumers would be protected by the reimposition of regulation.

[120] *See supra* notes 3-47 and accompanying text (*First Computer Inquiry, Second Computer Inquiry*, and imposition of separation on BOCs).

[121] They delineated activities that (1) were unregulated based on the strength of the competition, and (2) were to be offered by the separate subsidiary and not by the provider of regulated services. The FCC recently proposed to eliminate separation and to rely on market analysis of competition rather than technology-based definitions to determine the scope of regulation. Amendment of Section 64.702 of the Commission's Rules and Regulations (Third Computer Inquiry), 50 Fed. Reg. 33,581, at 33,589 (Aug. 20, 1985).

[122] *See e.g.*, Custom Calling Services II, 88 F.C.C.2d 1 (1981) (denying a request for waiver to allow AT&T to offer on an unseparated basis a voice store-and-forward service involving subscriber interaction with stored information; service has not become widely available from other suppliers); Petitions for Waiver of § 64.702 of the Commission's Rules (Second Computer Inquiry), 50 Fed. Reg. 13,573 (Apr. 5, 1985) (protocol conversion services).

Some definitional disputes would have been far simpler if decisions on deregulation did not impose separation.[123] Commissions could focus on the need for cost-based rate regulation of an offering, resulting in simpler, faster, and less costly proceedings. Telephone companies could plan the development, provision, and marketing of a new service without having to await a regulatory resolution on how to define the service. Yet commissions will continue to need to distinguish regulated from unregulated activities, and the basis for this distinction should minimize regulatory disputes and facilitate efficient planning by telephone companies and customers. Moreover, given the difficulties in determining the scope of regulated services, it would be easier for regulators and courts to make such determinations absent structural separation. Uncertainties in the scope of activities subject to separation raise its costs.

11.3 CONCLUSION

No reliable cost-benefit analysis has shown the need for separation. Furthermore, the diseconomies of separation are not necessary to achieve reasonable cost-based rate regulation, or to deter anticompetitive conduct. Problems with the definitions of activities subject to separation can actually impede deregulation, new offerings, and competition.

Regulators and courts should expeditiously end structural separation requirements for telephone companies. As less restrictive alternatives, they may consider other regulatory tools, such as separate books of account, prohibitions on bundling and discrimination, and information disclosure rules. Because a complete and accurate cost-benefit analysis is unrealistic and unworkable, regulators and courts should not demand an empirical weighing of the costs and benefits of separation. Rather, they should use changing technologies and market conditions, and experiences with separation and rate regulation to justify ending structural separation requirements for the telephone companies.

---

[123] The only consequence of such decisions would be whether to require tariffs. *See supra* notes, 55-64 and accompanyng text (deregulation without structural separation of interexchange services offered by exchange telephone companies).

Chapter 12

An Introduction to The FCC's Third Computer Inquiry

HERBERT E. MARKS and JAMES L. CASSERLY*

Heraclitus observed that "There is nothing permanent except change."[1] In the ensuing centuries, philosophers have continued to wrestle with the subject of change: its benefits, its burdens, its inevitability. On a more practical plane, business people and their attorneys must also grapple with change, especially in high technology markets where life cycles of products and services are increasingly rapid and unpredictable. In the context of regulated industries, the difficulties of accommodating change are multiplied because, at the same time that advances in technology present new challenges and opportunities, the governing policies and regulations undergo constant adjustment, revision, and—periodically—fundamental reconsideration.

These general observations apply with full force to current developments in telecommunications. The Federal Communications Commission is now considering major changes in its regulatory approach to communications and data processing and the decisions that result will inevitably be of substantial consequence for computer manufacturers, computer service vendors, and computer users. The potential effect of pending proceedings are of sufficient magnitude to warrant the close attention of computer industry professionals; those who are caught unaware may miss significant economic opportunities or, worse, pay substantial economic penalties if they cannot accommodate (and, ideally, influence) the course of change.

---

*Reprinted from *The Computer Lawyer,* Vol. 2, No. 10 (Oct. 1985) with permission. Copyright 1985 by Law & Business, Inc. All rights reserved.
[1] Heraclitus, Fragment, reprinted in Evans Dictionary of Quotations at 95 (Avenel Books 1968).

12.1 BACKGROUND

In no sector of the American economy have the past several years brought more change than in the communications industry. Virtually every American citizen and business has been affected by the tumult accompanying the restructuring of American Telephone and Telegraph Company (AT&T). Divestiture has imposed new burdens and responsibilities on users of communications services, on providers of services that depend on communications facilities, and on manufacturers of equipment that is connected, directly or indirectly, to the telephone network.

These and other developments in telecommunications have especially affected the computer industry. In an era of increasingly distributed processing and evergrowing volumes of data traffic, communications is far more important to computers than when all computing power was centralized in large mainframes and programs and data were physically input by delivering tapes or punchcards to the computer room. As use of (and interaction with) the telephone network has increased, computer manufacturers, computer service vendors, and users have acquired a much more immediate and substantial interest in the rules governing the telephone facilities and services. (AT&T, in turn, after years of concentration on communications, has sought and obtained the freedom to become a direct participant in the computer and data processing markets.)

The most obvious way in which computer industry professionals are affected by regulatory developments affecting telecommunications involves the rates charged for transmission facilities needed for computers to communicate with one another, with terminals, or with other intelligent devices. The FCC's approach to tariff regulation has not always followed a consistent course, but that subject must be deferred to another article. Here, the focus is on more fundamental, structural issues whose resolution should be of interest to computer professionals. For example:

1. What rules will govern the participation of communications common carriers in the computer services markets? How will those who control "bottleneck" facilities be prevented from leveraging their dominance in communications to gain unfair advantage in computer services? To what extent should the rules differ for American Telephone and Telegraph Company (AT&T), the Bell Operating Companies (BOCs), and independent telephone companies?

2. What will be the situs of computer intelligence used to provide various enhanced services, from traditional remote access data processing to more limited code and protocol conversion services? To what extent will the intelligence be integrated into telephone switching systems, or other equipment located in telephone companies' facilities, rather than equipment located at end users' premises?

3. What rules will govern the interoperation of equipment outside of the telephone network with computer intelligence located in the telephone network? For example, to what extent will telephone companies have to disclose

technical information needed by manufacturerers to produce equipment that can successfully interoperate with telephone company facilities and services?

4. If greater functionality is permitted to be deployed in the network, will there arise a greater need to permit users to select smaller, discrete elements of carriers' offerings and to provide for non-traditional forms of network access and interconnection? Will pure transmission capability, unadorned by any enhancements, remain available on a regulated, unbundled basis?

5. Will key pieces of equipment, or certain functions, be classed as exclusively within the domain of telephone companies rather than within the province of enhanced service providers or end users?

6. To what extent should customer-premised equipment (CPE) and enhanced services be regulated when offered by a telephone company? By a noncarrier?

7. How will the United States implement "integrated services digital networks" (ISDNs)? What benefits will ISDNs produce? Will these benefits offset potential detriments?

The foregoing list of issues is by no means exhaustive, but it does illustrate the potentially enormous impact of pending FCC decisions on the computer industry. These and related issues are under consideration in a variety of FCC proceedings, but it is the recently instituted *Third Computer Inquiry*[2] that most directly addresses these matters and that most assuredly warrants the close attention of computer lawyers.

It may be useful to begin by providing a brief description of the predecessor proceedings—the *First* and *Second Computer Inquiries*.

12.2 THE FIRST COMPUTER INQUIRY

In the late 1960's, the Commission first began to grapple with the regulatory issues raised by the growing convergence of data processing and communications technologies and by the interest of telephone companies in expanding beyond their traditional sphere of activities. The *First Computer Inquiry (Computer I),*[3] concluded in 1971, determined that "communications" services would continue to be regultaed under Title II of the Communications Act, that "data processing" services would not be regulated, and that "hybrid" services involving elements of both communications and data processing would be wholly regulated or unregulated depending on whether the data processing feature was "incidental" to the transmission objective, or vice versa.

---

[2] *Amendment of Sections 64.702 of the Commission's Rules and Regulations (Third Computer Inquiry),* FCC 85-397 (released Aug. 16, 1985).

[3] *Regulatory and Policy Problems Presented by the Interdependence of Computer and Communications Services and Facilities,* 28 FCC 2d 267 (1971), *aff'd in part sub nom. GTE Service Corporation v. FCC,* 474 F.2d 724 (2d Cir. 1973), *on remand,* 40 FCC 2d 293 (1973).

Computer I also determined that communications common carriers would be permitted to provide data processing and hybrid data processing service only through separate corporate entities whose relations with the carriers were to be governed by a policy of maximum separation. This policy was implemented by various specific structural separation requirements, some of which were struck down by the court of appeals, while others survived judicial review. One requirement that remained was that the separate corporation utilize separate computing equipment and facilities to provide its data processing services; another forbade common carriers from selling or leasing any of the excess capacity of the computers used in providing communications services.

Computer I did not address AT&T's role in data processing (except as incidental to AT&T's communications or hybrid communications services), because AT&T was then subject to the narrow line-of-business limitations established by the 1956 Western Electric Consent Decree.[4] Among other things, that Decree generally prohibited AT&T from providing data processing services and form manufacturing computer equipment.

12.3 THE SECOND COMPUTER INQUIRY

Within a few years, the Commission reached the tentative conclusion that the framework adopted in the First Computer Inquiry had outgrown its utility. In particular, the FCC believed that the *Computer I* rules were ambiguous as applied to hybrid services and as applied to certain types of equipment located on end users' premises.[5] The Commission also perceived that its *Computer I* rules unnecessarily constrained AT&T from participating in the burgeoning data processing market. In addition, the Commission wished to further promote the growth of CPE competition, which was not yet then particularly well established but which had already proved its value in stimulating innovation, reducing prices, and increasing the range of features available to the consumer.

In 1980, the Commission adopted the *Computer II* rules which, in summary form, distinguish between "basic services," *i.e.*, the offering of a pure transmission capability, and "enhanced services," which "employ computer processing applications that [1] act on the format, content, code, protocal, or similar aspects of the subscribers' transmitted information; [2] provide the subscriber additional, different, or restructured information; or [3] involve subscriber interaction with stored information."[6] Thus, enhanced services include everything from a com-

---

[4] *United States V. Western Electric Co.*, 1956 Trade Cas. ¶ 68,246 (D.N.J.).

[5] For example, the Commission encountered a major controversy over the proper classification—as "communications" or "data processing"—of an intelligent terminal used in conjunction with remote access data processing systems. *Data speed 40/4*, 62 FCC 2d 21 (1977), *aff'd sub nom. International Business Machines Corporation v. FCC*, 570 F.2d 452 (2d Cir. 1978).

[6] *Second Computer Inquiry*, 77 FCC 2d 384, *on recon.*, 84 FCC 2d 50 (1980), 88 FCC 2d 512 (1981), *aff'd sub nom. Computer and Communications Industry Association v. FCC*, 693 F.2d 512 (1982), *cert. denied*, 461 U.S. 938 (1983).

munications service with a protocol conversion capability to sophisticated remote access data processing services.[7] Basic services are regulated under Title II (the "common carrier" provisions) of the Communications Act; enhanced services are not, although they are claimed to be subject to the Commission's "ancillary" jurisdiction under Title I (at least when offered by an entity otherwise subject to Title II).

The *Computer II* orders also held that CPE should be unbundled from transmission services and, after a transition, removed from direct Title II regulation. The concept of requiring a separate corporation for a carrier to engage in enhanced services was retained, but the applicability of the rule was substantially modified. Specifically, the structural separation requirement was removed from the carriers to which it previously had applied and was extended instead to AT&T.

Computer II purported to create a means for AT&T to avoid the line-of-business constraints of the 1956 Consent Decree, at least to the extent necessary to engage in data processing. Although this action was of dubious validity, any doubts were mooted by the entry of the 1982 Modification of Final Judgement[8]— which eliminated the 1956 Decree and required AT&T's divestiture of the Bell Operating Companies.

12.4 THE THIRD COMPUTER INQUIRY

In the months following AT&T's divestiture of the Bell Operating Companies on January 1, 1984, the Commission began increasingly to question whether its *Computer II* scheme, like the *Computer I* framework before it, required change. Previously, between the announcement of the divestiture agreement and its implementation, the Commission had decided to retain the structural separation requirement for AT&T and to apply it, with modifications, to the BOCs.[9] But AT&T and the BOCs launched intense campaigns to secure relief from the structural separation requirements, claiming the *Computer II* rules imposed unnecessary costs by necessitating duplication of facilities and functions, constrained them from realizing their innovative potential, and denied consumers alternatives that only the telephone companies could offer.

---

[7] Packet switching, without more, is a basic service, as is providing the capability for speed conversion between disparate terminals. *American Telephone and Telegraph Co.*, 91 FCC 2d 1 (1982); *American Telephone and Telegraph Co.*, 94 FCC 2d 48 (1983); *Communications Protocols under Section 64.702 of the Commission's Rules and Regulations*, 95 FCC 2d 584, 601 n.5 (1983).

[8] *United States v. American Telephone & Telegraph Co.*, 552 F. Supp. 131, 226-234 (D.D.C. 1982), aff'd sub nom. *Maryland v. United States*, 460 U.S. 1001 (1983).

[9] *Policy and Rules Concerning the Furnishing of Customer Premises Equipment, Enhanced Services and Cellular Communications Services by the Bell Operating Cos.*, 95 FCC 2d 1117 (1983), aff'd sub nom. *Illinois Bell Telephone Co. v. FCC*, 740 F.2d 465 (7th Cir. 1984), on recon., 49 Fed. Reg. 26,056 (1984), aff'd sub nom. *North American Telecommunications Ass'n v. FCC*, No. 84-2216 (7th Cir. Aug. 27, 1985).

These arguments were sharpened in the context of several requests for waivers of the *Computer II* rules. In one, AT&T sought permission to have its "separate corporation," the unregulated CPE and enhanced services company, market transmission services on a "resale" basis, thus obviating the need for users to deal with AT&T's regulated transmission services company. In another, AT&T sought permission for its CPE and enhanced service company to procure software developed by the unseparated elements of AT&T without creating any right for third parties to procure the software on similar terms. The BOCs sought permission for their CPE companies (sometimes called separate subsidiaries) to act as sales agents for the regulated transmission companies of their affiliated carriers. In another major waiver request, the BOCs sought to perform protocol conversions (*e.g.*, between asynchronous terminals and X.25 hosts) in conjunction with their transmission services.

In each instance, the Commission granted much of the relief requested, though it also imposed conditions to minimize the danger of anticompetitive abuse.[10] During this process, however individual Commissioners and members of the Commission's staff recently expressed concern that the *ad hoc* waiver process was too slow, too uncertain, and too constraining. And they began to suggest, with increasing frequency, that certain enhanced services of potential value to the American public could be made available—and affordable—only if they were integrated (in one way or another) with the carriers' basic services.

Ultimately, these developments led to the release, in August 1985, of the *Computer III Notice of Proposed Rulemaking (Notice)*. The *Notice* is long, detailed, and complex, and it is premature to attempt much more than a thumbnail sketch of the Commission's proposals. The brevity of the description should not detract from the significance of what the Commission is contemplating.

In essence, the *Notice* has three principal elements:

• proposals for specific changes to the Computer II framework: "evolutionary" proposals which could be adopted promptly to address certain perceived problems, while still preserving much of the Computer II rules;

• a somewhat more "revolutionary" framework that that would completely displace the existing rules; and

• a pair of miscellaneous issues, not elsewhere addressed concerning which the Commission suggests that its decisions under existing rules have perhaps produced undesirable results.

---

[10] *American Telephone and Telegraph Co. Provision of Basic Services via Resale by Separate Subsidiary*, 98 FCC 2d 478 (1984), *on reconsideration*, FCC 85-379 (released Aug. 1, 1985), *appeal pending sub nom. MCI Telecommunications Corp. v. FCC*, No. 84-1402 (D.C. Cir. filed Aug. 9, 1984); *Furnishing of Customer Premises Equipment and Enhanced Services by American Telephone and Telegraph Co.*, FCC 85-56 (released Feb. 22, 1985); *American Information Technologies Corp. et al.*, 98 FCC 2d 943 (1983), *petition for reconsideration pending, appeal pending sub nom. North American Telecommunications Ass'n v. FCC*, No. 84-1430 (D.C. Cir. filed Aug. 20, 1984); Petitions for Waiver of Section 64.702 of the Commission's Rules (Computer II) filed by Pacific Bell et al., 100 FCC 2d 1057 (1985).

The *Notice* makes clear that the issues and proposals contained in its various sections are not mutually exclusive and that features of each may be combined. So, the concepts and notions discussed in one of the following sections may ultimately be employed or adapted in an entirely different context.

12.5 EVOLUTIONARY ASPECTS OF COMPUTER III

The "evolutionary" aspects of the *Notice* are intended to resolve certain issues that have proved controversial under the *Computer II* framework. For example, several alternative proposals would address the issue of protocols processing by AT&T and the BOCs in conjunction with basic service. The common objective of the different proposals is to facilitate the provision by carriers of services now encompassed within the first clause of services now encompassed within the first clause of the *Computer II* definitions (quoted above) of enhanced services, but one of the alternatives would go much further. Each of the three raises important and controversial issues.

Under the *first* proposal, the definition of enhanced service would be left virtually intact, but the Commission would remove the structural separation requirement for so-called "first clause" enhanced services for those dominant carriers which procure underlying transmission capability from themselves on a resale basis (*i.e.,* pursuant to tariffs). A *second* proposal would essentially maintain the current definition and retain the separate subsidiary requirement as a general rule. It would, however, permit AT&T and the BOCs to collocate or integrate facilities used in the provision of *all* enhanced services with facilities used to provide basic service under certain conditions (*e.g.,* compliance with the accounting and tariff structure requirements established in the Commission's decision conditionally granting the BOCs' asynchronous-to-X.25 protocol conversion waivers). The *third* proposal would create a new term, "network processing," that would encompass most of the first clause applications and would permit this type of service to be basic (*i.e.,* regulated) when provided by a carrier but enhanced (*i.e.,* unregulated) when offered by a non-carrier. From a computer industry perspective, it is curious that the first proposal equates processing that affects the content of transmitted information with processing that affects the code or protocol of information (both are included within the first clause of the enhanced service definition), while the third alternative would omit content processing from the new service category created for carrier's code and protocol conversions.

What all of the three alternatives have in common is that they would increase the computer intelligence that could be deployed in the network. And each of the proposals would lessen or eliminate the structural separation requirements that currently separate carrier facilities used in communications from those used in enhanced services. What is not addressed in this portion of the *Notice*, but is likely to be a major topic of the debate concerning these proposals, is the question of what specific conditions or alternative safeguards should be imposed to fulfill the role formerly played by structural separation. Since this question must be addressed under either the "evolutionary" or "revolutionary" framework, it warrants a brief disgression.

12.6 ALTERNATIVES TO STRUCTURAL SEPARATION: BEHAVIORAL SAFEGUARDS, COLLOCATION, AND "COMPARABLY EFFICIENT INTERCONNECTION"

The *Notice* identifies several forms of anticompetitive conduct which structural separation is intended to prevent: discrimination in the provision of network services (timing, quality, pricing); unfair advantages resulting from advance information about network improvements or modifications; and unique access to information regarding subscribers to basic network services. These potential problems, the Commission contends, can perhaps be avoided by the use of alternative measures. The Commission's growing disenchantment with structural separation and its increasing willingness to rely on non-structural safeguards is best evidenced by a recent order (adopted, but not released at the time of this writing) that relieves AT&T of the structural separation requirement for CPE.[11]

The *Notice* is especially tentative in its identification of specific alternative safeguards or behavioral conditions that may be imposed on carriers which provide computer processing services, but it does at least identify the major categories of issues that might be addressed in conditions designed to replace the structural separation requirement. These include:

1. *capitalization:* to limit dominant carriers' investments in "ancillary to communications" (see below) and noncommunications activities;
2. *cost separation:* to prevent the costs of CPE and enhanced services from being shifted to regulated communications services;
3. *technical information:* to permit non-carrier CPE manufacturers and enchance service providers to design equipment and services with sufficient knowledge of network characteristics and planned changes;
4. *customer information:* to delimit the use communications carriers may make, in their unregulated activities, of information they possess about the customers of their regulated services;
5. *limited structural separation:* rules containing some subset of the existing requirements for divisions between communications activities and other activities;
6. *common carrier obligations:* to determine whether communications services underlying an enhanced service offering should be regulated or not;
7. *enforcement matters:* to permit better oversight of carriers' conduct in an unseparated environment; and

---

[11] "Structural Separations Requirement Removed for AT&T's Provision of CPE (CC Docket 85-26)," FCC News Release (Sept. 18, 1985).

8. *conditions:* a shorthand reference to unbundling, pricing, and interconnection requirement along the lines established in the protocol conversion waiver order.

The notion of conditions includes a variety of elements, such as rational apportionment of the costs of equipment used for both regulated and unregulated services, and parity of treatment between the carriers' and non-affilates' enhanced services in terms of the pricing and availability of elements of underlying basic service. Perhaps the most interesting potential condition from a computer or data processing perspective is the notion of "comparably efficient interconnection" (CEI). This concept is alluded to on several occasions in the Notice and then is taken up in a separate section devoted to CEI, collocation (the Commission inquires whether it would be desirable or feasible to require carriers to permit third parties to collocate their processing equipment in telephone company central offices), and ISDNs. The resolution of the issues raised under this heading may substantially affect the deployment of computer intelligence in, or outside of, the telephone network.

The concept of comparably efficient interconnection is, as yet, somewhat amorphous, but it evidently could include a variety of ways in which users and third party enhanced service providers might be permitted to enjoy some of the same economies a carrier attains by locating its processing equipment in the central office, or by integrating processing functions into the central office switch. The extent of the economies realized by collocation and integration surely will be actively debated, but even greater energies will probably be devoted to the effort to develop a common understanding of CEI and appropriate rules for its implementation. Depending on how it is developed, the CEI concept could pay valuable dividends from a computer industry perspective.

The issues of integration and comparable efficient interconnection assume greater complexity in the context of ISDN. For example, under current ISDN plans, the "D" channel can serve both to transport data and to control other channels (the "B" channels). Must access to the "D" channel be limited to carriers? Are there considerations of network congestion, or message integrity, that require limiting non-carrier use of the "D" channel? Or can users be provided comparable efficient interconnection to the "D" channel? If so, will users acquire a new level of control and freedom in their communications activities? Ultimately, the resolution of ISDN issues may determine the extent to which telephone company-provided services are open systems or, conversely, the extent to which proprietary and non-standard facilities and services may become a norm.

12.7 "REVOLUTIONARY" COMPUTER III PROPOSALS

Besides the previously described evolutionary proposals, the Notice includes somewhat more revolutionary proposals that would more substantially displace not only the structural separation requirements but also the definitions and regulatory framework of *Computer II*. Under the proposed *Computer III* framework, "basic communications" would be defined essentially as it is today, or in accordance with one variation or another of the proposed evolutionary redefinition; CPE and enhanced services would be labeled "ancillary to communications"; and everything else would be "non-communications." The greater departure from today's regulatory structure, however, would not be the redefinition just described but the new regulatory approach that would be applied to whatever is determined to be ancillary to communications. With respect to such services, a multi-step analysis would be conducted.

First, is the service provided by a carrier? No entity would be classified as a carrier unless it also provided basic communications service, and a non-carrier's provision of ancillary services would be completely unregulated. *Second*, if the service is provided by a carrier, is the carrier dominant? Only if the answer is yes would the analysis proceed. *Third*, if the service is provided by a dominant carrier, does the offering have "economic characteristics that tend toward competition (*i.e.*, limited economies of scale and/or scope)"? If not, the service would be regulated as basic communications. (**Note:** this could produce regulation of enhanced services, which the *Second Computer Inquiry* found to be unregulatable under Title II.) If so, another question would be asked: does the service depend on a bottleneck needed by others to compete with the carrier in the provision of the service? If not, it would be treated as non-communications and monitored only to the extent to prevent it from being subsidized by monopoly ratepayers. If so, some form of safeguards would be applied to limit discrimination in network access, to ensure disclosure of network information, and to limit the use in competitive contexts of carriers' access to customer information generated in the course of transmission services operations.

The proposed *Computer III* framework is said to be intended, *inter alia*, to eliminate or reduce the regulatory uncertainty now experienced by carriers, but it remains to be seen whether the present proposals would in fact achieve that result. Conceivably, if the *Computer III* proposals were adopted, every new service might be subject to review, and a variety of questions might have to be answered before the regulatory status of the service would be determined. Each branch in the decision tree could be a potential point of argument. In this sense, the *Computer III* proposals might magnify, rathr than reduce, regulatory uncertainty. This, however, can better be determined after public comments are filed in this proceeding in late October and November 1985.

12.8 MISCELLANEOUS ISSUES RAISED BY THE NOTICE

In addition to the foregoing, *Computer III* also raises some additional issues. The final sections of the Notice address two issues which have been exhaustively debated and thoroughly considered in the past, but which the current Commission suggests that the *Computer II* rules may have produced an unfortunate results. One of these involves voice message storage; the other one concerns network channel terminating equipment (NCTE).

12.8.1 Voice Message Storage

Shortly after *Computer II* was adopted, AT&T proposed a service known as Custom Calling II, which would have provided for voice messages to be stored in the network and delivered at times of the caller's, or the called party's, choosing. The Commission deemed the service to be enhanced, and it refused to grant a waiver of the structural separation requirement.[12] To the FCC's surprise and disappointment, no alternative suppliers of equivalent services have emerged. This, the Notice acknowledges, may be because would-be providers of such services could not obtain the types of interconnection needed to construct an alternative version of Custom Calling II. Nonetheless, the Commission seems determined to take the steps necessary to make the voice message storage service available. The ramifications for the computer industry are subtle, because the discussion of the issue is entirely in terms of voice messages. An electronic switch or other digital gear, however, does not know the ones and zeros in its memory comprise a voice message rather than computer data. And, if data *storage* is permitted in telephone company facilities, what types of data *processing* might be allowed as well?

12.8.2 Network channel terminating equipment

The Notice also hints at a possible shift in the demarcation point that marks the boundary between network facilities and CPE. It is now established that "network channel terminating equipment" (NCTE), which carriers previously claimed was part of the network (*i.e.*, part of their monopoly), is CPE and open to competition.[13] The Commission's principal proposal on NCTE is to eliminate the structural separation requirement rather than to change the network boundary, but the latter is a real possibility in view of the *Notice's* inquiry whether special treatment should be accorded certain NCTE functions. Moreover, the logic of any decision to bring some NCTE functions back across the network boundary could conceivably be invoked at a later time to shift the boundary still further. Certainly the notion that equipment is not CPE because "it is inserted in the [bit] stream" applies to a wide range of devices. Depending on the equipment configuration, the quoted characterization could be applied to modems, terminals, PBXs, and even computers.

12.9 CONCLUSION

Clearly, the *Third Computer Inquiry* reopens many important issues and complicates short-term planning—especially for those who produce computer equipment or provide computer services. *Computer II* was built on a philosophy that

---

[12] *American Telephone and Telegraph Co.*, 88 FCC 2d 1 (1981).

[13] *Petitions Seeking Amendment of Part 68 of the Commission's Rules Concerning Connection of Telephone Equipment Systems and Protective Apparatus to the Telephone Network*, 92 FCC 2d 1 (1982); 94 FCC 2d 5 (1983), *recon. denied*, FCC 84-145 (released Apr. 27, 1984).

assumed maximum benefits would result if the telephone network served only the transmission function, while data processing functions (except as needed to administer the network) were to be located outside the network in CPE or the equipment of enhanced service vendors. Now, the Commission seems to be moving towards a different view, *i.e.*, that many efficiencies and economies can be achieved only if computer intelligence needed to provide enhanced services is integrated into, or collocated with, telephone company facilities. Such a premise is certainly open to question, particularly since in the computer world the trend has been towards decentralization. Even if the premise is correct, the Commission should certainly consider whether the drive to achieve these economies is being pursued in a manner that limits the ability of users to retain (and increase) their control over their own computer networks.

Computer III also renews the debate over what measures are needed to make competition between carriers and non-carriers fair, and thereby to maximize user choice. As carriers are permitted to locate greater computer functionality in their networks, the opportunities for trading on their dominant position in communications will increase. The Notice does solicit suggestions for nonstructural safeguards, and it initiates consideration of entirely new forms and conditions of network access and interconnection.

The *Third Computer Inquiry* has just begun and it is far too early to speculate on its outcome. What is certain is that the Commission's decisions in this proceeding have the potential to affect, substantially, the price, quality and nature of both communications and computer processing. It behooves those with an interest in such matters to assist the Commission in its efforts to examine all the ramifications of its proposals—so that the rules that ultimately emerge promote, to the extent possible the progress of technology and the growth of a competitive environment in the communications and computer industries.

Chapter 13

Understanding the Computer III Inquiry

RICHARD E. WILEY and HOWARD D. POLSKY*

On November 13, 1985, the Federal Communications Commissin was deluged with opening comments in its complex and highly controversial *Computer III* rulemaking proceeding.[1] At last count, more than 100 parties filed pleadings totaling over 4,000 pages. Virtually every major company involved in the telecommunications and computer fields, as well as consumers of those products and services, voiced strong opinions in response to the agency's 78-page Notice of Proposed Rulemaking (Notice). With reply comments due on December 13, and a final FCC decision to follow in 1986, *Computer III* already has become one of the most heated proceedings currently before the agency.

And not without reason. In the Notice, the FCC has tentatively decided to make two major changes in the way it regulates AT&T and the divested local Bell Operating Companies (BOCs). First, the Commission is proposing to eliminate its current rules which require AT&T and the BOCs to offer any unregulated computer services and products through a separate corporate subsidiary. Thus, for the first time in modern telecommunications history, AT&T and the Bell Companies may be given the opportunity to vertically integrate their regulated and unregulated operations, and the public policy ramifications of this tentative decision are enormous.

Take AT&T, for example. The new *Computer III* regime would allow the company to combine its regulated long distance telephone business (AT&T Communications) with its unregulated computer services enterprise (AT&T Information Systems). A totally unified AT&T—with its unique nationwide transmission network and prodigious computer and telecommunications manufactur-

---

[1] Amendment of Section 64.702 of the Commission's Rules (Computer III), CC Docket No. 85-229, FCC 85-397, released August 16, 1985).

ing and research capabilities— could significantly alter the evolution of this country's information industry.

Second, the Notice proposes a novel "market power" test to determine whether certain "enhanced" offerings (services which combine computer processing and transmission functions) of AT&T and the BOCs should be rate regulated under the Communications Act. This economic approach to service regulation would replace the definitional schemes used by the FCC for the last 20 years to distinguish regulated communications from unregulated data processing. By focusing on the competitive characteristics of enhanced services rather than their functional attributes, the FCC is seeking to apply regulation only where monopoly traits exist. In the process, the Commission acknowledges that it may also have to reregulate some AT&T and BOC offerings that are completely unregulated at this time.

This article explores the important legal and policy issues raised by the Notice. We will also offer an assessment of the possible effects upon AT&T and the BOCs, their unregulated competitors, and consumers if the FCC were to adopt its tentative proposals. To accomplish all of this, however, it is necessary to place *Computer III* in its historical context.

13.1 COMPUTER I

The convergence of computer and communications technologies has created difficult regulatory problems for the FCC since the mid-1960s. In the *Computer I* proceeding, the Commission focused on its jurisdictinal responsibilities and decided not to regulate data processing companies, even though they typically offered communications capabilities with their services. The Commission concluded that the incidental use of telephone lines by data processors to permit access to their host computers did not amount to the offering of a common carrier communications service within the meaning of the Communications Act. Rather, the FCC defined such services as hybrid data processing and left them unregulated, along with stand-alone data processing which the agency found to be beyond its subject matter jurisdiction. Conversely, the FCC determined that the use of computers by carriers to switch telephone calls (i.e., for message switching) or for other transmission purposes were traditional communications or hybrid communications functions, and therefore subject to rate regulation under the Act.

Besides adopting this definitional scheme, the Commission decided in *Computer I* that common carriers should be able to compete in the unregulated data processing business. However, the agency was concerned that if parts of the same computers used for switching telephone calls were devoted to data processing, then the carriers could cross-subsidize their unregulated competitive activities by shifting a disproportionate share of the cost of those computers to communications service ratepayers. In addition, because data processors rely on telephone lines to serve their customers, the agency was fearful that communications carriers would discriminate against their unregulated competitors in installing and maintaining essential transmission facilities.

To guard against these anticompetitive practices, the FCC adopted its so-called "maximum separation" policy. Common carriers could enter the unregulated data processing business, but only through a separate corporate entity—with its own computing facilities, separate books of account, officers, and operating personnel. Maximum separation did not apply to AT&T (and its Bell Operating Companies) because the FCC believed that a 1956 antitrust consent decree then in effect precluded AT&T from engaging in any unregulated ventures.

13.2 COMPUTER II

By the late 1970s, the FCC claimed that the definitions adopted in *Computer I* had become obsolete. The advent of smart terminals and the ability for carriers to process information as it passed through their networks (known as distributed processing) had clouded the differences between communications and data processing. To address these problems, the FCC initiated *Computer II*; ultimately, however, the proceeding became a vehicle for deregulating major segments of the common carrier industry.

In its *Computer II* decision, the FCC sought to draw a "bright line" between the use of computer technology by common carriers to facilitate communications or to offer other processing services. Under the *Computer II* definitional scheme, services provided over communications facilities are classified as either basic or enhanced. A basic service is simply the offering of pipeline transmission capacity to move information from one point to another, such as plain voice and data transmission services. Basic services are the purest form of common carriage and presently are regulated pursuant to the FCC's *Competitive Common Carrier* scheme. Under this scheme, only dominant carriers, or those possessing market power, are rate regulated. AT&T and the BOCs are currently deemed to be dominant.

In contrast to the pipeline nature of basic services, enhanced offerings use computer technology to act on the content of information as it passes through the network, or offer subscribers interaction with stored information. The *Computer II* rules describe three types of enhanced offerings which are each found in a separate clause of the enhanced service definition. Specifically, enhanced offerings are:

> services which are provided over common carrier facilities, and which employ computer processing to: (1) act on the format, content, code, protocol or similar aspects of the subscriber's transmitted information; (2) provide the subscriber additional, different, or restructured information; or (3) involve subscriber interaction with stored information.

As explained below, most of the problems cited by the FCC as reasons for initiating *Computer III* have involved the so-called "first clause" services of this definition. An example of a first clause service would be the offering of protocol conversion, which can be used to permit otherwise incompatible facsimile machines, computers, or other devices to communicate with each other.

The establishment of the enhanced service category in *Computer II* served several important purposes. First, it relieved the FCC of the difficult task of distinguishing hybrid communications (which was regulated) from hybrid data processing (which was unregulated).

Second, it permitted the agency to deregulate. The FCC held that enhanced services are not common carrier offerings as a matter of law and, therefore, are not subject to regulation under Title II or the Communications Act (the common carrier provisions). As a result, an entire class of carriers, known then as value-added carriers, were instantly deregulated.

Third, it allowed AT&T to offer enhanced services and telephone terminal equipment (customer premises equipment or CPE) on an unregulated basis notwithstanding the 1956 consent decree. Because enhanced services and CPE involve a communications component, the FCC declared such offerings to fall under its ancillary jurisdiction, and thus subject to regulation within the meaning of the 1956 consent decree. For the first time, AT&T was permitted to enter the burgeoning computer communications and equipment market on an unregulated basis.

Notwithstanding all these changes, however, the FCC continued to recognize the need to protect AT&T's ratepayers from the harmful effects of cross-subsidization if AT&T were allowed to participate in unregulated markets. The FCC also was concerned that AT&T could use its control over the local exchange bottleneck to discriminate against enhanced service competitors that required access to those essential monopoly facilities.[2] Accordingly, the FCC conditioned AT&T's entry into the unregulated enhanced services and CPE market by requiring it to form a structurally separated corporate subsidiary to engage in such activities. AT&T Informatin Systems was organized to satisfy this requirement. In addition, the subsidiary's access to bottleneck transmission facilities had to be obtained under tariff, just like its competitors.

Not long after *Computer II* was adopted, new computer-communications technologies that could be integrated into the basic telephone network began to come into strong demand. The growing popularity of personal computers equipped with different communications protocols, for example, created the desire for users to be able to access remote databases and to communicate with each other. In addition, telephone subscribers began to demand new services, such as voice messaging.

While all of these capabilities could be integrated directly into the basic transmission network, the structural separation rules of *Computer II* required

---

[2] The local telephone exchange is considered a bottleneck because the vast majority of communications traffic must pass through it to reach end users. As a result, both the FCC and the Department of Justice traditionally have been concerned that monopoly exchange operators, if permitted into competitive enhanced markets, could favor their own local facilities requirements over a competitor that has a need for those exact same facilities.

either that these types of enhancements be offered through a separate corporate subsidiary or that a waiver of the *Computer II* rules be obtained. This often led to delays and litigation over the nature of the particular services at issue (basic vs. enhanced) and, in some cases, to decisions not to provide a service at all due to the added costs or inefficiencies resulting from the separate facilities requirement.

13.3 THE NOTICE

As a result of these particular problems, and the new industry structure created by the AT&T divestiture in 1984, the FCC has decided that there is now a need to reevaluate the efficacy of the *Computer II* regime. The *Computer III* Notice generally approaches this task from two different angles.

In Section III of the Notice, the Commission proposes to make what it calls evolutionary changes to the *Computer II* scheme. Essentially, these proposals would eliminate the separate subsidiary requirement only for first-class enhancements, thereby allowing AT&T and the BOCs to integrate protocol processing capabilities into the basic telephone network. First-clause services are considered to be more akin to facilitating the transmission of messages than to true information processing services.

However, the removal of structural separation for these services would be subject to conditions requiring comparably efficient interconnections ("CEI") for competitors and accounting rules to prevent cross-subsidization. The Notice indicates that these modifications to *Computer II* could cure most of the significant problems that have occurred to date, but questions the wisdom of still retaining the *Computer II* definitional scheme in a world of rapidly changing computer and communications technologies.

Thus, in Section II of the Notice, the Commission has tentatively decided to scrap the *Computer II* approach entirely and to replace it with a regulatory scheme based on two fundamental principles. First, the FCC proposes to use market power as the determinant for distinguishing between the regulated and unregulated endeavors of AT&T and the BOCs. After almost two decades of experience with definitions, the agency seems to have concluded that economic regulation of carrier services should depend on the competitive nature of the market, and not on whether computer processing functions are offered as part of those services. In short, the Commission seeks to extend the principles of its *Competitive Carrier* scheme for basic services (i.e., regulating dominant carriers and forbearing from regulation of non-dominant carriers) to the enhanced services market.

Second, where the FCC decides that the regulation of particular AT&T or BOC offerings is warrented, it proposes to rely on accounting controls instead of separate subsidiaries to ensure a proper allocation of joint and common costs between monopoly and competitive activities.

Based on these principles, the essence of the *Computer III* regulatory framework discussed in Section II consists of a process for identifying the non-competitive enhanced offerings of AT&T and the BOCs, and then applying various accounting and tariff controls to prevent them from abusing their market power over such offerings to the detriment of ratepayers or competitors. In a nutshell, here is how the FCC's Section II proposal works:

As a starting point, the agency has concluded that the offerings of AT&T and the BOCs will fall into three possible categories: (1) basic communications, (2) services ancillary-to-communications, and (3) non-communications. Basic communications services provide subscribers with the means to transport information and electrical signals from one locatin to another without changing the content thereof. This category is esentially the same as "basic" services under *Computer II*. Services ancillary-to-communications include any offerings that are within the subject matter jurisdiction of the FCC; i.e., some element of communications (as defined by the Communications Act) is associated with the ofering. An example is the offering of enhanced services as currently defined, but the category itself is broader. Finally, as its label approximately suggests, non-communication offerings encompass any other enterprise that a carrier may undertake, such as real estate or life insurance ventures.

Once the nature of an offering is identified (which ironically may recreate the very kind of definitional problems the FCC is seeking to avoid), the Commission would then apply its market power analysis to determine what form of regulation, if any, should be applied. If the offering is a basic communications service, the Commission would continue to apply the "current policies governing such services."[3] Basic services are presently deemed to be common carrier offerings and regulated under Title II of the Communications Act, as interpreted in the Commission's *Competitive Carrier* proceeding. Thus, where offered by a non-dominant carrier, such services would continue to be subject to regulatory forebearance by the Commission. When offered by a dominant carrier, like AT&T or the BOCs, traditional tariff regulation would still be maintained.

Whenever a carrier engages in a non-communications business, the FCC's concern is that the costs associated with such activities might be shifted to users of the carrier's regulated services, thereby resulting in unjust rates. To guard against the cost-shifting, *Computer II* requires AT&T and the BOCs to provide non-communications offerings only through separate corporate subsidiaries. The Notice takes the position that accounting mechanisms (in combination with other regulatory tools) can achieve the same result while also lowering the prices for both the regulated and non-communications services through efficiencies gained by sharing common costs. Accordingly, non-communications offerings made by AT&T and the BOCs would be subject to non-structural safeguards, such as accounting controls, reporting obligations, or investment oversight. Non-communications offerings made by non-dominant carriers would not be scrutinized

---

[3] Notice at ¶ 49.

because, in the FCC's view, such companies cannot sustain their positions in competitive markets of engaged in cost-shifting. If the non-dominant carrier's communications service rates became too high, customers would simply turn to other suppliers.

The most dramatic regulatory revisions in Section II are proposed for services ancillary-to-communications, such as enhanced services, that are offered by AT&T and the BOCs. The gist of the FCC's plan can best be described as a "sliding scale" approach: the level of regulation applied would be directly proportional to competitive market conditions. Using this approach, the ancillary offerings of AT&T and the BOCs that are "unlikely to receive effective competition"[4] would be the most tightly regulated. Specifically, the FCC proposes to regulate such offerings "directly together with basic communications services."[5] As a practical matter, this means that non-competitive enhanced services that are presently unregulated could very well be reregulated and tariffed under Title II of the Act. It also would require the FCC to engage in a service-by-service market analysis for all ancillary offerings, a process which could be more regulatory than the FCC may realize.

Next in order are ancillary services offered by dominant carriers that are subject to competition, but which also have control over bottleneck facilities needed by their competitors. In such circumstances, the Commission is concerned that the dominant carriers could favor their own ancillary offerings (e.g., by installing their own transmission facilities before their competitors) or acquire an unfair head start in offering ancillary services due to advance knowledge of improvements or modifications in their networks. Accordingly, the Notice proposes a set of accounting and tariff controls "to ensure that the ancillary product is not a burden to ratepayers of the basic service, and that the carrier does not gain an improper competitive advantage from its control of bottleneck facilities."[6]

Finally, ancillary products that are subject to competitoin, but which do not depend on bottleneck facilities, would be treated the same as a non-communications offering—that is, accounting devices would be used to ensure that those competitive services are not subsidized by ratepayers of monopoly or near-monopoly services. Ancillary services offered by non-dominant carriers or other entities, however, would continue to be unregulated, just as under the current *Computer II* scheme.

13.4 POLICY ANALYSIS

What does all this mean for the telecommunications and information processing industries? Reduced to its essentials, the proposed *Computer III* regulatory regime as proposed in Section II of the Notice benefits AT&T the most, frees the

---

[4] *Id.* at ¶ 29.
[5] *Id.*
[6] *Id.*

328 Understanding the Computer III Inquiry

BOCs to integrate service enhancements into the basic telephone network, and does not disturb the current unregulated status of non-dominant carriers (for both basic and enhanced offerings), enhanced service providers, and data processing vendors.

If the FCC affirms its tentative decision in Section II to eliminate the *Computer II* separate subsidiary requirement for AT&T and the BOCs (which it certainly appears inclined to do in light of its September 18 decision to relieve AT&T of this restriction for CPE), AT&T clearly will benefit the most. It would have the green light to combine the operations of its three subsidiaries: AT&T Communications (regulated telephone business), AT&T Information Systems (competitive, non-regulated information services), and AT&T Technologies (the old Bell Labs research and Western Electric equipment enterprises). The joint marketing alone of an AT&T nationwide telecommunications network and computer system—which such a decision permits—would be a formidable combination, even for the likes of IBM.

The only certain restriction that would be imposed on AT&T appears to be accounting controls. Should the FCC determine now, or in the future, that AT&T does not possess bottleneck facilities—a distinct possibility—then bookkeeping requirements would remain the lone check on AT&T's ability to leverage its substantial market power in telecommunications into unregulated services and products. As the opening comments indicate, the trade-off between the benefits of a vertically integrated AT&T and the threat to competition is one of the most heated issues before the FCC.

In this regard, it is interesting to observe that the sweeping solution proposed in Section II of the Notice (elimination of the separate subsidiary requirement for AT&T) bears little relationship to the problems encountered under *Computer II* (primarily the inability of the BOCs to provide first-clause type services—e.g., protocol conversion—as part of their basic network offerings). Indeed, as to AT&T, virtually the only reason cited in the Notice for doing away with structural separation is that the divestiture terminated AT&T's control over local bottleneck facilities. And as for the BOCs, their ability to offer enhanced first-clause services could be accommodated simply by modifying the *Computer II* definitions themselves, and allowing for limited collocation of enhanced facilities in BOC central offices, as outlined in Section III of the Notice.

Thus, many parties have taken the position in their opening comments that the efficiency problems associated with the separate subsidiary requirement could be readily cured by far less drastic measures than proposed in Section II. For this reason, it can be speculated that *Computer III* may simply represent a vehicle by which a deregulation-minded FCC can eliminate structural separations, just as *Computer II* terminated the regulation of enhanced carrier services and CPE.

Although the BOCs similarly would benefit from the ability to integrate enhancements into their basic network offerings, they would continue to be prohibited from offering second- and third-clause services, or true information services, because of the terms contained in the Modified Final Judgment (MFJ) in the AT&T antitrust case. The FCC does not believe, however, that the MFJ is a bar to the BOCs' offering of first-clause or protocols-type processing service in the basic network.[7]

Moreover, the Commission has indicated in the Notice that it still views local exchange carriers as monopolies due to their control over local bottleneck facilities. Thus, the BOCs likely would be subject to tariffing, disclosure, and other requirements in addition to accounting controls for their offerings of ancillary services which utilize the local networks. Nevertheless, it might be argued by some that even the BOCs are not bottlenecks due to the presence of other transmission alternatives, such as digital termination and cable TV systems.

In the absence of structural separations, enhanced service providers would have to depend on effective enforcement of strong accounting and other controls to ensure that the competitive enhanced offerings of AT&T and the BOCs are not being subsidized, and to guarantee the availability of comparable interconnections to the basic network. The price consumers pay for basic communications service would likewise be dependent upon the success of these controls, as would the proliferation of new services and service providers.

13.5 LEGAL QUESTIONS

The Notice also raises some intriguing legal issues that could put the entire Section II market power scheme in jeopardy. To begin with, the FCC stresses "that no entity [will] be classified as a 'carrier' solely because it is providing an ancillary services."[8] This is consistent with the FCC's determination in *Computer II* that enhanced services, which fall within the ancillary category, do not come within the Act's Title II definition of common carriage. However, the Notice goes on to say that if a dominant carrier offers an enhanced service that does not face competition, the Commission would "regulate the offering directly under Title II. . . ."[9] These positions are difficult to reconcile. If an entity is not a common carrier by offering only enhanced services, then how does the FCC find authority to regulate enhanced services under Title II simply because they are offered by a dominant carrier?

What appears to be happening is that the FCC has implicitly redefined the concept of common carriage to depend on the presence or absence of market power. Not only does the language of the Communications Act make no such distinction but, as indicated in *NARUC v. FCC*, 525 F.2d 630, 641 (D.C. Cir. 1976), such statutory definitions have been upheld "even where nothing approaching monopoly power exists." Furthermore, the very underpinnings of the Section II scheme are tied to the FCC's *Competitive Common Carrier* proceedings which applies forbearance to the basic offerings of non-dominant carriers and would extend forbearance to the enhanced services of non-dominant carriers as

---

[7] *Id.* at ¶ 18, n.16.
[8] *Id.* at ¶ 51.
[9] *Id.* at ¶ 53.

well. However, in *MCI Telecommunications Corp. vs. FCC*, 765 F.2d 1186 (D.C. Cir. 1985), the court recently reversed part of the FCC's *Competitive Carrier* scheme and raised several questions about the legality of the forbearance concept itself. In addition, the court observed that the FCC correctly "rejected a definitional approach" to common carriage based on market power in the *Competitive Common Carrier* proceeding. *Id.* at 1194. In short, the new Section II regulatory scheme, if adopted, is susceptible to a serious legal challenge.

* * *

With the release of the Notice, and the filing of opening comments, the issues in *Computer III* have been crystalized and the battle lines drawn. Essentially, *Computer III* questions whether the economies of scope and other advantages of vertical integration for the BOCs and AT&T can be secured without sacrificing the acknowledged benefits of a competitive marketplace or the rights of telephone subscribers to just and reasonable rates. The FCC's answer to this very difficult question will have a profound effect on the future development of the telecommunications and computer industries.

POSTSCRIPT

In June of 1986, the FCC released its final decision in *Computer III*.[10] To the surprise of many observers, the FCC abandoned the market power scheme proposed in Section II of the Notice (and discussed in the article above). The Commission concluded that "replacing the *Computer II* regulatory regime with the Part II 'economic analysis' approach would not create an environment in which the industry could implement the major improvements in efficiency and competition in the enhanced services marketplace that we initiated this proceeding to achieve."[11] Accordingly, the agency decided to pursue a more evolutionary approach, much like that proposed in Section III of the Notice (as discussed above). As a result, the new *Computer III* regulatory scheme consists of the following four elements:

First, the Commission retained the *Computer II* basic/enhanced definitional approach to service classifications. Thus, only basic common carrier services are regulated by the FCC and the enhanced service industry stays unregulated.

Second, the agency decided that it would eliminate the structural separation requirements of *Computer II*, subject to the implementation of a program of "non-structural safeguards." This program is designed to permit AT&T and the BOCs to achieve the efficiencies of integration and, at the same time, protect

---

[10] 104 F.C.C. 2d 958 (1986), *recon.*, 2 FCC Rcd 3035, *supplemental order*, 2 FCC Rcd 3072 (1987).

[11] 104 F.C.C. 2d at 1018.

enhanced service competitors and consumers from discriminatory practices and harmful cross-subsidization.

The centerpiece of the program for the total removal of structural separation is the development of a so-called "open network architecture" ("ONA") that will enable all enhanced service providers to interconnect to the telephone network on a technically equal basis to the enhanced operations of AT&T and the BOCs. Initial ONA plans are not due at the FCC until 1988, and full implementation may be well beyond that. In the interim, the FCC decided to retain its structural separation requirement, except that individual enhanced services may be offered by AT&T and the BOCs if they permit "comparably efficient interconnection" ("CEI") to enhanced service competitors pursuant to a plan approved by the FCC.

Besides the equal access requirements of ONA and CEI, the other nonstructural safeguards are designed to ensure that AT&T and the BOC: (1) do not favor their own enhanced service operations in the installation and maintenance of facilities; (2) provide advance notice of network design information to enhanced service competitors; and (3) do not use customer proprietary network information to disadvantage competitors. To prevent cross-subsidization, the *Computer III* decision also requires these "dominant" telephone companies to allocate costs in compliance with manuals approved by the FCC.

Third, the Commission prohibited the states from imposing their own separate subsidiary requirements for unregulated enhanced services, or requiring ONA or CEI tariff structures inconsistent with those approved by the FCC. Significantly, however, the *Computer III* decision did leave the regulation of intrastate ONA and CEI tariff rate elements to the states.

Fourth, the FCC decided that its *Computer III* regulatory scheme should apply only to AT&T and the BOCs. Thus, the major independent telephone companies (*e.g.*, GTE, United, Contel) may integrate enhanced services into their network offerings without an ONA or CEI plan. However, the independent telephone companies are subject to the accounting and cost allocation rules recently adopted by the Commission in another proceeding,[12] the agency's general network disclosure rules,[13] and the anti-discrimination provisions of the Communications Act.

One final but critical point must be mentioned. As noted above, the decree entered in the AT&T antitrust case (also known as the Modification of Final Judgment or "MFJ") prohibits the BOCs from providing "information services" to the public.[14] For all practical purposes, the definition of an information service under the MFJ is synonymous with the FCC's definition of an enhanced service under *Computer III*. Thus, while the FCC has established an elaborate regulatory

---

[12] *See* Separation of Costs of Regulated Telephone Service from Costs of Nonregulated Activities, 2 FCC Rcd 1298 (1987) ("Joint Cost Order").

[13] 104 F.C.C. 2d at 970; *see also* 47 C.F.R. § 68.110(b).

[14] *See* United States v. American Tel. & Tel. Co., 552 F.Supp. 131, 227 (D.D.C. 1982), *aff'd sub nom.* Maryland v. United States, 460 U.S. 1001 (1983).

scheme for the provision of enhanced services by the BOCs, the MFJ prohibits the BOCs from offering most enhanced services altogether. For example, the BOCs are not currently allowed to offer voice storage and retrieval services under the MFJ, although *Computer III* assumes that the BOCs can provide those services.

The restrictions in the MFJ do not mean that the *Computer III* regulatory regime is an academic matter, however. To begin with, the line-of-business restrictions on information services do not apply to AT&T (except for electronic publishing). Hence, AT&T will be relieved of the entire separate subsidiary requirement as soon as its ONA plans are approved by the FCC. As for the BOCs, the MFJ restrictions were never intended to be permanent, and the *Computer III* regulations now being developed at the FCC will be in place when the time does come for their removal. Moreover, any MFJ waivers granted to the BOCs to offer particular information services would trigger the FCC's *Computer III* requirements.

Chapter 14

Deregulation and Telecommunications Acquisition

WALTER SAPRONOV*

14.1 INTRODUCTION

In a recent address, Judge Harold H. Greene compared the impact of developments in computer and telecommunications technology upon society to James
Watt's invention of the steam engine. His commentary included the following
observation:

> The reorganization of the Bell System is playing a part in these developments, and
> its impact cannot but grow in the future. For if nothing else, that reorganization is
> introducing two new players in the game: competition into the telecommunications
> industry and AT&T into computers. . .

This paper focuses on those "two new players" and their effect upon the
acquisition strategy of today's telecommunications managers. Some prefatory
observations are in order.

A deregulated, competitive telecommunications marketplace constitutes a departure from traditional approaches to acquisition of the various products and
services of that market. Telecommunications services and data processing equipment are increasingly becoming *bundled as commodities*—for example, in smart
modems, intelligent network processors, integrated communications processors,

*Copyright 1985, Walter Sapronov. All rights reserved. Originally reprinted with permission by
the Society for Information Management in 2 *Spectrum* 4, August 1985.

[1] Address of Honorable Judge Harold H. Greene, U.S. District Court, District of Columbia at the
COMPUTER and COMMUNICATIONS LAW CONFERENCE, Arizona State University College of
Law, January 14, 1985.

and value-added PBX systems. Another change lies in the new offerings of computer product lines by common carrier subsidiaries such as AT&T Information Services. As a consequence of this industry realignment, the pricing and terms of computer and communications goods and services are changing, *with profound implications for acquisition and planning strategies.*

This paper addresses some of those implications in the areas of contracting and negotiating in the new telecommunications environment. While this discussion is based on the perspective of the network user-purchaser, these considerations are equally significant for other industry participants, including carriers, vendors, resellers, and, to some extent, residential ratepayers.

14.2 DOMESTIC REGULATORY POLICIES: A REVIEW

A brief review of the U.S. regulatory policies and developments follows as background. Considerable literature is available on the details of these policies.[2] This review is only a summary and is not intended to be an exhaustive or comprehensive discussion.

Domestic telecommunications regulation is grounded in the U.S. Constitution: federal regulation of interstate communications carriage *qua* interstate commerce is empowered by the "Commerce Clause"; state regulation of intra-state communications is based on the "reserved powers" clause of the Ninth Amendment. There are numerous legislative roots underlying the regulatory environment, including 19th century transportation and telegraphy legislation, the Sherman-Clayton Anti-Trust Act, the Communications Act of 1934 (as amended), and the Satellite Act of 1962, among others. Telecommunications has traditionally been viewed as a "natural monopoly" and thus properly offered to the public for hire by government controlled carriers. A number of regulatory agencies having administrative, legislative, and judicial powers are responsible for regulating the activities of such carriers. Since 1934, the Federal Communications Commission (FCC) has been the agency responsible for regulatory oversight of interstate communications carriers and *inter alia* the electromagnetic spectrum in general.[3] State regulatory agencies (often called public service commissions or PSCs) have regulatory control over intrastate communications to the extent not pre-empted by the FCC.[4]

The nature of regulation is essentially characterized by its stated purpose in providing communications service to the public at reasonable, nondiscriminatory rates. Pursuant to that objective, Title II of the Communications Act empowers the FCC to regulate interstate carriers through mechanisms such as tariffs,

---

[2] See generally, Marks, Regulation and Deregulation in the United States and Other Countries, 25 JURIMETRICS 1 (Fall 1984); TELECOMMUNICATIONS IN THE U.S.: TRENDS AND POLICIES (ed. L. Lewin 1981).

[3] 47 U.S.C. §201 et. seq.

[4] See e.g., N. Carolina Utilities Commission v. FCC, 437 F.2d 787 (4th Cir. 1977) where FCC jurisdiction held preemptive over equipment used for joint interstate and intrastate communications.

complaint procedures, and entry and exit (Section 214) authority.[5] Title I of the Act broadly establishes the purview of the FCC to include all carriers (so-called "ancillary jurisdiction"), whereas Title III of the Act further extends the FCC's regulatory oversight to all radio communications. State carrier regulations generally mirror federal regulations and extend over intra-state communications only. Following divestiture and the introduction of Local Access Transport Areas (LATAs), state regulatory control extends over both local exchange carriers, such as the divested Bell Operating Companies, and inter-exchange carriers, such as AT&T Communications, for intra-LATA and inter-LATA service, respectively.

Since the early Hush-A-Phone and Carterfone cases, regulators and the courts have been pursuing a deregulatory trend in their treatment of carriers. The underlying policy objective is the transformation of the telecommunications industry from a government-regulated monopoly to an unregulated, competitive marketplace. Numerous landmark decisions have furthered that trend, including the Resale and Shared-Use Proceeding,[6] the Competitive Carrier Rulemaking.[7] Computer Inquiry II,[8] and the settlement of the Justice Department's anti-trust suit against AT&T (styled as a modification of the 1956 Western Electric Consent Decree–MFJ).[9] A stated purpose of the MFJ was to bring about deregulation while safeguarding the industry from anticompetitive abuses by the traditional Bell system.

Following divestiture, that deregulatory trend has continued, notably in the FCC's gradual relaxation of regulatory constraints imposed by Computer Inquiry II and subsequent rulemakings upon dominant carriers such as AT&T and the Bell Operating Companies.[10] The regulatory constraints currently undergoing review include structural separation requirements, currently prescribing that the sale and provision of "enhanced" communications services and customer premise equipment (CPE) be done only through such carriers' separate, unregulated affiliates. Further deregulation of the dominant carriers at this time is not uncontroversial. Critics point to the dangers of a marketplace shakeout for the other carriers, cross-subsidation between unregulated and regulated services and potential anti-competitive practices. Nonetheless, the expectation of a "Com-

---

[5] 47 U.S.C. §§ 203, 207, 208, 214.

[6] Regulatory Policies Concerning Resale and Shared Use of Common Carrier Services and Facilities, 60 F.C.C. 2d 261 (1976), on reconsideration, 62 F.C.C. 2d 588 (1977), aff'd sub nom. AT&T Co. v. FCC, 572 F. 2d 17 (2d Cir. 1978).

[7] Policy and Rules Concerning Rates for Competitive Common Carrier Services and Facilities and Authorization Therefore, 6th Report and Order (released January 4, 1985) (CC Docket 79-252), 50 FR 1215 ("Competitive Carrier").

[8] Amendment of Section 67.702 of the Commission's Rules and Regulations, 77 F.C.C. 2d 384, on reconsideration, 84 F.C.C. 2d 50 (1980), on further reconsideration, 88 F.C.C. 2d 512 (1981), aff'd sub nom. Computer and Communications Industry Association v. FCC, 693 F.2d 198 (D.C. Cir. 1982), cert. denied, 103 S.Ct. 2109 (1983).

[9] United States v. AT&T Co., 552 F. Supp. 131 (D.D.C. 1982), aff'd sub nom. Maryland v. U.S., 460 U.S. 1001 (1983).

[10] See generally ENDING SEPARATE SUBSIDIARIES FOR TELEPHONE COMPANIES, Law & Business, Inc./Harcourt Brace Jovanovich, Publishers (1985).

puter III Inquiry" in the near future points to a policy statement by the FCC that the marketplace has sufficiently changed so as to merit re-examination and, in all likelihood, continued deregulation.

Some specific effects of these policy trends on the user recipients follow.

14.3 TELECOMMUNICATIONS ACQUISITION PRACTICES

Following the 1956 Western Electric Consent Decree and the line-of-business restrictions imposed upon AT&T, the telecommunications industry remained separated into two major segments:

1. **telecommunications services** and related equipment falling under the "network" classification;
2. **business machines** connected to the network but proscribed from provision by AT&T according to those restrictions.

Telecommunications services, initially voice and subsequently data, traditionally have been acquired by users under tariff from a sole-source monopoly supplier. Business machines, however, have always been acquired commercially through negotiation, contracts, competitive vendor proposals, and open pricing.

The line separating these segments has eroded over the years, especially in the distinction between network equipment and business machines, both of which fall under the general category of "computers." Following the deregulation of CPE (e.g., analogue modems, terminals) in Computer Inquiry II, and other deregulation of digital network channel termination equipment[11] and user-owned satellite earth stations,[12] much of the previously tariffed telecommunications equipment base has found its way into the competitive marketplace. Consequently, the acquisition practices associated with user purchase of such telecommunications equipment likewise have changed to resemble those traditionally used in commercial business machine acquisition.

The division between the regulated and unregulated portion of the telecommunications market has changed in the area of telecommunications services as well. Traditionally, both interstate and intra-state communications services have been offered solely under tariffs subject to FCC and state PSC scrutiny, respectively. Over the years, however, many services have been deregulated and are now offered on a competitive basis. For example, interstate resale carriers are free from all regulation other than the general requirement of providing reasonable, nondiscriminatory service. "Enhanced services," those involving a carrier's action upon the form, content, or code of transmission, were deregulated according to the terms of Computer Inquiry II (as opposed to "basic services," end-to-

---

[11] Petitions Seeking Amendment of Part 68, 94 F.C.C. 2d 5, 34 (1983), on reconsideration, FCC 84-145 (released April 27, 1984).
[12] Re: Regulation of Domestic Receive Only Satellite Earth Stations, 74 F.C.C. 2d 205 (1979).

end transmission transport, which continue to be regulated). Furthermore, the commission has pursued a policy of forbearance from regulation with respect to nondominant, "other common carriers" (OCCs), such as GTE and MCI, which culminated in the requirement that all OCCs cancel their existing tariffs (see *Forbearance* discussion *infra*). As with CPE, all such nonregulated services fall into the sphere of competitive, commercial acquisition from the standpoint of prospective purchasers.

The impact of deregulation on telecommunications acquisition practices is most decidedly felt in differences between acquiring such goods and services under tariffs as opposed to acquiring them under commercial contracts.

14.4 TARIFFS

Carrier tariff filing represents a key element of telecommunications regulation. Pursuant to Section 203 of the Communications Act, all interstate common carriers are required to file tariffs defined as "schedules of charges and other information related to use of communications service" with the FCC. Intra-state carrier tariffs must be filed with the appropriate state regulatory commission and generally mirror federal filings in form and structure. Tariff charges are subject to requirements of "reasonableness" and "non-discrimination" under the Communications Act and are often challenged on those grounds. Notice requirements and presumptions of lawfulness vary for different carriers, depending upon the extent of FCC regulation (e.g. full regulation, streamlined, forbearance). However, as discussed below, the extent to which tariff filings are subject to FCC discretion has become highly controversial.

Generally speaking, for purposes of communications acquisition, users should note the following tariff characteristics:

1) Tariffs definitively take precedence over and may not be varied by any other agreements between carriers and users as to prices and terms of service.[13]
2) Common carriers traditionally use tariffs, both federal and state, to limit their liability.[14]
3) User complaint procedures involving tariffs must adhere to statutory formalities and are generally heard before regulatory agencies rather than courts of general jurisdiction.[15]

---

[13] 47 U.S.C. § 203(c). See Selwyn, "From Tariff to Contract: The Changing Telecommunications' Business Environment," published in NEGOTIATING TELECOMMUNICATIONS CONTRACTS: BUSINESS AND LEGAL ASPECTS, Law & Business, Inc./Harcourt Brace Jovanovich, Publishers (1985).

[14] See e.g. Western Union Telegraph Co. v. Esteve Brothers and Company, 256 U.S. 567, 569 (1921); American Satellite Corp. v. Southwestern Bell Co., 64 F.C.C. 2d 503, 510 (1977); Valentine v. Michigan Bell Telephone Co. (1972) 388 Mich. 19, aff'd 31 Mich. App. 18 (1972).

[15] 47 U.S.C. §§207, 208; See Anderson "The Commission's Complaint Process: What it is, How it Works" in 1 TELEMATICS 4 (Aug. 1984).

From a technical standpoint, the tariffed telecommunications environment is familiar to many users responsible for both voice and data circuit acquisition. Relevant considerations include pricing structure (e.g. plotted according to V and H coordinates) and additional features such as line conditioning, grades of bandwidth (capacity) and line termination charges. Transmission and cost optimization techniques in this environment, including multiplexing, concentration and tail-circuit configurations, are also familiar.[16] For many networks, divestiture and LATAs have introduced complications into such systems analyses, often requiring network topology review where circuits cross LATA boundaries.

Once the topology has been selected, however, it is worth emphasizing that the terms and prices of tariffed services are non-negotiable. Given this inflexibility, two factors weigh heavily to the user's detriment in the acquisition process.

First, tariffs typically limit both the carrier's liabilities and the remedies available to users who suffer damages by carrier action (or inaction). Such limitations have been upheld by courts on both federal and state levels. Typically, such limitation of liability limits a carrier's out-of-pocket damages to a pro-rata refund for outage duration during a disruption of service. Consequential damages related to circuit failure or other carrier wrongdoing are generally disallowed, unless there is a showing of willful or malicious action on the part of the carrier. Thus, from the standpoint of allocation of risk, the user is disadvantaged by such limitations available to tariffed carriers.

Secondly, users alleged to have suffered damages from carriers are limited in their choice of forum for sounding complaints. A court of general jurisdiction will usually refuse to hear a subscriber's complaint according to the doctrine of "primary jurisdiction." One version of this doctrine holds that the subscriber's complaint is properly construed as a challenge to the tariff and therefore, is properly heard before the appropriate regulatory agency and not in the courts.[17] For interstate carriers, the criteria for referring a case to the FCC on "primary jurisdiction" grounds includes such factors as the experience of the judiciary in dealing with technical questions at issue and the danger of inconsistent rulings.[18] State courts sometimes apply the doctrine on the grounds that the tariff forms part of the contract between the carrier and subscriber.

There are some exceptions to the application of "primary jurisdiction." The Communications Act provides alternative remedies for potential plaintiffs: a party may seek relief from a district court of competent jurisdiction or through FCC complaint procedures but not both.[19] State courts sometimes draw a distinction between actions of a contractual nature, properly heard by the Public Service Commission, and action in tort (e.g., alleging the carrier's negligence or willful

---

[16] See J. Martin, SYSTEMS ANALYSIS FOR DATA TRANSMISSION (1972).

[17] See 67 A.L.R. 3rd 84, 89.

[18] RCA Global Communications, Inc. v. Western Union Telegraph Co., 521 F. Supp. 998, 1006 (S.D. N.Y., 1981). See generally 74 Am Jur 2d. Telecommunications §20.

[19] 47 U.S.C. §207.

tariff violation). The latter may sometimes be heard in a state court general jurisdiction. From the subscriber's viewpoint, remand of a case to a regulatory agency may well be disadvantageous for reasons of inconvenience, duration of hearings and inexperience with regulatory formalities.

14.5 FORBEARANCE

Given these considerations involving tariffs, it seems evident that the user's negotiating position in dealing with tariffed suppliers is compromised from the outset. In a regulated environment, the protection of carriers is viewed to be in the interests of public policy and, therefore, to be expected. With deregulation, however, such regulatory protection is replaced with the rules of the competitive marketplace. Pursuant to that goal, the FCC has adopted fully deregulated policies for some carriers (enhanced service providers) and "forbearance" from regulation for others (OCC's).[20]

In the Competitive Carrier Rulemaking, the FCC first permitted (Second Report and Order) and eventually mandated (Sixth Report and Order) carriers subject to forbearance policies to cancel their existing tariffs. This rulemaking has met with vehement objections and is currently on appeal to the Circuit Court of the District of Columbia.[21] For subscribers, the opposition is revealing. Appellant arguments cite the necessity of negotiating individual contracts with users as an instance of their damages if this rulemaking were to be upheld.

The FCC's position on this issue is clear. In the aforementioned Second Report and Order, the FCC asserted that contracts between carrires and subscribers fall within the legislative intent of the Communications Act. In the Sixth Report and Order, the commission affirmed its intention to continue to administer (Section 208) complaint procedures and to ensure that forborne carrier rates continue to be just and reasonable under subscriber contracts. In particular, the commission contemplated the following advantages to its ruling:

> The use of tariffs can restrict consumers from seeking the most advantageous service arrangements. A tariff may be restrictive because it fosters an image that all possible service arranagements are defined within its text. Customers may be reluctant to ask for arrangements outside of the tariff because they may think such specific arrangements are unavailable or technically not feasible or are not willing to wait for the required lengthy tariff update procedures to be completed. The cancellation of tariffs will naturally force forborne carrires to be more competitive and they would be more apt to adapt general service offerings as their customers' needs change.[22]

However, even if this ruling withstands appeal small users will probably be subjected to "contracts of adhesion" in lieu of tariffs and thus still be limited in

[20] See Competitive Carrier at 1216.
[21] See Telecommunications Reports, June 10, 1985 at 11, 13.
[22] See Competitive Carrier at 1220.

their negotiating capability. In all likelihood, the cancelled tariffs would probably form the basis of such contracts.[23] Large users, however, can be expected to exercise "clout" in such a non-tariffed environment and thereby enhance their negotiating leverage.

14.6 COMPUTER CONTRACTS AND CPE

While tariff regulation will continue for some time, at least for dominant carriers, the CPE marketplace has been for the most part deregulated (see Telecommunications Acquisition Practices supra). Telecommunications "hardware" continues to be offered under tariff only where such equipment falls under the definition of "basic" service or is construed to be part of the network and not CPE—for example, as in Centrex devices. Parenthetically, one may note that relief from structural separation requirements for the provision of CPE has been granted for AT&T and may soon be forthcoming for the BOC's as well; thus one can expect regulated entities to provide CPE albeit not under tariff and not bundled with other regulated services.

Nonetheless, the deregulation of CPE is a significant development for purchasers. A recent Justice department memorandum has explicitly included computers within the CPE classification.[24] As indicated above, transactions involving CPE thus become legally equivalent to other computer transactions. This resemblance triggers the applicability of "computer law" to the buyer-seller relationship.

The term "computer law" refers to the application of traditional legal issues and principles to the provision and acquisition of computer goods and services. The issues have become familiar through a line of cases spanning the last two decades.[25] These issues include applicability of the Uniform Commercial Code (UCC) (as opposed to state codifications of the common law of contracts), express and implied warranties, the validity of disclaimers, the legal effect of parol representations by sales representatives and advertisements, consequential damages and fraudulent misrepresentations by vendors. While an examination of these issues is beyond the scope of this paper, it is worth noting that the principles of computer law are directly applicable to CPE acquisition. Some selective observations follow.

It may be to the customer's advantage if the UCC applies to CPE acquisition in view of implied warranties and other protections. The UCC will apply to CPE

---

[23] See supra note 21 at 12.

[24] United States v. Western Electric Co., No. 82-0192, Memorandum at 20 n. 40 (D.D.C. filed December 14, 1984).

[25] See generally, R. Raysmann and P. Brown, COMPUTER LAW: DRAFTING AND NEGOTIATING FORMS AND AGREEMENTS, Law Journal Seminars Press (N.Y. 1984); Cooper "Contracting for Computer Hardware and Software" in COMPUTER PROCUREMENT SEMINAR. Institute of Continuing Legal Education (Athens, Georgia, 1984).

purchases if the sale in question is deemed to be for "goods" (rather than services).[26] While CPE hardware seems clearly to fall within the UCC definition of "goods"—items moveable at the time of sale—there is some question as to the nature of bundled purchasers for CPE and telecommunications services. For such bundled purchases, the UCC will apply if the transaction is primarily for "goods." The user should therefore style or unbundle the contract or purchase agreement accordingly.

Some of the express warranties provided by CPE vendors should address the specifics of satisfactory telecommunications operation. Thus, for example, data transmission rates, measured response time, message throughput, error rates, protocol conversions and adherence to specific industry standards (e.g. recent CCITT standards for packet switched networks) should constitute such express warranties. Ideally, CPE operation according to such warranties should be demonstrable, for example, through benchmarks incorporated into the contract by reference. It is worth noting that courts have upheld an action in breach where a terminal has failed to perform according to advertised data transmission rates.[27]

A vendor will usually insist upon the operation of a force majeure clause to excuse non-performance for so-called "Acts of God" or reasons outside the seller's control. Following divestiture, such factors could include delays in circuit acquisition or other carrier actions directly affecting satisfactory operation of the CPE hardware. The customer should negotiate for appropriate equitable rescission clauses for relief from payment obligations in the event of such unforeseen circumstances.

The FCC imposes registration requirements (Section 68 of the Commissions Rules) upon all CPE for the safety and protection of the public telephone network.[28] Such registration requirements are the obligation of the manufacturer as a necessary condition for attachment to the public network. As such, their compliance should be a condition to the contract for sale and should be emphasized when dealing with new or untested equipment, OEM suppliers or foreign vendors. Moreover, such registration implies nothing about the functional performance of CPE and should not be confused with other warranties.

Finally, one must anticipate that networks and interface standards change. This is especially relevant when dealing with new digital interface standards (T-1 Carrier, DS-1 message framing specifications) and fiber optic links. Under the FCC's network disclosure rules, the carrier is under a Computer Inquiry II obligation (the "disclosure rule") to make such technical information relating to network changes public.[29] The CPE purchaser should therefore consider the

[26] O.C.G.A. §11-2-105 et. seq.; See generally, J. White and R. Summers, HANDBOOK OF THE LAW UNDER THE UNIFORM COMMERCIAL CODE (2nd Ed. 1980) at 52 et. seq.
[27] See Consolidated Data Terminals v. Applied Digital Data Systems, 708 F. 2d 391 (9th Cir. 1983).
[28] For FCC proposed streamlining of equipment registration, see revisions to Part 68 of the Commissions Rules; Deregulatory Options and Streamlined Application Processing, Notice of Proposed Rulemaking, 49 FR 39349, October 5, 1984.
[29] 47 C.F.R. 64.702 (d)(2) 1985, See Computer and Business Equipment Assn., 93 F.C.C. 2d 1226, 1249. (1983).

effect of such network changes and negotiate for the continued compliance of the purchased equipment.

14.7 CONCLUSION

This paper has attempted to underscore some of the practical effects of deregulation upon today's telecommunications users. The discussion is by no means complete. Nor is the state of deregulation static or even consistent. Nonetheless, as the marketplace continues to evolve toward full competition, users will have to become increasingly self-reliant so as to ensure continued just and reasonable rates in the absence of government oversight.

Chapter 15

Procurement of Customer Premises Equipment: Contracting in a Nontariffed Environment

Frederick L. Cooper, III, Esq.

As a result of the Federal Communications Commission's Second Computer Inquiry, telecommunications users are able to acquire customer-premises equipment in privately-negotiated transactions, subject to the pressures of the market and free of the constraints previously imposed by tariffs.[1] "Customer-premises equipment," or "CPE," includes telephone handsets, key systems, modems, computers, terminals, digital Network Channel Termination Equipment ("NCTE"), PBXs (private branch telephone exchange systems), and PABXs (private automatic branch telephone exchange systems). Today, a well-negotiated and well-drafted contract is absolutely essential in any large-scale acquisition of CPE. Because the terms and conditions of CPE acquisition are no longer prescribed by tariff, they must be incorporated into the acquisition contract. Moreover, users are now able to negotiate with vendors for terms and conditions, as well as prices, that may have been unavailable under tariffs. In a nontariffed marketplace, it is important to remember the oft-repeated homily: "If it's not in the contract, it's not in the deal."

The author gratefully acknowledges the research and assistance of J. Reid Hunter, Esq., an associate in the Computer/Communications Department of Hurt, Richardson, Garner, Todd & Cadenhead.

[1] See In re Amendment of Section 64.702 of the Commission's Rules and Regulations (Second Computer Inquiry), 77 F.C.C. 2d 384 (1980), *on reconsideration*, 84 F.C.C. 2d 50 (1980), *on further reconsideration*, 88 F.C.C. 2d 512 (1981), *aff'd sub nom*, Computer & Communications Industry Ass'n v. FCC, 693 F.2d 198 (D.C. Cir. 1982), *cert. denied*, 461 U.S. 398 (1983) (Customer-premises equipment may not be offered under tariff, may not be bundled with tariffed services and may only be offered by AT&T or the Bell Operating Companies through their respective deregulated subsidiaries.). *See also* 47 C.F.R. § 64.702(e) (1982).

Contracting for the procurement of CPE presents the user's attorney with a unique negotiating and drafting challenge. Customer-premises equipment often involves highly complex technology and a single CPE system may consist of telecommunications, data processing, and software components.

Telecommunications technology and standards are constantly changing. Unless CPE vendors are required to warrant continuing compliance with network and interface standards, the acquired CPE may be incompatible with public communications systems soon after acquisition. CPE procurement also involves the user's attorney in new and often unfamiliar nomenclature, such as "baud rates," "digital loop back-testing," "PCM," and "TDM," just to name a few. Furthermore, as we enter the "information age," data management and communication are becoming vital parts of every business and profession. As a result, consequential damages from a CPE failure may be astronomical in proportion to the acquisition cost.[2] Today's attorney must be prepared to assist businessmen and professionals as they venture into the unregulated, "free for all" CPE marketplace.

In a nontariffed environment, counsel must apply existing legal principles to a complex and changing technology in order to assist telecommunications users in planning, negotiating, and contracting for a large-scale CPE acquisition. Counsel must understand the many important implications of the Uniform Commercial Code in order to draft crucial acceptance test provisions and performance warranties. Moreover, the Magnuson-Moss Warranty—Federal Trade Commission Improvement Act may affect the vendor's ability to limit its warranties to the user. Finally, procurement of large interconnect telephone systems (PBXs, PABXs) raises special additional issues that must be addressed by counsel. Only by negotiating, drafting, and reviewing the acquisition contract with these implications and issues in mind may counsel take advantage of the many opportunities presented to users by deregulation while preserving the protections formally afforded in part to users by tariffs.

15.1 ORGANIZING FOR CPE PROCUREMENT

Large-scale CPE procurement should be deliberately planned from the outset. Once a user has decided to enter the CPE marketplace, the user should define his or her CPE needs in very broad terms. Next, the user should survey the market to determine whether these needs can be met. Using the results of this survey, the user should conduct a "cost-benefit" analysis to re-define his or her needs into a rough set of functional specifications.

Next, the user should establish a negotiating "team" and specific negotiating objectives. The negotiating team should include (1) management personnel

---

[2] See Chatlos Systems, Inc. v. Nat'l Cash Register Corp., 670 F.2d 1304 (3d Cir. 1982) (per curiam), *cert. denied*, 457 U.S. 1112 (1982) (User of computer system which failed recovered more than nine times the purchase price.).

directly affected by the acquisition, (2) the user's purchasing agent or agents, (3) the user's financial advisor (controller or outside certified public accountant), and (4) the user's legal counsel (in-house counsel or outside special counsel). Financial and tax planning considerations usually induce most users to include financial advisors at a very early stage of the acquisition process. Unfortunately, most users fail to include legal counsel until later stages of the acquisition. Often, counsel does not learn of the proposed acquisition until he or she is asked to review the vendor's standard "form contract." Optimally, users should include legal counsel at a very early stage—one at which the user has maximum leverage—so that the user may maximize his or her protection via a well-negotiated and well-drafted acquisition contract.

The acquisition team may be an organized "task force" that meets on a regular basis, or it may be nothing more than a list of individuals who are available for consultation on a "as needed" basis, but who never actually meet as a group. "Task force" organization is particularly appropriate for acquisitions that critically affect the user's business. In either event, counsel for the user and the lead negotiator designated by the user should consult with team members frequently throughout the acquisition process.

The negotiating team's first responsibility should be to formulate contracting objectives which will guide the team throughout the acquisition process. Although contracting goals and objectives will vary with each user, all users should, at a minimum, negotiate to accomplish the following:

1. Achieve contractual parity with the CPE vendor in the "battle of the forms";
2. Contract for functional results, rather than for specific assets;
3. Attempt to control the costs of the acquisition;
4. Capitalize on the opportunities previously unavailable in the tariffed environment, keeping in mind that CPE vendors can no longer "hide behind their tariffs," and
5. Require CPE vendors to guarantee continued compliance with changing network and interface standards.

The negotiating team should not overlook the vendor's goals and objectives. As a general rule, CPE vendors are most concerned with the following:

1. Limiting their exposure to liability;
2. Protecting valuable proprietary rights in their technology; and
3. Controlling their costs.

Only after carefully considering both parties' respective contracting objectives is the negotiating team prepared to solicit bids from CPE vendors.

The negotiating team should develop and use a "request for proposal" to solicit bids from vendors. A request for proposal, or an "RFP," is a written request developed by the user and its negotiating team that is submitted to possible vendors. The RFP invites vendors to make a bid and stipulates the features, performance criteria, and conditions required by the user. In a non-tariffed environment, it is vital that a user devote a considerable amount of time and effort to developing a RFP. A well-drafted RFP optimizes the user's leverage at a point in the procurement process when that leverage is greatest—bid submission time.

A carefully drafted RFP also gives the user a decided advantage over the vendor in the familiar "battle of the forms." [3] Because the terms contained in the form first submitted often are controlling in the event of conflicting terms, [4] the RFP should include all contract provisions considered vital to the acquisition, including risk-shifting provisions that will affect both the vendor's exposure and the cost of the transaction. Alternatively, the user might attach his or her standard form contract to the RFP and stipulate that its terms will govern the acquisition. The user also might require that the RFP, along with the vendor's response, be attached to, and incorporated into, the final contract, thereby forcing the vendor to warrant the desired features and performance criteria.

Responses to the RFP will assist the negotiating team in refining its prior market survey and functional specifications. By circulating the RFP widely, the team may solicit responses from a large number of vendors. If vendor responses indicate that the user's requirements cannot be met, or can be met only a greater-than-anticipated costs, the team can reformulate the RFP for submission to vendors.

After the RFP is reformulated and a sufficient number of responses are received, the negotiating team should conduct preliminary negotiations with several vendors before choosing a vendor. The negotiating team should continue to work with the designated negotiators and the team's counsel throughout the negotiation and drafting of the final acquisition contract. The team should conduct a final review of the final draft of the contract before it is submitted to the vendor for signature.

15.2 APPLYING THE UNIFORM COMMERCIAL CODE IN CPE ACQUISITIONS

Article Two of the Uniform Commercial Code (the "UCC") governs "transactions in goods" in 49 states and the District of Columbia. [5] The UCC defines "goods" as follows: "All things (including specially manufactured goods) which are movable at the time of identification to the contract for sale other than the money in which the price is to be paid, investment securities . . . and things in action." [6] Most CPE qualifies as goods under this definition. Consequently, the

---

[3] *See generally* J. WHITE & R. SUMMERS, UNIFORM COMMERCIAL CODE § 1-2, at 24-39 (2d ed. 1980); U.C.C. § 2-207 (1977).

[4] *See generally* J. WHITE & R. SUMMERS, *supra* note 3, § 1-2, at 24-39.

[5] U.C.C. § 2-102 (1977). *See e.g.*, Meiske v. Bartell Drug Co., 92 Wash. 2d 40, 593 P.2d 1308 (1979) (en banc).

[6] *See* U.C.C. § 2-105(1) (1977).

UCC will govern most CPE acquisitions that are structured as sales. In many jurisdictions, the UCC also will govern leases of CPE. Finally, the UCC provisions will govern the licensing of software in many CPE acquisitions. Before disregarding its provisions, counsel for a user should make a well-researched determination that the UCC does not apply to a particular acquisition.

Clearly, a sale of goods is a "transaction in goods" with the scope of Article Two of the UCC.[7] Sales of services are not governed by the UCC.[8] The provision of services incidental to the sale will not render the UCC inapplicable to the sale.[9] On the other hand, if the contract is predominantly for the provision of services (*i.e.*, maintenance, development, and/or consulting services), the UCC probably will not apply.[10]

Leases of CPE, whether from the CPE manufacturer, or from a leasing company in a third-party leasing arrangement, also may be governed by the UCC. Some courts have held that the UCC is never applicable to lease transactions.[11] Other jurisdictions have held that Article Two of the UCC applies in its entirety to leases.[12] Still other courts look through the form of the transaction and apply an "economic realities" test to determine if the "lease" is in fact a lease, governed by lease principles, or if it is a sale by the "lessor" subject to a security interest in the goods, governed by Article Two of the UCC.[13] Still other courts have compared the economic considerations of leasing to a sale of goods and have applied some provisions of Article Two by analogy to lease transactions.[14]

Much of today's CPE also incorporates computer software components. As a technical matter, most software is licensed and not sold. However, courts have held that when software is "bundled" with computer hardware which is sold, the entire transaction is a "sale" of "goods" under the UCC.[15] An increasing number

---

[7] *See, e.g.*, Mansfield Propane Gas Co. v. Folger Gas Co., 231 Ga. 868, 204 S.E.2d 625 (1974).

[8] *See, e.g.*, Liberty Fin. Mgmt. Corp. v. Beneficial Data Processing Corp., 670 S.W.2d 40 (Mo. App. 1984) (UCC does not govern a contract to provide data processing services).

[9] *See* Dynamic Corp. of America v. International Harvester Co., 429 F. Supp. 341 (S.D.N.Y. 1977).

[10] *See* Computer Servicenters, Inc. v. Beacon Mfg. Co., 328 F. Supp. 653 (D.C.S.C. 1970), *aff'd.*, 443 F.2d 906 (4th Cir. 1971) (per curiam); Data processing v. L. H. Smith Oil Corp., 492 N.E.2d 364 (Ind. App. 1974).

[11] *See, e.g.*, DeKalb Agresearch, Inc. v. Abbott, 391 F. Supp. 152 (N.D. Ala. 1974), *aff'd* 511 F.2d 1162 (8th Cir. 1975); Martin v. Ryder Truck Rental, Inc., 353 A.2d 581 (Del. Super. 1976); Mays v. Citizens & Southern Nat'l Bank, 132 Ga. App. 602, 208 S.E.2d 614 (1974); Bona v. Graefe, 264 Md. 69, 285 A.2d 607 (1972); Leasco Data Processing N.Y.S.2d 288 (App. Term 1973) (per curiam), *aff'd mem.* 360 N.Y.S.2d 189 (App. Div. 1974).

[12] Hertz Commercial Leasing Corp. v. Transp. Credit Clearing House, 59 Misc. 2d 226, 298 N.Y.S.2d 392, *rev'd on other grounds*, 64 Misc. 2d 910, 316 N.Y.S.2d 585 (Sup. Ct. 1970).

[13] *See, e.g.*, Citicorp Leasing, Inc. v. Allied Institutional Distrib., Inc., 454 F. Supp. 511 (W.D. Okla. 1977); Crest Inv. Trust, Inc. v. Atl. Mobile Corp., 252 Md. 286, 250 A.2d 246 (1969).

[14] *See, e.g.*, Glenn Dick Equip. Co. v. Galey Constr., Inc., 97 Idaho 216, 541 P.2d 1184 (1975); Briscoe's Foodland, Inc. v. Capital Assoc., Inc., No. 55,033 (Miss. Feb. 19, 1986) (available Dec. 21, 1986 on LEXIS) (Robertson, J., concurring).

[15] *See, e.g.*, Triangle Underwriters, Inc. v. Honeywell, Inc., 457 F. Supp. 765, 769 (E.D.N.Y. 1978), *aff'd in part, rev'd in part*, 664 F.2d 737 (2d Cir. 1979), *aff'd after remand*, 651 F.2d 132 (2d Cir. 1981).

of courts are treating licenses of standard, noncustomized, non-bundled software packages (*i.e.*, spreadsheet packages, inventory packages, etc.), as sales of goods, even where incidental services are provided with the software.[16] By analogy, sales of CPE that include related software should be treated as sales of goods for UCC purposes, even if a majority of the purchase price is allocated to software components.

Counsel should negotiate and contract with the UCC in mind because its provisions affect issues that are particularly critical in CPE acquisition. The UCC will fill any "gaps" left in the acquisition agreement. Absent agreement to the contrary in the contract, the UCC will govern acceptance, rejection, revocation of acceptance, and risk of loss of the CPE. The UCC also will govern any agreement reached by the parties regarding warranties (express and implied), warranty disclaimers and remedies for breach of these warranties. Because many vendors skillfully draft their standard form agreements so as to be favorably supplemented by the UCC regarding many important issues, counsel must review a vendor's contract with the utmost care.

15.3 DRAFTING ACCEPTANCE AND RISK OF LOSS PROVISIONS

15.3.1 Acceptance Under the UCC

Acceptance is probably the most critical issue in any CPE acquisition. Because the user's payment obligation in many transactions does not arise until acceptance occurs,[17] a user's leverage is greatest prior to acceptance. Moreover, a user may more easily cause the CPE vendor to take back defective or otherwise nonconforming equipment before acceptance than after acceptance.[18] In many cases, after acceptance the user must live with the tendered CPE and look to warranty-related remedies or maintenance provisions for relief.

If the parties do not include an acceptance provision in the contract, the UCC will govern the time and effect of acceptance.[19] However, from the user's perspective, the UCC provisions governing the time of acceptance are often poorly suited for CPE acquisitions. Unless otherwise specified in the contract, "acceptance" under the UCC occurs as follows:

1. When the user signifies, after a reasonable opportunity to inspect, that the CPE conforms to the contract, or that the CPE is nonconforming, but he or she will accept it anyway;

---

[16] *See, e.g.*, RRX Industries, Inc. v. Lab-Con, Inc., 772 F.2d 543 (9th Cir. 1985). *Compare* Data Processing v. L. H. Smith Oil Corp., 492 N.E.2d 314 (Ind. App. 1986) (contract for development and sale of customer computer programming was not a sale of goods under the UCC). *See also* Note, *Computer Programs as Goods under the UCC*, 77 MICH. L. REV. 1149 (1979).

[17] U.C.C. § 2-607(1) (1977).

[18] *See* WHITE & R. SUMMERS, *supra* note 3, § 8-3 at 301.

[19] U.C.C. §§ 1-102(3), 2-606 (1977).

2. When the user fails to make an effective rejection of the CPE, provided that he or she has had an opportunity to inspect it; or
3. When the user does any act inconsistent with the vendor's ownership of the CPE (unless such act is wrongful as against the vendor, in which case the vendor must ratify the act for it to constitute an acceptance).[20]

If the acquisition is for the purchase of a "commercial unit,"[21] the user accepts the entire system when he or she accepts any part of the system.[22]

15.3.2 Rejection and Revocation of Acceptance under the UCC

Prior to acceptance, a user may "reject" CPE that fails in any respect to conform to the requirements of the contract.[23] Rejection must be within a reasonable time of tender or delivery and the user must "seasonably" notify the vendor of his or her intent to reject.[24] Notification should be in writing and should carefully state the basis upon which the equipment is rejected.[25] A rejecting user must take care not to use the CPE after rejection, because any "exercise of ownership" by the user is wrongful against the vendor.[26] Moreover, the user must exercise his or her right to reject nonconforming CPE very carefully, as wrongful rejection will entitle the vendor to recover damages for nonacceptance.[27]

The UCC also provides vendors a right to cure certain nonconforming tenders of CPE, and thereby cause the user to retain nonconforming CPE. A vendor has a right to cure a rejected tender of "nonconforming" CPE if (1) the vendor had reasonable grounds to believe the tendered equipment would be acceptable *and* (2) the vendor "seasonably" notifies the user of his or her intent to cure.[28] However, a user may preclude the vendor's right to cure by including in the contract language that requires rigid compliance and that precludes replacements of defective equipment.[29]

If a user receives equipment that proves to be defective, but does not discover the defects until he or she has accepted it, he or she must either "revoke acceptance" or retain the equipment and sue for breach of warranty.[30] Revocation of acceptance, like rejection, entitles the user to cancel his or her obligations

---

[20] *Id.* §§ 1-102(3), 2-606(1).

[21] A "commercial unit" is defined in the UCC as "a unit of goods as by commercial usage is a single whole for purposes of sale and division of which materially impairs its character or value on the market or in use." *See* U.C.C. § 2-105(6) (1977).

[22] U.C.C. § 2-606(2) (1977).

[23] *Id.* §§ 2-601, 607(2).

[24] *Id.* § 2-602(1).

[25] *See id.* § 2-605(1).

[26] *See id.* § 2-602(2)(a).

[27] *See id.* §§ 2-602(3), -703.

[28] *Id.* 2-508(2). A non-conforming tender is effectively cured by substituting conforming equipment within a reasonable time of rejection by the user. *See id.*

[29] *See id.* § 2-508 comment 2.

[30] *See id.* §§ 2-607(2), 608(1), 714(1). *See also id.* § 2-714 comment 2.

under the contract and return the equipment to the vendor.[31] Revocation of acceptance differs from rejection in that the procedural requirements are more numerous and more difficult.

A user may revoke acceptance of the entire CPE system, or of some part, in two narrow instances:

1. If a user knows of nonconformities in the CPE at acceptance, he or she may revoke acceptance only if he or she accepted the equipment on the reasonable assumption that they would be cured, and in fact they were not;[32] or
2. If the user accepted the equipment without discovering the nonconformity, he or she may revoke acceptance if acceptance was reasonably induced by either the vendor's assurances or by the difficulty of discovering the nonconformities.[33]

In either case, any nonconformity must substantially impair the value of the CPE to the user.[34]

To be effective, revocation must occur within a reasonable time after the defect is discovered or should have been discovered and before any substantial change in the condition of the CPE (excepting changes in the CPE caused by their own defects).[35] Revocation of acceptance is ineffective until the user notifies the vendor.[36] Although it is not clear what amount of time is a reasonable time within which to revoke acceptance, Professors White and Summers suggest that the nature of the defect, the complexity of the goods involved, and the sophistication of the buyer are factors that should be considered.[37] Courts have held that a buyer may afford the vendor an opportunity to correct any defects in goods without jeopardizing his or her right to revoke acceptance should the remedial efforts fail.[38] However, continued use of goods after acceptance has been revoked may be inconsistent with the vendor's ownership, thereby invalidating a revocation of acceptance.[39]

---

[31] *See id.* § 2-711(1); CMI Corp. v. Leemar Steel Co., 733 F.2d 1410 (10th Cir. 1954).

[32] U.C.C. § 2-608(1)(a) (1977).

[33] *Id.* § 2-608(1)(b).

[34] *Id.* § 2-608(1).

[35] *Id.* § 2-608(2).

[36] *Id.*

[37] J. WHITE & R. SUMMERS, *supra* note 3, § 8-3 at 310.

[38] *See, e.g.,* Warren v. Guttanit, Inc., 69 N.C. App. 103, 317 S.E.2d 5 (1984); Trailmobile Div. of Pullman, Inc. v. Jones, 118 Ga. App. 472, 164 S.E.2d 346 (1968).

[39] Computerized Radiological Serv. v. Syntex Corp., 786 F.2d 72 (2d Cir. 1986) (use of CAT scanner for 22 months after revocation of acceptance precluded revocation). *But see* Minsel v. El Rancho Mobile Home Center, Inc., 32 Mich. App. 10, 188 N.W.2d 9 (1971) (use of mobile home for six weeks after revocation of acceptance while searching for a new residence held reasonable); Fablok Mills, Inc. v. Cocker Mach. & Foundry Co., 125 N.J. Super. 251, 310 A.2d 491 (1973) (continued use of machines reasonable where no other machines available and alternative was going out of business).

15.3.3 Acceptance Test Provisions

The UCC rules regarding acceptance, rejection, and revocation leaves a number of unanswered questions when applied to the typical CPE acquisition. Of the issues raised, the following are most significant to the user:

1. What is a "reasonable time" for an inspection to trigger acceptance?
2. Is it possible for the CPE to conform to the contract, precluding rejection or revocation of acceptance, but to not perform as represented by the vendor?
3. By using CPE during installation and testing, does a user engage in acts inconsistent with the vendor's ownership, precluding rejection of the CPE?
4. If the user accepts one of several interrelated components of a system, has he or she accepted part of a "commercial unit," and thereby accepted the entire system, notwithstanding the fact that other components may be nonconforming?
5. If the vendor is entitled to cure a tender of nonconforming equipment, what is a "further reasonable time to substitute a conforming tender"?
6. Where a user has informed the vendor of his or her intent to revoke acceptance, does continued use of the working components of CPE until substitute CPE can be cut over invalidate revocation of acceptance? Is such continued use of the defective CPE excusable mitigation of damages?

In a CPE acquisition, certainty as to the time of acceptance and the right to reject and revoke acceptance is crucial to both parties. Under the UCC, the precise time of acceptance and the effectiveness of a rejection or revocation of acceptance are highly fact-intensive and depend on the circumstances of the particular transaction.[40] Counsel for users should not rely on the UCC to resolve these issues, but should draft detailed acceptance provisions enabling the user to withhold payment until the CPE performs satisfactorily.

User's counsel should review carefully any acceptance provisions drafted by the vendor. Typically, vendors' standard form contracts define acceptance in terms even more favorable to the vendor than would the UCC. For example, acceptance may be deemed to occur upon shipment of the CPE or upon certification by the vendor that the CPE is installed and ready for use. Moreover, standard form contracts often are silent on the issues of rejection and revocation of acceptance, thereby triggering the UCC provisions relating to these matters.

Well-drafted acceptance test provisions prescribe those performance and reliability tests that must be satisfied before CPE will be deemed accepted by the user. Acceptance test provisions should also specify the effects of acceptance. Acceptance should trigger the user's payment obligation and the initiation of any warranty responsibilities assumed by the vendor. Optimally, risk of loss of the CPE and, consequently, the corresponding obligation to insure, should also be tied to acceptance.[41]

---

[40] *See generally* J. WHITE & R. SUMMERS, *supra* note 3, § 8-1 to -3, at 293-318.
[41] *See* Section III.D. *infra*.

A well-drafted acceptance test provision must be tailored to the specific CPE acquisition. Only where CPE performance is not crucial to the user's business or where the damages from CPE failure would be *de minimus* should the user agree to simple acceptance test procedures. In the more likely case where CPE failure would cause substantial consequential harm, or where complex CPE systems (*i.e.*, large PABX systems) are involved, counsel should demand comprehensive acceptance test provisions. Comprehensive acceptance test provisions should measure the conformity of CPE to the contract in terms of the following criteria:

1. Performance, (*i.e.*, response time, data handling capability, usable memory, etc.); and
2. Reliability (*i.e.*, system uptime).

The standards included in the acceptance test provisions also may be used as the benchmark for ongoing CPE performance under the express warranties. The acceptance test provision should contain remedies and penalties that are triggered by the vendor's failure to comply strictly with the prescribed criteria within an agreed time period.

The negotiation and drafting of comprehensive acceptance test provisions may often be complex and time-consuming. Continuing access to technical expertise is absolutely essential to enable counsel to develop and refine performance and reliability criteria. However, the benefits to the user far outweigh the burdens of negotiating and drafting such provisions.

15.3.4 Risk of Loss Provisions

Another important issue in CPE acquisition contracts is risk of loss. Because CPE often must be shipped to the user's site by common carrier, the user and vendor should consider who will bear the loss should the equipment be damaged or destroyed in transit. If the parties do not expressly allocate the risk of loss in transit within the acquisition contract, the UCC provisions will determine the point and time at which the risk shifts to the user.[42] As with many other "gap filling" provisions, the risk of loss provisions of the UCC often favor the CPE vendor.

Where the contract provides for shipment by a carrier, the UCC determines when the risk of loss shifts according to whether the contract is a "shipment" contract or a "destination" contract. A contract that does not require the vendor to deliver the equipment to a particular destination is a "shipment contract."[43] Risk of loss passes to the user under a shipment contract when the vendor puts the goods in the possession of the carrier and makes a reasonable contract for their transportation.[44] If the CPE is damaged or destroyed after it is delivered to the

---

[42] *See generally* U.C.C. § 2-509 (1977).
[43] *See* J. WHITE & R. SUMMERS, *supra* note 12, § 5-2 at 180.
[44] U.C.C. §§ 2-509(1)(a), -504 (1977).

carrier, the user is liable for the purchase price and must look to the carrier, and not the vendor, to recover for the damages or loss.[45]

If the contract requires the vendor to deliver the equipment at a particular destination (*i.e.*, the user's site), risk of loss passes to the user when the carrier tenders delivery[46] and a contract is termed a "destination contract."[47] Under a destination contract, the vendor absorbs the damages for goods lost or damaged in transit.[48] In addition, the vendor will be liable to the user for nondelivery unless he or she tenders substitute goods.[49] The UCC makes it clear that courts should presume a contract is a shipment contract, unless the vendor specifically agrees to deliver to a particular destination or the contract otherwise expressly allocates loss.[50] This result obtains even if the vendor has agreed to pay shipping costs.[51]

Risk of loss is most often allocated in the contract by using F.O.B. ("free on board") terms. If the contract provides that shipment is to be F.O.B. "the place of shipment," (*i.e.*, the vendor's loading dock), the contract is a shipment contract and the vendor's responsibility is to place conforming goods in to the possession of the carrier and make an appropriate contract for shipment.[52] Risk of loss then passes to the user.[53] If the contract provides that shipment or the price is F.O.B. "the place of destination," (*i.e.*, the user's site), the contract is a destination contract and the vendor must "at his own expense transport the goods to that place and there tender delivery of them. . . ."[54] Risk of loss will pass to the user only when the equipment is tendered at the user's site.[55]

Finally, tender or delivery of substantially nonconforming goods by the vendor will alter the risk of loss rules in the user's favor. If, upon receipt by the user, the tendered CPE is so nonconforming that the buyer is entitled to reject it, risk of loss will remain on the seller until the vendor cures the nonconformities or the user accepts the equipment.[56] If the user accepts the nonconforming equipment but rightfully revokes acceptance, he or she may look to the vendor to recover any losses not covered by his or her insurance.[57]

In negotiating risk of loss provisions, the user's objectives are relatively simple. Ideally, risk of loss should not pass to the user until the CPE passes the acceptance test provisions. Of course, such a provision requires the vendor to

---

[45] *Id*. § 2-709(1). *See also* J. WHITE & R. SUMMERS, *supra* note 3, § 5-1 at 174-79.
[46] U.C.C. §§ 2-509(1)(b) (1977).
[47] *See* J. WHITE & R. SUMMERS, *supra* note 3, § 5-2 at 180.
[48] U.C.C. §§ 2-503(3), (1977).
[49] *Id*. § 2-711(1); J. WHITE & R. SUMMERS, *supra* note 3, § 5-1 at 174-75.
[50] U.C.C. § 2-503 comment 5 (1977); J. WHITE & R. SUMMERS, *supra* note 3, § 5-2 at 182.
[51] U.C.C. § 2-503 comment 5 (1977).
[52] *Id*. §§ 2-319(1)(a), -504 (1977); J. WHITE & R. SUMMERS, *supra* note 3, § 5-2 at 180.
[53] U.C.C. § 2-509(1)(a) (1977).
[54] *Id*. § 2-319(1)(b).
[55] *Id*. § 2-509(1)(b).
[56] *Id*. § 2-510(1).
[57] *Id*. § 2-510(2).

insure the equipment until acceptance, and, moreover, a vendor may simply pass the insurance cost to the user in the form of a higher price. Except in a large acquisition by a user with substantial bargaining power, counsel should consider accepting a shipping- or destination-type contract in exchange for a meaningful acceptance test provision.

15.4 DRAFTING WARRANTIES AND WARRANTY DISCLAIMERS UNDER THE UCC

Except for the acceptance test provisions, no provisions of a CPE acquisition contract are more crucial than those containing the warranties and warranty disclaimers. Most vendors' form contracts disclaim any warranties that the CPE sold is fit for the user's needs and include only a limited "repair or replace" warranty against defects in materials and workmanship. Typical vendor form contracts also limit the user's remedies for breach of the warranty. In the competitive, nontariffed marketplace created by the Second Computer Inquiry, users and their counsel should not accept boilerplate warranty language. Instead, users should negotiate for warranty provisions that guarantee continuing CPE performance.

Several bodies of law affect the making and disclaiming of warranties. The UCC defines warranties and governs the ways in which they can be made, disclaimed and modified, as well as the remedies available for their breach. The Magnuson-Moss Warranty—Federal Trade Commission Improvement Act (the "Magnuson-Moss Act"),[58] and the Federal Trade Commission regulations promulgated thereunder, prescribe additional requirements for, and limitations on, warranties made with respect to "consumer products." In addition, various state consumer protection acts affect warranties made by a sellers of certain products.[59] Although a discussion of these state acts is beyond the scope of this article, counsel for users should consult the statutes of the states in which the vendor and user do business for applicable legislation.

15.4.1 Warranties and the UCC

15.4.1.1 Express Warranties

The UCC lists five ways in which a vendor may create an express warranty. Any *affirmation of fact* or *promise* made by the vendor that relates to the equipment and becomes a "part of the basis of the bargain" creates an express warranty that the goods will conform to the affirmation or promise.[60] In addition, any *descrip-*

---

[58] 15 U.S.C.A. §§ 2301-2312 (West 1982). *See also* 16 C.F.R. §§ 700-703.
[59] *See e.g.*, O.C.G.A. § 10-1-370 to -375 (1982); O.C.G.A. § 10-1-390 to -407 (1982 & Supp. 1986).
[60] U.C.C. § 2-313(1)(a) (1977).

tion of the equipment that was made which becomes "a part of the basis of the bargain" creates an express warranty that the equipment conforms to that description.[61] Finally, any *sample* or *model* that is made "part of the basis of the bargain" will create an express warranty that the equipment conforms to the sample or model.[62]

The meaning of the phrase "basis of the bargain" does not appear in the UCC and courts differ widely in construing it. Some courts have held that a user must rely on a seller's affirmation for it to become part of the basis of the bargain,[63] while others have held that no reliance is required.[64] In any event, express written representations in a contract generally are considered a part of the basis of the bargain and will create express warranties.[65]

The UCC provisions on warranties protect a user's reasonable expectations. No specific language is required in order to create an express warranty. The terms "warrant" or "guarantee" are not required, nor is a specific intent to create a warranty.[66] However, mere "puffery," including statements of value, opinion, or recommendation, do not create an express warranty.[67]

CPE acquisitions typically will involve several or all of the five types of express warranties. A vendor's published specifications and documentation will create an express warranty if the court determines that they were part of the basis of the bargain.[68] Sales and promotional literature published by a vendor may become a part of the basis of the bargain and create an express warranty.[69] Arguably, a vendor's response to the user's RFP constitutes a description of the equipment, and if incorporated into the contract as recommended above, should create an express warranty that the equipment will conform to the description therein. Samples or models of the CPE demonstrated by the vendor also may rise to the level of express warranties.

Nonetheless, counsel should not rely on these representations that the CPE will perform properly, but should demand ongoing performance warranties coupled with specified remedies for any breach. As with acceptance test provisions, compliance with the warranty should be measured by performance and reliability criteria set forth in the warranty.

Because performance warranties are only as good as the remedies available for their breach, the warranty provisions must specify how and when the vendor will

---

[61] *Id.* § 2-313(1)(b).

[62] *Id.* § 2-313(1)(c).

[63] *See, e.g.*, Speed Fastners, Inc. v. Newsom, 382 F.2d 395 (10th Cir. 1967); Hagenbuch v. Snap-On Tools Corp., 339 F. Supp. 676 (D.N.H. 1972).

[64] *See, e.g.*, Young & Cooper, Inc. v. Vestring, 214 Kan. 311, 521 P.2d 281 (1974); Hawkins Constr. Co. v. Matthews Co., 190 Neb. 546, 209 N.W.2d 643 (1973).

[65] *See* Consolidated Data Terminals v. Applied Digital Data Systems, Inc., 708 F.2d 385 (9th Cir. 1983).

[66] U.C.C. § 2-313(2) (1977).

[67] *See id.*

[68] Consolidated Data Terminals, 708 F.2d at 391-92. *See also* U.C.C. § 2-313 comment 5 (1977).

[69] *See, e.g.*, Drayton v. Jiffee Chemical Corp. 395 F. Supp. 1081 (N.D. Ohio 1975); Harris v. Belton, 258 Cal. App. 2d 595, 65 Cal. Rptr. 808 (1968).

correct any failure to meet these criterias. Routine and emergency CPE failures should be defined and response times for each specified. Finally, the vendor's maintenance obligations should commence at the end of the express warranty period and should require the vendor, upon payment of a maintenance fee, to continue to maintain the CPE in conformance with the warranted performance and reliability criteria.

15.4.1.2 IMPLIED WARRANTIES

By operation of law, vendors also may make certain implied warranties in transactions involving CPE that are covered by the UCC. A CPE vendor who is a merchant with respect to the equipment sold impliedly warrants that the equipment is merchantable.[70] The UCC defines a merchant as:

> a person who deals in goods of the kind or otherwise by his occupation holds himself out as having knowledge or skill peculiar to the practices or goods involved in the transaction or to whom such knowledge or skill may be attributed by his employment of an agent or broker or other intermediary who by his occupation holds himself out as having such knowledge or skill.[71]

To be merchantable, CPE need not be defect-free. "Merchantable" equipment must be fit for the ordinary purposes for which it is used and must pass without objection in the trade under the contract description.[72]

If at the time of contracting, the vendor has reason to know of a particular purpose for which the equipment is required and that the user is relying on his or her skill or judgment to select or furnish suitable goods, the vendor impliedly warrants that the equipment shall be fit for that particular purpose.[73] This warranty is commonly known as the "implied warranty of fitness for a particular purpose." Some courts have held that implied warranties of merchantability and fitness arise in leases of personal property.[74]

Other warranties arise by operation of law in a "contract for sale" of CPE. By entering a contract for sale, a vendor warrants that the title conveyed is good and that transfer thereof to the user is rightful.[75] The vendor also impliedly warrants that the equipment is delivered free from any security interest or other liens of which the user has no knowledge at the time of contracting.[76] Finally, a merchant regularly dealing in the CPE warrants that the equipment is delivered free of any

---

[70] U.C.C. § 2-314(1) (1977).

[71] *Id.* § 2-104(1).

[72] *Id.* § 2-314(2)(a), (c).

[73] *Id.* § 2-315.

[74] *See, e.g.,* Quality Acceptance Corp. v. Million & Albers, Inc., 367 F. Supp. 771 (D. Wy. 1973) (public policy requires that the warranties of fitness and mechantability be implied in a lease or bailment of business machines); Knox v. N. Am. Car Corp., 80 Ill. App.3d 683, 399 N.E.2d 1355 (1980) (lessor of boxcars impliedly warranted that they would be fit for the lessee's purposes).

[75] U.C.C. § 2-312(1)(a) (1977).

[76] *Id.* § 2-312(1)(b).

rightful claims by third parties "of infringement or the like" (unless the user furnished specifications to the vendor, in which case the user must indemnify the vendor against claims of infringement arising out of the vendor's compliance with the specifications).[77] One court recently held that this provision requires only that the goods be "delivered" free of infringing claims, and that it does not protect the user against patent infringement claims arising out of their subsequent use.[78] Finally, the official comments to Section 2-313 of the UCC suggest that these implied warranties may also apply to nonsale transactions.[79]

15.4.2 Disclaimers of Warranties and the UCC

The implied warranties created by the UCC are frequently disclaimed. Any modification or disclaimer of the implied warranty of merchantability must specifically mention "merchantability," and if done in writing, the disclaimer or modification must be conspicuous.[80] Modification or exclusion of the implied warranty of fitness for a particular purpose must be in writing and conspicuous.[81] Exclusion or modification of the warranty of title and of the warranty against infringement requires specific language or circumstances sufficient to "give the buyer reason to know that the person selling does not claim title in himself or that he is purporting to sell only such right or title as he or a third person may have."[82]

Most CPE vendors' standard form contracts will purport to exclude both the implied warranties of merchantability and fitness for a particular purpose. Disclaimers of the warranty of title and the warranty against infringement are rare. These disclaimers probably will not be negotiable, so users should devote their time to bargaining for comprehensive express warranties that guarantee some specified level of performance.

Unlike implied warranties, express warranties, once made, usually are not disclaimable. Most vendors' form contracts will contain some form of general disclaimer which purports to exclude all implied and express warranties other than the vendor's express "repair or replace" warranty. If words or conduct of warranty cannot be harmonized with language or conduct negating or limiting a warranty, the negating or limiting language is inoperative.[83] Therefore, express written representations that form a part of the basis of the bargain will be enforced against the vendor, despite any general disclaimer language to the

---

[77] *Id.* § 2-312(3).

[78] Motorola, Inc. v. Varo, Inc., 33 PAT. TRADEMARK & COPYRIGHT J. (BNA) 52, 53 (N.D. Tex. Dec. 7, 1986).

[79] U.C.C. § 2-313 comment 2 (1977) ("[T]he warranty sections of this Article are not designed in any way to disturb those lines of case law growth which have recognized that warranties need not be confined . . . to sales contracts . . . . They may arise in other appropriate circumstances . . . .").

[80] *Id.* § 2-316(2).

[81] *Id.*

[82] *Id.* § 2-312(2).

[83] *Id.* § 2-316(1).

contrary.[84] General disclaimer language is of some usefulness to vendors. General disclaimers, when coupled with "merger" or "integration" clauses, usually will prevent representations made outside the contract documents from becoming "warranties."[85]

Most warranty disclaimers are accompanied by a "merger" or "integration" clause. A typical merger or integration clause provides that there are no understandings, agreements, representations, or warranties other than those specified in the contract and that the written contract is the complete and exclusive statement of the terms of the agreement. Merger or integration clauses preclude users from introducing evidence of oral representations made *prior* to the execution of the contract.[86] However, a merger or integration clause will not prevent the introduction of parol evidence to explain an ambiguity in the contract[87] or one created by related contracts.[88] A merger or integration clause also will not prevent the introduction of evidence of course of dealing, usage of trade or course of performance to explain or supplement the terms of the contract.[89]

In negotiating warranty provisions for the CPE contract, counsel's best strategy will be to bargain for favorable "results oriented" express warranties. Counsel should avoid the typical "free from defects in materials and workmanship" language and instead seek performance warranties. As in the acceptance test provisions, compliance should be measured against specified performance and reliability benchmarks. Counsel also should demand an intellectual property rights warranty in which the vendor warrants that the CPE system, as installed, does not infringe the copyright, patent, trademark, or any other intellectual property rights of, and does not misappropriate the trade secrets or confidential information of, any third party. Within the warranty, the vendor should covenant to indemnify the user for any damages suffered as a result of any *claims* of infringement by any third party.

---

[84] *See* Consolidated Data Terminals, 708 F.2d at 391 (statements contained in written specifications of computer terminals prevail over a general disclaimer of warranty liability.)

[85] *See, e.g.,* Pennsylvania Gas. Co. v. Secord Bros., Inc., 73 Misc. 2d 1031, 343 N.Y.S.2d 256 (Sup. Ct. 1973), *aff'd* 44 A.D.2d 906, 357 N.Y.S.2d 702 (1974).

[86] *See e.g.,* Applications Inc. v. Hewlett Packard Co., 501 F. Supp. 129 (S.D.N.Y. 1980); National Cash Register Co. v. Modern Transfer Co., 224 Pa. Super. 138, 302 A.2d 486 (1973). *See also* U.C.C. § 2-202 (1977); *But see* O'Neil v. International Harvester Co., 40 Colo. App. 369, 575 P.2d 862 (1978) (evidence of oral warranties admissible notwithstanding warranty disclaimer and integration clause where buyer alleges oral warranties made prior to execution of contract and post-sale conduct tending to show such warranties were made).

[87] *See* Nat'l Cash Register Co. v. Modern Transfer Co., 224 Pa. Super. at _____ , 302 A.2d at 489 (dictum); Bob Robertson, Inc. v. Webster, 679 S.W.2d 683 (Tex. App. 1984) (The integration clause was contradicted by the instrument itself where the contract referred to delivery numerous times but contained no delivery date, and consequently, oral proof of the delivery date was admissible.).

[88] *See* W. R. Weaver Co. v. Burroughs Corp., 580 S.W.2d 76 (Tex. Civ. App. 1979) (extrinsic evidence admissible to resolve ambiguity created by multiple contract documents, some of which contained integration clauses and one of which did not).

[89] U.C.C. § 2-202(a) (1977).

15.4.3 Limitations of Remedies and the UCC

Damages recoverable by a user for a vendor's breach of a CPE contract may often be substantial. Upon a breach of any of the UCC warranties, a user may recover the difference "at the time and place of acceptance" between the value of the CPE as warranted and the value of the CPE as accepted.[90] Typically, this difference is equal to the cost of repair or replacement of the defective goods.[91] Users may also recover the loss suffered for any other "nonconformities" in the equipment tendered.[92] Incidental damages, and foreseeable consequential damages proximately resulting from the vendor's breach, also are recoverable.

Because the sum of direct, consequential, and incidental damages resulting from a breach of a CPE contract may be extremely high, vendors will insist upon limitations on the user's remedies for breach of any warranty. The UCC allows vendors to contractually prescribe the remedies available to a user for breach of the vendor's obligations.[93] However, unless the prescribed remedy is expressly agreed upon as the exclusive remedy, resort to it by a user is optional.[94] Moreover, if an exclusive or limited remedy fails of its essential purpose, a user may recover all of the remedies provided by the UCC for breach of a warranty.[95] One recent decision held that if a limited or exclusive remedy fails of its essential purpose, otherwise validly disclaimed consequential damages are recoverable.[96] "Repair or replace" warranties, which are common in CPE form contracts, should be held to fail of their essential purpose if the vendor is unable or unwilling to make the equipment or system perform the warranted function within a reasonable time.[97]

Vendors also may limit or exclude their liability for consequential damages, unless the limitation or exclusion is determined to be unconscionable.[98] In the sale of "consumer goods," the limitation of consequential damages for personal injury is prima facie unconscionable.[99] Arguably, CPE purchased primarily for use in a business or profession is not "consumer goods" under the UCC,[100] and,

---

[90] *Id*. § 2-714(2).

[91] *See generally* J. WHITE & R. SUMMERS, *supra* note 3, § 10-2 at 377-383.

[92] U.C.C. § 2-714(1) (1977).

[93] *Id*. § 2-719(1)(a).

[94] *Id*. § 2-719(1)(b).

[95] *Id*. § 2-719(2). *See, e.g.*, Ford Motor Co. v. Mayes, 575 S.W.2d 480 (Ky. Ct. App. 1978).

[96] *See, e.g.*, RRX Industries, Inc. v. Lab-Con, Inc., 772 F.2d 543 (9th Cir. 1985). *But see* Chatlos Systems, Inc. v. Nat'l Cash Register Corp., 635 F.2d 1081 (1980), *cert. dismissed*, 457 U.S. 1112 (1982). (Separate disclosure of consequential damages is not invalidated unless unconsciousable under U.C.C. § 2-719(3).).

[97] *See* Chatlos Systems, Inc., 635 F.2d at 1085.

[98] U.C.C. § 2-719(3) (1977).

[99] *Id*.

[100] The UCC defines "consumer goods" as goods that are used or bought for use primarily for personal, family or household purposes. U.C.C. §§ 2-103(3), 9-109(1) (1977).

therefore, vendors may disclaim liability for personal injury. Disclaimers and limitations of liability for consequential economic loss usually are upheld.[101] Finally, some commentators suggest that the UCC precludes sellers who warrant their goods from so limiting the buyer's remedies as to deprive the buyer of the "substantial value of the bargain."[102] As these commentators read the UCC and the cases interpreting it, sellers must provide buyers at least a "fair quantum of remedy" for breach of the seller's obligations or their disclaimers will be struck down.[103]

Counsel must carefully evaluate the proposed exclusive remedies that are to be incorporated in the express warranty provisions. The provisions should set out response times for both emergency and routine problems. Emergency and routine malfunctions must be defined, as must response time, and the warranty provisions should describe any penalties for failure to meet response times.

The parties might also include a "backup" remedy in the warranty provisions. As courts continue to strike limited remedy provisions from contracts because they fail their essential purpose, vendors should become more willing to allow users to rescind after acceptance. Users should demand that vendors agree to take back CPE that fails to meet performance benchmarks after a reasonable number of attempts, and to refund all or a substantial portion of the purchase price. From a vendor's standpoint, such a backup remedy may preclude the recovery of otherwise properly disclaimed consequential damages in the event that the exclusive remedies are determined to have failed of their essential purpose.[104] From the user's standpoint, such provisions are added assurance that he or she will receive the benefit of the bargain.

Finally, wherever relevant, users should consider negotiating for what is becoming known as a "Part 68 Warranty." Part 68 of the regulations promulgated by the FCC prescribes technical interface specifications for CPE that will be connected to the public telephone network.[105] The "Part 68 Warranty" should require the vendor to warrant the continuing compliance of the CPE with the interface requirements of Part 68 of the FCC regulations.

---

[101] B. CLARK & C. SMITH, THE LAW OF PRODUCT WARRANTIES ¶ 8.04[3][a] at 8-65 (1984).

[102] See generally id. ¶ 8.04[3][b] at 8-65 to -68.

[103] Id.

[104] See Garden State Food Distrib., Inc. v. Sperry Rand Corp., 512 F. Supp. 975 (D.N.J. 1981) (clause in computer lease purchase agreement providing for recovery of all charges paid by buyer if seller failed to repair or replace defective parts upheld despite buyer's contention that the "repair or replace" remedy failed of its essential purpose); Computerized Radiological Serv., Inc. v. Snytex Corp., 595 F. Supp. 1495 (E.D.N.Y. 1984), aff'd in part, rev'd in part, 786 F.2d 72 (2d Cir. 1986) (clause in contract limiting recovery for breach of warranty to purchase price affords plaintiff adequate remedy if "repair or replace" remedy fails of essential purpose). But see RRX Industries, Inc. v. Lab-Con, Inc., 772 F.2d 543 (9th Cir. 1985) (consequential damages recoverable when limited "repair or replace" warranty failed of its essential purpose, notwithstanding a clause in the contract limiting damages for breach of the contract to the software purchase price).

[105] 47 C.F.R. § 68.1-.506 (1985).

15.5 DRAFTING WARRANTIES AND DISCLAIMERS UNDER THE MAGNUSON-MOSS ACT

The Magnuson-Moss Act affects warranties made with respect to some CPE. The Act does not preempt the UCC warranty provisions, but it does have a significant impact upon "suppliers" and "warrantors" of "consumer products." The Act defines a "supplier" as "any person engaged in the business of making a consumer product directly or indirectly available to consumers."[106] A "warrantor" is "any supplier or other person who gives or offers a written warranty or who is or may be obligated under an implied warranty."[107] Most, if not all, vendors will be suppliers or warrantors under the Act with respect to any CPE marketed which qualifies as a "consumer product."

The Act defines a "consumer product" as "any tangible personal property which is distributed in commerce and which is normally used for personal, family or household purposes. . . ."[108] In determining whether an item is a "consumer product" under the Act, "the percentage of sales or the use to which a product is put by an individual buyer is not determinative."[109] According to the rules promulgated by the Federal Trade Commission, ambiguity is to be resolved in favor of coverage under the Magnuson-Moss Act.[110] Under these rules, CPE that is designed and marketed for use both in business and in the home probably will qualify as "consumer products."[111]

The Magnuson-Moss Act, and the regulations promulgated thereunder, govern the contents and effect of written warranties made with respect to "consumer products." The Act does not require any vendor to make a written warranty. However, vendors who qualify as "warrantors" must comply with specific disclosure requirements in drafting their warranty provisions. Moreover, the Act substantially limits a supplier's ability to disclaim or modify the UCC implied warranties if the supplier makes a written warranty or enters a service contract with respect to "consumer product" CPE.

With respect to all CPE that qualifies as "consumer products," the warrantor must disclose "fully and conspicuously . . . in simple and readily understood

---

[106] 15 U.S.C.A. § 2301(4) (West 1982).
[107] *Id.* § 2301(5).
[108] *Id.* § 2301(1).
[109] 16 C.F.R. § 700.1(a) (1986). *See* Business Modeling Techniques, Inc. v. Gen. Motors Corp., 123 Misc.2d 605, 474 N.Y.S.2d 258 (Sup. Ct. 1984) (automobile was consumer product, notwithstanding the fact that it may have been used primarily for business purposes). *But see* Balser v. Cessna Aircraft Co., 512 F. Supp. 1217 (N.D. Ga. 1981) (determining factor should be the use to which the product actually is put by the purchaser); Richards v. Gen. Motors Corp., 461 So.2d 825 (Ala. Civ. App. 1984) (state law determines whether Act applies and, therefore, characterization depends upon the primary use by the individual buyer).
[110] 16 C.F.R. § 700.1(a) (1986).
[111] *See* Tandy Corp. v. Marymac Ind., Inc., 213 U.S.P.Q. 702, 705-06 (S.D. Tex. 1981) (even a small amount of "normal" consumer use is sufficient to make the entire product line subject to the Magnuson-Moss Act; held, Tandy TRS-80 microcomputer treated as a consumer product under the Act); *See also* 16 C.F.R. § 700.1(a) (1986).

language the terms and conditions of such warranty."[112] Furthermore, any written warranty made by a warrantor on a "consumer product" costing more than $15.00 must clearly and conspicuously indicate the following:

1. who is protected by the warranty, if enforceability is limited;
2. what is included and what is excluded from warranty coverage;
3. what the warrantor will do in the event of a defect, malfunction, or failure to conform, including the items or services that the warrantor will or will not pay for or provide;
4. the duration of the warranty and the commencement date, if different from the purchase date;
5. a step-by-step explanation of the procedure that the consumer must follow to obtain performance of any warranty obligation;
6. information regarding the availability of any informal dispute settlement mechanisms;
7. any limitations on the duration of implied warranties, accompanied by the statement, "Some states do not allow limitations on how long an implied warranty lasts, so the above limitation may not apply to you";
8. Any exclusions or limitation on incidental or consequential damages, accompanied by the statement, "Some states do not allow the exclusion or limitation of incidental or consequential damages, so the above limitation or exclusion may not apply to you."; and
9. The following statement: "This warranty gives you specific legal rights, and you may also have other rights which vary from state to state."[113]

The Act defines a "written warranty" as any written affirmation of fact or written promise made in connection with the sale of a consumer product, which promise or affirmation becomes a part of the basis of the bargain and either (a) relates to the nature of material or workmanship, affirming or promising that it is defect free, or (b) promises that the product will meet a specified level of performance over a specified period of time, or (c) in which the warrantor undertakes to refund, repair, replace, or take other remedial action if such product fails.[114] Certain vendors must make the terms of any written warranty on consumer products available to the user prior to the sale.[115] Vendors who are warrantors also must designate written warranties made respecting consumer products costing more than $10.00 as either "full" or "limited."[116]

The typical industry practice among CPE vendors is to refrain from granting warranties that qualify as "full" warranties under the Magnuson-Moss Act. A

[112] 15 U.S.C.A. § 2302(a) (West 1982).
[113] 16 C.F.R. § 701.3(a) (1986).
[114] 15 U.S.C.A. § 2301(6) (West 1982).
[115] Id. § 2302(b)(1)(A); see generally 16 C.F.R. § 702 (1986).
[116] 15 U.S.C.A. §2303(a) (West 1982).

warranty designated as "full" must meet the federal minimum standards for warranties set out in the Act. Under a full warranty, the warrantor must remedy any defect, malfunction or failure to conform with the warranty within a reasonable time and without charge.[117] The warrantor may not disclaim nor limit the duration of any implied warranties,[118] and may only exclude or limit consequential damages if such exclusion or limitation conspicuously appears on the face of the warranty.[119] After a reasonable number of attempts to remedy defects or malfunctions in the CPE, a warrantor making a full warranty must allow the customer to elect a refund or a replacement of the product.[120] The warrantor may not impose any duty other than notification upon the user as a condition to the warrantor's performance under the warranty unless the warrantor can demonstrate such additional duties are reasonable.[121] Any warranty designated by a supplier as a "full" warranty shall be deemed to incorporate these federal minimum standards for warranties.[122] In addition, designating a warranty that does not meet these federal minimum standards for warranties as a "full" warranty is a violation of the Act.[123]

Possibly the most significant impact of the Magnuson-Moss Act on CPE acquisitions is its effect on a vendor's ability to disclaim implied warranties. A supplier who makes a "written warranty" on any CPE that is a consumer product or who enters a "service contract" for the CPE within 90 days of its sale may not disclaim the implied warranties of fitness for a particular purpose and merchantability,[124] but may only limit their duration to that of the express written warranty if such duration is reasonable and is set forth in clear and unmistakable language prominently displayed on the face of the warranty.[125] A supplier enters a "service contract" if he or she contracts in writing to perform maintenance or repair services on a consumer product over a fixed period of time or for a specified duration.[126] Any attempted disclaimer, modification, or limitation of the implied warranty in violation of these requirements is ineffective under state law[127] and may also subject the supplier to punitive damages in a suit brought by a damaged consumer.[128]

Failure to comply with the requirements of the Magnuson-Moss Act is a violation of 15 U.S.C. § 45(a)(1) (proscribing unfair methods of competition and

---

[117] *Id.* § 2304(a)(1).
[118] *Id.* §§ 2304(a)(2), 2308(a).
[119] *Id.* § 2304(a)(3).
[120] *Id.* § 2304(a)(4).
[121] *Id.* § 2304(b)(1).
[122] *Id.* § 2304(e).
[123] *Id.* §§ 2303(a)(2), 2310(b).
[124] *Id.* § 2308(a).
[125] *Id.* § 2308(b).
[126] *Id.* § 2301(8).
[127] *Id.* § 2308(c).
[128] *See* In re General Motors Corp. Engine Interchange Litigation, 594 F.2d 1106 (7th Cir. III. 1979), *cert. denied*, 444 U.S. 870 (1979). *But see* Feinstein v. Firestone Tire & Rubber Co., 535 F. Supp. 595 (D.C.N.Y. 1982).

unfair and deceptive acts or practices), and may be redressed by Federal Trade Commission action or by the consumer in a private action.[129] The Act authorizes actions by the Federal Trade Commission and the Attorney General to obtain temporary restraining orders or preliminary injunctions without bond in order to restrain any warrantor from making a "deceptive warranty" with respect to a consumer product or to restrain any person from failing to comply with, or from violating, the Act.[130] The Commission must file a complaint under 15 U.S.C. § 45 within ten days to prevent dissolution of the order or injunction.[131] A consumer who is damaged by a violation of the Act or by a vendor's failure to comply with a written warranty, implied warranty, or service contract may sue in state or federal court.[132] Warrantors may require consumers to resort to an informal dispute settlement procedure prior to commencing a civil action under the Act.[133] A consumer who prevails in a civil action may recover his or her costs and expenses, including attorneys fees, reasonably incurred in the prosecution of the suit.[134] In addition, consumers may bring class actions for failure to comply with any obligation under any written or implied warranty, or under a service contract.[135]

The Magnuson-Moss Act may prove to be a significant body of law in the deregulated telecommunications market-place. Although the Act has been in effect since 1975, plaintiff's attorneys are just beginning to discover the usefulness of the Act.[136] To the extent that the Act applies to CPE acquisitions, a user may have more favorable remedies under the Act than under the UCC.[137] One court has held that a consumer need not show privity in order to sue a warrantor for breach of warranty under the Act.[138] A user may disregard disclaimers or limitations of UCC implied warranties that violate the Act and sue the vendor for breach of the implied warranties.[139] The Act also makes suit for breach of warranty more feasible by allowing consumers to recover attorneys' fees and by authorizing suit in federal court.

The applicability of the Magnuson-Moss Act to CPE is an important issue that remains largely unaddressed. As of this writing, one court has applied the

---

[129] 15 U.S.C.A. § 2310(c)(1) (West 1982).
[130] *Id.*
[131] *Id.*
[132] *Id.* § 2310(d)(1).
[133] *Id.* § 2310(a)(3).
[134] *Id.* § 2310(d)(2).
[135] *Id.* § 2310(e). *But see id.* § 2310(d)(3) (No claim may be brought by a consumer in federal district court if the amount in controversy of any individual claim is less than the sum or value of $25.00, the amount in controversy is less than the sum or value of $50,000, counting all claims in the suit, or in a class action, the number of named plaintiff's is less than 100.)
[136] *See* Bixby, *Judicial Interpretation of the Magnuson-Moss*, 22 AM. BUS. L.J. 125, 125 (1984).
[137] *See generally* Smith, *The Magnuson-Moss Act: Turning the Tables on Caveat Emptor*, 13 CAL. W.L. REV. 391 (1977).
[138] *See* Ventura v. Ford Motor Co., 180 N.J. Super. 45, _____ , 433 A.2d 801, 808-11 (1981). *But see* Feinstein v. Firestone Tire & Rubber Co., 535 F. Supp. at 605 n. 13.
[139] *See id.* at 808, 809-10.

Magnuson-Moss Act to the sale of personal computers.[140] A determination that additional items of CPE constitute "consumer products" under the Act will enhance considerably the user's position *vis-à-vis* the CPE vendor. Although the Act arguably was not intended to protect buyers who have sufficient bargaining power to negotiate warranty provisions with sellers, counsel should assume that the Act applies to acquisitions of CPE until court decisions indicate otherwise.

15.6 DRAFTING PBX AND PABX ACQUISITION CONTRACTS

Procurement of large interconnect telephone systems is a highly complex undertaking that is in many ways similar to a construction project. Because a PBX (or PABX) must be constructed on the user's premises before any acceptance testing can be done, contracting for PBXs and PABXs involves elements of construction contracting, software licensing, and major equipment procurement contracting. Moreover, purchase and implementation of the system may take as long as two years. In negotiating and drafting the PBX or PABX acquisition contract, counsel for the user must consider a number of special issues in addition to those already discussed.

15.6.1 The System Description and Implementation Schedule

Counsel, and the other negotiating team members, should devote particular attention to the system descriptions contained in the RFP and the final contract documents. Painstaking time and effort devoted to development of a RFP will yield substantial benefits later. Preparing a thorough RFP for a large PBX (or PABX) system should take three to six months. The RFP should include a functional description of all PBX (PABX) features desired, including system capacity and performance specifications. The RFP also should specify any other features that might affect the system price. For instance, the RFP should describe the installation requirements and the desired expandability, and should include the user's warranty requirements, maintenance requirements, desired maintenance response times, and the target cutover date. Drafting a detailed RFP also enables the user to compare competing bids on an "applies to apples" basis.

A comprehensive description of the system is equally important in the final procurement contract document. Only by including the system specifications in the contract will the user assure himself or herself of receiving that for which he or she bargained. Counsel should incorporate both the RFP and the vendor's response in the contract by reference, along with all hardware and software feature manuals.

In order to assure timely installation and cutover of the new system, counsel should view the system implementation conceptually as a construction project. The vendor and user should agree upon and specify project milestones and

---

[140] Tandy Corp., v. Marymac Ind., Inc., 213 U.S.P.Q. 702 (S.D. Tex. 1981).

corresponding completion dates. Contract payments should be tied to the vendor's timely performance in accordance with each project milestone.[141] As in a construction contract, the user should "hold-back" an appreciable percentage of payment until the system is accepted. The contract also should specify liquidated damages on a per diem basis for failure to meet project milestones.[142] Suggested milestones include installation of the switch, installation of the PBX (PABX) station, system cutover, and system acceptance.[143]

15.6.2 PBX/PABX Acceptance Test Provisions

As discussed above, a critical element of any acquisition contract is the acceptance test provision. This is especially true in a PBX or PABX acquisition contract. The functional specifications provided in the RFP should be used to design acceptance tests for system performance and reliability. Because cutover is not easily reversed and the system must properly interface with common carriers' telecommunications lines and equipment, pre-cutover acceptance testing should be extensive.[144] Users should design off-line tests that simulate actual system traffic in order to test all functions of the system, as well as the total capacity of the system.[145] Only after successful completion of off-line testing should on-line acceptance testing begin.[146] The on-line test period should be long enough to allow the system to negotiate a full range of normal and peak load traffic.[147]

The remedy provisions of the acceptance test provisions are particularly important in a PBX or PABX contract. Since substantial "progress" payments will have been made before acceptance testing can be begun, the user lacks the leverage he or she would have if the entire purchase price were withheld until acceptance. Consequently, the acceptance test provisions must prescribe detailed, result-oriented remedies for failure of the system to pass any acceptance tests, coupled with some guarantee that the user may recover all payments made upon ultimate system failure.

Remedies should be tailored to the user's system needs. The contract might grant the vendor an extended cure period, during which the vendor' pays increasing liquidated damages as the delay in acceptance continues, and reserving to the user a right to terminate the contact and receive a complete refund upon the vendor's failure to conform the system within a prescribed time.[148] Alterna-

---

[141] *See* Wallace, *Contracting for Interconnect Telephone Systems: Some Do's and Don'ts*, TELEMATICS, July, 1984, at 26, 27.

[142] *Id.*

[143] *Id.*

[144] Rosenbaum, *Busy Signals—Telecommunications Contracting Demands Special Approaches*, COMPUTER LAW STRATEGIST, Nov. 1984, at 1, 4.

[145] *Id.*

[146] *Id.*

[147] *See id.*

[148] *See* Wallace, *supra* note 141 at 29.

tively, the contract might provide the user with a right to rescind the contract, thereby revesting title to the equipment in the vendor.[149] This right to rescind might be drafted as a "put option," in which the seller agrees to buy back the system at an agreed price equal to the amounts paid towards the purchase price upon the system's failure to pass the acceptance tests. By drafting the user's remedy for acceptance test failure as a put option, counsel will remove all doubts regarding the disposition of all parts of the system upon failure. If the contract provides for termination by either party, it should require the vendor to continue system operation and support until either cutover to a new system or return to service by a common carrier.[150] Vendors should be allowed to set-off a reasonable amount for the temporary use of the defective system from any refund due the user upon termination.

15.6.3 Title and Risk of Loss Provisions

Because of the typically long interim period between delivery of PBX (PABX) equipment to the user and actual acceptance of the system, title to the equipment and risk of loss of the equipment may present negotiating dilemmas. Absent express contractual agreement, title passes from the vendor to the user (1) at the time and place of shipment under a shipment contract, and (2) at the delivery of the goods to their destination under a destination contract.[151] When the contract of sale requires the seller to install the goods, title may not pass until installation.[152] PBX (PABX) vendors may prefer that title to the equipment not pass until most or all of the purchase price will have been paid under the progress payment schedule. On the other hand, users may probably desire title to equipment early, especially with respect to those items that have been installed and have become a fixture on their premises.

Risk of loss provisions present a similar dilemma. Vendors will not want to insure equipment installed on the user's premises until acceptance, but will bargain to shift risk of loss to the user on delivery to a common carrier or to the user's site. Users may prefer that risk of loss remain on the vendor through installation and acceptance testing.

Counsel for users might resolve the dilemma by suggesting that title to each item of equipment passes to the user upon installation, subject to an UCC Article 9 security interest in the equipment to secure payment of all "held back" amounts. Preferably, risk of loss should remain with the vendor until acceptance. However, counsel might agree that it pass as early as delivery to the user's site, but no earlier. Although the availability of rejection and revocation of acceptance under the UCC is unaffected by the title to the goods,[153] counsel should specify

---

[149] *See id.*
[150] *See id.*
[151] U.C.C. § 2-401(2) (1977).
[152] *See* 3 R. ANDERSON, UNIFORM COMMERCIAL CODE § 2-401(4) (3d ed. 1983).
[153] U.C.C. § 2-401 (1977).

clearly when the risk of loss and title to the equipment pass in order to avoid any uncertainties should the system fail acceptance testing.

15.6.4 Reconfiguration Provision

PBX and PABX acquisition agreements should include a reconfiguration clause. A reconfiguration provision enables the user to add features and upgrade the equipment during the period between the contract execution and system cutover. Typical standard vendor contracts contain configuration provisions that limit allowable additions or deletions by dollar value or some percentage of the contract price.[154] Frequently, vendor contracts also include a date beyond which configuration changes are not allowed (a "firm configuration date").[155] Counsel should negotiate for maximum allowable additions or deletions under the reconfiguration provision. Counsel should also seek the ability to make additional changes after the firm configuration date, subject to the payment of a reasonable penalty.

15.6.5 Technical Data Access Provisions

Users must recognize problems that may arise should the PBX (PABX) vendor discontinue adequate system maintenance and support or go out of business. If the vendor fails to maintain the PBX (PABX), the user will need operating manuals, schematic diagrams, maintenance flow charts, as well as software source code, in order to enable third parties to maintain and repair the system. However, such documents contain valuable proprietary information of the PBX (PABX) vendor.

Maintenance of the system software presents particularly difficult issues. Because most vendors protect software under trade secret law as well as copyright law, vendors license software in object code (machine-readable) form only and subject to strict confidentiality covenants and restrictions.[156] These restrictions typically apply to software documentation as well as code.[157]

Although some commentators suggest that users should contract for access to technical manuals and software source code in the event of a vendor's insolvency or failure to maintain the system,[158] few PBX or PABX vendors will even negotiate entrusting their valuable technical manuals or source code to a user or an escrow agent. In addition, vendors constantly update and change system software, and as a result, the cost of keeping the user's version (or escrow version) updated would be prohibitively high. Consequently, most vendors will

---

[154] Jarrett, *A Practical Perspective on PBX Contracts*, DATA COMMUNICATIONS, Nov. 1986, at 171, 1972.

[155] *Id.*

[156] *See generally* F. COOPER, LAW AND THE SOFTWARE MARKETER: HOW TO DEVELOP A LEGAL PROTECTION GAME PLAN (to be published 1987).

[157] *Id.*

[158] Jarrett, *supra* note 154, at 176; Wallace, *supra* note 141, at 30-31.

be unable to contract for access to source code or other technical data, but instead will be forced to rely on the vendor's stability and reputation.

If a user has a large amount of bargaining power or if he or she is dealing with a relatively small vendor, the user may be able to negotiate software code access in the form of a source code escrow or trust arrangement. Source code escrows have enjoyed more prevalent use, but commentators recently have questioned their utility in bankruptcy.[159] Arguably, a source code escrow is an executory contract. Because the source code held in escrow belongs to the vendor, the trustee in bankruptcy may be able to reject the contract and prevent the user from obtaining the source code out of escrow—a result contrary to the intention of both parties.[160] To avoid this possibility, users should consider using a source code trust agreement. Because a trust agreement vests title to the source code in the trust upon execution, the trustee agreement arguably is not executory and therefore is not voidable by the trust in bankruptcy.[161] It is doubtful that the automatic stay provisions of the bankruptcy code would preclude the trustee from releasing the source code upon the vendor's bankruptcy.[162] Therefore, the source code trust is the preferable arrangement with vendors who are willing to give access to software code.

In the more likely event that the PBX (PABX) vendor is unwilling to grant access to software code and other technical data, the user must rely on well-drafted maintenance provisions and the vendor's service record to assure the continued utility of the system. Large users can bargain for on-site maintenance personnel to assure them of virtually uninterrupted PBX (PABX) service. The problem of insuring the user's access to source code and other data in the event of the vendor's insolvency is a much more perplexing one with no satisfactory solutions. Perhaps the best strategy is to deal with an established vendor that has shown a strong commitment to the PBX (PABX) market, paying special attention to the vendor's commitment to maintenance and support of its installations in the user's geographic area.

15.6.7 Warranty and Maintenance Provisions

Warranty and maintenance provisions are crucial elements of any PBX of PABX contract. The well-drafted PBX (PABX) acquisition contract will combine comprehensive warranty provisions with post-warranty maintenance provisions which, in effect, assure the user of a specified level of performance for as long as the user owns the system. Counsel should not accept "reasonable efforts" warranties or maintenance provisions, but should insist upon vendor performance

---

[159] *See* Gilburne, *The Use of Escrows for Source Code and Technical Design Specifications in OEM Transactions*, THE COMPUTER LAWYER, May 1984, at 1, 5 (1984); Wallace, *supra* note 140, at 30.

[160] *See id.; See also* 11 U.S.C.A. § 365 (West 1979 & Supp. 1986).

[161] *See generally* F. COOPER, *supra* note 156.

[162] *See id.;* 11 U.S.C.A. § 362(a) (West 1979 & Supp. 1986).

warranties, compliance with which is measured in terms of data transmission rates, measured response times, message through-put, error rates, protocol conversions, adherence to specific industry standards, and precise response times.[163] The maintenance provisions should also require the vendor to provide new releases of the system software as they are released. Vendors should warrant that the CPE will continue to comply with changing networks and interface standards.[164]

The response time guarantees contained in the warranty provision should apply to the vendor's maintenance obligations as well. In both warranty and maintenance provisions, emergency situations, such as those involving a loss of a defined significant percentage of call-carrying capacity, should require an immediate vendor response. Vendors should be afforded longer response times for routine system failures. Response time should be measured from the time the vendor is notified of a problem until the problem is remedied. The user should be entitled to liquidated damages on the vendor's failure to meet such response times.[165] Failure to meet response times for routine failure should not trigger liquidated damages.

In addition to performance warranties and maintenance provisions, the user should demand regulatory compliance warranties and intellectual property rights warranties. The vendor should warrant that the system complies with all federal and local regulations affecting the system, including local building and electrical codes, OSHA regulations, as well as the applicable portions of Title 47 of the Code of Federal Regulations.[166] Because many regulations impose obligations on the user as well as the manufacturer of CPE equipment, these warranties must not be overlooked.[167]

Users should also insist upon a warranty that no parts of the system infringe the intellectual property rights of any third party. As discussed above, the warranty should be accompanied by an indemnity provision, under which the vendor covenants to indemnify and hold harmless the user from all damages, including attorney fees and court costs, suffered by the user as a result of any *claims* of alleged infringement. The user should also demand that if his or her use of the system is enjoined because of an alleged infringement, the vendor will, within an agreed time, either (1) procure for the user rights to continue using the system or, (2) modify or replace the system so that it is no longer infringing. After any such modification or replacement, the system should meet or exceed the performance and reliability specifications set out in the performance warranty provisions.[168]

---

[163] Rosenbaum, *supra* note 144, at 4; Sapranov, Deregulation and Telecommunications Acquisition, SPECTRUM, Aug. 1985, at 1, 4.

[164] See *id*.

[165] *See* Wallace, *supra* note 141, at 31.

[166] 47 C.F.R. § 15, 68 (1986); Wallace, *supra* note 141, at 31.

[167] Wallace, *supra* note 141, at 31.

[168] *Id*. at 32.

15.6.8 Arbitration Clause

Finally, counsel for the user should consider including an arbitration clause in the acquisition contract. Litigation is always a slow, agonizing, and expensive process. Moreover, courts of law are poorly suited for resolving disputes involving telecommunications issues. However, counsel also should consider the shortcomings of arbitration to resolve disputes. In most of today's arbitration matters, as in most litigation, the parties desire to take discovery prior to arbitration. Because there are no rules to govern such discovery, disputes regarding discovery may remain unresolved at the arbitration hearing. Also, there is no tribunal to force the parties to proceed to arbitration by a specific date. Finally, some attorneys believe that since the parties often must resort to a court of law to enforce or escape the arbitration award, they might just as well have started out there. If counsel chooses to include an arbitration clause, it should address each of these problems. Any arbitration clause also should stipulate the method for choosing the panel of arbitrators and the rules to be followed. The contract should provide that the arbitrators' decision will be binding on the parties.

15.7 CONCLUSION: CONTRACTING TO ALLOCATE RISK

As a result of the deregulation of the telecommunications industry, corporate counsel can expect to be called upon to assist his or her clients in large-scale acquisitions of CPE. Moreover, as information management becomes increasingly important to all businesses and professions, small- and medium-sized users will be entering the nontariffed CPE marketplace. Consequently, today's corporate counsel must recognize and address the respects in which drafting a CPE contract differs from the drafting of other major acquisition contracts.

As with any other acquisition transaction, the primary focus of the contract document is the express allocation of risks between the parties. Vendors limit their risks by inserting favorable acceptance provisions and limited repair or replace warranty provisions in their standard form contracts. Vendors typically disclaim all implied warranties and limit the user's remedies for breach of any warranties made. Because they are not insurers, vendors contend, their pricing is not structured to enable them to expose themselves to unlimited liability for incidental and consequential damages resulting from CPE failures.

Unfortunately, the highly technical nature of CPE requires users to rely upon the vendor's skill and judgment in selecting suitable equipment. The deregulation of the CPE marketplace means that users are no longer protected by regulatory agency rulings and filings. Users can ill afford to bear the risks of CPE failure and the accompanying disasterous consequential damages. The vitality of dependable telecommunications equipment and services to modern-day business requires that a workable compromise be reached on these issues.

If a vendor and the user cannot agree on the allocation of risk in large-scale CPE acquisitions, counsel should suggest shifting the risk to third-party insurance carriers. Computer lawyers presently counsel parties in high exposure computer related acquisition contracts to shift liability using insurance specifically tailored for the computer industry. Similarly, the parties to a CPE acquisition should consider comprehensive general liability coverage to insure against ordinary lawsuits, accompanied by professional liability insurance to assure against loss caused by errors and omissions. Property insurance contracts might be amended to include loss of data as a covered loss. Only by shifting certain risks inherent in a large-scale CPE procurement transaction to third-party insurance carriers who are equipped to handle such risks may enlightened vendors and users strike a deal that is not only acceptable, but economically feasible, to both parties.

Chapter 16

Negotiating Shared Tenant Service Agreements: Protecting the Building Owner's Interests

HENRY D. LEVINE

Once a building owner knows what shared tenant services (STS) is and decides that he wants to offer it in his buildings, he must find a communications company that can manage or operate the business and negotiate the terms on which that company will come into the building. This article is about the last step—negotiating the agreement to protect the owner's interest.

There are three ways to organize a shared tenant service venture. The first, in which the building owner himself sponsors the offering was never very popular and has grown rarer with time. Most owners have (wisely) concluded that they are in the real estate business, not the communications business, and have not attempted to operate STS operations on their own. The other forms of organization—a joint venture between the owner and a communications company (a "provider"), and a "franchise" in which a provider offers STS service in a building in return for a fee or other consideration—are conceptually different but have become quite similar in practice. Even in a "franchise" environment, building owners want some control over the provider's activities and, increasingly, are "investing" in shared tenant services. Most STS agreements end up looking like "franchise" agreements, and that is the model used for this discussion.

The shared tenant service industry, in its modern form, is two to three years old. Some of the major companies now participating in the industry include RealCom (a subsidiary of IBM), Wang, Fairchild Industries, Electronic Office Centers of America (which is partially owned by Westinghouse), Telecom Plus, and Bell South Systems Technology. Two years ago the industry experienced its first major shake-out when ShareTech, a partnership of AT&T and United

---

*Used with permission of Henry D. Levine.

Technologies and one of the two largest and most active providers, was dissolved by its owners and left the business. An increasing number of major and minor communications companies are still actively looking for STS projects, but the demise of ShareTech has had a significant effect on the negotiating environment. In a marked change from two years ago, providers are no longer bidding against each other to build market share. Contract terms other than compensation have, however, become steadily more favorable to building owners. The smart building owner, who looks at STS primarily as a building amenity or enhancement whose value lies in faster lease-up and higher rents over the long term, can negotiate an STS agreement that will create a more attractive project, expose him to the least possible risk and produce a modest amount of direct income.

CONTRACT ISSUES

Shared tenant service agreements can run 40 pages or more, much of it fine print. The following, therefore, only highlights seven general issues about which building owners should be especially concerned.

First, a provider wants, and generally should be granted, the exclusive right to serve a building. The exclusivity that an owner is able to grant, however, is quite limited. Tenants must be allowed to shop freely for telecommunications equipment and services, and efforts to keep the local telephone company out or restrict its activities in a building are foolish and futile. Another aspect of a grant of exclusivity is its scope. Some providers will seek to broaden their rights of exclusivity by requesting a "franchise" on services that are unrelated to communications or data processing, (e.g., copying and temporary personnel). Granting a provider the exclusive right to provide such services is often bad for the building and providers can (and almost always will) live without it.

At the opposite end of the exclusivity issue, some building owners are interested in restricting an STS provider's right to provide STS in competing buildings within the same geographic area. Some providers will not give exclusivity of this kind because it ruins their (hoped-for) economies of scale. Others will, although they usually seek to minimize the scope and duration of such restrictions.

Second, developers and providers alike are frequently concerned about the scope of an STS offering, that is, what services will be provided. As a general rule, providers should only be *required* to offer telephone instruments connected to a full-featured PBX, access to local service, long distance service, and maintenance (including moves, adds and changes). Other additional services are usually optional, and the provider will offer them if he feels it is profitable to do so. The owner should obtain the right to require that such an additional service be offered if the owner is willing to pay the provider's net out-of-pocket costs of doing so, as well as the right to have a third party come into the building and offer such services if the provider is asked to do so but refuses. Some enhanced services, (e.g., mail and message centers), have become common. Others, notably video teleconferencing and shared data processing, are often promoted with great fanfare, but have rarely proven profitable and have not been included in most recent offerings.

A third key issue is developer control. The issue here is not control of the details of pricing or services *per se*, but of broader provider activity that can or will impact the building owner or his tenants. An STS agreement should include strict requirements that the provider obtain prior approval before making any structural changes to the building, do nothing that might disrupt building or tenant operations or put the owner in default under a lease or any other agreement, etc. The building owner should have the right to approve the provider's on-site personnel or to have unsatisfactory representatives of the provider transferred. Finally, good STS agreements incorporate firm performance standards, including maximum response times to requests for service.

Fourth, the term of STS agreements average ten years, although contracts as short as five years and as long as fifteen are not uncommon. More and more agreements include a specific provision for a short term renewal or extension near the end of the initial term of a contract, usually at the owner's option, if the provider has a major prospect but needs to sign an equipment lease or service agreement of five years or more in order to compete with alternative providers of service and equipment.

Fifth, although STS is not a major source of revenue to a building owner, compensation continues to be hotly negotiated. Few guidelines can be given because what a developer can get depends on many things, notably the desirability of a particular project (*i.e.*, its size, location, and tenant mix) and the owner's willingness to invest in communications-related infrastructure. Typical franchise or concession fees range from 1 to 3 percent of gross revenues and often include special provisions for long distance revenues and the exclusion of revenue from services that a provider may not be permitted to mark-up. Many agreements include a "sliding scale" that increases fees as a provider's gross revenues rise. This type of provision reduces the provider's overhead during the critical start up period and gives the building owner an added incentive to promote STS to tenants and prospective tenants.

The provider's space lease is closely related to the issue of compensation. Some providers seek free space, but most will lease a modest amount of space (*e.g.*, 1,000-2,000 square feet) at market rates with concessions typical of (or perhaps slightly better than) the market. Since rent payments on even a relatively small amount of space can equal or exceed expected concession fees, lease terms obviously have an impact on concession fee negotiations.

A key (and potentially contentious) side issue is the relationship of the lease terms to the STS agreement. Standard building leases contain a number of clauses that are unsuitable in an STS environment. For example, leases almost always prohibit tenants from running wire outside of their own space and include indemnification provisions that are often unacceptable to providers. One solution is to slog through the lease, modifying it as necessary. Another solution is to let provisions in the STS agreement control space used in connection with the provision of shared tenant services (including the provider's switch room) while using a lease to govern the provider's activities as a lessee of office space in the building.

Sixth, the issue of termination—often given short shrift in STS contracts—deserves attention.[1] No one wants to talk about divorce at a wedding, but it is essential that an STS agreement including provisions governing termination caused by a default by the building owner or the provider, destruction or condemnation of the building, regulatory problems, and the sale of the building to a purchaser who does not wish to continue offering STS or who wishes to change providers. Some providers seek the right to terminate a contract if, after a reasonable period (five years is common), it can't make a go of the business. The termination section of an STS agreement must include provisions outlining who will have control over the disposition of STS equipment and agreements and, as far as possible, the prices to be paid at termination for STS equipment (*e.g.*, tax basis, or fair market value as determined by an independent appraiser). Typically, there are two sets of terms depending upon who defaults or is responsible for termination. There must also be a provision mandating the continuation of service until a suitable replacement provider can be found. The priority here is maintaining service to tenants—if they lose telephone service because of a fight between a provider and the owner, STS will quickly become a liability, not an amenity.

Seventh, STS agreements should address issues of insurance, liability, and indemnification.[2] Reputable providers will readily agree to carry suitable amounts of insurance, but liability and indemnification have traditionally been strong points of contention between owners and providers. Citing data processing equipment contracts and local telephone company tariffs, providers seek to avoid liability for consequential damages suffered by the owner if a provider defaults. More importantly, some providers refuse to agree to indemnify a building owner if the owner is held liable because of the action or inaction of the provider in offering STS. The solution to this problem is to find a provider who will give adequate protection or, at the very least, to make sure that the provider includes in its agreements with tenants clear and complete language to the effect that the tenant's lease and its communications service agreement are separate and that the tenant will not under any circumstances hold the developer liable for inadequate or improper provision by the provider of STS. Some providers complain that this type of requirement will hurt their marketing efforts, but no responsible provider refuses to include such provisions.

---

[1] *See* Levine, "Crucial STS Contract Issues: Term and Termination." *Shared Tenant Services News*, March, 1986, pp 7-10.

[2] *See* Levine, "Indemnification by Shared Tenant Service Providers: a Trap for the Unwary Developer, "*Tenant Communications*, November, 1985, pp 4-5.

CONCLUSION

Many other issues can arise during the negotiation of an STS agreement, but the bottom line for building owners is that shared tenant services should enhance the prestige and leasability of their property, pose minimal risk, and present some prospect of producing direct income. Responsible providers willing to meet these requirements exist (although you wouldn't know it from their form contracts), and with enough lead time and diligence, building owners can secure STS agreements that are more than adequate to meet their needs.

STS is a new business, still in its embryonic phase. I have no doubt that as the industry matures contract terms will become more and more standard, and the very complicated negotiations which make this a legal "boutique business" will become more straightforward.

Chapter 17

Term and Termination in Shared Tenant Service Agreements

HENRY D. LEVINE

None of the clauses in a contract under which a communications company is to provide shared tenant services (STS) in an office building or other real estate project is more basic than the term (*i.e.*, duration) of the agreement. Basic, however, is not the same as simple. This article discusses the interests of real estate developers and communications companies in the term and related issues, and outlines the contract arrangements that have developed in the industry to address these concerns.

17.1 TERM

Shared tenant service agreements generally run five to fifteen years, with most clustering into the 8 to 12 year time frame. Those on the shorter end often include one or more options for periods of up to five years, exercisable by the developer, the provider, or both. There is usually a provision requiring notice of termination by one of the parties six months or a year prior to the end of the term, with an automatic one year renewal if notice is not given. That prevents either party from cancelling at the last minute, leaving its partner (and customers) in the lurch.

Five to fifteen years may seem long as commercial agreements go, though it is roughly comparable to the term of many large office leases. The length is dictated by the time required to sign up tenants in a project and to amortize the PBX and other equipment that the provider must install to offer service. Most pro formas for shared tenant service projects do not show breakeven cashflow until the third year or so, due to heavy upfront costs and the time required to sign up tenants. Overall project profitability is typically acceptable only over a period of seven years or more.

Used with permission of Henry D. Levine.

The "special case" on term is the multi-phase project, such as an office park to be developed over the course of a decade. There is no easy way to address the length of an STS agreement covering such a project. Anything long enough to give the provider a "fair shot" at the completed project is likely to be much too long (*e.g.*, 20 years) for the first completed buildings. One possible solution is a contract covering the first building(s) only, with a clause providing that substantially similar contracts will be executed for subsequent buildings if specified criteria covering penetration and performance are met. The "master agreement's" economic terms must then be subject to renegotiation, at the developer's option, at a specified point—perhaps seven or ten years down the road—again with a presumption of renewal (albeit with renegotiated fee provisions) if the provider has met stated performance criteria.

17.2 MARKETING STS NEAR THE END OF THE CONTRACT TERM

After the actual length of the contract, the most important issue involving term is the problem of marketing to tenants in the later years of an agreement. Consider a ten year STS agreement executed in 1984 for a new 600,000 sq. ft. downtown office building. In 1990, a new anchor tenant moves into the project, leasing 150,000 sq. ft. The tenant was previously a Centrex customer, and does not therefore have CPE of its own. Obviously, the STS provider would like a shot at the tenant—a subscriber of this size can make or break a project. The problem is that the equipment portion of most STS tenant agreements—like the lease of a PBX and associated station equipment—typically runs five to seven years. Shorter lease terms are available, but the rates are much higher, and a provider has to be able to offer 5 year deals to compete with PBX manufacturers. Since it is 1990, the STS provider's franchise in our hypothetical building has only four years left to run. How then can he market to the new anchor tenant?

One possible answer is that he can't, and some STS agreements include a provision that no contract with any tenant will extend beyond the term of the agreement. Two years ago I was recommending such a provision. Given the 8-12 year length of most STS agreements the provider should be able to make its money even with such a clause. But it does present problems in the later years of a contract, particularly when major opportunities come along, such as a new anchor tenant). And a strict limitation can be counterproductive for the developer, threatening the commitment of the provider and thus the quality of service in the declining years of the agreement and reducing the developer's concession income.

One alternative is to allow the provider to negotiate an appropriate equipment contract with the tenant, including in it a provision for assignment of that contract to the landlord (or the provider's successor in the building) if the provider's "franchise" is terminated before the end of the contract term. That makes a sale at competitive rates theoretically possible, but it can create new issues. The equipment manufacturers from whom STS providers lease the equipment they offer may have a few choice words about the arrangement, for example. It may also increase tenant resistance, since the tenant will not be able to count on having the party with whom it contracted around to service its needs for life of the deal. Finally, it can create pressures on the landlord; if the agreement with the STS provider expires without renewal and (for whatever reason) no subsequent provider is brought in, the landlord may be obligated (legally or otherwise) to continue maintaining the PBX and providing access to network services to a subscribing tenant whose contract has not expired.

A third way to deal with this problem involves a contract clause that addresses marketing in the out years by specifying that the STS provider may ask the developer to extend the term of the agreement for a period long enough to serve a new tenant. The developer may grant or deny the requested extension; approval may be in the developer's sole discretion or may be "not unreasonably withheld" as the parties see fit. Of course, once the STS agreement is extended for one tenant, it is extended for all. What this clause therefore amounts to is a specialized and somewhat restricted short-term renewal option.

In the end, commercial realities will likely supersede contract negotiation in this area. If a shared tenant services agreement is going well and the parties are happy with each other, a way will be found to accommodate the late sign-up of a major customer, possibly by early renegotiation of the contract to extend it for seven to ten years. Conversely, if the parties are not happy with each other, e.g., because the project has not gone well and penetration is low, marketing efforts are likely to be minimal in the later years of the contract, whatever its provisions for renewal or extension.

17.3 WHAT HAPPENS TO THE SYSTEM WHEN THE CONTRACT ENDS?

A good STS agreement includes not one termination clause, but three or four. Either party must be allowed to terminate the agreement in the event of a material breach or default by the other. Beyond that, there should be provision for termination of an agreement in the event of destruction, condemnation or sale of the underlying project. Issues such as continuation of service while another provider is found, purchase of the provider's equipment; assumption of lease and tenant obligations, compensation to the provider in the event of termination; and liability to tenants before and after the termination should be addressed during negotiation of an STS agreement. These issues should not be left to be "worked out" if and when the need arises. In the heat of a dispute in which termination looks increasingly likely, neither party is likely to focus on the need to provide continuous, high quality service. Indeed, service—and the tenants who need it—can become little more than a bargaining chip. When that happens everyone—especially the developer—loses.

Two crucial issues in any termination are payment to the provider for its switch and other equipment, and whether the purchase of the system by the developer (or the provider's successor, if there is one) is to be at the option of the developer or the provider. These issues are squarely presented in a "natural termination," *i.e.*, the end of the relationship due to expiration of an unrenewed STS agreement. While the issue may well be moot if the business has been unprofitable, if the provider is making money the developer and provider are likely to have very different views of the world. The provider sees a going business that it developed over a decade (more or less) being summarily shut down for what will inevitably be viewed as "no good reason." He feels entitled to be paid the "going concern" value of the enterprise, *i.e.*, its capitalized earnings. The developer, on the other hand, sees something that closely resembles the expiration of a long term lease, and views the provider like a tenant who has no interest in the location at the end of its lease and should, indeed, be required to surrender all "tenant improvements" to the landlord without compensation of any kind. At most, the developer may feel that the provider is entitled to the tax basis of the equipment in place, which is likely to be very small by the close of the agreement term.

The point is not that either of these positions is correct—though as an attorney who generally represents developers I incline to the view that a provider who signed up for a fifteen year franchise should have reasonably expected to make his profits over the life of the agreement, and is entitled (at most) to the option of removing the equipment or selling it to the developer for salvage value at the end of the term. Rather, the point is that the time to think about termination is when the initial agreement is being negotiated and not ten years later, lest the building's and the provider's reputations suffer when tenants hear (or start) rumors that they are about to lose their telephone service.

One way to reduce (but not eliminate) agony at termination is to have the developer take title to those portions of the system best described as fixtures, either by paying for their installation or being given them upon termination of the agreement for any reason. If the developer owns the distribution frames, conduit, risers, and switch room improvements the chance of interrupted service is substantially reduced, and haggling over system value can be ameliorated if not eliminated.

17.4 CONCLUSION

Most of the time spent negotiating an STS agreement is devoted to compensation, indemnification, and marketing issues (the services to be offered, cooperation in advertising, etc.) The term of the agreement, and events that will occur close to or at the end of that term, may seem mundane and not worth the time and trouble required to resolve them. To the contrary, both providers and developers must be aware that he who ignores these issues at the birth of a deal may be haunted by them at its death.

Chapter 18

Indemnification in Shared
Tenant Services Contracts*

HENRY D. LEVINE

The indemnification clause—sometimes called the "hold harmless" clause—in a shared tenant services (STS) agreement between a communications company and a developer is the section of the contract in which the communications company (the provider) promises to defend any claims against the developer or landlord arising out of the provision of STS in the landlord's building, and to pay any damages awarded (or settlements reached) as a result of such claims. Because the major providers of STS reject full indemnification, the issue has become one of the most important in the industry.

To understand indemnification you have to understand the developer's view of shared tenant services. To most landlords, STS is an "extra"—an amenity that may marginally increase lease-up rates and rents, and could generate very modest direct revenues, i.e., ten to 25 cents per square foot. Typically, a developer makes no cash investment in the provision of STS; sometimes he puts in or pays for conduit, riser cable, and distribution frames. In short, the developer does not view himself as being in the telecommunications business, any more than allowing a newspaper stand in his lobby puts him in the publishing business. He is in the real estate business, and that is where he intends to stay.

18.1 CONSEQUENTIAL DAMAGES

Indemnification clauses assure that the risks of providing STS will be borne by the provider, rather than the developer. They are important because of the remote (but not infinitesimal) threat of consequential damages, a term that is best

384 Indemnification in Shared Tenant Services Contracts

explained through an example. Suppose Merrill Lynch has a branch in an office building in which STS is offered, and subscribes to the service. The phones go dead for three days, and the office loses $100,000 in commissions. The *direct* damages are the costs of repairing the system and/or obtaining alternative service in the interim. The consequential damages are the $100,000 in lost commissions.

Consequential damages are not a problem for regulated telephone companies. Their rates and terms of services are governed by tariffs filed with state and federal regulators which, once approved have the force of law. Those tariffs always limit telephone company liability, and specifically disclaim any liability for consequential damages. The courts have repeatedly upheld such limitations, often on a theory that if consequential damages are awarded, the general body of ratepayers (i.e., the public at large) will end up footing the bill. If your phones go down for a week, you get a refund equal to one week's local service charges, and not a penny more.

Shared tenant services providers, however, are not typically utilities—they have resisted classification and regulation as such—so they don't get the benefits of the tariff shield. STS providers are not powerless to limit their liability for consequential damages—like computer and telephone equipment manufacturers, they can (and do) put language in their contracts with subscribers that limits their liability to direct damages (sometimes less) and expressly disavows any liability for incidental or consequential damages. If asked—and savvy developers always ask—providers will also insert express provisions in their contracts with tenants to the effect that the building owner is *not* a party to the contract and will not be liable in any way for failure to deliver adequate service or equipment.[1]

Most of the time, language like that discourages tenants from suing, much less collecting, on a consequential damages claim. But there have been few if any) cases to date, and the industry is gripped by the nagging fear that in a sufficiently egregious case in a pro-plaintiff state (like California) a court or jury will disregard contractual language and award consequential damages to a small, poor tenant whose business has been damaged (perhaps fatally) by a large, wealthy communications company. The risk is very small but the potential liability is enormous, and cannot be insured against. Landlords share in this risk because like it or not they are viewed by tenants subscribing to shared tenant services as co-providers of the service or at least agents of the provider.[2]

---

[1] It is also a good idea to ask the provider to insert in his contracts with tenants a clause to the effect that the contract for telephone services is separate and apart from the tenant's lease, and the tenant expressly agrees not to withhold rent if telephone services are unsatisfactory or regard the provider's failure to deliver adequate service as a constructive eviction.

[2] Indeed, most shared tenant services agreements expressly provide that the developer will arrange for his leasing agents to promote the service, and will cooperate in making it available to his tenants.

18.2 LEVELS OF INDEMNIFICATION

Hence the need for indemnification and the current dispute. There are four levels of indemnification, the providers agree to insure the developer against any liability of any kind arising out of the provision of STS. Less favorable to the developer, but usually acceptable, is an indemnification clause that excludes from the "insurance" any liability flowing from the landlord's negligence, breach of contract, or other wrongdoing. Still less favorable to the developer is an indemnification clause that only covers liability arising out of the negligence, breach of contract or other wrongdoing of the provider, which can leave a developer high and dry if there has been a system failure, and a tenant collects for it, but fault cannot be clearly established. Finally, and most ominously, each of the first three kinds of indemnification can be restricted by limiting the provider's obligation to direct damages, so that no matter what happens or who was at fault, the provider will not be required to indemnify the developer for awards for lost profits or other consequential damages.

There are nuances and variations on these themes—some providers like to negotiate for indemnification of the provider by the developer if a claim arises out of the developer's negligence or breach of contract—but the four kinds of indemnification outlined above are by far the most common. Typically, a developer will try for the first and, depending upon his bargaining power and the importance of other issues, settle for the second or the third.

There are a lot of arguments to be made in this area. A stonewalling provider may note, for example, that telephone equipment and elevator manufacturers always exclude consequential damage liability from their contracts. Of course, the issue here is *not* the direct liability of a provider to developer for consequential damages, e.g., lost rents if the service is so bad that tenants leave the building to escape it. That kind of liability is routinely excluded from STS agreements, precisely because of the telephone and computer equipment precedents cited above. Another argument is that the risk is very small, even negligible—but of course if the providers really believe this they would readily accept the risk.

The decision to accept a shared tenant services agreement that limits indemnification is a business decision for the developer, not a legal one for his advisers. The business problem is that limiting indemnification to direct damages, regardless of who is at fault, changes the STS proposition presented to a developer from one that offers modest gains with modest commitments and very little risk to one that offers modest gains with modest commitments and a not inconsequential risk of extremely large losses. Developers and their counsel who care about indemnification would therefore do well to require prospective providers to state where they stand on the question at the outset of negotiations, not when the champagne has been chilled and the press conference scheduled.

Chapter 19

Technical and Regulatory Issues are Challenging ISDN's Progress*

WALTER SAPRONOV

Although much progress has been made in turning ISDN (Integrated Services Digital Network) into a reality, a cloud of confusion still envelopes the ISDN concept. Many users do not understand exactly how far the communications vendors have progressed or what users can do to influence the still-evolving standards.

Similarly unclear is the technical and regulatory future of ISDN. Making any predictions on this front requires a careful examination both of the published CCITT (International Telegraph and Telephone Consultative Committee) I-Series recommendations plus the FCC's (Federal Communications Commission) notice of inquiry and first report on ISDN, along with related decisions. At this point, neither the CCITT nor the FCC efforts are close to completion. Nonetheless, the importance of ISDN to the communications industry merits its study as early in the planning stages as possible.

Three distinct areas deserve specific attention:

1. Technical requirements of ISDN interfaces.
2. The business opportunities associated with the demand for such interfaces.
3. The current regulatory and legal requirements imposed on ISDN-provision by carriers and others.

(For an overview of ISDN's progress in the United States, see DATA COMMUNICATIONS, May, 1985 p. 45.)

As with any major development in communications technology, the advent of ISDN will be associated with an extensive transition period. Estimates of the duration of this period vary: Some carriers are planning isolated ISDN testing this year, while the U.S. National Telecommunications and Information Administration (NTIA) projects that ISDN networks will completely encircle the globe as early as the beginning of the next century.

Historically, transitions of this type—such as the emergence of IBM's SNA (Systems Network Architecture), packet-switching networks, and local area networks—have been accompanied by certain recognizable characteristics:

1. Customers' range of choices in communications products or services expands, thus complicating and confusing the selection process.
2. Older, existing equipment must be adapted to the new technology for the remainder of its useful life.
3. In-place networks or even simple teleprocessing arrangements must be accommodated through gateways or other interconnection mechanisms.

Given the almost universal expectations of ISDN development, each of these characteristics can be expected to influence the communications industry as the transition to ISDN continues. For equipment manufacturers and service providers, this means that new markets will emerge during the interim period that will ease the pain of the transition. Examples of such transitional business opportunities are found today in the markets for protocol converters, gateway software, and emulation equipment.

A few specific industry segments seem most likely to experience a significant impact during the ISDN transition period. These groups include the regulated carriers, the value-added networks (VANs), and the independent suppliers of network products and services.

Insofar as ISDN planners contemplate provision of voice and nonvoice services over the local exchange loop, they necessarily affect the carriers that provide those services today. In the United States, these include both local exchange and interexchange carriers as well as dominant and other common carriers (OCCs). As will be discussed below, the provision of ISDN is a contemporary issue for the regulatory community, the eventual decisions of which will determine the scope of carrier participation in the ISDN marketplace. Naturally, a number of carriers are involved in anticipatory planning and field testing (DATA COMMUNICATIONS, "AT&T's ISDN begins its earthly descent," May, 1985 p. 45).

The planning efforts of a number of Bell operating companies (BOCs) have already yielded a significant marketplace for high-capacity digital switches. Some examples include AT&T's No. 5 ESS, ITT's System 12, and Northern Telecom's DMS 100. Some of these switch manufacturers have leveraged their technical experience in ISDN implementations outside the United States to enhance domestic marketing efforts. For example, Northern Telecom's efforts in Canada and Siemens' work in Germany will both prove to be directly applicable to implementations of ISDN in the United States.

In addition to digital switching, ISDN requirements include Common Channel Interoffice Signaling, specifically CCIS/CCITT Signaling System Number 7.

Stated simply, common channel signaling allows the use of additional bandwidth capacity over existing circuits because signaling is handled over separate channel facilities. For example, North American D-type channel bank facilities today reduce 64-kbit/s digital signal rates to 56 kbit/s because certain frames use one out of every 8 bits for signaling (DATA COMMUNICATIONS, "Long overdue, T1 takes off—but where is it heading?" June, 1985 p. 120).

The introduction of common channel signaling into the Bell System antedated the publication of CCITT No. 7 as an ISDN recommendation. Moreover, the various carriers have agreed to implement common channel signaling irrespective of ISDN timetables. (According to some industry sources, the carriers have agreed on October 1987 as the deadline.)

The introduction of ISDN facilities into the local loop has been profoundly complicated by the divestiture decree (known as "MFJ," modified final judgment). This decree had several important provisions in relation to ISDN.

For instance, according to the MFJ, the BOCs can supply local exchange services only within circumscribed LATAs (Local Access and Transport Areas). All interexchange (inter-LATA) services, whether interstate or intrastate, must be provided by an interexchange carrier (IEC)—such as AT&T or one of the OCCs—and are strictly prohibited to BOCs. A further provision of the decree mandates that the BOCs upgrade their local switching exchanges to provide equal access to all interexchange carriers by 1986. A technical upgrade to local exchange switches will permit subscribers to access their IEC of choice by means of a five-digit selection prefix "10NNN," where NNN is the IEC designation. This feature, termed Feature Group D, is scheduled to replace the predivestiture access arrangements. Furthermore, equal quality of access to OCCs will be facilitated by the introduction of access tandem switches. These enable a subscriber to reach an OCC directly from a local exchange switch (and thus implement a "trunk side connection") rather than using the equivalent of a switched connection from one subscriber to another (known as a "line side connection").

In addition to imposing a jurisdictional demarcation between local exchange and interexchange carriage, the MFJ imposed a separation of assets between AT&T and the BOCs. Included in the asset base assigned to AT&T were the network-control-point and signal-transfer-point hardware, the vehicles for introducing common channel signaling (initially, CCIS No. 6) throughout the old Bell network. Following divestiture, the common channel signaling efforts of AT&T became proprietary and isolated from counterpart efforts by the BOCs. Tandem switches handling intra-LATA connections and toll switches handling inter-LATA traffic were also divided between the BOCs and AT&T, even though they might reside at the same facility.

19.1 ISLANDS

Overall, the net effect of divestiture was to delay severely, and perhaps alter, ISDN's introduction into the United States, especially in comparison with ISDN efforts in Europe and Japan.

First, the LATA boundaries and interexchange service prohibitions imposed on the BOCs presage the eventual rise of multiple ISDN "islands" in the United States, in contrast to the monolithic ISDNs envisioned in other countries. ISDN services will also be separated across local exchange/interexchange lines, thus dividing ISDNs supplied by BOCs from those provided by AT&T and the OCCs. While planners from these organizations are studying proposed interconnections—notably, in the ECSA (Exchange Carrier Standards Association) ISDN T1D1 subcommittee—a true integration of domestic ISDN service is a regulatory fiction. The subcommittee can make recommendations to the carriers but has no actual control over them. Thus, nothing could prevent one carrier from offering one set of ISDN features while another carrier deems a slighly different set of features more profitable. At best, there will be a multiplicity of local and interexchange ISDNs with (it is hoped) suitable gateway interconnections.

Secondly, BOC efforts to upgrade the local exchange facilities to accommodate ISDN will require coordination with complementary efforts by the IECs. These efforts must adhere to the equal access mandate of the MFJ. Yet, AT&T has an obvious advantage over its competitors because it has been pursuing a common channel signaling base for some time. This may, in fact, preempt the other carriers' participation in offering interexchange ISDN services. Consequently, it seems that ISDN subscriber access for voice-grade communications service to AT&T, but not to the OCCs, is inherently "unequal."

Furthermore, IEC participation will also be required to map any future ISDN numbering plan to the aforementioned equal access dial-up sequences of the local exchange. Finally, stored program control (SPC) upgrades to end office (class 5) BOC switches must eventually be matched by similar upgrading of interexchange toll switches, access tandems, signal transfer points, and other interexchange facilities. (The SPC upgrades are designed to introduce ISDN local service gradually.) Other complications in coordinating local exchange and interexchange ISDN upgrades will stem from continued deployment of optical-fiber and packet radio facilities.

Apart from divestiture, the complications of introducing clear channel signaling (64 kbit/s) into the existing, North American digital plant are well known. Specifically, the basic impediments lie in the "bit robbing" of DS1 signal formats for in-band, control signaling purposes, and in the bipolar zero suppression coding schemes used in T1 carrier systems. Effectively, this sets a maximum transfer rate for digital (pulse code modulation encoded) voice or voiceband data signals at 56 kbit/s. According to CCITT Recommendation I.464, this imposes a rate adaptation requirement called "restricted 64-kbit/s transfer" onto the user-network interface and onto internetworking functions for connecting restricted 64-kbit/s ISDNs with unrestricted ISDNs.

BOC implementations of ISDN will obviously occur gradually, largely because newly defined subscriber-to-network interfaces require extensive testing. According to curent I-Series specifications (the CCITT "redbook"), the interface will require integration of time-compression multiplexing and/or echo cancellation techniques over local two-wire loops. Future ISDN interfaces using fiber-optic or broadband technologies will eventually require testing and integration as well. Until the current regulatory controversy over BOC provision of certain types of network connection devices is settled (see discussion of NT1 equipment below), these testing and integration efforts are likely to incur complications or delays.

On first impression, ISDN services from BOCs portend still more competition in the VAN marketplace. Other recent competitive developments affecting the VAN providers have included the following carrier-supplied packet-switching transport services, such as AT&T's Accunet Packet-Switched Services (formerly Bell Packet-Switching Service, or BPSS) and the BOCs' LADT (local area data transport), FCC waiver grants permitting resale of AT&T Communications basic service by AT&T Information Systems, async-to-X.25 protocol conversion by BOCs, and voice/data private network alternatives, such as software-defined networks (sometimes called "virtual private lines"). From the user's perspective, ISDN, if viewed as still another transmission service, further complicates the telecommunications manager's selection options.

On the other hand, those VANs already providing customers with value-added services, such as remote database access, stock quotation services, and credit card authorizations, may well view ISDN as a distribution mechanism. Thus, VAN/ISDN combined services conceivably can extend their reach to a larger subscriber base than either service in isolation.

Another CCITT document addresses the interconnection of VANs and ISDNs. Recommendation X.31 envisions both a minimum and maximum integration scenario (Figure 19.1).

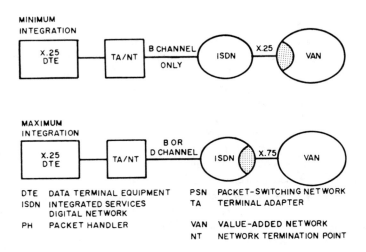

Figure 19.1 Scenarios. In (a), only B-channel access to ISDN interconnections to packet-switching networks (PSN) is permitted. Call setup requires LAP-D signaling procedures to a port on the PSN. By contrast, in (b) the ISDN includes packet handler functions, and LAP-D multiplexing allows signaling and data transmission.

VAN/ISDN interconnection methods are conceptually similar to X.25/X.75 interconnection schemes that connect different packet-switching networks. There are additional conversion requirements that include the use of common channel signaling, (D- or E-channel procedures) in an internetworking context. Details remain to be worked out about handling call-setup and progress signaling over network boundaries. Presumably, these and other ISDN gateway interconnection specifications will be published under the CCITT 1.500 recommendations sometime in the future.

ISDN will create new competition among communications equipment vendors. Some of the new lexicon for ISDN gear is listed below.

1. NT1: Network termination equipment corresponding to OSI layer 1, which is associated with the physical and electrical termination of the network.
2. NT2: Network termination equipment corresponding to layers 1, 2, and 3 (physical, data link, and network, respectively).
3. TA: Terminal equipment providing adaptation of pre-ISDN terminal equipment (for example, devices that are compatible with X.21 and V.24).
4. TE1: Terminal equipment complying with ISDN interface specifications (for example, digital telephones).
5. TE2: Pre-ISDN terminal equipment not complying with ISDN interface specifications.

19.2 THE INDEPENDENT SUPPLIERS

In accordance with the FCC's decision regarding network channel-terminating equipment (see below), ISDN network equipment falls under the deregulated CPE category and is thus open to competition among independent suppliers. This competition encompasses equipment manufacturers of NT1, NT2, terminal adapter, and various types of ISDN terminals. Some analysts project that NT1 devices will consist of microcomputer "plug-in" boards. Again, as with testing of ISDN loop transmission techniques, the industry must await final FCC resolution of the regulatory status of NT1 and relevant modifications to the rules (specifically found in the Code of Federal Regulations Part 68) for the attachment of foreign devices to the public network.

NT2 devices, however, seem firmly established as CPE and thus open to competition among independent suppliers. Notably, IBM's comments to the FCC ISDN inquiry included concern that ISDN specifications be made sufficiently simple so that users would not be encumbered with undesired, additional functionality called for by complex, feature-laden standards. (An overly complex interface is inconsistent with federal regulations that establish minimal standards only to prevent network harm and do not recommend network efficiency or design standards.) Since such functionality would have a direct bearing on cost, this directly affects future NT2 manufacturers.

NT2 devices are functionally equivalent to ISO/OSI layers 1 through 3 and are anticipated to provide X.25 packet service over both B and D channels. The type of packet service varies (Fig. 2) and may or may not require a terminal adapter (TA) for an interface to pre-ISDN equipment (the ISDN lexicon for this gear is "type TE2"). The existing pre-ISDN equipment base ("type TE1") will make the TA function a critical resource for adapting older equipment to ISDN facilities as they become available. Given the similarity of the NT2 ISDN function to current X.25 standards, the market for NT2 and TA devices should prove a natural for native X.25 and protocol-converter suppliers.

Accommodating pre-ISDN equipment requires adaptation of functions and transmission rates. For X.25 terminals, ISDN adaptation is defined in CCITT Recommendation X.31 (from I.462) and in the familiar V-series terminal interfaces (RS-232-C) contained in Recommendations I.460 and I.463. Other adaptations are defined as well. Rate adaptation involves techniques, such as "flag stuffing," that allows terminals operating at less than 64-kbit/s rates to use a B channel. An example of function adaptation is the handling of link layer differences between X.25 and ISDN specifications (LAP-B and LAP-D, respectively). Again, such adaptation techniques should prove familiar to vendors who are supplying X.25-to-SNA protocol conversion and thus are already handling similar link layer differences between HDLC LAP-B and SDLC protocols.

19.3 REGULATORY ISSUES

The importance of addressing regulatory ramifications early in the ISDN planning process was recognized in 1983 by both the State Department and the FCC. In its report, the National Telecommunications Information Agency (NTIA) concluded that "because of the far-reaching impact of ISDN on competition, equipment and service trade, it is important that the U.S. Government provide a reasonably specific policy framework on which future U.S. efforts to develop ISDN standards could be based." For its part, the FCC issued a Notice of Inquiry (Gen. Docket 83-841) and adopted a First Report (released on April 2, 1984) that addresses issues relating to ISDN.

Other regulatory decisions germane to ISDN planning include the MFJ, Computer Inquiry II, the Digital NCTE decision (GCC Docket 81-216), the Communications Protocols decision (Gen. Docket 80-756), and the recently issued BOC Protocol Conversion Order (FCC 85-101). The Commission has also called for comment on ISDN issues related to colocations of ISDN source facilities by carriers and noncarriers in the recently convened Computer Inquiry III. The Commission announced that it would further examine ISDN issues in a reconsideration of Computer Inquiry II policies sometime this year. To date, these issues have been couched in the deregulatory and structural separation provisions of those policies, much to the dissatisfaction of the dominant carriers and their allies.

The salient regulatory issues concerning ISDN focus on two major controversies: the demarcation point issues and the basic/enhanced dichotomy of Computer Inquiry II.

The demarcation point at issue separates the regulated portion of the network from the customer premises equipment. Following Computer Inquiry II, CPE was deregulated and unbundled from regulated carrier offerings. According to the terms of the MJF, the BOCs are permitted to provide but not manufacture CPE. Computer Inquiry II and subsequent affirmations, however, require that such provision by AT&T and the BOCs be done only through a separate affiliate (the structural separation requirement) in nontariffed competition with independent suppliers. The digital NCTE decision further established that digital NCTEs—such as DSU (data service unit) and CSU (channel service unit)—also fall under the deregulated CPE category and are not to be provided by carriers as part of a regulated network service.

Upon examination of ISDN NT1 and NT2 devices, the FCC found them sufficiently similar to NCTE to warrant their classification as CPE. It decreed a "U" reference point as the demarcation point between the ISDN network and the customer premises. NT1 (or NT1 and NT2 combined equipment), therefore, may not be provided under tariff or bundled with ISDN network services. In this respect, the U.S. demarcation differs from the CCITT version. The latter proposes that the network be separated from the subscriber premises at the "T" reference point, with the implication that NT1 devices can be provided as part of the carrier's communications network.

As expected, the carriers have vociferously denounced the FCC's position. Some argued that the NCTE decision should be changed to accommodate the international ISDN definitions. The commission and other commentators, such as IBM, disagreed. Moreover, IBM expressed a concern that a carrier-prescribed ISDN may be needlessly complex and slanted toward provision of voice rather than data.

Given the FCC position on NCTE, the issue of locating the demarcation point leads to the question of whether the carriers may supply ISDN NT devices under waiver of present policies. Here, the discussion becomes reminiscent of the Hugh-A-Phone and Carterfone cases. The legal principle articulated in those decisions is as follows: customer-supplied equipment attachments to the public telephone network are allowed to the extent that they are privately beneficial without being publicly harmful; the burden of proof that such equipment is harmful lies heavily on the carriers. A waiver of present policies allowing carriers to effectively supply an "ISDN access arrangement" for reasons of preventing public harm would have to meet that burden.

As a proleptic argument in support of such anticipated carrier waivers, one may point to possible ISDN network harm with unstable loop characteristics, remote testing requirements, and potential "hacker" access to the D- or E-channel signaling infrastructure. Nonetheless, the FCC resolved in the NCTE decision to address such circumstances on an ad hoc basis only and foreclosed the possibility of exclusive provision of NCTE (and thus ISDN NT1) by carriers on a regulated basis.

19.4 DISTINCTION

The "basic/enhanced" services dichotomy comes from Computer Inquiry II and remains active until and unless the FCC reconsiders its position. Generally, basic services are subject to FCC regulation under Title II of the Communications Act, while enhanced services are not regulated under Title II. Basic services may be viewed as end-to-end transmission capacity without alteration of the message at either end of the transmission. Enhanced services, on the other hand, have a twofold definition. First, they "employ computer processing applications that act on the form, content, code, protocol, or similar aspects of the subscriber's transmitted information." Second, they are able to "provide . . . additional, different, or restructured information, or involve subscriber interaction with stored information.

The FCC further ruled that enhanced services may not be offered under tariff nor bundled with basic services. Additionally, provision of enhanced services by AT&T or the BOCs is subject to the same structural separation requirements as the provision of CPE. Where the FCC deems it to be in the public interest, however, the separation requirements may be relaxed or waived—for example, in resale of basic AT&T Communications services by its deregulated subsidiary.

ISDN raises the following questions in this context: To what extent are ISDN services enhanced? Can applicable structural separations for ISDN carriers be waived so as to permit bundling of enhanced ISDN services (such as telemetry) with basic ISDN service (such as digitized voice)?

According to the FCC Report on ISDN, the current CCITT ISDN bearer/teleservices division appears to "accommodate" the basic/enhanced dichotomy—at least to the extent that typical basic services, such as voice. Telex, and telegraph, are grouped under bearer services. Teleservices, on the other hand, seem clearly to fall under the enhanced category.

ISDN packet services (Figure 19.2) require further scrutiny. In the Protocols Decision, the commission exempted "network processing"—such as call establishment, on/off hook, and dial signaling, for both packet- and circuit-switched networks—from the enhanced category. Thus, D- E-channel connection establishment and CCITT System 7 signaling may also escape classification as enhanced services.

Furthermore, packet-switching transport services, such as AT&T's Accunet and BOC LADT, have also been held to be basic on the ground that the contents of the message (X.25 packet) entering into and exiting from the network are identical and that network internal conversions are irrelevant for classification purposes. Arguably, packet-switching bearer services over B- or D-channel connections can be considered basic following similar reasoning.

The classification of bearer services as basic is fraught with implications for the ISDN industry. Such services could, therefore, be regulated, tariffed, bundled with other basic services (such as conventional voice), and would not be subject to separate costing or accounting provisions.

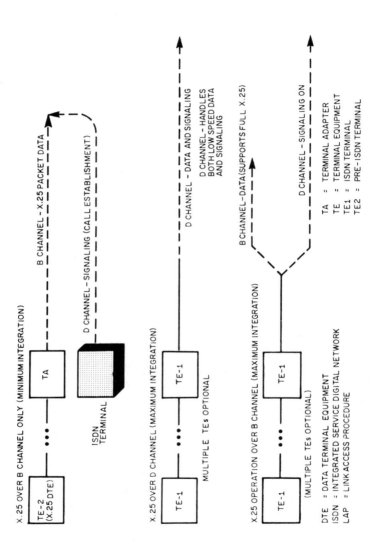

Figure 19.2 Packet-switching service over ISDN channels. In minimum integration (a), the TA and TE2 interface appears as native interface to ISDN. In maximum integrations (b), the D channel is used for both signaling and low-speed data. In native operation (c), the B channel supports full X.25 service.

The issue then turns to teleservices and waiver potential. As an example, teleservices includes teleconferencing, remote database access, and alarm services, appear to fall under the *second* part of the enhanced definition. That is, teleservices seem to involve "additional," "different," and "subscriber interaction with stored information." It is important to note that the Protocols Decision clearly states that only those services falling under the first part of the definition are subject to waiver relief from structural separation requirements; those falling under the second part are not.

Consequently, it would appear that the aforementioned teleservices would be ineligible for the type of waiver relief recently afforded to the BOCs for provision of async-to-X.25 protocol conversion. If valid, such reasoning would further preclude the carriers from sharing or colocating bearer and teleservices central-office facilities.

A final observation on ISDN regulation concerns the other side of divestiture, namely the MFJ and the continuing jurisdiction of the Consent Decree Court. FCC rulings notwithstanding, the BOC provision of information services (the MFJ equivalent of enhanced services) is prohibited under the Consent Decree on anticompetitive grounds. Legally speaking, FCC decisions are not binding on the Consent Decree Court regarding issues under the MFJ. Thus, any BOC provision of ISDN services may still have to pass Justice Department recommendation and Consent Decree Court approval if such services are deemed to violate the information services prohibitions of the Decree.

The nascent ISDN industry will grapple with the regulatory issues in the foreseeable future. The outcome of these decisions will inevitably affect the market share for ISDN equipment and services between regulated carriers and unregulated independents. There is merit to the concerns of all parties involved. Regulatory stifling of carrier participation is ISDN premises equipment technology may have an inhibiting effect on ISDN development. On the other hand, excessive indulgence of carrier activity in deregulated ISDN areas may lead to a juggernaut that can undermine the goals of divestiture. It remains for the regulators, courts, and advocates to strike the proper balance.

Chapter 20

"Back to the Future": A Model for Telecommunications*

MARK S. FOWLER, ALBERT HALPRIN, and
JAMES D. SCHLICHTING†

20.1 INTRODUCTION

Since World War II, new technologies and the introduction of competition have transformed the nature of the telecommunications industry in the United States. Technological advances in telecommunications have allowed the transfer of larger volumes of information than ever before at faster speeds and with superior accuracy—all at steadily declining costs. These changes have led to the introduction of competition in the provision of telecommunications goods and services that formerly were subject to a single source of supply. The resulting benefits are clear: a proliferation of new products and services for all consumers; more sophisticated means of transferring information; and, more generally, greater value for every telecommunications dollar.

In this vibrant and fast-growing sector of our economy, traditional public utility regulation of telecommunications has come under greater and greater stress. The infirmities of the traditional approach increasingly have become apparent in recent years, especially in the wake of the divestiture of AT&T. The absence of a prior national debate and consensus on divestiture contributed not only to substantial industry and customer confusion, but also to an unfortunate disruption in the formulation of a more coherent national telecommunications

*Reprinted with permission from *38 Federal Communications Law Journal* 145. Copyright 1986, Federal Communications Bar Association/Regents of the University of California. All rights reserved.

†The authors wish to express their deeply felt gratitude to Sandra B. Eskin, William J. Kirsch, and Thomas J. Sugrue for their long hours of assistance on this article and to acknowledge the contributions of Margot Bester and Curt Chambers.

policy. Divestiture has given those so inclined an opportunity to attempt to thwart progress with short-term fixes at the expense of those who recognize the need for a long-term vision of a vibrant telecommunications industry that serves as the model for specific regulatory decisions.

This article seeks to refocus the current debate on the more fundamental issues by reaching back to the American ideal of a free enterprise economy to map out the future of telecommunications in this country. It advances a competitive industry paradigm as the proper long-term vision for domestic telecommunications. It also presents a proposal for trial deregulation of all telecommunications goods and services in states willing to undertake such an experiment. The hope is that this proposal might simultaneously accelerate the transition to a competitive telecommunications marketplace and avoid the costs of a gradualist approach to deregulation.

Both the competitive industry paradigm and our specific deregulatory proposal are designed merely to serve as points of departure for a serious, substantive debate on national telecommunications policy in the United States. They establish the basis for what we hope will be a continuing dialogue by all interested parties on the model that best ensures use of our nation's telecommunications resources so as to allow a continued flourishing of new communications services and the maximization of overall benefits to society.

These conclusions are grounded in a reexamination of telecommunications regulation and its recent history. The article begins with a discussion of the fundamental societal goals for telecommunications in this country. It then explores the application of the traditional public utility paradigm and examines the societal costs of this approach. The next sections trace the role of developing technologies in the introduction of competition in telecommunications and suggest that these developments render a competitive industry paradigm the most appropriate model for the telecommunications industry in this country.

The article then proceeds to identify some of the key obstacles on the road to a competitive marketplace and suggests basic guiding principles for the transition to competition, such as encouraging use of the public switched network through a policy of pricing flexibility and through a movement from structural regulation of dominant carriers to an open network architecture with nonstructural regulation. The article concludes by presenting for discussion a specific proposal built on these principles for a three-year trial of total deregulation of telecommunications. This alternative to the gradualist approach to deregulation could well accelerate our transition to a competitive telecommunications marketplace.

20.2 FUNDAMENTAL GOALS FOR AMERICAN TELECOMMUNICATIONS

Consideration of a long-term model for telecommunications regulation should begin with the overarching goals of fairness and efficiency. These goals were identified at least as early as 1934, when Congress enacted the Communications

Act, charging the Federal Communications Commission with the duty "to make available, so far as possible, to all the people of the United States a rapid, efficient, Nation-wide, and worldwide . . . communication service with adequate facilities at reasonable charges."[1]

The mandate for fairness encompasses the fundamental goals of reasonable rates, the absence of unjust discrimination, and universal service. This last goal reflects the broad-based consensus in our society that basic telephone service should not be just an ordinary service, but an "essential" service available to all our nation's citizens.[2] In this nation, telephone penetration—that is, the proportion of households with telephone service—has remained just above 90 percent in recent years. If anything, it has been rising.[3] The universal service goal precludes implementation of any regulatory policy leading to a significant decline in telephone penetration.[4]

The mandate for efficiency requires the Commission to seek to obtain for American consumers the greatest value from our telecommunications resources at the least cost. In a free market economy, where individual consumers express their preferences among competing goods through free choice in their purchases, price becomes the principal arbiter of relative values. And where prices reflect the underlying production costs of these goods—either through the exacting discipline of competition or through regulation—consumer choice will lead to the most efficient levels of production for these various goods, at which the last consumer consuming a product benefits just enough to cover the cost of producing that product. If prices are artificially higher than costs, output will be inefficiently limited and consumers willing to pay more than the costs of producing the good will have to go without. Conversely, if prices are artificially held

---

[1] 47 U.S.C. § 151 (1982). Fairness and efficiency are not, of course, the only priority concerns of federal telecommunications regulators. The Communications Act also expressly recognizes that network development must take account of national defense concerns, in times of peace as well as war. *Id.*

[2] The "universal service" goal is not expressly mentioned in the Communications Act, but has been inferred from the broad language of the Act. *See, e.g.,* MTS/WATS Market Structure (Phase I), 93 F.C.C.2d 241, 266-67, 53 R.R.2d 479, 499 (1983) [hereinafter cited as MTS/WATS Third Report and Order].

[3] The Census Bureau survey data for March 1986 showed that 92.2 percent of American households had a telephone in their home. This is an all-time high, slightly above the 91.9% level for November 1985 and significantly higher as a statistical matter than the 91.4% predivestiture penetration level measured in November 1983. Federal Communications Commission, Telephone Subscribership in the U.S. (May 27, 1986).

[4] The Commission recently has conducted two studies in this general area, examining the effects of federal decisions on local telephone service rates and service discontinuation. The Commission's initial report concluded, among other things, that existing federal policies would not cause minimum charges for residential telephone service to increase sharply or cause residential subscribers to discontinue service. Petition by the State of Michigan Concerning the Effect of Certain Federal Decisions on Local Telephone Service ("Michigan Report"), 96 F.C.C.2d 491 (1983). The second report, issued in January 1985, affirmed this conclusion, which also is consistent with recent telephone penetration statistics. Further Report on the Effects of Federal Decisions on Universal Service, FCC 84-636 (released January 9, 1985).

below costs, output will be inefficiently stimulated to produce goods for consumers unwilling to pay the underlying costs.[5] Society suffers an unnecessary reduction in its economic welfare through the inefficient misallocation of its productive resources in telecommunications.

The cost to consumers of any uneconomic misallocation of telecommunications resources has been steadily increasing in light of the rapid pace of technological development. The world is fast approaching a new Information Age in which a significant portion of productive global resources will be directed to collecting, analyzing, transmitting, and reporting information. The United States can rightly claim at present to be at the cutting edge as we enter the Information Age. Only sound regulatory policies that optimize efficient use of our telecommunications network will allow continued innovation by this country's greatest economic resource, the private sector. Regulatory policies must ensure that society does not have to invest more resources than necessary in its telephone network and that investment in the network be allocated so as to maximize benefits.[6]

20.3 THE PUBLIC UTILITY PARADIGM IN TELECOMMUNICATIONS

For much of this century, fairness and efficiency in American telecommunications have been sought through the public utility paradigm of governmental regulation.[7] The paradigm is expressly premised on the assumption that the industry constitutes a "natural monopoly" in which a single entity can provide better service at lower costs than a number of competing suppliers.[8] Under the public utility paradigm, it is thought to be both more efficient and more fair for government to grant an exclusive franchise to one company than to let market forces reign. The governmentally bestowed monopoly, however, creates strong incentives for overpricing and reduced output of the monopoly services.[9] In addition, as explained in more detail below,[10] governmentally granted market power can be used to leverage other markets through anticompetitive conduct, such as the discriminatory provision of regulated services to competitors and their

---

[5]For further discussion of the concept of "incremental" or "marginal" cost, see P. Samuelson, Economics 426-37 (1980).

[6]Efficiency and fairness are not intrinsically inconsistent concerns. To the contrary, it would appear that improved efficiency in the network would in many respects increase the fairness of the system. For instance, rational cost-based pricing actually increases fairness insofar as it results in end users paying the costs they impose on society rather than requiring other end users to bear those costs. Kahn, *The Road to More Intelligent Telephone Pricing,* 1 Yale J. on Reg. 139, 146 (1984).

[7]*See generally* G. Brock, The Telecommunications Industry 158-61, 177-99 (1981).

[8]2 A. Kahn, The Economics of Regulation 2,146 (1971).

[9]*See, e.g.,* Averch and Johnson, *Behavior of the Firm under Regulatory Constraint,* 52 Am. Econ. Rev. 1053 (1962).

[10]*See infra* pages 164-65.

customers in these other markets or the cross-subsidization of competitive offerings through improper cost allocation between regulated and unregulated services.

The public utility paradigm employs intrusive governmental regulation to combat these possible harms. To prevent the reduced output of monopoly services, the public utility paradigm strictly controls entry and exit, closely regulates both the prices and the conditions of service, and imposes an obligation to serve all applicants under reasonable conditions.[11] The use of governmentally granted market power to leverage other markets is prevented by setting prices for regulated services and by severely restricting the utility's participation in competitive markets.

Telecommunications services—both local and long distance—traditionally have been included among the core of industries falling within the public utility paradigm. The view that telecommunications is a "natural" monopoly has been defended with a number of arguments, such as: (1) simple economies of scale in the provision of a standardized service dictate that one firm should provide that service; (2) aggregate investment costs can be minimized if the planning for the installation and expansion of capacity is done on a system-wide basis; (3) the demand for higher standards of service necessitates centralized responsibility and control; and (4) no company is likely to assume the responsibility of providing a truly national network—one that enables almost everyone at any moment to reach anyone else in the most isolated part of the country—unless it has a monopoly status.[12]

The public utility paradigm has incorporated a number of specific regulatory practices to implement entry/exit regulation and rate-of-return ratemaking in telecommunications. First, costs that are joint or common to more than one service[13] and local plant costs have been recovered from telephone services according to social and political objectives, with little regard for the social welfare benefits of economic efficiency. Second, uneconomically slow depreciation of investment has artificially depressed current rates while maintaining a high level of investment on which companies have earned a return. Third, widespread averaging of costs and rates has allowed a nationwide sharing of the costs of wiring the entire country for universal service,[14] but has greatly limited

---

[11] A. Kahn, The Economics of Regulation 3 (1970).

[12] *See* 2 A. Kahn, *supra* note 8, at 127-29. Some, however, have seriously contested this view. *See, e.g.,* Evans and Heckman, *A Test for Subadditivity of the Cost Function with an Application to the Bell System,* 74 Am. Econ. Rev. 615 (1984); Eldor & Sudit, *Alternative Specifications of Returns to Scale and Joint Estimation of Factor Demands and Production Functions in Telecommunications,* 18 Rev. Bus. and Econ. Research 15 (1982). *See also* Raj & Vinod, *Bell System Scale Economies Estimated from a Random Coefficients Model,* 34 J. Econ. & Bus. 247 (1982). *See also infra* note 20.

[13] For an explanation of joint and common costs, see page 168 and note 61 below.

[14] Universal service was also achieved through the Rural Electrification Act of 1936, which provided additional funds to provide service to rural areas of the country. *See* 7 U.S.C. § 901 *et seq.* (1982).

telephone companies' incentives to run their operations efficiently. Finally, possible anticompetitive use of governmentally granted market power was not merely restrained, but affirmatively prohibited under the 1956 Consent Decree, barring AT&T, which through its Bell System affiliates had also become the preeminent local exchange carrier, from engaging in any business other than the provision of common carrier communications services.[15]

An important, although not immediately apparent, effect of a national telecommunications monopoly subject to government regulation has been the imposition of significant direct and indirect (or opportunity) costs on society. The public utility paradigm has exacted significant efficiency costs in resource allocation: distorting investment decisions, limiting private incentive to innovate with new technology, and worse, affirmatively discouraging innovation that would render obsolete vast amounts of embedded equipment that is included in the rate base. Moreover, regulation has tended to discourage price competition and provided only limited incentives to cut costs or increase management efficiencies. Regulation has tended as well to limit the choices available to consumers: regulatory price ceilings prevent the supply of higher-quality, higher-priced offerings; regulatory price floors discourage the supply of low-quality inexpensive options that many consumers would find attractive. Furthermore, it has limited the ability of market participants to respond quickly to changes in demand and supply. Regulation also tends to react much more slowly than the marketplace to the changing reality of technology.[16] In addition, substantial private and public resources have been spent simply administering the entire regulatory system. Finally, regulatory ratemaking not only has led to significant direct administrative costs, but also has been subject to serious practical difficulties, making terribly elusive the goal of keeping prices close to costs.[17]

Perhaps the most costly aspect of traditional public utility regulation, however, has been its self-perpetuating character. It is impossible to test its central premise—that telecommunications is a natural monopoly—for regulation itself erects barriers to entry and provides existing firms with the opportunity to block or delay the plans of a firm wishing to offer a new product or service or to enter a new market.[18] The costs and delays inherent in obtaining regulatory approval for such entry undoubtedly have led many firms to avoid entering the market when

---

[15]Similarly, Western Electric, AT&T's wholly owned equipment manufacturing subsidiary, was precluded from manufacturing equipment other than the type of equipment used by the Bell System for furnishing common carrier communications services. AT&T and Western Electric also were required to license their patents to all applicants upon payment of appropriate royalties. *See* United States v. Western Electric Co., 1956 Trade Cas. (CCH) ¶ 68,246 (D.N.J. Jan. 24, 1956).

[16]A primary effect of regulation is, in fact, to slow down change. It has been argued that the pace of progress under regulation will be determined by existing firms, with the ability of new firms to make changes reduced or eliminated. *See* G. Brock, *supra* note 7, at 14-15. *See also* V. Goldberg, *Regulation and Administered Contracts,* 7 Bell J. Econ. 426 (1976).

[17]*See* G. Brock, *supra* note 7, at 15-16.

[18]*Id.* Existing firms can also create barriers to entry by such methods as building excess capacity. *Id.* at 25-34.

they were otherwise ready, willing, and able to provide a service or product that consumers would buy at market price.

Thus, the direct and indirect costs of applying the public utility paradigm in markets where competition could thrive have been significant in terms of foregone social welfare benefits. Therefore, where competition can prevail, the public interest demands that regulators attempt to take advantage of the corresponding efficiency benefits.

20.4 THE BREAKDOWN OF THE PUBLIC UTILITY PARADIGM

The past thirty years have made it clear that the public utility paradigm does not apply, and perhaps should never have been applied, across-the-board to the entire telecommunications industry. The persistence of potential competitors, plus the development of new technologies, has effectively undermined the notion that outside companies can never become effective competitors of the telephone companies. Open entry was first introduced into the markets for customer premises equipment (CPE)[19] and interexchange private line services.[20] As open-entry policies actually led to entry by non-telephone company firms, competitive pressures increased on telephone companies, highlighting the inefficient practices that were part and parcel of public utility regulation. As a result, regulation of the rates and conditions for telephone products and services had to be relaxed, allowing the benefits of competition to be realized by the American consumer. The public utility paradigm had collapsed with respect to large segments of the telecommunications industry.

Open entry first came to telecommunications with respect to CPE as a result of the persistence of CPE competitors. For many years, AT&T's tariffs prohibited its customers from connecting to its network any device not supplied by the telephone company. A series of Commission and federal court decisions ultimately found that the application of this restriction to the "Hush-A-Phone"—a simple cup-like device designed to provide some privacy and to help eliminate background noise when attached physically to a telephone's mouthpiece—constituted "an unwarranted interference with the telephone subscriber's right rea-

---

[19]CPE encompasses not only the "plain old telephone," but also sophisticated terminal equipment that can incorporate information retrieval and processing capabilities, and private branch exchanges that can perform switching and traffic concentration functions on the customer's premises.

[20]It is indeed possible that those markets were never properly regarded as natural monopoly markets. In a lengthy inquiry in Docket No. 20003, the Commission undertook a broad fact-finding inquiry into the economic consequences of the regulatory policies and pricing practices for telecommunications services and facilities, particularly those subject to competition. The Commission concluded that no immediate adverse harm had been demonstrated either in regard to interconnection competition or private line service competition. *See* Customer Interconnection, 75 F.C.C.2d 506 (1980). And, in an analysis appended to this report, the Commission staff declared that "[b]oth conceptually and empirically, the record of this docket is insufficient to support a finding that the Bell system is a natural monopoly." *Id.* at 565. *See also supra* note 12.

sonably to use his telephone in ways that are privately beneficial without being publicly detrimental."[21]

The Commission extended open entry in 1968 to CPE that connected electronically and not just physically, to the network when it found unlawful AT&T's prohibition of the use of the Carterfone, a device that interconnected two-way mobile radio systems with the wireline telephone network.[22] The Commission in *Carterfone* expressly limited restrictions on the interconnection of equipment to those aimed at protecting the telephone network from technical harm,[23] a decision it implemented in detail in 1975 through its terminal equipment registration program.[24]

The initial opening for competition in the interexchange services market came through the proposed use of microwave facilities for private line services. Finding a need for private services and foreseeing no risk of harm to established services, the Commission authorized private microwave networks in 1958.[25] In 1969, the Commission approved MCI's limited point-to-point system between Chicago and St. Louis "designed to meet the interoffice and interplant communications needs of small businesses."[26] This approval prompted a deluge of applications seeking authorization of similar microwave facilities. Two years later, in a rulemaking proceeding, the Commission decided to allow the entry of new carriers into the specialized communications field to provide alternatives to certain interstate transmission services traditionally offered only by the telephone companies.[27] Next came the approval of an interstate packet-switched communications network offering that introduced "value-added networks," which resold data processing

---

[21]Hush-A-Phone Corp. v. United States, 238 F.2d 266, 269 (D.C. Cir. 1956). The case was remanded to the FCC, which ordered telephone companies to revise their tariffs to allow customer use of the Hush-A-Phone and any other devices that were not injurious. The revised tariffs, which became effective by operation of law, still contained language prohibiting interconnection of non-telephone-company-provided communications systems.

[22]Use of the Carterfone Device in Message Toll Telephone Service, 13 F.C.C.2d 420, 13 R.R.2d 597, *aff'd on recon.* 14 F.C.C.2d 571, 14 R.R.2d 185 (1968).

[23]AT&T's tariff revisions after *Carterfone* permitted interconnection through protective coupling devices—"connecting arrangements" and "network control signalling units"—provided by the telephone company. *See* North Carolina Util. Comm'n v. FCC, 552 F.2d 1036, 1041 (4th Cir.), *cert. denied,* 434 U.S. 874 (1977).

[24]*See* 47 C.F.R. §§ 68.1-68.506 (1985). The Part 68 registration program allows users to connect any terminal equipment (including main station telephones, key telephone systems, and PBX equipment) to the telephone network if such equipment is connected through protective circuitry registered with the Commission or if the terminal equipment is itself registered. *See* Interstate and Foreign Message Toll Telephone, First Report and Order, 56 F.C.C.2d 593 (1975), *modified on recon.,* 58 F.C.C.2d 716 (1976), Second Report and Order, 58 F.C.C.2d 736 (1976), *aff'd sub nom.* North Carolina Util. Comm'n v. FCC, 552 F.2d 1036 (4th Cir.), *cert. denied,* 434 U.S. 874 (1977).

[25]*See* Allocation of Frequencies in Bands Above 890 Mc., 27 F.C.C. 359, 18 R.R. 1767 (1959), *modified on recon.,* 29 F.C.C. 825, 20 R.R. 1602 (1960).

[26]Microwave Communications, Inc., 18 F.C.C.2d 953, 953, 16 R.R.2d 1037, 1039-40 (1969).

[27]Specialized Common Carrier Services, First Report and Order, 29 F.C.C.2d 870, 22 R.R.2d 1501, *aff'd on recon.,* 31 F.C.C.2d 1106, 23 R.R.2d 1501 (1971), *aff'd sub nom.* Washington Util. & Transp. Comm'n v. FCC, 513 F.2d 1142 (9th Cir.), *cert. denied,* 423 U.S. 836 (1975).

functions through basic private line circuits.[28] Shortly thereafter, approval was given for unlimited resale and shared use of private line services and facilities.[29]

The use of new transmission technologies was not limited to provision of private line services through microwave antennas. Open entry and competition came to ordinary switched long-distance service after a series of commission and federal court decisions in the late 1970's.[30] Tariff restrictions against the resale and shared use of these services were removed in 1980.[31] The potential for the use of satellites for long-distance services was recognized by 1972, when the Commission established a policy of open entry for domestic satellites.[32] With the Commission's recent authorization of a large number of new satellites and its reduction in satellite spacing to allow the placement of more satellites in orbit, the skies have been broadly opened to both regulated entities and private operators.[33]

The actual competitive entry of non-telephone company firms into markets formerly the sole preserve of telephone companies highlighted the competitive vulnerabilities of various inefficient practices under regulation. The Commission concluded that a relaxation of the regulation of the rates and conditions of telephone company goods and services newly subject to competition was necessary to allow the marketplace to reclaim those competitive markets. In *Computer I,* the Commission confirmed that data processing, whether provided in the form of CPE or services, should not be subject to regulation, but that the provision of communications services, even if provided through CPE, should be regulated.[34] In *Computer II,* the Commission decided to deregulate all offerings of CPE, determining that CPE constituted a category separate from offerings of telecom-

---

[28]Packet Communications, Inc., 43 F.C.C.2d 922 (1973).

[29]Resale & Shared Use of Common Services, 60 F.C.C.2d 261, 38 R.R.2d 141 (1976), *recon.*, 62 F.C.C.2d 588, 39 R.R.2d 765 (1977), *aff'd sub nom.* American Tel. & Tel. Co. v. FCC, 572 F.2d 17 (2d Cir.), *cert. denied,* 439 U.S. 875 (1978).

[30]MCI Telecommunications Corp. v. FCC, 561 F.2d 365 (D.C. Cir. 1977) (Execunet I), *cert. denied,* 434 U.S. 1040 (1978), *motion for order directing compliance with mandate granted,* 580 F.2d 590 (D.C. Cir.) (Execunet II), *cert. denied,* 439 U.S. 980 (1978). *See generally* MTS/WATS Market Structure, Report and Third Supplemental Notice of Inquiry and Proposed Rulemaking, 81 F.C.C.2d 177, 178-95 (1980).

[31]Resale and Shared Use, 83 F.C.C.2d 167, 48 R.R.2d 1067 (1980).

[32]Domestic Communication-Satellite Facilities (DOMSAT), First Report and Order, 22 F.C.C.2d 86, 18 R.R.2d 1631 (1970), Second Report and Order, 35 F.C.C.2d 844, 24 R.R.2d 1942 (1972), *aff'd sub nom.* Network Project v. FCC, 511 F.2d 786 (D.C. Cir. 1975).

[33]Domestic Fixed-Satellite Service, 94 F.C.C.2d 129, 53 R.R.2d 1597 (1983), *recon.*, FCC 84-32 (released Feb. 2, 1984), *further recon.*, FCC 84-181 (released May 15, 1984); Satellite Orbital Spacing, 54 R.R.2d 577 (1983); Assignment of Orbital Locations to Space Stations in the Domestic Fixed-Satellite Service, 50 Fed. Reg. 35,228 (1985). *See also* Domestic Fixed Satellite Transponder Sales, 90 F.C.C.2d 1238, 52 R.R.2d 79 (1982).

[34]Computer Use of Communications Facilities, Tentative Decision, 28 F.C.C.2d 291 (19) [hereinafter cited as First Computer Inquiry Ten tative Decision], Final Decision and Order, 28 F.C.C.2d 261 (1971) [hereinafter cited as First Computer Inquiry Final Decision], *aff'd in part and reversed in part sub nom.* GTE Service Corp. v. FCC, 474 F.2d 724 (2d Cir. 1973), *decision on remand,* 40 F.C.C.2d 293 (1973). AT&T and the Bell System companies were prohibited from providing unregulated data processing services by the 1956 Consent Decree (*see supra* page 152), so the effect of this deregulation was limited to other telephone companies.

munications services and mandating an end to carrier provision of CPE "bundled" with basic communications services.[35] The Commission expressly found that the terminal equipment market was subject to an increasing amount of competition, that consumers were deriving substantial benefits from these competitive forces, and that these benefits could be jeopardized by continued regulation of CPE.[36] The Commission "unbundled" CPE from basic transmission services by discontinuing rate regulation of CPE and requiring that it be sold separately in a competitive market.

The Commission similarly moved to achieve the benefits of competition in the interexchange services market by reducing regulation of rates and conditions. In the *Competitive Carrier* decisions, the Commission reduced the regulatory burdens on competitive carriers without market power by applying streamlined regulation and forebearance.[37] In *Computer II*, the Commission also eliminated regulation of the rates and conditions of enhanced services in light of competition in the marketplace.[38]

20.5 A COMPETITIVE INDUSTRY PARADIGM

These significant recent changes in telecommunications regulation suggest that the time has come to replace the traditional public utility paradigm of government regulation with a competitive industry paradigm. The effects of the recent injection of competition into significant segments of interstate telecommunications, the benefits flowing from deregulation in other industries formerly regulated as public utilities, and the promise of new technologies on the brink of realization all demonstrate the necessity for changing our model for telecommunications. Unless mistaken regulatory approaches either retard or limit the industry's potential, telecommunications should become a largely competitive marketplace in which competition drives prices to costs and lowers costs to the

---

[35]Second Computer Inquiry, Final Decision, 77 F.C.C.2d 384, 47 R.R.2d 669 [hereinafter cited as Second Computer Inquiry Final Decision], *modified on recon.*, 84 F.C.C.2d 50, 48 R.R.2d 1107 (1980) [hereinafter cited as Second Computer Inquiry Reconsideration], *further modified on recon.*, 88 F.C.C.2d 512, 50 R.R.2d 629 (1981), *aff'd sub nom.* Computer & Communications Indus. Ass'n v. FCC, 693 F.2d 198 (D.C. Cir. 1982), *cert. denied*, 461 U.S. 938 (1983), *aff'd on second further recon.*, FCC 84-190 (released May 4, 1984).

[36]Second Computer Inquiry Final Decision, *supra* note 35, 77 F.C.C.2d at 439, 441.

[37]Competitive Carrier Rulemaking, Notice of Inquiry and Proposed Rulemaking, 77 F.C.C.2d 308 (1979), First Report and Order, 85 F.C.C.2d 1 (1980), Further Notice of Proposed Rulemaking, 84 F.C.C.2d 445 (1981), Second Report and Order, 91 F.C.C.2d 59, 52 R.R.2d 187 (1982), *recon.*, 93 F.C.C.2d 54, 53 R.R.2d 735 (1983), Second Further Notice of Proposed Rulemaking, 98 F.C.C.2d 792 (1982), Third Further Notice of Proposed Rulemaking, 48 Fed. Reg. 28,292 (1983), Third Report and Order, 48 Fed. Reg. 46,791 (1983), Fourth Report and Order, 95 F.C.C.2d 544, 54 R.R.2d 1037 (1983), Fourth Further Notice of Proposed Rulemaking, 96 F.C.C.2d 922 (1984), Fifth Report and Order, 98 F.C.C.2d 1191 (1984), Sixth Report and Order, 99 F.C.C.2d 1020 (1985), *vacated and remanded sub nom.*, MCI Telecommunications Corp. v. FCC, 765 F.2d 1186 (D.C. Cir. 1985).

[38]Second Computer Inquiry Final Decision, *supra* note 35, 77 F.C.C.2d at 430-35. For a definition of enhanced services, see note 118 below.

minimum, in which products and services are provided whenever end users are willing to pay the necessary costs of production, and in which only minimal subsidies, if any, are necessary to maintain universal service to every consumer who wishes telephone service. Realization of these efficiency benefits of competition will provide greater value in the future for every telecommunications dollar.

The benefits of competition in the markets for CPE and interexchange communications are clearly evident today. It is indisputable that the market for telecommunications equipment is vigorously competitive, with numerous well-financed ventures holding significant market shares.[39] AT&T's predominant market share of the new private branch exchange (PBX) and key system markets has declined drastically in the last few years so that it no longer can be said to dominate any segment of the equipment marketplace.[40] The benefits of such competition are palpable. It is estimated that sales revenues in the CPE market increased by nearly 50% between 1983 and 1985.[41] More than 2000 vendors are supplying end users with $14 billion worth of terminal equipment.[42] The introduction of competition has also provided consumers with a wider variety of CPE options and with less expensive alternatives than existed in the earlier monopoly market. Consumers can obtain such new CPE features as automatic redial, hold, and other call-handling options. A wide variety of new terminal equipment has also appeared, including wireless telephony, customized dialing, and other speciality phones, as well as varieties of decorator phones. It is estimated, for instance, that there are currently 3 million cordless telephones in use. The benefits for business users have also been substantial; PBX and key system prices have been dropping.[43] Nevertheless, the capabilities of business CPE have increased, with such features as high-speed facsimile and integrated data and voice capabilities now being commonplace.

It is also apparent that the interexchange market is well on the way to complete competition. The majority of Americans now have a choice of long-distance carriers. A number of competitors with substantial resources have obtained significant market shares in a few short years. Because of the advent of these

---

[39]*See* Customer Premises Equipment, 100 F.C.C.2d 1298, 1313-16 (1985); Furnishing of Customer Premises Equipment and Enhanced Service, Order, 102 F.C.C.2d 655 (1985) [hereinafter cited as AT&T Structural Relief Order], *aff'd in principal part on recon.* Memorandum Opinion and Order on Reconsideration, FCC 86-341 (released Aug. 7, 1986) [hereinafter cited as AT&T Structural Relief Reconsideration].

[40]*See* AT&T Structural Relief Order, *supra* note 39, 102 F.C.C.2d at 676-77.

[41]Telecommunications: A Market Profile, Wall St. J., Feb. 24, 1986, § 4 (Telecommunications Special Report), at 5D.

[42]*See* Furnishing of Customer Premises Equipment by the Bell Operating Telephone Companies, Notice of Proposed Rulemaking, FCC 86-113, para. 32 (released Mar. 28, 1986) [hereinafter cited as BOC Structural Relief NPRM].

[43]Zorpette, *The Telecommunications Bazaar,* IEEE Spectrum, November 1985, at 59 & 61. For instance, the average wholesale price of a key system has dropped from $300 per unit in 1983 to $225 in 1985. *Id.* at 59.

competitors and movement toward more rational economic pricing of regulated services,[44] usage rates for interstate MTS and WATS services have decreased more than 20% in two and one-half years, stimulating significant additional usage of the public switched network.[45] With the achievement of "equal access" for long-distance competitors, as mandated by the *Modification of Final Judgment (MFJ)* and the Commission,[46] the shape of the interexchange market should be determined primarily by competitive forces.[47]

Similarly, in other sectors of the economy formerly subject to the public utility paradigm, increasing reliance on competition rather than regulation has led to significant improvements in both efficiency and productivity. In ground and air transportation, regulation resulted in artificially designed route structures. Deregulation has permitted greater systemwide planning and efficiency gains, most notably in the form of hub-and-spoke delivery systems.[48] Deregulation in the airline industry has also resulted in a wider choice of discounted fares, aircraft,

---

[44]*See infra* pages 167-83.

[45]Press Release, "Interstate Long Distance Rate Reductions Worth More Than $2 Billion Become Effective," Mimeo No. 4871 (released May 30, 1986).

[46]The Modification of Final Judgment in the AT&T antitrust case requires the divested Bell Operating Companies (BOCs) to provide all interexchange carriers with local exchange access "on an unbundled tariffed basis that is equal in type, quality and price to that provided to AT&T and its affiliates." *See* United States v. American Tel. & Tel. Co., 552 F. Supp. 131, 226, 227 (D.D.C. 1982) (*"Modification of Final Judgment"* or *"MFJ"*), *aff'd sub nom.* Maryland v. United States, 460 U.S. 1001 (1983). GTE is required to implement equal access pursuant to a consent decree entered into with the Department of Justice to settle an antitrust challenge to GTE's acquisition of Southern Pacific Communications Company. United States v. GTE Corp., 603 F. Supp. 730 (D.D.C. 1984). The remaining independent telephone companies are required to implement equal access in certain end offices pursuant to an FCC order. *See* MTS/WATS Market Structure (Phase III), 100 F.C.C.2d 860, 57 R.R.2d 1303 (1985).

[47]The Commission recently determined that current policies governing competition in the interexchange marketplace and the transition to equal access are fundamentally sound. *See* OCC Joint Petition for Expedited Rulemaking, Notice of Proposed Rulemaking, 50 Fed. Reg. 50,316 (1985) [hereinafter cited as OCC NPRM]. The Commission is committed, however, to taking all actions needed to ensure a level playing field for competition in this market. *See* Separate Statement of Chairman Mark S. Fowler, *id.* at 50,328-29. For example, the Commission has addressed a number of transitional problems resulting from the presubscription process under which customers select their primary interexchange carrier before conversion of their telephone company central office to equal access. In particular, the Commission found that the routing to AT&T of all traffic from customers who fail to presubscribe was unreasonable and discriminatory. It mandated instead a uniform *pro rata* allocation plan that became effective May 31, 1985. Moreover, the Commission resolved a number of questions related to presubscription, including, *inter alia,* the controlling indication of customer choice, the retroactive allocation of customers converted to equal access prior to the default order, and the applicability of charges for customers requesting changes to their initial presubscription. *See* Investigation of Access and Divestiture Related Tariffs, 101 F.C.C.2d 911, *modified on recon.,* 102 F.C.C.2d 503 (1985).

[48]Hub-and-spoke operations permit suppliers to aggregate traffic and thus to increase loads and decrease costs by taking advantage of vehicle-size economies. This type of operation also discourages abandonment of routes where there is insufficient traffic to support frequent non-stop service. *See, e.g.,* Leonard, *Airline Deregulation: Grand Design or Gross Debacle,* 17 J. Econ. Issues 453 (1983). Competition and deregulation also have resulted in a lowering of labor costs and a revision of work rules that have significantly increased labor productivity. Regulation permits, perhaps even provides incentives for, large wage increases that are passed along to the consumer in the form of higher prices.

and carriers than ever before and a closer match of product supplies with customer demand.[49]

It also appears that developing technologies and financial innovation may make the competitive industry paradigm the most appropriate long-term model for the local exchange markets. Those markets still must primarily be considered monopoly markets in most areas. They have, at least until now, experienced the least amount of technological innovation. Limited local exchange competition, however, has already begun to appear.[50] Digital Termination Systems (DTS), a microwave digital service, has been introduced in several cities for data transmission. Cellular radio systems have begun to operate in a number of cities across the country and will be extended into hundreds of additional cities during the next five years. As cellular technology advances and costs are reduced, cellular systems may become direct competitors of local exchange carriers. Similarly, fixed microwave or cellular systems may prove to be more efficient for hooking up end users in rural states than traditional copper wire. At least some interexchange carriers have begun to provide interexchange access service directly to end users in competition with the local exchange carrier. Some real estate developers have started placing electronic switches in multitenant buildings to provide tenants with more efficient access to the local exchange carrier's central office and to various interexchange carriers.[51] Apartment buildings with master antennas and cabling for TV could also be providing local telephone services in the near future. Competition is likely to develop between cable companies and local exchange carriers for the provision of local voice, data, and video services as the telephone companies lay more wide-band capacity and institute an Integrated Services Digital Network (ISDN), and the cable companies begin installing switches in their existing systems.[52]

The appearance of competitive markets throughout the telecommunications industry will allow a maximization of public benefits with only a minimum of regulation. As competition invades the entire marketplace, producers will have to price their services at cost and to lower costs as much as possible, or risk losing customers. This efficient telecommunications pricing system could well reduce the use of averaging, allowing prices to vary more directly with the marginal

---

[49]Leonard, *supra* note 48, at 457, 459-60. *See also* S. Morrison & C. Winston, The Economic Effects of Airline Deregulation (The Brookings Institution, 1986); Bailey, *Deregulation and Regulatory Reform of U.S. Air Transportation Policy,* in Regulated Industries and Pub. Enterprise 29 (B. Mitchell and P. Kleindorfer eds. 1980).

[50]*See, e.g.,* Pepper, *Competition in Local Distribution: The Cable Television,* in Understanding New Media: Trends and Issues in Electronic Distribution of Information 147 (B. Compaine ed. 1984).

[51]*See, e.g.,* Aronow, *Smart Buildings and Shared Tenant Services: A Preliminary Analysis,* 37 Fed. Com. L. J. 521 (1985).

[52]An ISDN would provide end-to-end voice and data communications through the same digital transmission media. At present the Communications Act prohibits telephone companies from providing video programming directly to subscribers in their telephone service areas. 47 U.S.C.A. § 613(b).

costs of serving customers.[53] At a minimum, it appears likely that firms will find it necessary to treat customers or classes of customers with reasonable marketplace alternatives, and therefore high demand elasticities, on a special basis in order to retain them on the network. Many carriers are likely to employ two-part tariffs, with lump-sum access charges for non-traffic-sensitive costs of the local loop and separate usage-sensitive charges for traffic-sensitive costs. As in other competitive markets, a firm's ability to judge accurately the relative cost efficiencies of various pricing alternatives will be an important factor determining its success in the marketplace. Only firms using the most efficient methodologies will ultimately be able to provide the greatest values to consumers and thus survive the discipline of the marketplace.

Besides precipitating changes towards more rational pricing of telecommunications products and services, the advent of a competitive marketplace will leave no companies with sufficient market power to present a significant danger of anticompetitive behavior. Whenever a firm attempts to engage in improper cost-shifting or to discriminate against competitors, it will run serious risks of losing customers and revenues. Regulation to constrain such acts simply will be unnecessary.

The significant increase in technological and financial innovation caused by competition in telecommunications may also in fact resolve the chief fairness issue in telecommunications today, ensuring that everyone who desires telephone service can obtain it at an affordable price. Competition may drive prices and costs so low that no need will exist for subsidies for telephone service to any American consumer. If a need for subsidy exists, the amount will be reduced to a bare minimum. As a matter of economic theory, the most efficient way of providing such subsidies is directly through general revenue funds.

Thus, achievement of a competitive world in telecommunications promises enormous benefits in efficiency and fairness. Prices will accurately reflect costs, leading to the production of goods and services only when there are consumers willing to pay those costs. All companies will find it necessary to reduce costs to the minimum, seeking more efficient methods of organizing the production of telecommunications services. Both these developments will advance fairness in the industry. No longer will ratepayers be denied the benefits of a truly competitive marketplace—lower prices and a greater variety of services. No longer will certain classes of ratepayers be required to contribute toward the costs of providing services to others who have the ability to pay for them. And no longer will the costs to society of providing universal service be significantly higher than necessary.

---

[53]Kahn, *supra* note 6, at 149. Of course, the entire fragmentation of the network by individual customer is unlikely to occur because it would be administratively inefficient. Most businesses in competitive markets today use some averaging techniques to achieve administrative or transactional efficiencies that may more than counterbalance losses from pricing inefficiencies.

20.6 THE SIGNIFICANT REGULATORY PROBLEMS OF AN ASYMMETRIC TRANSITION

The day of full competition across the telecommunications market has not yet arrived, however. Local exchange service and even access for interexchange telecommunications service still are generally provided on a monopoly basis. Moreover, in an increasingly competitive interexchange market, AT&T retains a predominant market share and some significant market power. As a result, it is clear that the concerns that led to traditional public utility regulation of telecommunications services still apply to the local exchange market and, to a lesser degree, to the interexchange market.

We must allow competition, however, to flourish wherever and whenever possible, while avoiding the trap of merely protecting individual competitors. The fundamental premise for the transitional marketplace must be that telecommunications regulation should not block competitive entry of new firms and new services into the market. Market considerations of probable prices and costs, rather than regulatory hurdles, should determine when competition develops in the various sectors of the telecommunications market.[54] If regulators fail to honor this premise, the absence of competitive entry may reflect not the continued existence of a natural monopoly, but only the existence of regulatory barriers to entry. Yet it appears likely that developing new technologies will eventually force a stay of the visible regulatory hand in favor of Adam Smith's invisible hand. Thus, the question is whether regulators will manage the transition responsibly or whether they will unsuccessfully attempt to stem such change, at great cost to society as a whole.

The transitional marketplace is asymmetric, with some firms having significant market power and other firms having little. This marketplace poses substantial problems for the industry and its regulators. The entry of nondominant firms into formerly monopolistic telecommunications markets has been pressuring, and will continue to pressure, telephone companies to align prices with costs in various areas and thus to discontinue several traditional public utility pricing practices. Regulators have thus far allowed telephone companies to implement certain competitive measures in response. But as competition continues to develop, telephone companies will have to implement several additional responses with the approval of regulators.

The participation in competitive markets of firms with market power in other telecommunications markets, however, also requires regulators to remain vigilant

---

[54]The significance of barriers to entry and exist restrictions as impediments to the realization of competitive market benefits has been emphasized recently by proponents of the contestable markets theory. *See, e.g.,* Bailey & Baumol, *Deregulation and the Theory of Contestable Markets,* 1 Yale J. on Reg. 111 (1984); W. Baumol, J. Panzar, & R. Willig, Contestable Markets and the Theory of Industrial Structure (1982); Schwartz & Reynolds, *Contestable Markets: An Uprising in the Theory of Industry Structure: Comment,* 73 Am. Econ. Rev. 488 (1983); Baumol, Panzar, & Willig, *Contestable Markets: An Uprising in the Theory of Industry Structure: Reply,* 73 Am. Econ. Rev. 491 (1983).

to prevent such dominant carriers from engaging in anticompetitive practices in their newly competitive roles. Such major carriers might be able to use their market positions in basic transmission services to discriminate against other vendors' competitive services and products that rely on those basic services. For instance, they could adopt or change network interconnection standards so as to prevent or limit competition by other companies. They could make other changes in their monopoly network for the introduction of new products and services that, absent advance disclosure, would provide them with significant strategic advantages over potential competitors. They could also favor their own competitive service customers by providing them with basic services, including installation and maintenance, that are superior to or less expensive than those provided customers of competitors.

Dominant carriers could also engage in improper cross-subsidization of competitive services by regulated services. Cross-subsidization occurs when costs—most prominently some joint costs and common costs—that are attributable to unregulated activities are improperly shifted into the revenue requirements for regulated activities.[55] Cost-shifting wrongly inflates the prices paid by ratepayers for regulated services and artificially lowers the costs of the carrier's unregulated services and products, which could result in predatory pricing by the carrier in the competitive sphere.[56]

The 1956 Consent decree took perhaps the most draconian approach to these problems: it prevented AT&T and the Bell Operating Companies from engaging in anticompetitive conduct in unregulated areas simply by barring them from unregulated activities.[57] As we have seen, the solution of prohibiting competition between telephone companies and other firms did not endure.[58]

As competition develops throughout the transitional marketplace and limits the potential for anticompetitive conduct, regulators will have to be ready to eliminate restrictions on carrier behavior that are no longer necessary and inhibit development toward full competition. These problems are extremely difficult and complex and will require careful consideration by regulators. Some guiding principles should be helpful to regulators in fulfilling their public interest obligations in these difficult times.

---

[55]See, e.g., Second Computer Inquiry Final Decision, supra note 35, 77 F.C.C.2d at 463; Amendment of Section 64.702 of the Commission's Rules and Regulations (Third Computer Inquiry), Notice of Proposed Rulemaking, 50 Fed. Reg. 33,581, 33,590 (1985) [hereinafter cited as Third Computer Inquiry NPRM]; AT&T Structural Relief Order, supra note 39, 102 F.C.C.2d at 658, 673-75.

[56]Cross subsidies do not include the simple investment of earnings from the regulated sphere in unregulated activities. Assuming regulated earnings are themselves proper on regulatory grounds—that is, they are based on reasonable expenditures and investments and do not exceed the carrier's authorized rate of return—and assuming investment in regulated activities is sufficient to maintain quality network services, those earnings may either be paid out as dividends to shareholders or invested in regulated or unregulated businesses. Such corporate dividend investment decisions are matters of business judgment, entrusted to company management, for which the risks lie with shareholders.

[57]See supra note 15.

[58]See supra pages 153-58.

20.6.1 Guiding Principles for the Transition

Forward-looking regulators will recognize and endorse the efficiency benefits from growing competition in telecommunications today and will take steps to keep their hands steady on the tiller. Perhaps the key objective for public interest regulation in the transitional marketplace should be to stimulate use of the public switched network to the efficient levels that would be attained in a competitive marketplace. The public switched network is a critical national resource that has been underutilized because of inefficient pricing, limitations on the permissible activities of important players in the market, and limitations on access to the network by competitive service providers. Regulators should therefore seek to allow dominant carriers some pricing flexibility, to adjust the regulatory measures used to prevent possible anticompetitive behavior by dominant carriers, and to encourage implementation of an open network architecture.

A new policy of dominant carrier pricing flexibility should serve to increase use of the public switched network. As competition enters new markets, existing companies should be allowed to innovate in pricing so as to recover their joint or common costs and fixed costs by the more efficient methods that are required in competitive markets. Subsidies necessary to preserve universal service should be limited to those subscribers who could not afford telephone service if they were required to pay the full costs of such service, and should be structured so as to cause the least distortion in the economic signals given by the market for both the relative costs incurred in providing new services and the prices reflecting the individual preferences of consumers.

The removal of costly structural safeguards increases utilization of the public switched network by allowing more efficient provision of telecommunications goods and services by dominant firms. Thus, regulation has been moving, and should continue to move, from an era of structural safeguards to an era of open network architecture and other nonstructural safeguards. Implementation of open network architecture should increase use of the public switched network by opening the network to new enhanced services providers, who will thereby be assured access to the local exchange network as nearly equal as possible to that of the local exchange carriers themselves. Those providers will be able to compete with dominant carriers in offering sophisticated services that employ the basic regulated services as underlying building blocks.

In this new era, the marketplace will determine whether particular types of services will be offered in the network, in competitive enhanced service provider facilities, or in CPE. Furthermore, competition in this area should allow for the introduction of efficient new series that until now have in large part been precluded by regulatory burdens.

20.6.2 Dominant Carrier Pricing Flexibility

The movement toward more economically efficient use of the public switched network has been quite evident in the increasing competitive pressures for change in various pricing practices under the traditional public utility paradigm. For instance, depreciation practices have been significantly modified during the last five years. Traditionally, depreciation rates were uneconomically low, artificially maintaining low current rates for consumers and high earnings to shareholders.[59] With newly developing technologies and the advent of competition, the Commission found it necessary to make depreciation practices more economic.[60] Two other areas of particular importance, where pricing is currently inefficient, are the pricing of joint or common costs and the recovery of fixed or "non-traffic-sensitive" costs.

1. Pricing Flexibility for Services With Joint or Common Costs—Pricing flexibility for regulated common carrier services with joint or common costs has become one of the most important issues in telecommunications today because of the gradual, but inexorable emergence of competition. Before the advent of competitive services, allocation of joint costs and common costs among services was considered primarily a question of social policy with only theoretical economic significance. However, with the development of services competitive with some, but not all, of these offerings, joint and common cost allocation has acquired critical importance. Regulated dominant carriers must be able to respond competitively so that we can realize the benefits of a free marketplace. At the same time, limits must be set to ensure that such firms do not engage in practices that improperly burden ratepayers or harm competition.

a. The Problems of Allocating Joint and Common Costs—The problems posed by the allocation of costs that are joint or common to several services are well-known. Services that are provided using, at least in part, the same plant or productive operation have "joint or common costs."[61] By definition, these types of costs would have to be incurred even if only one of the multiple services was

---

[59]This result obtained because of the following: lower depreciation rates meant that less investment was depreciated each year into expenses to be recovered during the year from ratepayers, so they received short-term benefits in lower-than-economic rates. The lower depreciation rates also increased company earnings, however, by keeping artificially high the rate base on which the carriers received their rate-of-return.

[60]In the first of two orders, the Commission accepted the use of "equal life group" and "remaining life" depreciation methods as a means of conforming the regulatory treatment of depreciation more closely to the actual decline in value and eventual retirement of plant. Property Depreciation, 83 F.C.C.2d 267 (1980), recon. denied, 87 F.C.C.2d 916 (1981). In the second order, the Commission decided that it no longer would treat expenditures for "inside wiring" of residences and businesses as a capital investment subject to inclusion in the rate base and to depreciation. Instead, it decided to treat those costs as current expenses to be recovered as part of the carrier's revenue requirement in the year in which they were incurred. Uniform System of Accounts, 85 F.C.C.2d 818 (1981). Even with these reforms in the Commission's depreciation practices, AT&T has already taken some writedowns of depreciation reserves on its financial books, concluding that their recovery in competitive markets is no longer possible. It also appears possible that, as competition increases, the BOCs might have to take writedowns in the near future as well.

[61]Production costs are joint only when two products or services can be economically produced only in fixed proportions. Costs are common when producing service A uses capacity that otherwise could be used to produce service B. See 1 A. Kahn, supra note 11, at 77-79.

being provided. If all services are regulated, the difficulty comes in properly allocating these costs among services for purposes of ratemaking.[62] Traditionally, regulators have permitted the use of Fully Distributed Cost (FDC) methods of allocation in which the costs are allocated among all the services on the basis of some seemingly equitable principle. Because there are several possible principles, different FDC methods may lead to strikingly different results. More important, FDC methods may have some undesirable effects with respect to economic efficiency. In many instances, the use of an FDC allocator, such as the common one of relative usage, can lead to inefficient fragmentation of services. In those circumstances, each service will have to pay the entire common costs individually, even though there would be less total expenditure if the services shared those costs.[63] Use of an FDC allocator can even lead to the total absence of services that might be provided under a more efficient allocation principle.

Economists have long advocated the use of some form of marginal cost allocation as being more efficient.[64] When costs are common, definable shares of the costs may sometimes be causally attributed to each service: the marginal cost of one service would be the additional joint production costs incurred by increasing the output of that service while holding the output of others constant.[65] Use of such marginal costs would in those instances be most appropriate. If costs are joint, however, allocation among services has an element of arbitrariness. A number of economists advocate that the most efficient allocation of joint costs is to mark up the prices of the various services above marginal costs in inverse proportion to their elasticities of demand, so-called Ramsey pricing, which would maximize the total consumer surplus.[66] Yet these demand elasticities may be difficult to measure, and Ramsey pricing, while achieving efficiency, may have redistributional effects that impose other social costs. As a result, Ramsey pricing may not always be desirable. Nevertheless, the efficiency costs of alternative allocation methods should clearly be recognized.

Certain other allocation methods, though not as efficiency-maximizing as Ramsey pricing, may be more efficient than current methods. Under the Long Run Incremental Cost (LRIC or "incremental cost") method, the revenues brought in by a service when produced jointly are required to equal or exceed that

---

[62]When some of the services sharing joint or common costs are regulated and some are unregulated, the difficulty arises in properly allocating these costs among services for the purpose of ensuring that there is no improper cross-subsidization of unregulated services by the customers of regulated services. *See supra* page 165.

[63]*See, e.g.,* E. Zajac, Fairness or Efficiency 87-88 (1978).

[64]*See, e.g.,* P. Samuelson, *supra* note 5, at 435-46.

[65]1 A. Kahn, *supra* note 11, at 78-79.

[66]*See* E. Zajac, *supra* note 63, at 21-32; 1 A. Kahn, *supra* note 11, at 144; S. Breyer, Regulation and Its Reform 288-90 (1982). Breyer explains Ramsey pricing using the following example: a bridge is a natural monopoly that costs $25 million to build, but has significantly lower maintenance costs. In answering the question of how the fixed costs of building the bridge should be divided among users, Ramsey pricing would suggest that the bridge authority should increase bridge tolls most above incremental costs for those who are least likely to stop using the bridge as a result, and least for those who would be most easily discouraged from using the bridge. *Id.* at 288-89.

service's long run incremental cost, that is, the additional cost necessary to provide that service jointly with other existing services. Under the stand-alone test, the customers of a service are never required to bear more costs when all the services are produced jointly than they would have to pay if their service were provided on a stand-alone basis.[67]

b. Commission Consideration of Cost Allocation Methods—The Commission has long recognized that newly emerging competition has heightened the importance of these cost allocation questions. As early as 1955, AT&T began filing tariffs in response to perceived competitive threats to its monopoly.[68] By the early 1970s, competition in private line services had developed sufficiently so that the Commission consolidated various ongoing proceedings into Docket No. 18128, in which the Commission expressly considered how AT&T should allocate joint costs.[69] AT&T proposed a LRIC method, with seven different FDC allocation methods as alternatives. In the context of a telecommunications marketplace where many services were, at best, minimally competitive and thus could bear the economic brunt of a significant shifting of common costs without revenue losses by AT&T, the Commission rejected the theoretically superior LRIC approach both because it was unnecessary to allow sufficient competitive response by dominant carriers and because it was unlikely in practice to constrain predatory practices adequately. The Commission instead chose AT&T's FDC Method 7, in which common plant costs were allocated to the services the plant was intended to provide when built. The Commission also divided services into several different categories, including seven kinds of private line services. Each of these services was required to limit its revenues to stay within the Commission's maximum allowable rate of return. This limitation placed more restriction on carrier pricing freedom than did the Commission's traditional method of examining only a carrier's aggregate rate of return.[70]

The Commission ran into difficulty implementing its decision in Docket 18128. Because of these difficulties, joint and common costs tended to be allocated among services in proportion to each service's use of the common plant.[71] It proved impossible to allocate common costs to so many different

---

[67]*See* 1 A. Kahn, *supra* note 11, at 142-43, 166-67; E. Zajac, *supra* note 63, at 88-89, *see also* 2 A. Kahn, *supra* note 8, at 222; L. Johnston, Competition and Cross-Subsidization in the Telephone Industry 16-19 (1982); Northeastern Tel. Co. v. American Tel. & Tel. Co., 651 F.2d 76, 90 (2d Cir. 1981), *cert. denied*, 455 U.S. 943 (1982); MCI Telecommunications Corp. v. American Tel. & Tel. Co., 708 F.2d 1081, 1124 (7th Cir.), *cert. denied*, 464 U.S. 891 (1983).

[68]*See* S. Breyer, *supra* note 66, at 303-05.

[69]For a summary of Commission actions in this area before Docket No. 18128, see Separation of Costs of Regulated Telephone Service From Costs of Nonregulated Activities, Notice of Proposed Rulemaking, FCC 86-146, paras. 12-13 (released Apr. 17, 1986) [hereinafter cited as Joint Cost NPRM].

[70]*See* AT&T Long Lines Department, 61 F.C.C.2d 587, 38 R.R.2d 1121 (1976), *modified on recon.*, 64 F.C.C.2d 971, 40 R.R.2d 1289 (1977).

[71]S. Breyer, *supra* note 64, at 308.

services according to planned expenditures. As a result, the Commission took two actions: it undertook to revise its Uniform System of Accounts (USOA), which had been adopted in 1935, and it began consideration of an AT&T Cost Allocation Manual. The purpose of the USOA revision, which was recently completed, was to obtain more reliable figures for revenues, expenses, and investments broken down by jurisdiction and by individual service categories.[72] The adoption of an Interim Cost Allocation Manual (ICAM) addressed the question of cost allocation directly.[73] The ICAM divided the world of services into only four categories: MTS, WATS, private line, and ENFIA. It expressly selected an FDC allocation of costs based on relative usage. The ICAM attempted to prevent predatory pricing in part by requiring tariffs for the first three categories to be targeted to earn at the authorized rate-of-return. Within the relatively large category of private line services, the ICAM also sought to prevent predatory pricing by relying on the relatively high cross-elasticities of demand among the various private line services. If a carrier priced one service predatorily, customers would quickly transfer from the other private line services to that one, preventing the carrier from, subsidizing that service with revenues from any of the others in that category.

c. Commission Policy of Pricing Flexibility—Building on the general foundation of these cost allocation methodologies, the Commission has moved toward an express policy of pricing flexibility in particular areas by adopting guidelines for private line tariffs and for Optional Calling Plans for MTS services.

In its *Private Line Guidelines* decision,[74] the Commission sought to increase carrier flexibility by specifying five basic guidelines for consistent, integrated private line tariff rate structures that would allow carriers to develop, and receive approval for, new private line tariffs more quickly. With the continued increase in competition for private line and MTS/WATS services, it was becoming both more difficult for dominant carriers to find services unaffected by competition into which costs could be shifted safely and more important for those carriers to be able to respond to the competitive prices of their deregulated competitors. Thus, the Commission took a significant step toward allowing use of a LRIC allocation of common costs as a standard for judging whether competitive price responses in the form of volume discounts were predatory. It expressly rejected the use of FDC allocations on the ground that such allocations would merely

---

[72]Uniform System of Accounts for Telephone Companies, Notice of Proposed Rulemaking, 70 F.C.C.2d 719 (1978), First Supplemental Notice of Proposed Rulemaking, 44 Fed. Reg. 47,359 (1979), Second Supplemental Notice of Proposed Rulemaking and Order, 88 F.C.C.2d 83 (1981), Further Notice of Proposed Rulemaking, 100 F.C.C.2d 480 (1985), Report and Order, FCC 86-221 (released May 15, 1986).

[73]AT&T Manual and Procedures for the Allocation of Costs, 84 F.C.C.2d 384 (1981), *aff'd in principal part on recon.*, 86 F.C.C.2d 667 (1981), *aff'd sub nom.* MCI Telecommunications Corp. v. FCC, 675 F.2d 408 (D.C. Cir. 1982). For a description of ENFIA, see note 94 below.

[74]Private Line Rate/Volume Discounts, 97 F.C.C.2d 923 (1984).

serve to maintain a price floor above marginal cost that would impair competition on the basis of relative economic efficiency.[75] The Commission declined to adopt any economic methodology for testing predation and instead decided to focus primarily on the existence of a consistent, integrated rate structure under its five guidelines.[76]

With the development of competition for MTS and WATS services, a similar need developed in that market to permit nonpredatory; competitive responses by regulated carriers. In response to filings by AT&T for Optional Calling Plans (OCPs) for MTS services, the Commission recently increased carrier flexibility by permitting various alternative tariff structures in OCPs, including multipart tariffs, subscription charges, minimum monthly charges, termination charges, and postalized (non-distance-sensitive) rates.[77] And it allowed greater flexibility in its guidelines for consideration of OCP lawfulness by adopting a net revenue standard as a close proxy for a LRIC approach.[78] The net revenue standard requires that an OCP as a whole increase the carrier's net revenue from switched services, that is, its total switched service revenues less its total costs of providing switched service offerings, including access charges.[79] This standard is functionally equivalent to requiring OCPs to make a contribution to overhead.[80] In a market with usage-sensitive carrier access charges for switched services, this test encourages the development of OCPs that stimulate demand for switched access to the public network because such plans will reduce the carrier's access rates as it spreads the constant costs of fixed plant over a greater number of minutes and may even reduce the carrier's total access costs.[81] The OCP guidelines represent an important step in implementing a program of pricing flexibility in the transition to a competitive marketplace.

---

[75]*Id.* at 945-46.

[76]The Commission also required showings of competitive necessity and mandated that the rates for the private line category be targeted to earn the authorized rate of return. The Commission indicated that volume discounts would have to be reviewed on an individual basis to determine their lawfulness.

[77]Guidelines for Dominant Carriers' MTS Rates and Rate Structure Plans, 50 Fed. Reg. 42,945, 42,955-56 (1985).

[78]The Commission declined to adopt a pure marginal cost standard, concluding that there were serious practical difficulties in implementing such a standard in these circumstances. For instance, the current imposition of a usage-sensitive access charge for a significant portion of non-traffic-sensitive (NTS) costs would tend to distort the economic effects of a pure marginal cost standard. Most importantly, under this standard NTS costs would be borne entirely by other MTS customers. Because these costs would not be increased by implementation of an OCP, the marginal NTS cost would be zero. *Id.* at 42,948-49.

[79]*Id.* at 42,951-52. The selection of all switched services as the test standard has at least two consequences: (1) it gives the carrier credit for the decrease in costs, including access costs, that OCP-stimulated MTS demand may cause for other switched services, and (2) a plan will not be regarded as compensatory merely because it attracts additional revenues from other switched services. *See id.* 42,952.

[80]*Id.* at 42,953.

[81]The Commission expressly required that any carrier claiming a decrease in access costs because of stimulated demand demonstrate that the minutes in fact constitute newly stimulated demand and not merely minutes taken from other services or a competitor. *Id.* at 42,952.

2. Recovery of Non-Traffic-Sensitive-Costs—The major portion of local tele-phone plant costs, which in turn comprise the largest segment of the total costs of the public switched network, are non-traffic-sensitive (NTS)—that is, they do not vary with the extent to which the facilities are used.[82] The allocation and the recovery of NTS costs have been the source of some controversy for a number of years. The first question in our federal system, where regulatory authority is shared between federal and state authorities, has been how NTS costs should be allocated between the federal and state jurisdictions. The second, and in many respects more important, question has been how NTS costs should ultimately be recovered from end users. Historically, although not as a matter of necessity, the answers to these two questions have been related. NTS costs assigned to the interstate jurisdiction traditionally have been included in usage-sensitive inter-states toll rates. By contrast, at the state level, NTS costs have been recovered through flat-rate local exchange service charges as well as usage-sensitive intras-tate toll charges. During the last three years, the Commission has started to move toward economically more efficient pricing by imposing a flat-rate interstate end user charge. Additional modifications still appear to be necessary for a successful transition to a competitive telecommunications marketplace.

a. History of NTS Cost Recovery—The costs of local exchange plants were originally "separated"—allocated betweens state and federal jurisdictions for purposes of ratemaking—pursuant to a "board-to-board" approach.[83] The United States Supreme Court's decision in *Smith v. Illinois Bell Telephone Co.*,[84] however, required an end to a pure board-to-board approach. In response, the Bell System companies began to include in their separations studies a station-to-station approach, under which a portion of the costs of connecting the originating and terminating stations for long-distance calls, including the costs of the local loops, is allocated to the interstate revenue requirement. In 1943, the Bell System companies adopted a pure station-to-station approach for long-distance ratemak-ing, an approach later mandated by the first "Separations Manual" developed

---

[82]NTS costs consist primarily of the costs of installing and maintaining the local loop between each subscriber's premise and the local telephone company. Hence, such costs are a function of such factors as the number of subscribers connected to the network and the distance between subscriber premises and local telephone company central offices.

[83]Under this method, the costs of all facilities used in the provision of local service were recovered through local exchange service charges, mostly flat per-month charges, regulated at the state level. Only the costs of facilities used solely for interexchange purposes—those located on the trunk side of the originating local switchboard (e.g., long distance transmission lines and toll switches)—were allocated to toll operations. Toll rates thus reflected transmission costs from one long distance switchboard to another, but not any fixed costs of the local plant.

[84]282 U.S. 133 (1930). The Court there held that at least some of local telephone plant costs fell within the jurisdiction of federal, rather than state, authorities because interstate long-distance calls used the local telephone company exchange plant at the originating and terminating ends.

jointly by the Commission and the National Association of Regulatory Utility Commissioners (NARUC).[85]

The Separations Manual underwent a number of revisions over the years, gradually shifting greater and greater portions of local plant costs to the federal jurisdiction.[86] The last revision that increased the interstate allocation of NTS costs was the so-called Ozark Plan, adopted in 1970, which replaced the existing subscriber line usage (SLU) allocator for NTS costs with a "Subscriber Plant Factor" (SPF) formula that in effect took SLU and approximately tripled it.[87] Under the SPF regime the interstate allocation of NTS costs grew very rapidly.[88] Largely as a result, the Commission convened a Federal-State Joint Board[89] in 1980 to reexamine separations procedures, including the allocation of NTS plant between federal and state jurisdictions.[90] The Joint Board recommended, and the Commission adopted, proposals to freeze the SPF allocation of each company at its 1981 level and then to phase-in a nationwide allocation factor that assigned 25 percent of most NTS costs to the federal jurisdiction.[91]

---

[85]The manual, which was introduced in 1947, apportioned part of local exchange company plant costs to the interstate jurisdiction according to a "subscriber line use" factor (SLU), which measured the relative use of subscriber lines for interstate calls. The 1947 manual transferred approximately $19 million in revenue requirements from intrastate to interstate operations. See R. Gabel, Development of Separations Principles in the Telephone Industry 50-52 (1967). For a short summary of general separations procedure, see joint Cost NPRM, *supra* note 67, at paras. 5-10.

[86]The separations manual was repeatedly revised after 1947, with each plan, although based on the station-to-station approach and employing usage measures, further increasing the allocation of costs to the interstate jurisdiction. These plans included the Charleston Plan (1952), the Modified Phoenix Plan (1956), the Denver Plan (1965), and the FCC Plan (1969). For more on the history of the Separations Manual and the various plans, see NARUC-FCC, Cooperative Committee on Communications, Separations Manual 5-8 (Feb. 1971).

[87]*See* Prescription of Procedures for Separating and Allocating Plant Investment, Operating Expenses, Taxes and Revenues Between the Intrastate and Interstate Operations of Telephone Companies, 26 F.C.C.2d 247 (1970). In 1970, the overall Bell System interstate SLU was 5.08% and the interstate SPF was 16.71%. It was estimated at the time that the Ozark Plan would shift roughly $130 million in costs from the intrastate to the interstate jurisdiction. *See id.* at 260 (Comm'r Johnson, dissenting). The SPF formula was not applied on a uniform, nationwide basis, but on a company-by-company basis within each state.

[88]By 1980, 7.8% of actual exchange plant usage apparently was for AT&T's interstate services, and 25.8% of local exchange costs were assigned to AT&T's interstate rate base. Because of the application of SPF, increases in interstate usage resulted in proportionately greater increases in NTS cost allocations to interstate operations. *See, e.g.,* Kovach, *Access Charge Issues,* in The New Telecommunications Era After the AT&T Divestiture 87, 94-96 (1985).

[89]Section 410(c) of the Communications Act states that the Commission must refer any proceeding regarding the jurisdictional separation of common property and expenses between the interstate and intrastate operations to a Federal-State Joint Board. A Joint Board is composed of three FCC Commissioners and four State Commissioners. The Joint Board's role is to provide a recommended decision for review and action by the Commission. *See* 47 U.S.C. § 410(c).

[90]In 1972, $1.9 billion in NTS costs were allocated to the interstate jurisdiction. By 1978, this had risen to $5.1 billion. Moreover, NTS costs, as a percentage of interstate MTS and WATS revenues, had increased over this period from 28 to 34 percent. *See* Amendment of Part 67, 78 F.C.C.2d 837, 842 (1980).

[91]The Joint Board recommended the interim SPF freeze at the same time it recommended that CPE be phased out of the separations process over a five-year period in light of the Commission's decision to detariff CPE. Amendment of Part 67, Recommended Interim Order, 46 Fed. Reg. 63,354 (1981); Amendment of Part 67, Recommended Decision and Order, 46 Fed. Reg. 63,344 (1981). The

The introduction of competition into the interstate switched services market also forced a reevaluation of interstate NTS cost recovery. The OCCs purchased only local exchange service in providing their customers access to their MTS/WATS-like services and thus were not party to the division of revenues/settlements process by which local exchange carriers in effect received a contribution from AT&T Long Lines for their interstate operating costs.[92] This created a dilemma: on the one hand, the OCCs were able to avoid making the contribution for local plant costs required of AT&T Long Lines despite the fact that the OCCs, like AT&T Long Lines, used local facilities in originating and terminating their customers' interstate calls.[93] On the other hand, the access provided to the OCCs was inferior in many respects to that provided AT&T for its long-distance services. The network originally had been engineered to provide the superior access enjoyed by AT&T to only one long-distance carrier.

Commission adopted the interim SPF freeze, as well as the CPE phase-out, with a number of technical modifications. Amendment of Part 67, 89 F.C.C.2d 1, *aff'd on recon.*, 91 F.C.C.2d 558 (1982), *aff'd sub nom.* MCI Telecommunications Corp. v. FCC. 750 F.2d 135 (D.C. Cir. 1984). At the time it was frozen, SPF allocated approximately 28% of total nationwide NTS costs to the interstate jurisdiction, about 3.3 times the amount that would have been allocated by SLU. SPFs for individual telephone company operations within a given state varied greatly, however, reaching as high as 85% of a company's NTS costs. After implementation of the interim SPF freeze, the Joint Board recommended a transition to the 25% basic allocation factor and the provision of assistance to companies with high NTS costs. Amendment of Part 67, Second Recommended Decision and Order, 48 Fed. Reg. 46, 556 (1983). The Commission adopted that recommendation in all material aspects. Amendment of Part 67, 96 F.C.C.2d 781 (1984). The Joint Board later recommended several changes in the original transition to the 25% basic allocation factor and to the high-cost company assistance program. MTS/WATS Market Structure and Amendment of Part 67, Recommended Decision and Order, 49 Fed. Reg. 48, 325 (1984). These changes were also adopted by the Commission. MTS/WATS Market Structure and Amendment of Part 67, Decision and Order, 50 Fed. Reg. 939 (1985) [hereinafter cited as Decision and Order], *aff'd on recon.*, MTS/WATS Market Structure and Amendment of Part 67, Memorandum Opinion and Order, FCC 86-56 (released Jan. 30, 1986). Under the current schedule, the phase-out of frozen SPF and the phase-in of the uniform nationwide 25% basic allocation factor is to be accomplished over an eight-year period that began January 1, 1986. The annual change in any telephone company's interstate allocation is limited to five percentage points, however. Thus, companies with an 85% interstate allocation under frozen SPF will move to the basic allocation factor over a twelve-year period.

[92]Before divestiture, the Bell System (AT&T Long Lines and the Bell Operating Companies) and the independent telephone companies joined together in dividing revenues pursuant to private contractual arrangements that followed the principles of the NARUC-FCC Separation Manual and the Commission's rules. AT&T Long Lines filed tariffs for interstate toll services, with the independents and the BOCs concurring in those tariffs. Similarly, independents concurred in the intrastate toll tariffs filed by the BOCs. The arrangements between the Bell System and independent telephone companies were known as "settlements," while those between the members of the Bell System (AT&T Long Lines and the BOCs) were known as "division of revenues." Under the "division of revenues/settlements" process, all interstate toll revenues were in effect aggregated into a single nationwide interstate revenue pool and paid to the local exchange carriers for their operating expenses attributable to the interstate jurisdiction. The remaining revenues were then effectively divided on the basis of each company's investment in interstate operations. *See generally* MTS/WATS Market Structure, Second Supplemental Notice of Inquiry and Proposed Rulemaking, 77 F.C.C.2d 224, 226-29 (1980).

[93]Commission decisions permitting the sharing and resale of private line services, the rates for which did not include NTS costs of the public switched network, further exacerbated the problems of the existing costing and pricing methodologies. *See supra* note 29.

The issue of compensation by the OCCs for use of the local exchange was addressed in a series of negotiations between AT&T and the OCCs in 1978 and 1979. The result of these negotiations, the "ENFIA" agreement, established charges that the OCCs would pay for their use of local exchange facilities in the provision of MTS/WATS-equivalent services.[94] Those charges were substantially smaller than the contributions toward NTS costs made by AT&T Long Lines through the division of revenues/settlements process.

The implementation of "equal access" for OCCs by the local exchange carriers[95] provided an opportunity for resolving this problem. The Commission's Access Charge Plan has replaced the pre-divestiture division of revenues/settlements arrangements and the ENFIA agreement with a system of tariffed access charges administered by the National Exchange Carrier Association (NECA).[96] As part of that plan, the Commission now requires that the OCCs continue to receive a discount for inferior access until they are provided by the exchange carriers with the opportunity to obtain "equal access" to end users.[97]

b. Movement Toward More Efficient Recovery of NTS Costs—There are other, more economically significant problems with traditional NTS cost recovery resulting from the circumstance that recovery from end users of costs unaffected by usage has been accomplished through usage-sensitive long-distance rates. Such a recovery method significantly skews the price signals concerning consumption of telecommunications services. Because each interstate minute of use is burdened with costs that do not reflect actual costs caused by that minute, interstate usage is artificially depressed below optimum levels. Consumers for

---

[94]The ENFIA agreement was an interim measure to bridge the gap between the court decisions in the Execunet cases, which permitted the OCCs to offer services in direct competition with MTS and WATS unless and until the Commission found that such competition was not in the public interest, and the Commission's later determination of an appropriate access rate structure for all interexchange carriers. The access to the local exchange provided these OCCs was inferior to that provided AT&T for its interstate services and, as a result, the ENFIA agreement included rates substantially below those paid by AT&T for local exchange access services. *See* Exchange Network Facilities (ENFIA), 71 F.C.C.2d 440 (1979).

[95]*See supra* note 44 (discussion of the equal access obligations of the BOCs, GTE, and the independent telephone companies).

[96]MTS/WATS Third Report and Order, *supra* note 2, *modified on recon.*, 97 F.C.C.2d 682, *further modified on recon.*, 97 F.C.C.2d 834 [hereinafter cited as MTS/WATS Second Reconsideration Order], *aff'd in principal part and remanded in part, Nat'l Ass'n of Regulatory Util. Comm'rs v. FCC*, 737 F.2d 1095 (D.C. Cir. 1984), *cert. denied*, 105 S.Ct. 1224, 1225 (1985), *modified on further recon.*, 99 F.C.C.2d 708 (1984), 100 F.C.C.2d 1222, *aff'd on further recon.*, 102 F.C.C.2d 899 (1985), *appeal docketed*, U.S. Telephone, Inc. v. FCC, No. 84-115 (D.C. Cir. March 23, 1984). For a further discussion of NECA, see MTS/WATS Third Report and Order, *supra* note 2, at 333-361. *See also* 47 C.F.R. §§ 69.601-69.611.

[97]The *MFJ* established a schedule for the implementation of equal access by the BOCs, providing that it must be available at end offices serving one-third of the BOC exchange access lines by September 1, 1985, and, subject to certain exceptions and possible waivers, at all end offices upon bona fide request by an OCC by September 1, 1986. United States v. American Tel. & Tel. Co., *supra* note 46, 552 F. Supp. at 227. By the end of 1985, approximately 51% of all BOC access lines were converted to equal access, with these lines representing approximately 70% of all lines that are to be converted by September 1986. *See* OCC NPRM, *supra* note 47, at para. 34.

whom the value of additional long-distance calling is greater than the additional costs actually caused by that calling, but less than those costs plus the added portion of NTS costs, will not make those calls even though such calling would produce net benefits. By their nature, the NTS costs that cause those consumers to refrain from making those calls will not be saved by their forbearance, but will instead have to be collected from interstate calls that are made. Their forbearance only increases the per-minute rate applied to interstate calls, thereby further uneconomically depressing interstate demand.

In addition, the recovery of NTS costs through usage-sensitive toll charges provides heavy long-distance users with significant incentives to bypass the local exchange's switched access functions even when such bypass is economically more costly than switched access.[98] When those users drop off the switched network, it increases the usage-sensitive rates to be borne by other users, causing even more users to consider bypassing the network.[99]

The Commission addressed these problems in its Access Charge Plan by proposing to shift most NTS costs from usage-sensitive charges to "subscriber line charges," fixed-rate charges paid by end users.[100] With prices more aligned with how costs are incurred, consumers would receive more accurate price signals to guide them in deciding between alternative methods for connecting to long-distance carriers and between telecommunications and other activities, allowing efficient utilization of our national telecommunications resources.

The transition to this efficient pricing system has proved extremely complex. To help ensure the preservation of universal service, the Commission decided, for instance, that subscriber line charges for residential and single-line business users

---

[98]The usage rate charged by the local exchange carrier to the interexchange carrier includes a "contribution" toward the payment of the fixed costs of providing a network of subscriber loops. In order to pay this "contribution," the interexchange carrier must charge its customers rates that are higher than the costs of providing long-distance service. These higher-than-cost rates are only charged when an end user's call passes through the local "switch" to the interexchange carrier.

[99]The Commission has conducted two studies on bypass. In February 1983, the Commission released a staff study of bypass activities as part of the Third Report and Order in the MTS/WATS Market Structure proceeding. See MTS/WATS Third Report and Order, supra note 2, at App. F ("Status Report on Near-Term Local Bypass Developments") [hereinafter cited as First Bypass Report]. The Second Bypass Report represented a more detailed investigation of bypass. See FCC Common Carrier Bureau, Bypass of the Public Switched Network (Dec. 19, 1984) [hereinafter cited as Second Bypass Report]. The Second Bypass Report drew several important conclusions. First, it confirmed the finding of the First Bypass Report that bypass is occurring and would continue to grow. Second, it concluded that service bypass—that is the use of private lines in lieu of switched access—would initially be the most prevalent form of bypass. Third, it concluded that the establishment of direct links between the long-distance carriers and points with large concentrations of traffic appeared to be the most likely source of growth in bypass in the near future. And finally, it concluded that bypass is likely to divert a great deal of traffic from the public switched network. MTS/WATS Market Structure and Public Notice No. 3206 Seeking Data, Information and Studies Relating to Bypass of the Public Switched Network, Order, FCC 84-635, para. 2 (released Jan. 18, 1985) (adopting Second Bypass Report).

[100]The Plan never contemplated relying on subscriber line charges to recover all NTS costs of those exchange carriers with particularly high NTS costs because of the expected negative impact on universal service. MTS/WATS Third Report and Order, supra note 2, 93 F.C.C.2d at 281-82.

should be introduced on a gradual, limited basis.[101] The Commission also determined that the NTS costs of the public switched network should be recovered through a mandatory pool administered by NECA that would help companies with high interstate NTS costs by providing for a uniform nationwide carrier common line charge (CCLC).[102] At the same time, the Commission, in conjunction with the Joint Board, instituted several specific measures to help insure that universal service is maintained. First, they established a High Cost Fund or Universal Service Fund to ensure that local telephone service remains affordable in high-cost areas.[103] Second, they established mechanisms for providing lifeline assistance to low-income households.[104] Third, they undertook a continuing effort to monitor the effects of these subscriber line charges on universal service. In addition, the Commission recently initiated a proceeding to examine the effect of subscriber line charges, high-cost assistance, and lifeline assistance on universal service, uneconomic bypass, economic efficiency, and pricing discrimination among interstate services resulting from the inconsistent methods used to recover interstate loop costs, and asked the Joint Board to prepare recommendations for possible further action.[105] Any Commission action

---

[101]A $1 residential and single-line business subscriber line charge was implemented on June 1, 1985. This increased to $2 on June 1, 1986. *See* Press Release, "Subscriber Line Charge Accompanied by Major Reduction in Long Distance Rates," Mimeo No. 4872 (May 30, 1986). Full subscriber line charges for multi-line business customers, subject to a cap of $6 per month, have been in effect since May 1984. *See* MTS/WATS Second Reconsideration Order, *supra* note 96, 97 F.C.C.2d at 83.

[102]MTS/WATS Third Report and Order, *supra* note 2, at 328. The mandatory NECA pool, of course, is not the only means to this end. Another method of recovering NTS costs across the country may prove to be more refined and involve less masking of the true economic costs and benefits of alternative local network designs.

[103]Assistance to subscribers in high cost areas is provided through an interstate allocation of local loop costs in addition to the basic 25% allocation. For small telephone companies—that is, those with fewer than 50,000 working loops—an additional 50% of the relevant cost per loop falling between 115% and 150% of the national average is to be allocated to the federal jurisdiction, as is 75% of the relevant cost per loop in excess of 150% of the national average. Thus, after complete phase-in of the 25% basic allocation factor, the interstate allocation is to include all relevant loop costs in excess of 150% of the national average. Larger telephone companies also are eligible for high-cost assistance, but the percentage in the first cost band is reduced to 25% of the relevant cost per loop. Decision and Order, *supra* note 91, 50 Fed. Reg. at 940-41.

[104]The Joint Board recommended and the Commission adopted a two-phase approach concerning assistance for low-income households. The Commission first established an option program providing for the equivalent of a waiver of the subscriber line charge. Customers are eligible for a 50% reduction in the subscriber line charge if they satisfy a state-determined means test subject to verification and if their states implement an equal monetary reduction in the local exchange rate. *Id.* at 941. Subsequently, the Commission established an optional program providing for a full waiver of the subscriber line charge if the state provides an equivalent amount of assistance under a highly targeted lifeline assistance program. The federal assistance is funded through the carrier common line charge and is available for a single telephone line for the principal residence of eligible households. The state contribution that is subject to matching federal assistance may include reduced rates for local telephone service, connection charges, or customer deposit requirements, and may be derived from any state source. *Id.* at 941-43.

[105]MTS/WATS Market Structure and Amendment of Part 67, Further Notice of Proposed Rulemaking, Mimeo No. 5537 (released July 2, 1986).

to consider an increase in the level of these charges has been deferred until after the Joint Board study.

In the meantime, further movement has occurred toward more efficient recovery of the NTS costs of WATS closed-end access lines. Access charges for these lines had been identical to those for common lines carrying MTS traffic because the separations process, for historical reasons, did not distinguish between the costs of these lines. Thus, after separations, the interstate jurisdiction faced one lump-sum revenue requirement for the interstate NTS costs of switched services, the major portion of which, as described above, was recovered through usage-sensitive charges. Changes were recently made, however, in the separations process to assign the costs of WATS access lines directly to either the interstate or intrastate jurisdiction.[106] The Commission took an important step toward competitive cost-based pricing by removing the usage-sensitive CCLC on WATS access lines and assessing a separate, flat monthly charge.[107]

The current state of affairs, although perhaps a prudent initial step in transition, is inherently unstable and will have to be modified to avoid serious difficulty. The still significant loading of NTS costs into MTS toll rates on a usage-sensitive basis has continued the skewing of price signals concerning the optimal allocation of resources. Substantial incentives also remain for uneconomic bypass. Thus, the Commission has taken certain steps to try to avoid problems during the transition. For instance, it has loaded proportionally more of the interstate NTS revenue requirement now collected through usage-sensitive charges on the terminating end of MTS calls. The rationale is that, at present, it appears to be technologically more difficult to bypass there than on the originating end.[108]

In addition, the Commission has provided exchange carriers with some flexibility in their collection of access charges. For instance, the Commission recently indicated that it was prepared to grant waivers of the Part 69 rules to permit local exchange carriers to utilize peak/off-peak pricing for traffic-sensitive access charges.[109] The Commission also has adopted guidelines for exchange carriers to seek waiver of the Part 69 rules in order to implement interim NTS plans.[110] The guidelines permit exchange carriers to file interim NTS plans that initially are effective for one year, impose the uniform, nationwide CCLC for terminating switched access, and do not alter the fundamental operations of the mandatory

---

[106]See MTS/WATS Market Structure and Amendment of Part 67, Recommended Decision and Order, 50 Fed. Reg. 47,774, 47,778 (1985) (recommending changes); MTS/WATS Market Structure and Amendment of Part 67, Decision and Order, 51 Fed. Reg. 7,942, 7,943 (1986).

[107]See WATS-Related and Other Amendments of part 69, 59 R.R.2d 1418, paras. 3-17 (1986) [hereinafter cited as WATS Access Charge Order].

[108]Id. at paras. 38-55. The Commission also has applied the higher CCLC to the open end of calls with one open end and one closed end, such as WATS, 800 service, and FX. Id.

[109]See id. at paras. 30-37. See also Kahn, supra note 6, at 153.

[110]Petitions for Waiver of Various Sections of Part 69 of the Commission's Rules, Memorandum Opinion and Order, FCC 86-145 (released Apr. 28, 1986).

pool of NTS costs and revenues administered by NECA. The Commission also set forth guidelines for two specific models of interim NTS plans: the IXC capacity charge model, and the direct end user charge model.[111] It is hoped that these steps will provide exchange carriers with sufficient pricing flexibility to cope with the continued uneconomic recovery of NTS costs.

20.6.3 Transition from Structural Regulation of Dominant Carriers to an Open Network Architecture

Underutilization of the public switched network also results in part from the structural regulatory measures currently imposed to prevent possible anticompetitive conduct by dominant telephone companies. Traditionally, the primary concern has been that the monopoly, or dominant, status of carriers in regulated markets might allow them to engage in various forms of anticompetitive conduct to the detriment of consumers in the competitive markets and ratepayers in the regulated markets. More recently, as competition has come to major sectors of the telecommunications industry, concern has increased that the direct and indirect costs of preventive regulatory measures are now inordinately high, resulting primarily in higher prices to the consumer and underutilization of the public switched network. Thus, a priority for regulators in the continuing transition to a competitive marketplace should be an adjustment of these regulatory measures so as to encourage the introduction of new enhanced services on the network. This appears to be best accomplished by replacing current structural regulation with effective nonstructural measures and by extending the concept of "equal access" to require local exchange carriers to provide an open network architecture for enhanced service providers.

1. The Use of Structural Regulation to Prevent Anticompetitive Practices— Perhaps the most extreme structural approach to the problem of possible anticompetitive conduct was that of the 1956 Consent Decree, which prohibited competition between the telephone companies and non-telephone companies.[112] That approach ultimately proved unsustainable. The Commission instituted the *First Computer Inquiry (Computer I)* in 1966 as it came to be recognized that at least

---

[111]Under the first model, exchange carriers can collect their carrier common line (CCL) revenue requirement through either capacity charges levied on IXCs or interim surcharges imposed on special access lines (including WATS closed ends) used for designated services considered close MTS substitutes, or both. Under the second model, the exchange carrier can bill its originating CCL costs directly to the end user on a usage-sensitive basis, pursuant to a volume discount. In some respects, this second model is similar to declining block tariffs used in electric utility pricing and to self-selecting two-part tariffs, in which end users are charged according to flat-rate entry fees and usage charges that differ with usage level. Some academics champion this tariff structure as an efficient method for pricing access costs. *See* Kahn, *supra* note 6, at 152; E. Zajac, *supra* note 63, at 39-40; Oi, *A Disneyland Dilemma: Two-Part Tariffs or a Mickey-Mouse Monopoly?*, 85 Q. J. Econ. 77 (1976).

[112]*See supra* page 152 and note 15.

some computer use by carriers was not common carrier communication subject to regulation under Title II of the Communications Act.[113] In *Computer I,* the Commission decided to distinguish between the use of computers to perform message or circuit switching, which was deemed a regulated communications service, and the use of computers for the processing of information, which was left to the discipline of the marketplace.[114] Carriers other than Bell System companies, which were still subject to the 1956 Consent Decree,[115] could participate in the unregulated data processing market, but only subject to a "maximum separation" requirement mandating that a separate corporate entity provide such services and equipment.[116]

The structural regulation of *Computer I* was relaxed in the *Second Computer Inquiry (Computer II).* The Commission found that competition in telecommunications had increased, reducing the potential for abuse and thus the need for harsh preventive regulatory measures.[117] In *Computer II* the Commission re-divided the telecommunications world into basic services, enhanced services, and CPE.[118] The Commission permitted carriers other than AT&T to enter the enhanced services market and to sell their unbundled CPE without structural separation.[119] The Commission decided that certain nonstructural safeguards, such as requiring these carriers to sell basic services to themselves at tariffed rates, were sufficient to prevent abuse in light of the carriers' lack of market power. The Commission also attempted to clear the way for AT&T to provide services and equipment that *Computer I,* in conjunction with the 1956 Consent

---

[113]The goal of *Computer I* was to distinguish, if possible, between computer use by common carriers for purposes of monopolistic communications services and unregulated carrier use of computers for other purposes. Computer Use of Communications Facilities, Notice of Inquiry, 8 F.C.C.2d 11 (1967). *Carterfone,* which allowed end users to connect non-carrier-supplied CPE to the network, also ensured that carriers and non-carriers would be squaring off in the marketplace. *See supra* pages 154-55 and notes 22-24.

[114]First Computer Inquiry Tentative Decision, *supra* note 34, 28 F.C.C.2d at 295-96. The status under the Communications Act of "hybrid" services combining both communications and data processing services was to be determined according to which of the two aspects was predominant. *Id.* at 305; First Computer Inquiry Final Decision, *supra* note 34, 28 F.C.C.2d at 276-79.

[115]First Computer Inquiry Final Decision, *supra* note 34, 28 F.C.C.2d at 282; First Computer Inquiry Tentative Decision, *supra* note 34, 28 F.C.C.2d at 298-99, 305.

[116]First Computer Inquiry Final Decision, *supra* note 34, 28 F.C.C.2d at 268-71.

[117]Second Computer Inquiry Final Decision, *supra* note 35, 77 F.C.C.2d at 391-93, 433-34. By this time, AT&T's revenues in both the interstate private line and the interstate MTS/WATS markets were subject to competition, thus making it more difficult for the company to assign costs from other services to those markets and maintain market shares.

[118]Only basic services were regarded as communications services subject to Title II entry/exit and rate-of-return regulation. Second Computer Inquiry Reconsideration, *supra* note 35, 84 F.C.C.2d at 105-09; Second Computer Inquiry Final Decision, *supra* note 35, 77 F.C.C.2d at 490-95. Enhanced services, which the Commission declared to be outside the ambit of Title II, were defined as services "offered over common carrier transmission facilities used in interstate communications, which employ computer processing applications that act on the format, content, code, protocol or similar aspects of the subscriber's transmitted information; provide the subscriber additional, different, or restructured information; or involve subscriber interaction with stored information." 47 C.F.R. § 64.702(a).

[119]Second Computer Inquiry Final Decision, *supra* note 35, 77 F.C.C.2d at 388-89.

Decree, arguably had foreclosed.[120] Because of AT&T's pervasive market power, however, the Commission imposed strict structural separation requirements on its provision of enhanced services and CPE.[121]

The antitrust restrictions on AT&T and Bell System companies, of course, have recently changed pursuant to the *Modification of Final Judgment (MFJ)*.[122] Under the *MFJ*, AT&T was required to divest itself of its 22 wholly-owned Bell Operating Companies (BOCs).[123] AT&T retained its embedded CPE, its enhanced services business, and its manufacturing, research, and interLATA[124] toll facilities. In addition, AT&T was freed from the requirements of the 1956

---

[120]The Commission sought to accomplish this by declaring that CPE and enhanced services, although not Title II services, were subject to regulation under the Commission's ancillary jurisdiction under Title I of the Communications Act. Thus, the argument went, because CPE and enhanced services were subject to Commission regulation, AT&T and the other Bell System companies would be permitted to engage in these competitive activities under the 1956 Consent Decree. Second Computer Inquiry Reconsideration, *supra* note 35, 84 F.C.C.2d at 105-09; Second Computer Inquiry Final Decision, *supra* note 35, 77 F.C.C.2d at 490-95.

[121]Under these *Computer II* rules, strict requirements were imposed on the scope of permissible activities for all segments of AT&T's corporate structure. Any separate subsidiary providing unregulated goods or services was required: to have separate officers; to maintain separate books of account; to employ separate personnel for operations, installation, and maintenance; to undertake its own marketing, including all advertising; to deal with any affiliated manufacturing entity on an arms' length basis; and to utilize separate computer facilities in the provision of any enhanced services. The subsidiary was prohibited from owning any network or local distribution facilities and equipment and from providing any basic services. Second Computer Inquiry Final Decision, *supra* note 35, 77 F.C.C.2d at 475-86; Second Computer Inquiry Reconsideration, *supra* note 35, 84 F.C.C.2d at 75-79; 47 C.F.R. § 64.702(c).

AT&T's regulated basic service entities were also subject to certain limitations. They were not permitted to engage in the sale and marketing of CPE or enhanced services and were required to disclose network design and other information whenever such information was provided to the separate subsidiary. Second Computer Inquiry Final Decision, *supra* note 35, 77 F.C.C.2d at 475-86; Second Computer Inquiry Reconsideration, *supra* note 35, 84 F.C.C.2d at 75-86; 47 C.F.R. § 64.702. The disclosure requirement was later refined in an order that dealt specifically with AT&T's disclosure obligations for its network services. Computer and Business Equipment Manufacturers Association, Report and Order, 93 F.C.C.2d 1226 (1983) [hereinafter cited as Disclosure Order]. In addition, AT&T was subject to a general network disclosure requirement imposed on all carriers that mandated disclosure, reasonably in advance of implementation, of any information regarding any new service or change in the network. Second Computer Inquiry Reconsideration, *supra* note 35, 84 F.C.C.2d at 82-83; 47 C.F.R. § 68.110(b) ("All Carrier Rule").

In the *Second Computer Inquiry Final Decision* the Commission imposed the structural separation requirements on both GTE and AT&T. 77 F.C.C.2d at 466-475. In the *Second Computer Inquiry Reconsideration Order*, however, the Commission concluded that the costs of applying those requirements to GTE exceeded the benefits, and therefore limited their application to AT&T. 84 F.C.C.2d at 72-75.

[122]*See supra* note 44.

[123]The Court approved a Plan of Reorganization filed by AT&T under which the 22 BOCs and their assets were consolidated into seven separate Regional Holding Companies (RHCs). United States v. Western Electric Co., Inc., 569 F. Supp. 1057, 1061-62 (D.C. Cir. 1983).

[124]The term "LATA," which stands for "Local Access and Transport Area," originated in the antitrust proceeding in order to designate those areas that serve as "exchanges" within which the BOCs are allowed to provide communications services. United States v. Western Electric Co., Inc., 559 F. Supp. 990, 993 nn. 4 & 9 (D.C. Cir. 1983).

Consent Decree, including the restrictions on its engaging in unregulated businesses.[125]

On the other hand, the *MFJ* subjected the BOCs, as owners of local bottleneck exchange facilities, to a series of line-of-business restrictions. The BOCs were limited to providing exchange telecommunications, exchange access, information service access, Yellow Pages, directory services, and CPE.[126] The BOCs were specifically prohibited from providing any interLATA services or information services and from manufacturing equipment (including CPE). The BOCs were allowed to provide any prohibited service only upon court approval of a specific waiver for that service. In a subsequent order establishing standards for these line-of-business waivers, the court prohibited the seven Regional Holding Companies[127] from earning revenues from nonexchange communications businesses greater than 10% of their total revenues.[128]

After the decision approving the Bell System divestiture under the *MFJ*, the Commission examined the propriety of applying its *Computer II* structural separation requirements to the BOCs. The Commission decided that the potential for cross-subsidization and discrimination then warranted imposition of modified structural separation requirements on the BOCs, but promised to review the appropriateness of these requirements within two years.[129]

2. Transition from Structural Regulation to an Open Network Architecture—All these structural restrictions have imposed significant costs on society, both directly through the duplication of costs and indirectly through the absence of services and products for which the public would be willing to pay their true costs.[130] They also have precluded major firms from providing complete telecom-

---

[125]The only restriction imposed on AT&T was a seven-year prohibition against engaging in "electronic publishing." United States v. American Tel. & Tel. Co., *supra* note 44, 552 F. Supp. at 231.

[126]All embedded CPE was transferred from the BOCs to AT&T at the time of divestiture. *Id.* at 192, 226-27.

[127]*See supra* note 121.

[128]United States v. Western Electric Co., Inc., 1984 Trade Cas. (CCH) ¶ 66,121, at page 66,283 (D.D.C. July 26, 1984).

[129]Policy and Rules Concerning the Furnishing of Customer Premises Equipment, Enhanced Services and Cellular Communications Equipment by the Bell Operating Companies, 95 F.C.C.2d 1117, *aff'd sub nom.* Illinois Bell Telephone Co. v. FCC, 740 F.2d 465 (7th Cir. 1984), *aff'd on recon.*, 49 Fed. Reg. 26056 (1984), *aff'd sub nom.* North American Telecommunications Ass'n v. FCC, 772 F.2d 1282 (7th Cir. 1985). *See also* American Information Technologies Corp., BellSouth, and NYNEX, Interim Capitalization Plans for the Furnishing of Customer Premises Equipment and Enhanced Services, 98 F.C.C.2d 943 (1984), *modified on recon.*, FCC 85-582 (released Nov. 11, 1985).

[130]One possible example of such a service is AT&T's Custom Calling II, a proposed voice storage and retrieval service. The Commission denied AT&T's petition for waiver of Second Computer Inquiry restrictions to permit it to offer Custom Calling II without structural separation. AT&T had contended that while such services could be offered on a separated basis, it would be uneconomical to do so. In denying the petition, the Commission concluded that competition between AT&T's separate subsidiary and other service providers would create comparably desirable offerings, if left unper-

munications systems and end-to-end services that customers desire. With the
continued growth of competition in the marketplace, it is important that we
constantly reexamine the benefits of such safeguards to ensure that these costs are
not imposed unnecessarily. It appears likely that, in the very near future, implementation of an open network architecture, along with other nonstructural safeguards, may prove an efficient and effective method of preventing anticompetitive conduct that will increase use of the public switched network.[131]

With respect to the provision of CPE, reexamination is showing that the net
benefits of structural regulation are now less than the net benefits of nonstructural
safeguards. The Commission recently reached this conclusion with regard to
AT&T's participation in the CPE marketplace. It concluded that as a result of
developments since the *Computer II* decision, including the Bell System divestiture and the growth of competition in both the CPE and interexchange
services marketplace, the *Computer II* structural separation requirements with
respect to AT&T's offerings of CPE are no longer warranted.[132] The Commission
found that AT&T's ability to engage in improper cost-shifting without suffering
competitive harm has substantially diminished; that AT&T's ability to engage in
discriminatory practices with respect to its provision of basic transmission services likewise has been significantly reduced; that the CPE market's vulnerability
to anticompetitive practices has lessened; and that the costs of structural separation, both direct and indirect, are still significant.[133] Based on these conclusions,
as well as a reassessment of the efficacy of nonstructural safeguards, the Commission concluded that certain nonstructural safeguards could protect against the
potential for anticompetitive conduct at substantially lower costs than structural
separation. It therefore replaced the structural separation requirements with
various nonstructural safeguards designed to prevent anticompetitive practices by
AT&T: it required accounting measures to prohibit improper cost-shifting; it
required network information disclosure; it prohibited discrimination in favor of
AT&T CPE customers with respect to access to basic network services; and it
established procedures whereby end users can control the availability of their

---

turbed by AT&T's proposed integration of Custom Calling II with AT&T's basic services. Yet no such
services emerged in the years that followed. *See* AT&T Company Petition for Waiver of Section
64.702, 88 F.C.C.2d 1 (1981).

[131]The Commission has initiated a rulemaking to adopt a system of accounting separation for
allocating joint and common costs among regulated telephone services and nonregulated telephone
company activities. *See* Joint Cost NPRM, *supra note* 67. This proceeding will provide an important
foundation for the new regulatory regime of open network architecture and other nonstructural
safeguards. After extensive review, the Commission also has revised its uniform system of accounts,
which was originally adopted in 1935, to provide for a modern, stable information base that will
allow improvements in cost allocations and separations. Revision of the Uniform System of Accounts, Report and Order, FCC 86-221 (released May 15, 1986).

[132]AT&T Structural Relief Order, *supra* note 39.

[133]*Id.* at 673-79, 697.

telephone service information to AT&T's CPE personnel and to AT&T's CPE competitors for the design of competitive telecommunications systems.[134]

The Commission has tentatively reached a similar conclusion in its reexamination of structural regulation of the BOCs' provision of CPE.[135] The benefits of structural safeguards appear to be not as significant as originally thought in light of the BOCs' limited ability to engage in improper cross-subsidization or discrimination. The Commission has tentatively concluded that the potential for cross-subsidization is limited by the robustly competitive CPE marketplace and the continued growth in bypass technologies and services.[136] The Commission also has tentatively concluded that improper discrimination against the BOCs' CPE competitors may be unlikely because of the Commission's CPE interconnection requirements, the readily detectable nature of BOC departures from voluntary network standards affecting CPE interconnection, and other, improved nonstructural safeguards.[137] Finally, the Commission has tentatively concluded that the direct and indirect costs of structural safeguards are substantially greater than those of various nonstructural regulations.[138]

A similar analysis of the relative costs and benefits of structural and nonstructural regulation applies as well to the provision of enhanced services by dominant carriers. Indeed, the absence of any significant market for enhanced services could well indicate that the direct and indirect costs of structural separation have led to the absence of various enhanced services that could otherwise be economically provided.[139] Thus, the Commission has concluded in its *Third Computer Inquiry (Computer III)* that structural separation requirements with respect to enhanced services provided by AT&T and the BOCs should be replaced by various nonstructural safeguards.[140]

There is, however, a critical new linchpin in the application of nonstructural regulation to the provision of enhanced services: open network architecture. Open network architecture is an extension of the concept of equal access, which has been employed successfully in the areas of equipment and interexchange services, to the provision of enhanced services. The Part 68 registration program for CPE established that all manufacturers should have access to the network equal to that of the telephone companies by requiring that all plugs and jacks to the network be standardized, that network interface information be made available, and that all changes in the network or its services that would affect CPE

---

[134]*Id.* at 679-99

[135]BOC Structural Relief NPRM, *supra* note 41.

[136]*Id.* at paras. 32-33.

[137]*Id.* at para. 34.

[138]*Id.* at para. 35.

[139]Amendment of Section 64.702 of the Commission's Rules (Third Computer Inquiry), Report and Order, FCC 86-252, paras. 79-80, 89-90, (released June 16, 1986) [hereinafter cited as Third Computer Inquiry Report and Order]; *see also* Third Computer Inquiry NPRM, *supra* note 53, 50 Fed. Reg. at 33,582-83.

[140]Third Computer Inquiry Report and Order, *supra* note 139, at paras. 3, 46-99, 111-265.

interconnection be disclosed in advance.[141] The requirement that the exchange carriers provide equal access to all providers of basic interstate interexchange services is another significant application of the equal access concept.[142]

As explained in *Computer III*, open network architecture consists of "the overall design of a carrier's basic network facilities and services to permit all users of the basic network, including the enhanced service operations of the carrier and its competitiors, to interconnect to specific network functions and interfaces on an unbundled and 'equal access' basis."[143] No matter how implemented, an important goal of an open network architecture is the reduction in the effect of any local bottleneck, opening provision of enhanced services to non-telephone companies and thus stimulating both the development of new technologies for such services and use of the public switched network.[144] It would also generate significant competitive pressures on carriers and thus reduce the potential for anticompetitive conduct.[145]

Similar analysis may well lead to the conclusion that at least some of the structural prohibitions in the *MFJ* should also be modified. For instance, it may be appropriate to remove restrictions on BOC manufacture of telecommunications equipment if it appears unlikely that the BOCs would be able successfully to engage in improper cross-subsidization through internal procurement or other anticompetitive activities.[146] In addition, because exchange carrier control of any local exchange bottleneck facilities would appear to permit no improper discriminatory treatment of rivals, there may be no need for *MFJ* structural restrictions

---

[141]*See supra* note 26. Both in the *Computer II* proceeding and in the subsequent Disclosure Order, the Commission continued and expanded on these requirements through the imposition of additional network disclosure requirements on carriers deemed most capable of anticompetitive conduct. *See* Second Computer Inquiry Reconsideration, *supra* note 35, 84 F.C.C.2d at 82-83, para. 95; 47 C.F.R. § 64.702(d)(2); Disclosure Order, *supra* note 121, at 1226, 1225-36, 1238, 1244 (1983). The Commission further modified and extended these disclosure requirements in lifting from AT&T the structural separation requirement with respect to CPE. AT&T Structural Relief Order, *supra* note 39, 102 F.C.C.2d at 682-88; AT&T Structural Relief Reconsideration, *supra* note 39, at paras. 11-32.

[142]*See supra* note 46.

[143]Third Computer Inquiry, Report and Order, *supra* note 142, at para. 113. *See generally id.* at paras. 111-16, 147-50, 210-22.

[144]With respect to implementation, the Commission has directed AT&T and the BOCs to file plans detailing specific network designs for implementing open network architecture by February 1, 1988. *Id.* at paras. 114, 220-22.

[145]The Commission decided to allow unseparated offerings by AT&T and the BOCs of particular enhanced services before implementation of a general open network architecture, if they satisfy the equal access standard by providing potential competitors with comparably efficient interconnection (CEI) opportunities on a service-by-service basis. *Id.* at paras. 111-16, 127-31. The Commission tentatively concluded that as a general principle the CEI requirements should apply not only to AT&T and the BOCs, but also to independent telephone companies that control bottleneck facilities. It nevertheless requested further comment on their application to independent companies. *Id.* at para. 132; Amendment of Section 64.702 of the Commission's Rules (Third Computer Inquiry), Supplemental Notice of Proposed Rulemaking, FCC 86-253, paras. 60-68 (released June 16, 1986).

[146]Conditions casting some doubt on the BOCs' ability to engage in anticompetitive activities with regard to equipment manufacture include the extremely competitive equipment marketplace and the Commission's planned implementation of various nonstructural safeguards against anticompetitive practices.

prohibiting the BOCs from participating in markets totally unrelated to telecommunications, from earning more than 10% of their revenues from competitive ventures, from providing competitive services outside their local exchange service area, and from providing non-switched international services.[147] Finally, implementation of an open network architecture requirement plus other nonstructural safeguards may well be adequate protection against any anticompetitive conduct related to BOC provision of information services. Serious examination of these and the other structural prohibitions in the *MFJ* is clearly warranted at the present time to ensure that outmoded structural regulation does not stifle the current transition to a competitive marketplace. Such examination must continue to ensure that adequate structures exist to maintain fair competition and to protect ratepayers of less competitive services.

Thus, it appears that the transition to a competitive telecommunications marketplace has progressed sufficiently to allow the replacement of several remaining structural impediments to dominant carrier participation in competitive markets with an open network architecture and other nonstructural safeguards. This should stimulate the development of new telecommunications products and services, by telephone companies and by other firms, that would not have been offered to consumers given the existence of structural restrictions, and should provide for a marketplace determination of the most efficient methods—within the network or without—of providing such new services.

20.7 ACCELERATING THE TRANSITION TO A COMPETITIVE INDUSTRY PARADIGM—A PROPOSAL

The fast-paced technological and market changes of recent years show no signs of abating. The telecommunications industry is evolving so rapidly that a competitive industry paradigm should be considered the most appropriate model or the entire industry in the relatively near future. The task of regulators is to ensure that the transition to a competitive marketplace is completed quickly, effectively, and at the least cost to consumers. As explained above, this transition should, at a minimum, be based on a continued commitment to universal service and the implementation of a regime of open network architecture that permits: (1) open entry by potential competitors both free of regulatory burdens and protected against anticompetitive conduct by telephone companies, and (2) pricing flexibility that permits telephone companies to respond competitively to such entry.

The more specific questions concerning how best to manage this transition are not susceptible to easy answers. It can be argued, for instance, that some of the

---

[147]NTIA has stated, for example, that "[t]here is virtually no strong public policy underpinning for restricting the business of the regional holding companies in foreign markets. Rather, there are strong policies which favor facilitating BOC participation in those markets." NTIA, Issues in Domestic Telecommunications: Directions for National Policy 58 (July 1985).

Commission's regulatory actions in the interexchange market that were designed to promote competition during transition, such as highly discounted access pricing for OCCs and restrictions on competitive pricing responses by AT&T, in fact have encouraged entry by uneconomic providers and uneconomic construction of excess capacity. If this is true, the gradualist approach to deregulation of interexchange markets will have resulted in substantial, unnecessary costs for society that never would have been incurred in a truly competitive marketplace. Moreover, this approach will have directly increased consumer costs by requiring regulated firms to charge higher prices to protect competitors during the transition.[148]

These considerations are especially relevant now because of recent developments in the provision of local exchange and access services. Such services, although not competitive now, are showing the same characteristics of supporting competition that appeared earlier with respect to CPE and interexchange services. Recent developments, such as advances in bypass technologies and shared telecommunications services, suggest that the time has come for an open entry approach to the provision of local exchange and access services. This article therefore puts forward a proposal to initiate discussion by industry participants, regulators and other policymakers, and academics on alternative approaches to the transition that might allow the swifter realization of the benefits of competition at lower costs to society.

Under this proposal, a three-year trial of total deregulation of telecommunications would be implememted in states willing to undertake such experiments.[149] Regulation of telecommunications goods and services would be largely suspended, including all entry/exit regulation, all rate-of-return regulation of individual service prices, and all structural regulation imposed by regulators or under the *MFJ*.[150] Competition and business freedom for the local exchange companies would be given an opportunity to bring their benefits to all sectors of the industry.

These trials would be subject to certain conditions. They would require implementation of an open network architecture for all telecommunications services—interexchange access, enhanced services, and local exchange service—to ensure that protential competitors of the telephone companies have a meaningful opportunity to provide those services as or more efficiently than the telephone companies. This comprehensive policy of equal access to the local exchange, an extension of this nation's historic practice of requiring carriers to

---

[148]*See* MacAvoy & Robinson, *Losing by Judicial Policymaking: The First Year of the AT&T Divestiture,* 2 Yale J. on Reg. 225 (1985).

[149]Because any such trials would be undertaken only in cooperation with state authorities, no questions would arise under Louisiana Pub. Serv. Comm'n v. FCC, 106 S.Ct. 1890 (1986).

[150]Thus, during the trial, there would be no need to seek government approval to extend or withdraw service or to change prices, to file cost support data justifying price levels, to adhere to artificially low depreciation rates prescribed by regulators, or to maintain costly structural safeguards.

interconnect with their competitors,[151] would constitute the final stage in the evolution of the concept of equal access traced above.[152]

These trials also would require a continued commitment on the part of regulators and telephone companies to maintenance of universal service. This commitment would be fulfilled most importantly through the rapid introduction of the positive forces of competition into the marketplace, which could well serve as the most effective mechanism for maintaining universal service by driving down costs to the absolute minimum. Local telephone companies are unlikely to find it in their economic interest to price local service at a level that causes any significant number of subscribers to drop off the network.[153] They instead are likely to have increased incentives to experiment with alternative rate structures and service options to continue affordable telephone service for the poor. For example, various local measured service alternatives to unlimited flat-rate calling could be tried, such as providing dial tone and a specific quantity of local calling for a flat monthly fee, plus a usage charge for additional calling. During these trials, this Commission and the state commissions would have to monitor developments carefully to ensure that universal service is not jeopardized. If telephone penetration levels dropped to any significant degree, corrective measures would have to be taken.

Under the terms of this proposal, any state or the federal government would remain free to regulate (*i.e.*, set a price and limit entry for) any service it was willing to subsidize from general tax revenues. The states may well determine to continue their regulation of local exchange service rates for residential and, perhaps, small business users, the services over which the local telephone companies are most likely to retain significant market power in the short term.[154] Because these services are currently priced below cost in most instances, continued regulation will bring with it a need for external funding.

The proposal advanced here would require that any continuation of below-cost provision of local exchange services for residential and small business customers be funded from the government's general tax revenues. Other approaches have been proposed. For instance, in California, a tax has been imposed on gross revenues received from the provision of intrastate, interexchange telecommunications services to collect monies for a state-administered Universal Service

---

[151]*See, e.g.,* I. Pool, Technologies of Freedom 206-09 (1983).

[152]*See supra* pages 190-91.

[153]This is so, at least in part, because the marginal cost of attracting new subscribers or retaining existing subscribers in areas that are already wired for telephone service is relatively small. Feeder cables to individual neighborhoods generally provide substantial excess capacity for the addition of new subscribers. In fact, it is common to bring the telephone wires to homes before the telephone company knows whether individual occupants want service. *See* Bell Telephone Laboratories, Engineering and Operations in the Bell System 289-90 (1983).

[154]Even for these services, new technology coupled with open network architecture and an unlimited ability to resell any telephone company offering should provide significant price discipline in many areas.

Fund.[155] Similarly, various proposals for state deregulation by "social contract" contemplate that the local telephone companies will have to increase rates or maintain rates at uneconomically high levels for their other services in order to recover any shortfall in local exchange service rates until such time as political and economic developments permit those rates to recover all costs of those services.[156] The approach suggested here brings at least two advantages over these alternative methods of financing telephone subsidies. First, it avoids the economic distortions in resource allocation that have so long plagued telephone pricing. The manifold economic efficiency benefits of competition detailed above[157] otherwise would be lost or severely compromised; allocation of investment among various telecommunications services would be distorted; and telephone companies, still needing a source of subsidy from other services, would be forced to price certain services above relevant costs, inducing uneconomic bypass by larger customers and leaving a dwindling customer base to pay the substantial fixed costs of the public switched network. Second, this approach makes clear the true costs of maintaining low residential service rates allowing an explicit public policy judgment on the appropriate level of subsidy. Until recently, the false impression has prevailed that low residential service rates were costless.

If, nevertheless, such subsidies for local exchange services are to be borne by other competitive telephone services, there appear to be advantages to allowing the local telephone companies to determine where to obtain the subsidy and how to target this assistance to needy end users, subject to the absolute requirement that universal service be maintained. Attempts by regulators to find sources for these subsidies are likely to result in significant distortions from competitive cost-based pricing that will lead to a marked misallocation of resources and "uneconomic bypass" of those extra charges by end users of the burdened services. By contrast, the telephone companies, who ultimately will feel the effects of the distorted pricing in an otherwise competitive marketplace, will be constrained to structure the subsidies so as to minimize any damaging distortions of the competitive marketplace. In particular, the companies should be best able to target the subsidies only to those who need them in order to afford telephone service, to ensure that the subsidies are only as large as necessary, and to obtain the subsidies from services in inverse relation to those services' demand elas-

---

[155]Cal. Rev. & Tax Code §§ 44000-44190 (West Supp. 1986); Cal. Pub. Util. Code § 739.2 (West Supp. 1986).

[156]Under "social contract" proposals, deregulation would take place through an agreement between state authorities and individual telephone companies. The companies would be required to limit local rate increases according to some external index, such as the Consumer Price Index, and to make specified capital investments during the contract period to maintain and upgrade their networks. In return, the companies would be freed from the burdens of rate-of-return regulation for all services and would be subject to minimal regulation, at most, of particular services. Obviously, the details of any social contract could vary widely depending on the concerns of state regulators and the telephone companies in different states.

[157]See supra pages 158-63.

ticities.[158] By contrast, the social contract approach of limiting prices on all basic local exchange service would result in a high percentage of the subsidy benefits going to recipients who have no need for them. It appears unlikely that the social benefits of this subsidy will outweigh the cost of the inefficiencies required to generate it.

Regulation of any services during trial deregulation would, of course, require measures to ensure that the providers of those services do not engage in anticompetitive conduct. This task could be accomplished through the continued application of various nonstructural safeguards, including most prominently the employment of minimal cost allocation measures and accounting safeguards to prevent cross-subsidization of competitive services by those services characterized by short-run or long-run market power. This would ensure that neither taxpayers nor ratepayers will bear a disproportionate share of any joint and common costs of regulated and unregulated services.

Although initiation of the trial period of deregulation could be tied to a specific event, such as implementation of open network architecture, there are significant advantages to beginning on a date certain after the provision of an open network architecture is practicable. Most important, designation of a specific date for implementing this proposal would encourage efficient planning by industry participants, including telephone companies, their current competitors and potential new entrants. The exact date of implementation on any particular state should be based on an assessment of a realistic date by manufacturers of telecommunications equipment, telecommunications service providers, and consumers. To develop and implement specific deregulatory measures, the Commission would work with the state commissions and the Department of Justice, and would help seek any necessary waivers from *MFJ* restrictions. For instance, in return for state adoption of this proposal for intrastate services, the Commission could deregulate the interstate access charges of that state's telephone companies.

The use of trial deregulation in willing states promises significant benefits for the country as a whole. The costs and benefits of this proposal or of other alternative approaches to introducing competition throughout the telecommunications network[159] could be determined on a geographically limited basis with the consent of the state authorities. They would provide the experience for possible later deregulation of the telecommunications industry by remaining states.

---

[158]*See supra* pages 169-70 & note 66 (discussion of Ramsey pricing).

[159]For instance, in June 1986, the Public Commissioner of Oregon initiated a proceeding seeking public comment on a significant deregulatory initiative. Adoption of the Universal Service Protection Plan, Order, AR 131 and UM 118 (Order No. 86-583, June 11, 1986); *see also* 1985 Or. Laws ch. 550 (H.B. 2200). Similarly, in April 1986, the state of Nebraska enacted a statute implementing a broad deregulatory framework or the telecommunications industry in that state as of January 1, 1987. Neb. Leg. Bill 835 (signed by Governor April 18, 1986) (to be codified at Neb. Rev. Stat. §§ 86-801 to 86-111).

20.8 CONCLUSION

The challenge generally faced by state and federal regulators is to develop thoughtful and viable policies that maximize consumer welfare. In the present circumstances, these policies must reflect not only an awareness of the readily apparent short-term direct costs of a transition from one industry model to another, but also a recognition of the heavy opportunity costs of failing to address the novel and rapidly changing aspects of American telecommunications. Contrary to what some would argue, the primary question today is not how to use regulation to carve up the telecommunications pie among competing interests, but how to take advantage of rapidly developing competition to increase the size of the pie and benefit society as a whole.

This article calls for a re-examination of government regulation of the telecommunications industry in the United States. It suggests that a competitive industry paradigm would best serve the public interest in telecommunications today. Finally, it advances for discussion a specific proposal designed to hasten the day of a completely competitive telecommunications marketplace.

The proposal admittedly is not a detailed plan for the transition to a fully competitive telecommunications industry. Nor should it be. Regulators should not at this point become enmeshed in developing a detailed plan for transition, for the debate should be focused on the fundamentals of telecommunications regulation. We should not be discussing how to tinker at the edges of a regulatory paradigm that is inappropriate for the modern era. As Peter Drucker has so aptly advocated, we should not be looking to do what we have always done "righter," but instead we should be asking what are the right things we should be doing. Any continued regulation should not result merely from inertia, but should depend upon an affirmative decision that such regulation serves the public interest. The costs in today's marketplace of unneeded regulation are simply too high.

In this effort, it will be crucial that there be active participation by the industry, users, and, in particular, state regulatory commissions. Industry participants will have to compete in the new environment and the rules for the transition must ensure that they all have an equal opportunity to compete with maximum freedom and flexibility. Users will be the major beneficiaries of the movement to the more consumer-oriented approach that is characteristic of competitive markets. And state regulators will continue to be on the front line protecting the public interest.

This proposal is not designed to impose a federal view on the states. Rather, it is a call for a sharing of ideas, and, if necessary, a greater sharing of authority to serve a greater good. In many instances, state regulatory authorities have been in the forefront of responding to the challenges of new technology and have served as beacons lighting the way for their federal counterparts. These and other visionaries, who see no value in preserving narrow and short-lived regulatory perogatives, should respond to this call for a debate on the government policies in order to ensure that the American telecommunications industry continues to lead the world in efficiency, equity, and excellence.

INDEX